# McGRAW-HILL SERIES IN CHEMICAL ENGINEERING
## SIDNEY D. KIRKPATRICK, CONSULTING EDITOR

# MASS-TRANSFER OPERATIONS

# McGRAW-HILL SERIES IN CHEMICAL ENGINEERING

SIDNEY D. KIRKPATRICK, *Consulting Editor*

## EDITORIAL ADVISORY COMMITTEE

## BUILDING FOR THE FUTURE OF A PROFESSION

Fifteen prominent chemical engineers first met in New York more than thirty years ago to plan a continuing literature for their rapidly growing profession. From industry came such pioneer practitioners as Leo H. Baekeland, Arthur D. Little, Charles L. Reese, John V. N. Dorr, M. C. Whitaker, and R. S. McBride. From the universities came such eminent educators as William H. Walker, Alfred H. White, D. D. Jackson, J. H. James, J. F. Norris, Warren K. Lewis, and Harry A. Curtis. H. C. Parmelee, then editor of *Chemical & Metallurgical Engineering*, served as chairman and was joined subsequently by S. D. Kirkpatrick as consulting editor.

After several meetings, this Editorial Advisory Committee submitted its report to the McGraw-Hill Book Company in September, 1925. In it were detailed specifications for a correlated series of more than a dozen text and reference books, including a chemical engineers' handbook and basic textbooks on the elements and principles of chemical engineering, on industrial applications of chemical synthesis, on materials of construction, on plant design, on chemical-engineering economics. Broadly outlined, too, were plans for monographs on unit operations and processes and on other industrial subjects to be developed as the need became apparent.

From this prophetic beginning has since come the McGraw-Hill Series in Chemical Engineering, which now numbers about thirty-five books. More are always in preparation to meet the ever-growing needs of chemical engineers in education and in industry. In the aggregate these books represent the work of literally hundreds of authors, editors, and collaborators. But no small measure of credit is due the pioneering members of the original committee and those engineering educators and industrialists who have succeeded them in the task of building a permanent literature for the classical engineering profession.

# THE SERIES

# MASS-TRANSFER
# OPERATIONS

**ROBERT E. TREYBAL**

*Professor of Chemical Engineering*
*New York University*

McGRAW-HILL BOOK COMPANY, INC.

New York     Toronto     London

1955

MASS-TRANSFER OPERATIONS

*Library of Congress Catalog Card Number 55-5699*

THE MAPLE PRESS COMPANY, YORK, PA.

# PREFACE

Of the many physical manipulations which we have come to know as the unit operations of chemical engineering, those described in this book perhaps more than any others are the responsibility solely of the chemical engineer. There is hardly a chemical process which does not include as an essential part some purification of a raw material, some separation of product from reaction mixture, for which these operations are appropriate. While most of them have been in practical use for many years, the development of sound methods of equipment design was begun much more recently but has proceeded at an accelerated pace. Indeed, the past fifteen years have seen phenomenal advances. Almost every issue of the chemical-engineering journals contributes to these advances but at the same time also broadens the gap between current practice and that which can ordinarily be taught in undergraduate university courses. It is the dual purpose of this book to provide a working text for teaching these subjects to the beginner and to provide the student with an entree to the modern technical literature so that the inevitable task of teaching himself will be perhaps less formidable.

Considerable thought was given to several treatments of the subject which are wholly different from that eventually used. It is possible, for example, to develop in detail completely generalized design methods at the beginning, and there is much that is appealing about such a procedure. But the student is usually impatient to begin the study of applications, and too long a period spent on abstract matters results in a loss of enthusiasm. The treatment here develops the generalized methods slowly throughout the book. The elegance of completely generalized methods, in any case, is perhaps more appreciated in hindsight. Major decisions respecting procedure, as well as many minor ones, were based on personal convictions as to the most effective methods of presentation developed during fifteen years of teaching this subject.

The presentation assumes that the student has an elementary knowledge of fluid flow and heat transfer, as well as a modest facility with calculations of material and energy balances and the use of the ideal-gas laws. The position of a course in this subject in the conventional chemical-engineering curriculum permits this. A course in physical chemistry should at least be taken simultaneously with this study, if not before, but the major topics of immediate importance, such as the various phase equilibria, are reviewed here with sufficient thoroughness for the purposes at hand.   There is more here than can ordinarily be treated in an undergraduate course, purposely so.   But the organization is planned so that entire chapters or sections of chapters are readily omitted from formal courses.   The student may then pursue these later by himself. The entire book may easily be covered in a first graduate course.   The literature references at the end of each chapter were carefully chosen with the beginning student in mind.   Many of them are the classics of our chemical-engineering literature, and if they are not the original sources, they at least lead to extensive bibliographies.

My own students will attest to the emphasis I have always placed on the importance of solving problems as a prerequisite to complete understanding of a subject.   The problems at the end of each chapter, of varying degrees of difficulty, cover all the major principles.   For the solution of these it is assumed that there is at hand some such collection of data as the "Chemical Engineers' Handbook," and no attempt has been made to provide extensive tables of physical properties.

I am indebted to many firms and technical journals through whose kind cooperation I am able to include many of the figures, and these are specifically acknowledged throughout the text.   I would be remiss if I failed to mention particularly the gracious cooperation of Clyde Berg, H. E. Degler, and E. J. Lyons, who represented some of the firms.   In addition I was favored by much thoughtful and constructive criticism of portions of the text by Thomas Baron, Harry Drickamer, Mott Souders, and C. R. Wilke, many of whose suggestions are incorporated in the text.   My colleagues at New York University, John Happel and Morris Newman, also patiently reviewed and criticized the manuscript. And as on a similar previous occasion, I am especially indebted to my wife, Gertrude I. Treybal, who helped so much with the tedious work of preparing a long manuscript.

ROBERT E. TREYBAL

# CONTENTS

ix

# CHAPTER 1

# INTRODUCTION

A substantial number of the unit operations of chemical engineering are concerned with the problems of changing the composition of solutions and mixtures through methods not involving chemical reactions. Most frequently these composition changes are analytical, i.e., it is desired to separate the original substance into its component parts. Such separations may be entirely mechanical, such as the separation of solid from liquid during filtration, or the classification of a granular solid into fractions of different particle size by screening. On the other hand, if the operations involve changes in composition of solutions, either solutions to which these operations are being applied or those introduced as agents, they are known as diffusional, or mass-transfer, operations, and it is these with which we are concerned. The substance undergoing the change in composition is most frequently itself a solution, but it may be a physical mixture or one which exhibits the properties of both.

The diffusional operations are characterized by a transfer of one substance through another, usually on a molecular scale. For example, when water evaporates from a pool into an air stream flowing over the water surface, molecules of water vapor diffuse through those of the gas at the surface into the main portion of the air stream, whence they are carried away. On other occasions, one molecular species may diffuse through another which is itself diffusing in the opposite direction. In every case, the mass transfer is a result of a concentration difference, the diffusing substance moving from a place of high to one of low concentration. The concentration difference is thus a driving force for the mass transfer in the same fashion as temperature difference is a driving force for the transfer of heat.

## CLASSIFICATION OF THE DIFFUSIONAL OPERATIONS

It is useful to classify the diffusional operations and to cite examples of each, in order to indicate the scope of the subject matter of this book. Separations may be brought about by:

1. Contact of two immiscible phases, with mass transfer or diffusion through the surface between the phases

2. Contact of miscible phases separated by a permeable or semi-permeable membrane, with diffusion through the membrane

3. Direct contact of miscible phases

This general scheme is the basis of the classification of Table 1.1. Of all the various methods, those in the first category are by far the most important.

TABLE 1.1. CLASSIFICATION OF THE DIFFUSIONAL OPERATIONS

| | Phase 1 | Phase 2 | All components present in both phases | All components not present in both phases | | |
| --- | --- | --- | --- | --- | --- | --- |
| | | | | Phase 1 pure | Phase 2 pure | Distributed component in both phases |
| 1. Contact of immiscible phases | Gas | Gas | None | None | None | None |
| | Gas | Liquid | Distillation Condensation | (Evaporation) ............. | Humidification Dehumidification | Absorption Stripping, desorption |
| | Gas | Solid | Fractional sublimation | (Sublimation) | (Condensation) | Adsorption Fractional adsorption Drying, desorption |
| | Liquid | Liquid | Liquid extraction Fractional extraction | None ............... | None ............. | Liquid extraction Fractional extraction |
| | Liquid | Solid | Fractional solidification | None | Dissolution (Crystallization) | Leaching Adsorption |
| | Solid | Solid | None | None | None | None |
| 2. Contact of miscible phases separated by a permeable or semipermeable membrane | Gas | Gas | Gas diffusion, gas effusion | | | |
| | Liquid | Liquid | Dialysis, fractional dialysis, electrodialysis, osmosis | | | |
| | Solid | Solid | None | | | |
| 3. Direct contact of miscible phases | Gas | Gas | Thermal diffusion, sweep diffusion, atmolysis, centrifugation | | | |
| | Liquid | Liquid | Thermal diffusion | | | |
| | Solid | Solid | None | | | |

**1. Contact of Immiscible Phases.** The three states of aggregation permit six possibilities: gas-gas, gas-liquid, gas-solid, liquid-liquid, liquid-solid, and solid-solid.

*Gas-Gas.* Since all gases are completely soluble in each other, this category cannot be practically realized.

*Gas-Liquid.* If all components of the system are present in appreciable amounts in both phases, the operation is known as *distillation.* In this instance the gas phase is created from the liquid phase by application of heat. For example, if a liquid solution of acetic acid and water is partially vaporized by heating, it is found that the newly created vapor phase and the residual liquid both contain acetic acid and water, but in proportions which are different for the two phases and different from those in the original solution. If the vapor and residual liquid are separated physically from one another and the vapor condensed, two solutions, one richer in acetic acid and the other poorer, are obtained. In this way a certain degree of separation of the original components has been accomplished. Conversely, should a vapor mixture of the two substances be partially condensed, the newly formed liquid phase and the residual vapor will differ in composition. In both instances an interdiffusion of both components between the phases eventually establishes their final composition.

All the components of the solutions involved may not be present in appreciable amounts in both gas and liquid phases, however. If the liquid phase is a pure liquid containing but one component while the gas contains two or more, the operations are known as *humidification* or *dehumidification,* depending upon the direction of the diffusion. For example, contact of dry air with liquid water results in evaporation of some of the water into the air (humidification of the air). Conversely, contact of very moist air with pure liquid water may result in condensation of part of the moisture in the air (dehumidification). In both cases relatively little air dissolves in the water, and for most practical purposes it is considered that only water vapor diffuses from one phase to the other.

Both phases may be solutions, each containing only one common component which distributes between the phases. For example, if a mixture of ammonia and air is brought into contact with liquid water, a large portion of the ammonia but relatively little air will dissolve in the liquid and in this way the air-ammonia mixture may be separated. The operation is known as *gas absorption.* On the other hand, if air is brought into contact with an ammonia-water solution, some of the ammonia leaves the liquid and enters the gas phase, an operation known as *desorption,* or *stripping.*

To complete the classification, one might mention the case where the gas phase contains but one component and the liquid several, as in evaporation of a salt-water solution by boiling. Here the gas phase contains only water vapor, since the salt is essentially nonvolatile. Such an operation does not depend on concentration gradients, but rather on the rate of heat transfer to the boiling solution, and is consequently not considered diffusional. But should the salt solution be separated by diffusion of the water into an air stream, the operation then becomes one of desorption, or stripping, and is diffusional.

*Gas-Solid.* Classification of the operations in this category according to the number of components which appear in the two phases is again convenient.

If a solid solution were to be partially vaporized without the appearance of a liquid phase, the newly formed vapor phase and the residual solid would each contain all the original components, but in different proportions, and the operation is *fractional sublimation.* As in distillation, the final compositions are established by interdiffusion of the components between the phases. While such an operation is theoretically possible, practically it is not generally done because of the inconvenience of dealing with solid phases in this manner.

All components may not be present in both phases, however. If a solid which is moistened with a volatile liquid is exposed to a relatively dry gas, the liquid leaves the solid and diffuses into the gas, an operation generally known as *drying*, sometimes as *desorption.* A homely example is the drying of laundry by exposure to air, and there are many industrial counterparts such as the drying of lumber or the removal of moisture from a wet filter cake by exposure to dry gas. In this case, the diffusion is, of course, from the solid to the gas phase. If the diffusion takes place in the opposite direction, the operation is known as *adsorption.* For example, if a mixture of water vapor and air is brought into contact with activated silica gel, the water vapor diffuses to the solid, which retains it strongly, and the air is thus dried. In other instances, a gas mixture may contain several components each of which is adsorbed on a solid but to different extents (*fractional adsorption*). For example, if a mixture of propane and propylene gases is brought into contact with activated carbon, the two hydrocarbons are both adsorbed, but to different extents, thus leading to a separation of the gas mixture.

The case where the gas phase is a pure vapor, such as in the sublimation of a volatile solid from a mixture with one which is nonvolatile, is an operation dependent more on the rate of application of heat than on concentration difference and is essentially nondiffusional. The same is true of the condensation of a vapor to the condition of a pure solid, where the rate depends on the rate of heat removal.

*Liquid-Liquid.* Separations involving the contact of two insoluble liquid phases are known as *liquid-extraction* operations. A simple example is the familiar laboratory procedure: if an acetone-water solution is shaken in a separatory funnel with carbon tetrachloride and the liquids allowed to settle, a large portion of the acetone will be found in the carbon tetrachloride-rich phase and will thus have been separated from the water. A small amount of the water will also have been dissolved by the carbon tetrachloride, and a small amount of the latter will have entered the water layer, but these effects are relatively minor. As another possibility, a solution of acetic acid and acetone may be separated by adding it to the insoluble mixture of water and carbon tetrachloride. After shaking and settling, both acetone and acetic acid will be found in both liquid phases, but in different proportions. Such an operation is known as *fractional extraction*.

*Liquid-Solid. Fractional solidification* of a liquid, where the solid and liquid phases are both solutions of variable composition containing all the components but in different proportions, is theoretically possible but is not ordinarily carried out, because of practical difficulties in handling the solid phase and because of the very slow diffusion rates in the solid.

The cases involving distribution of a substance between the solid and liquid phases are common, however. Solution of a component from a solid mixture by a liquid solvent is known as *leaching* (sometimes called solvent extraction), and as examples we may cite the leaching of gold from its ores by cyanide solutions, and the leaching of cottonseed oil from the cottonseeds by hexane. The diffusion is, of course, from the solid to the liquid phase. If the diffusion is in the opposite direction, the operation is known as *adsorption*. Thus, the colored material which contaminates impure cane sugar solutions may be removed by contacting the liquid solutions with activated carbon, whereupon the colored substances are retained on the surface of the solid carbon.

When the solid phase is a pure substance and the liquid solution is being separated, the operation is crystallization, but as ordinarily carried out this is more dependent upon heat-transfer rates and only indirectly on concentrations. The reverse operation is *dissolution*. No known operation is included in the category involving a pure liquid phase.

*Solid-Solid.* Because of the extraordinarily slow rates of diffusion within solid phases, there is no industrial separation operation in this category.

**2. Miscible Phases Separated by a Membrane.** In these operations the membrane is necessary to prevent intermingling of the phases, but it must be differently permeable to the components of the solutions if diffusional separations are to be possible.

*Gas-Gas.* The operation in this category is known as *gaseous diffusion*, or effusion. If a gas mixture whose components are of different molecular weights is brought into contact with a porous diaphragm, the various components of the gas will diffuse through the pores at different rates. This leads to different compositions on opposite sides of the diaphragm and consequently to separation of the gas mixture. In this manner, large-scale separation of the isotopes of uranium, in the form of uranium hexafluoride, is carried out.

*Liquid-Liquid.* The separation of a crystalline substance from a colloid, by contact of their solution with a liquid solvent with an intervening membrane permeable only to the solvent and the dissolved crystalline substance, is known as *dialysis.* For example, aqueous beet sugar solutions containing undesired colloidal material are freed of the latter by contact with water with an intervening semipermeable membrane. Sugar and water diffuse through the membrane, but the larger colloidal particles cannot. *Fractional dialysis* for separating two crystalline substances in solution makes use of the difference in membrane permeability for the substances. If an electromotive force is applied across the membrane to assist in the diffusion of charged particles, the operation is *electrodialysis.* If a solution is separated from the pure solvent by a membrane which is permeable only to the solvent, the solvent diffuses into the solution, an operation known as *osmosis.* This is not a separation operation, of course, but theoretically at least one could reverse the flow of solvent by superimposing a pressure to oppose the osmotic pressure.

*Solid-Solid.* This operation is unknown.

**3. Direct Contact of Miscible Phases.** The operations in this category, because of the difficulty in maintaining concentration gradients without mixing of the fluid, are not generally considered practical industrially except in unusual circumstances.

*Thermal diffusion* involves the formation of a concentration difference within a single liquid or gaseous phase by imposition of a temperature gradient upon the fluid, thus making a separation of the components of the solution possible. It was used, for example, in the separation of uranium isotopes in the form of uranium hexafluoride.

If a condensable vapor, such as steam, is allowed to diffuse through a gas mixture, it will preferentially carry one of the components along with it, thus making a separation by the operation known as *sweep diffusion.* If the two zones within the gas phase where the concentrations are different are separated by a screen containing relatively large-size openings, the operation is called *atmolysis.*

If a gas mixture is subjected to a very rapid *centrifugation*, the components will be separated because of the slightly different forces acting on the various molecules owing to their different masses. The heavier molecules thus tend to accumulate at the periphery of the centrifuge.

## CHOICES AMONG SEPARATION METHODS

The chemical engineer faced with the problem of separating the components of a solution ordinarily must choose between several possible methods. While the choice is usually limited owing to peculiar physical characteristics of the materials to be handled, the necessity for making a decision nevertheless almost always exists. Until the fundamentals of the various operations have been clearly understood, of course, no basis for such a decision is available, but it is well at least to establish the nature of the alternatives at the beginning.

One may sometimes choose between using a diffusional operation of the sort discussed in this book and a purely mechanical separation method. For example, in the separation of a desired mineral from its ore, it may be possible to use either the diffusional operation of leaching with a solvent or the purely mechanical methods of flotation. Vegetable oils may be separated from the seeds in which they occur by expression or by leaching with a solvent. A vapor may be removed from a mixture with a permanent gas by the mechanical operation of compression or by the diffusional operations of gas absorption or adsorption. Sometimes both mechanical and diffusional operations are used, especially where the former are incomplete, as in processes for recovering vegetable oils wherein expression is followed by leaching. A more commonplace example is the wringing of water from wet laundry followed by air drying. It is characteristic that at the end of the operation the substance removed by mechanical methods is pure, while if removed by diffusional methods it is associated with another substance.

One may also frequently choose between a diffusional operation and a chemical reaction to bring about a separation. Water may be removed from an ethanol-water solution either by causing it to react with unslaked lime or by special methods of distillation, for example. Hydrogen sulfide may be separated from other gases either by absorption in a liquid solvent or by chemical reaction with ferric oxide. Chemical methods ordinarily destroy the substance removed, while diffusional methods usually permit its eventual recovery in unaltered form without great difficulty.

There are also choices to be made within the diffusional operations. For example, a gaseous mixture of oxygen and nitrogen may be separated by preferential adsorption of the oxygen on activated carbon, by absorption, by distillation, or by gaseous effusion. A liquid solution of acetic acid may be separated by distillation, by liquid extraction with a suitable solvent, or by adsorption with a suitable adsorbent.

The principal basis for choice in any case is cost: that method which costs the least is usually the one to be used. Occasionally other factors also influence the decision, however. The simplest operation, while it may not be the least costly, is sometimes desired because it will be trouble-free. Sometimes a method will be discarded because of imperfect knowledge of design methods or unavailability of data for design, so that results cannot be guaranteed. Favorable previous experience with one

method may be given strong consideration.   Cost, however, remains as
the prime factor.

## METHODS OF CONDUCTING THE DIFFUSIONAL OPERATIONS

There are several characteristic methods of carrying out the diffusional operations upon which the extent of separation and the type of
equipment used strongly depend.   The nature of the flow of the phases
(whether in steady or unsteady state) and the method of contacting the
phases (whether in stagewise or continuous-contact fashion) are most
important considerations.

**Unsteady-state Operation.**   It is characteristic of unsteady-state
operation that concentrations at any position in the system change with
time.

If we have a purely *batch operation*, all the phases are stationary from
a point of view outside the system, or on a "forward-flow" basis, although
within the equipment there may be relative motion of the phases.   For
example, the familiar laboratory extraction procedure involving contact
of a solution with an immiscible solvent in a separatory funnel is a batch
operation, since, once the liquids are in place, there is no further flow of
liquid into or out of the vessel until the operation is completed.   During
the course of the extraction the solute diffuses from the solution into the
solvent, and the concentrations in both phases must therefore change
with time.   Provided the time of contact is great enough, the maximum
change in concentration which is possible is given when an equilibrium
exists between the phases, although in practice the operation may be
stopped before this occurs.   The entire operation is said to be equivalent
to one stage.   Each of the diffusional operations may be carried out in
this general fashion.

In a *semibatch operation*, one phase is stationary while the other flows
continuously into and out of the system.   As an example we may cite the
case of a drier where a quantity of wet solid is placed in an air stream
which flows continuously into and out of the drier, carrying away the
vaporized moisture.   The concentration of moisture in the solid and in
the leaving air stream must, of course, change with time.   Ultimately, if
sufficient time is permitted, the stationary phase will come to equilibrium with the influent phase as a maximum effect, and the operation
may be equivalent to one of many stages.

**Steady-state Operation.**   It is characteristic of steady-state operation
that concentrations at any position in the system remain constant with
passage of time.   This requires continuous, invariable flow of all phases
into and out of the system and a persistence of the flow regime within the
system.

In *parallel flow*, the phases move through the equipment in the same direction, entering and leaving together. The net effect in so far as concentrations are concerned is ultimately the same as for batch operation: if the phases are in contact long enough, the maximum concentration change will correspond to equilibrium between the effluent phases. The operation is equivalent to one stage.

In *countercurrent flow*, the contacted phases flow in opposite directions through the equipment. For example, in gas absorption the gas to be washed may flow upward through a tower while the washing liquid flows downward through the gas. As a maximum possible effect, one of the effluent phases will come to equilibrium with the other influent phase, although in practice insufficient time is available for this. The operation may be equivalent to many stages.

In *crossflow*, the phases flow at right angles to each other, as in the case of the air and water in an atmospheric water-cooling tower. The maximum possible concentration change occurs if one of the effluent streams comes to equilibrium with the other influent stream, and the operation may be equivalent to many stages.

There will be no difference in the ultimate concentration change possible in the three categories if one of the phases does not change its concentration, as, for example, the case of dissolving a pure gas in a liquid.

**Stagewise Operation.** If two insoluble phases are first allowed to come into contact so that the various diffusing components of the mixture may distribute themselves between the phases, and if the phases are then mechanically separated, the entire operation is said to constitute one *stage*. As an example, the laboratory batch extraction in a separatory funnel which was described earlier may be cited. The operation may be carried on in continuous as well as in batchwise fashion, however. Should a series of stages be arranged so that the phases are frequently contacted and separated once in each stage, the entire multistage assemblage is called a *cascade* and the phases may move through the cascade in parallel, countercurrent, or crossflow. In order to establish a standard for the measurement of performance, the *ideal*, or *theoretical*, *stage* is defined as one where the effluent phases are in equilibrium, so that longer time of contact will bring about no additional change of composition. The approach to equilibrium realized in any stage is then defined as the *stage efficiency*.

**Continuous-contact Operation.** In this case the phases flow through the equipment in continuous, intimate contact throughout, without repeated physical separation and contacting. The nature of the method requires the operation to be either semibatch or steady-state, and the resulting change in compositions may be equivalent to that given by a fraction of an ideal stage or by many stages. Equilibrium between two phases at any position in the equipment is never established; indeed, should equilibrium occur anywhere in the system, the result would be equivalent to the effect of an infinite number of stages.

The essential difference between stagewise and continuous-contact operation may then be summarized. In the case of the stagewise operation the diffusional flow of matter between the phases is allowed to reduce the concentration difference which causes the flow. If allowed to continue long enough, an equilibrium is established after which no further diffusional flow occurs. The rate of diffusion and the time then determine the stage efficiency realized in any particular situation. On the other hand, in the case of the continuous-contact operation the departure from equilibrium is deliberately maintained, and the diffusional flow between the phases may continue without interruption. Which method will be used depends to some extent on the stage efficiency that can be practically realized. A high stage efficiency can mean a relatively inexpensive plant and one whose performance can be reliably predicted. A low stage efficiency, on the other hand, may make the continuous-contact methods more desirable for reasons of cost and certainty.

### DESIGN PRINCIPLES

There are four major factors to be established in the design of any plant involving the diffusional operations: the number of ideal stages or their equivalent, the time of phase contact required, the permissible rate of flow, and the energy requirements.

**Number of Ideal Stages.** In order to determine the number of ideal stages required in a cascade to bring about a specified degree of separation, or the equivalent quantity for a continuous-contact device, the equilibrium characteristics of the system and material-balance calculations are required.

**Time Requirement.** In stagewise operations the time of contact is intimately connected with stage efficiency, whereas for continuous-contact equipment the time leads ultimately to the volume or length of the required device. The factors which help establish the time are several. Material balances permit calculation of the relative quantities required of the various phases. The equilibrium characteristics of the system establish the ultimate concentrations possible, and the rate of transfer of material between phases depends upon the departure from equilibrium which is maintained. The rate of transfer additionally depends upon the physical properties of the phases as well as the flow regime within the equipment.

It is important to recognize that, for a given degree of intimacy of contact of the phases, the time of contact required is independent of the total quantity of the phases to be processed.

**Permissible Flow Rate.**   This factor enters into consideration of semi-batch and steady-state operations, where it leads to the determination of the cross-sectional area of the equipment.   Considerations of fluid dynamics establish the permissible flow rate, and material balances determine the absolute quantity of each of the streams required.

**Energy Requirements.**   Heat and mechanical energies are ordinarily required to carry out the diffusional operations.   Heat is necessary for the production of any temperature changes, for the creation of new phases (such as vaporization of a liquid), and for overcoming heat-of-solution effects.   Mechanical energy is required for fluid and solid transport, for dispersing liquids and gases, and for operating moving parts of machinery.

The ultimate design, consequently, requires us to deal with the equilibrium characteristics of the system, material balances, diffusional rates, fluid dynamics, and energy requirements.   In what follows, basic considerations of diffusion rates are discussed first (Part I) and these are later applied to specific operations.   The principal operations, in turn, are subdivided into three categories, depending upon the nature of the insoluble phases contacted, gas-liquid (Part II), liquid-liquid (Part III), and solid-fluid (Part IV), since the equilibrium and fluid dynamics of the systems are most readily studied in such a grouping.   Part V considers contact of miscible phases.

## PROBLEMS

Classify the following simple operations according to whether they are (*a*) steady- or unsteady-state; (*b*) batch, semibatch, or continuous; (*c*) stagewise or continuous-contact; (*d*) single or multistage.

**1.** Solid salt is placed in a beaker of water, and the mixture stirred.   When the water is saturated, the solution is poured off, leaving the undissolved crystals behind.

**2.** Fresh water is added to the undissolved salt of Prob. 1, the mixture stirred and decanted, and the entire operation repeated five times.

**3.** Salt is placed in a beaker of water, fresh water is allowed to flow in continuously, the contents of the beaker are vigorously stirred, and the solution formed continuously overflows.   The salt ultimately completely dissolves.

**4.** A hot piece of metal is held in the cool running water stream from a water faucet until the metal is cold.

**5.** A hot piece of metal is placed in a beaker of cold water until metal and water are at the same temperature.

**6.** Coffee is prepared by allowing a portion of hot water to flow once through a bed of ground coffee beans, thus leaching out the desired soluble matter.

**7.** Coffee is prepared by pouring a portion of hot water repeatedly through the same ground coffee until no further leaching of the soluble matter occurs.

**8.** Coffee is prepared by stirring a sample of ground coffee with hot water in a container until the desired concentration in the solution is reached and the solid residue filtered from the liquid.

# PART I

# DIFFUSION AND MASS TRANSFER

If chemical engineering were sufficiently well developed, all our equipment could be designed, all our processes specified, and all the intricate phenomena observed in a chemical plant predicted from knowledge of the sciences of chemistry and physics, which are the foundation of chemical engineering. To the extent that we fail in this respect we resort to an experimental approach to solve our problems.

We have seen that there are certain characteristics common to all the diffusional operations: in every case, a fluid is brought into contact with another phase, a concentration gradient is established, and a transfer of matter from one phase to the other results. As a consequence there is an opportunity to coordinate and interrelate the operations one with another, with chemistry and physics providing the guiding principles. Such coordination is of considerable significance. It reduces the number of rules and empiricisms required to describe the operations, for example. It also simplifies experimental work, since it reduces the number of experiments required and permits experimentation on a small scale for use in large-scale design. Depending upon the extent of this development, forecasting the performance of engineering equipment is possible with increasing boldness as indicated in the following list of possibilities:

1. Prediction of performance of a given piece of equipment for new conditions from knowledge of its characteristics for one condition

2. Prediction of performance of a new piece of equipment from observation of another piece of equipment operating under similar, or even different conditions

3. Prediction of performance in one of the diffusional operations from observations made in another, for example, prediction for distillation from a knowledge of gas absorption

4. Prediction of performance in one of the diffusional operations from observations made in another, apparently unrelated

field, for example, predictions for gas absorption from a knowledge of fluid flow or heat transfer

5. Ultimate complete elimination of the need for additional experiments even in consideration of new operations and processes

The phenomena of diffusion and mass transfer between phases, and their relationship with the processes of momentum and heat transfer, are described briefly in Part I.   It will be seen that there are diverse stages of development in all the categories of the foregoing list.   Very substantial progress has been achieved in relatively recent years, and the field is advancing rapidly.   Indeed, it now seems reasonable to predict that the necessity for compartmenting the diffusional operations into some of the separate categories used in this book may be substantially eliminated in the foreseeable future.

# CHAPTER 2

# MOLECULAR DIFFUSION IN FLUIDS

It was shown in Chap. 1 that the diffusional operations always involve the contact of a fluid, either a gas or a liquid, with another phase, accompanied by transfer of material between the contacted phases. It is usually desirable to maintain the contacted phases in relative motion with respect to one another. Consequently, if molecules of one of the components present must move from one position to another in the system, it is clear that the nature of the bulk fluid movement will exert a profound influence upon the rate at which the transfer occurs.

**Diffusion and Fluid Flow.** Consider a fluid flowing past a solid interface such as the surface of a flat plate. Let the flow be rapid so that turbulent motion generally prevails. Assume also that the place under observation is relatively far removed from the edge of the plate, so that special conditions which prevail near the edge need not be considered. Extensive study has shown that the velocity of the fluid particles at various distances from the solid surface is not uniform but varies from zero at the surface to large values at positions far removed from the surface. Immediately adjacent to the interface there is a thin film in laminar or viscous flow. This film is characterized by an orderly movement of the fluid particles in persistent streamlines which parallel the contours of the surface, and there is no bulk movement in a direction perpendicular to the surface. The velocity increases linearly with distance from the surface within the laminar film. In the outer regions of the fluid, on the other hand, the flow is turbulent, characterized principally by large components of the velocity perpendicular to the surface. Relatively large portions of fluid, called eddies, move from one position in the fluid cross section to another, causing considerable mixing. The transition from laminar flow near the wall to turbulent flow in the outer fluid regions is gradual, giving rise to an intermediate buffer zone between the two principal zones. The relative thickness of the various zones depends upon the degree of turbulence existing, as measured by the Reynolds number, for example. These same phenomena are found whenever a fluid flows past a solid surface, flat or round, or past another insoluble fluid, although in the latter case the relative rather than the absolute velocity of the two phases at the interface is zero.

If a dissolved substance must diffuse through the various zones of such a moving fluid, it is clear that at least two separate mechanisms are necessarily involved. Diffusion in the laminar region is called *molecular diffusion*, that in the turbulent zone *eddy diffusion*.

**Molecular Diffusion.** Molecular diffusion is the transport of matter on a molecular scale through a fluid which is stagnant or, if in laminar flow, in a direction perpendicular to the flowing streamlines.

The kinetic theory of gases provides a means of visualizing what happens during a typical molecular-diffusion process. A molecule of a gas is imagined to travel in a straight line at a uniform velocity until it collides with another molecule, whereupon its velocity changes both in magnitude and direction. The average distance the molecule travels between collisions is called the mean free path, and the average velocity of the molecule is dependent upon the temperature. The molecule thus travels a highly complex zigzag path, and the net distance it moves in a given time is only a fraction of the distance along its actual path. For this reason, the net rate of diffusion is very slow, although we can expect it to increase with decreased pressure, which reduces the number of collisions, and with increased temperature, which increases the molecular velocity. The same general mechanism prevails also for the liquid state, although because of the considerably higher molecular concentration we find even slower diffusion rates. The phenomenon is frequently demonstrated by carefully pouring pure water over a copper sulfate solution in a glass cylinder, taking care not to mix the solutions during the process. If left to stand quietly, after a long period of time the copper sulfate will be found to have become uniformly distributed throughout the liquid, having diffused into the water. Similarly, perfume from an opened bottle will eventually pervade an entire room. Of course, in such gross experiments as these there may be superimposed upon the slow molecular diffusion the more rapid eddy diffusion resulting from mass movements of the fluids. It is difficult to demonstrate pure molecular diffusion over great distances since density differences resulting from nonuniform concentrations or temperatures give rise to convection currents in the fluid.

The phenomenon of molecular diffusion has been studied from several points of view, the most satisfactory of which is that of Maxwell and Stefan.[7,8,13] Briefly, for a binary solution of substances $A$ and $B$ which is not of uniform composition, there will be an interdiffusion of the substances which can be described in terms of the linear velocities of movement of $A$ and $B$. It is assumed that the drop in concentration of substance $A$, $-dc_A$, which acts as a driving force for the movement of $A$, is proportional to the relative linear velocity of $A$ with respect to $B$,

$u_A - u_B$; to the molecular concentrations of the substances, $c_A$ and $c_B$; and to the distance $dz$ through which the diffusion occurs,

$$-dc_A = \beta c_A c_B (u_A - u_B) \, dz \qquad (2.1)$$

This basic equation can now be treated to describe the various situations which may arise.[7]

## MOLECULAR DIFFUSION IN GASES

In the case of gases, the molar concentrations $c$ may be expressed as $\rho/M$ and the concentration gradient as $dp$. Equation (2.1) then becomes

$$-dp_A = \beta \, \frac{\rho_A \rho_B}{M_A M_B} \, (u_A - u_B) \, dz \qquad (2.2)$$

Define $N$ as the number of moles of gas diffusing per unit time, per unit area, in a direction perpendicular to that of the diffusion.

$$N = \frac{\rho u}{M} \qquad (2.3)$$

$$-dp_A = \beta \left( \frac{\rho_A u_A}{M_A} \frac{\rho_B}{M_B} - \frac{\rho_A}{M_A} \frac{\rho_B u_B}{M_B} \right) dz \qquad (2.4)$$

$$-dp_A = \beta \left( N_A \frac{\rho_B}{M_B} - N_B \frac{\rho_A}{M_A} \right) dz \qquad (2.5)$$

Applying the ideal-gas law,

$$\frac{p}{RT} = \frac{\rho}{M} \qquad (2.6)$$

Then $$-dp_A = \frac{\beta}{RT} \, (N_A p_B - N_B p_A) \, dz \qquad (2.7)$$

Since $$P = p_A + p_B \qquad (2.8)$$

$$p_B = P - p_A \qquad (2.9)$$

$$-dp_A = \frac{\beta}{RT} \, (N_A P - N_A p_A - N_B p_A) \, dz \qquad (2.10)$$

Let $$D_{AB} = \frac{R^2 T^2}{\beta P} \qquad (2.11)$$

$$\therefore \ -dp_A = \frac{RT}{D_{AB} P} \, (N_A P - N_A p_A - N_B p_A) \, dz \qquad (2.12)$$

1. *Steady-state Equimolal Counterdiffusion.* This is a situation which frequently pertains in distillation operations. $N_A$ and $N_B$ are constant, and $N_A = -N_B$. The concentrations at any point in the gas mixture remain constant with passage of time. Assuming $D_{AB}$ remains constant, Eq. (2.12) becomes

$$-\int_{p_{A1}}^{p_{A2}} dp_A = \frac{RT N_A}{D_{AB}} \int_{z_1}^{z_2} dz \qquad (2.13)$$

Letting $z_2 - z_1 = z$,

$$N_A = \frac{D_{AB}}{RTz}(p_{A1} - p_{A2}) \tag{2.14}$$

This equation is known as Fick's law, which parallels Fourier's equation for steady-state flow of heat, the concentration gradient in terms of partial pressures replacing the corresponding driving force in terms of temperature difference for heat transfer. It is frequently incorrectly

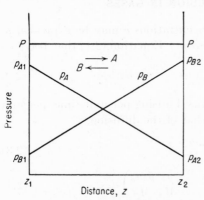

used in the determination of $D$, the *diffusion coefficient*, or *diffusivity*, under conditions where equimolal counterdiffusion does not occur. $D$ is a function of the temperature, pressure, and components of the gas mixture; it may depend very weakly upon the composition. It should be noted that the same diffusivity applies to both components $A$ and $B$, or $D_{AB} = D_{BA}$. Equation (2.14) may be represented graphically as in Fig. 2.1, where substance $A$ is shown diffusing in the direction of

Fig. 2.1. Equimolar counterdiffusion.

its drop in concentration or partial pressure $p_A$, with substance $B$ diffusing in the opposite direction.

2. *Steady-state Diffusion of A through Stagnant (Nondiffusing) B.* $N_B = 0$, $N_A$ = const. Equation (2.12) becomes

$$-dp_A = \frac{RTN_A}{D_{AB}P}(P - p_A)\,dz \tag{2.15}$$

Assuming $D_{AB}$ remains constant,

$$z = \int_{z_1}^{z_2} dz = -\frac{D_{AB}P}{RTN_A}\int_{p_{A1}}^{p_{A2}}\frac{dp_A}{P - p_A} = \frac{D_{AB}P}{RTN_A}\ln\frac{P - p_{A2}}{P - p_{A1}} \tag{2.16}$$

$$N_A = \frac{D_{AB}P}{RTz}\ln\frac{P - p_{A2}}{P - p_{A1}} \tag{2.17}$$

$$P - p_{A2} = p_{B2} \qquad P - p_{A1} = p_{B1} \qquad p_{B2} - p_{B1} = p_{A1} - p_{A2} \tag{2.18}$$

$$N_A = \frac{D_{AB}P(p_{A1} - p_{A2})}{RTz(p_{B2} - p_{B1})}\ln\frac{p_{B2}}{p_{B1}} \tag{2.19}$$

Letting

$$p_{BM} = \frac{p_{B2} - p_{B1}}{\ln(p_{B2}/p_{B1})} \tag{2.20}$$

$$N_A = \frac{D_{AB}P}{RTzp_{BM}}(p_{A1} - p_{A2}) \tag{2.21}$$

This equation can be shown graphically as in Fig. 2.2. Substance $A$ diffuses by virtue of its concentration gradient $p_{A1} - p_{A2}$. Substance $B$

does not diffuse, and its concentration gradient is maintained by inter-molecular friction between $A$ and $B$. Its hindering effect is included as the average concentration $p_{BM}$ in Eq. (2.21).

3. *Steady-state Diffusion of A through a Stagnant Multicomponent Mixture.* For the case where component $A$ diffuses through a stagnant mixture composed of constant proportions of components $B$, $C$, etc., Eq. (2.21) applies, provided an effective diffusivity of component $A$ through the mixture, defined as[17]

$$D'_A = \frac{1}{(Y_B/D_{AB}) + (Y_C/D_{AC}) + (Y_D/D_{AD}) + \cdots} \qquad (2.22)$$

is used. Here $Y$ refers to the mole-fraction compositions on an $A$-free basis. The average partial pressure $p_{iM}$ of the nondiffusing mixture is used in place of $p_{BM}$.

4. *Steady-state Simultaneous Diffusion in Multicomponent Mixtures.* Exact but complicated expressions for a ternary mixture have been presented,[11] and simpler approximations presumably applicable to any number of components are also available.[17] These situations are beyond the scope of this book.

**Illustration 1.** Oxygen ($A$) is diffusing through carbon monoxide ($B$) under steady-state conditions, with the carbon monoxide nondiffusing. The total pressure is 1 atm., and the temperature 0°C. The partial pressure of oxygen at two planes 0.2 cm. apart are, respectively, 100 and 50 mm. Hg. The diffusivity for the mixture

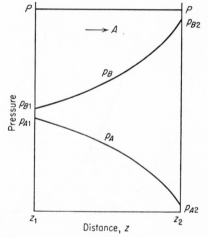

FIG. 2.2. Diffusion of $A$ through stagnant $B$.

is 0.185 sq. cm./sec. Calculate the rate of diffusion of oxygen in gm. moles/sec. through each square centimeter of the two planes.

*Solution.* Equation (2.21) applies. $D_{AB} = 0.185$ sq. cm./sec., $P = 1.0$ atm., $z = 0.2$ cm., $R = 82.06$ cu. cm. (atm.)/(gm. mole)(°K.), $T = 273$°K., $p_{A1} = 100/760 = 0.1317$ atm., $p_{A2} = 50/760 = 0.0658$ atm., $p_{B1} = 1 - 0.1317 = 0.8683$ atm., $p_{B2} = 1 - 0.0658 = 0.9342$ atm.

$$p_{BM} = \frac{p_{B1} - p_{B2}}{\ln (p_{B1}/p_{B2})} = \frac{0.8683 - 0.9342}{\ln (0.8683/0.9342)} = 0.901 \text{ atm.}$$

$$N_A = \frac{D_{AB}P}{RTzp_{BM}} (p_{A1} - p_{A2}) = \frac{0.185(1.0)(0.1317 - 0.0658)}{82.06(273)(0.2)(0.901)}$$
$$= 3.01(10^{-6}) \text{ gm. mole/(sec.)(sq. cm.)}$$

**Illustration 2.** Recalculate the rate of diffusion of oxygen ($A$) in Illustration 1, assuming that the nondiffusing gas is a mixture of methane ($B$) and hydrogen ($C$) in the volume ratio 2:1. The diffusivities are estimated to be $D_{O_2\text{-}H_2} = 0.690$ sq. cm./sec., $D_{O_2\text{-}CH_4} = 0.184$ sq. cm./sec.

*Solution.* Equation (2.21) applies. $P = 1.0$ atm., $T = 273°K.$, $p_{A1} = 0.1317$ atm., $p_{A2} = 0.0658$ atm., $p_{iM} = 0.901$ atm., $z = 0.2$ cm., $R = 82.06$ cu. cm (atm.)/- (gm. mole)(°K.) (see Illustration 1). $Y_B = 2/(2 + 1) = 0.667$, $Y_C = 1 - 0.667 = 0.333$, $D_{AB} = 0.184$, $D_{AC} = 0.690$ sq. cm./sec. Equation (2.22):

$$D'_A = \frac{1}{(Y_B/D_{AB}) + (Y_C/D_{AC})} = \frac{1}{(0.667/0.184) + (0.333/0.690)} = 0.244 \text{ sq. cm./sec.}$$

$$\therefore N_A = \frac{D'_A P}{RT z p_{im}} (p_{A1} - p_{A2}) = \frac{0.244(1.0)(0.1317 - 0.0658)}{82.06(273)(0.2)(0.901)}$$
$$= 3.97(10^{-6}) \text{ gm. mole/(sec.)(sq. cm.)}$$

**Diffusivity of Gases.** The diffusivity, or diffusion coefficient, $D$ is a property of the system dependent principally upon the temperature, pressure, and nature of the components of the system. Its dimensions on a

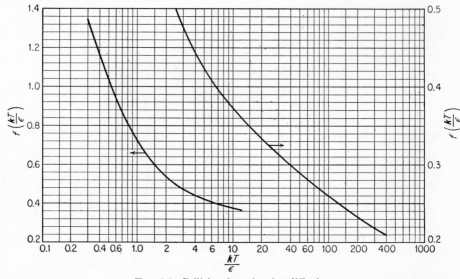

FIG. 2.3. Collision function for diffusion.

volumetric basis may be established by solving for $D$ in Eq. (2.14) and are (length)$^2$/time. In the c.g.s. system, sq. cm./sec. are ordinarily used, occasionally sq. cm./day. The corresponding English-system units are sq. ft./hr.

$$(D \text{ sq. cm./sec.})3.87 = D \text{ sq. ft./hr.}$$
$$(D \text{ sq. cm./sec.})86,400 = D \text{ sq. cm./day}$$

A few typical data are listed in Table 2.1.

Expressions for estimating $D$ in the absence of experimental data are ordinarily based on considerations of the kinetic theory, in the manner of Maxwell[9] and others. Hirschfelder, Bird, and Spotz[5] have summarized what appears to be the best method in the following equation,†

$$D_{AB} = \frac{0.0009292 T^{3/2} \left( \dfrac{1}{M_A} + \dfrac{1}{M_B} \right)^{1/2}}{P(r_{AB})^2 [f(kT/\epsilon_{AB})]}$$  (2.23)

where $D_{AB}$ = diffusivity, sq. cm./sec.

$T$ = abs. temp., °K.

$M_A$, $M_B$ = mol. wt. of $A$ and $B$, respectively

$P$ = abs. pressure, atm.

$r_{AB}$ = mol. separation at collision, A

    = $(r_A + r_B)/2$

$\epsilon_{AB}$ = energy mol. interaction, ergs

    = $\sqrt{\epsilon_A \epsilon_B}$

$k$ = Boltzmann const. = $1.38 \times 10^{-6}$ erg/°K.

$f(kT/\epsilon_{AB})$ = a collision function given by Fig. 2.3

TABLE 2.1. DIFFUSIVITIES OF GASES AT ATMOSPHERIC PRESSURE

| System | Temp., °C | Diffusivity, sq. cm./sec. | Ref. |
|---|---|---|---|
| $H_2$-$CH_4$ . . . . . . . . . . . . . . | 0 | 0.625 | 2 |
| $O_2$-$N_2$ . . . . . . . . . . . . . . . | 0 | 0.181 | 2 |
| CO-$O_2$ . . . . . . . . . . . . . . . | 0 | 0.185 | 2 |
| $CO_2$-$O_2$ . . . . . . . . . . . . . . | 0 | 0.139 | 2 |
| Air-$NH_3$ . . . . . . . . . . . . . | 0 | 0.198 | 18 |
| Air-$H_2O$ . . . . . . . . . . . . | 25.9 | 0.258 | 3 |
| | 59.0 | 0.305 | 3 |
| Air-ethanol . . . . . . . . . . . . | 0 | 0.102 | 6 |
| Air-$n$-butanol . . . . . . . . . | 25.9 | 0.087 | 3 |
| | 59.0 | 0.104 | 3 |
| Air-ethyl acetate . . . . . . . | 25.9 | 0.087 | 3 |
| | 59.0 | 0.106 | 3 |
| Air-aniline . . . . . . . . . . . . | 25.9 | 0.074 | 3 |
| | 59.0 | 0.090 | 3 |
| Air-chlorobenzene . . . . . . . | 25.9 | 0.074 | 3 |
| | 59.0 | 0.090 | 3 |
| Air-toluene . . . . . . . . . . . . | 25.9 | 0.086 | 3 |
| | 59.0 | 0.092 | 3 |

The quantities $\epsilon/k$ and $r$, such as those listed in Table 2.2, can be calculated from other properties of the gases, such as viscosity, or the equations of state. If necessary, they can be estimated for each component

† The listed units must be used in Eq. (2.23).

empirically, however,†

$$\frac{\epsilon}{k} = 0.75 T_{crit} \tag{2.24}$$

$$\frac{\epsilon}{k} = 1.39 T_{nbp} \tag{2.25}$$

$$r = 0.835 v_{crit}^{1/3} \tag{2.26}$$

where $T_{crit}$ = critical temp., °K.

$T_{nbp}$ = normal boiling point (n.b.p.), °K.

$v_{crit}$ = critical vol., cu. cm./gm. mole

Equation (2.23) is most satisfactory for mixtures of nonpolar gases or of a polar with a nonpolar gas.

TABLE 2.2. FORCE CONSTANTS OF GASES AS DETERMINED FROM VISCOSITY DATA†

| Gas | $\epsilon/k$, °K. | $r$, A. |
|---|---|---|
| Air | 97.0 | 3.617 |
| $H_2$ | 33.3 | 2.968 |
| $N_2$ | 91.46 | 3.681 |
| $CO_2$ | 190 | 3.996 |
| $N_2O$ | 220 | 3.879 |
| NO | 119 | 3.470 |
| $CH_4$ | 136.5 | 3.882 |
| $O_2$ | 113.2 | 3.433 |
| CO | 110.3 | 3.590 |
| A | 124.0 | 3.418 |
| Ne | 35.7 | 2.80 |
| He | 6.03 | 2.70 |

† By permission from Hirschfelder, Bird, and Spotz, *Trans. A.S.M.E.*, **71**, 921 (1949).

**Illustration 3.** Estimate the diffusivity of $O_2$ through CO at 1 atm., 0°C. (obsd. value = 0.185 sq. cm./sec.).

*Solution.* $T = 273$°K., $P = 1$ atm., $M_A = 32$, $M_B = 28$. From Table 2.2, for $O_2$, $\epsilon_A/k = 113.2$°K., $r_A = 3.433$ A; for CO, $\epsilon_B/k = 110.3$°K., $r_B = 3.590$ A.

$$\frac{\epsilon_{AB}}{k} = \sqrt{\frac{\epsilon_A}{k} \frac{\epsilon_B}{k}} = \sqrt{113.2(110.3)} = 111.6°K.$$

$$\frac{kT}{\epsilon_{AB}} = \frac{273}{111.6} = 2.44$$

From Fig. 2.3, $f(kT/\epsilon_{AB}) = 0.504$.

$$r_{AB} = \frac{r_A + r_B}{2} = \frac{3.433 + 3.590}{2} = 3.512 \text{ A}$$

† The listed units must be used in Eqs. (2.24) to (2.26).

Substitution in Eq. (2.23) gives

$$D_{AB} = \frac{0.0009292(273)^{3/2}(\frac{1}{32} + \frac{1}{28})^{1/2}}{1(3.512)^2(0.504)} = 0.175 \text{ sq. cm./sec.}$$

Alternatively, the critical properties of the gases might have been used to estimate the quantities, Eqs. (2.24) and (2.26). Thus, for $O_2$, $T_{crit} = 154.4°K.$, $v_{crit} = 74.5$ cu. cm./gm. mole. Thus $\epsilon_A/k = 0.75(154.4) = 116°K.$, $r_A = 0.833(74.5)^{1/3} = 3.50$ A. Similarly for CO, $T_{crit} = 134.2°K.$, $v_{crit} = 90$ cu. cm./gm. mole, and $\epsilon_B/k = 0.75(134.2) = 100.6°K.$, $r_B = 0.833(90)^{1/3} = 3.72$ A. These values lead to $D_{AB} = 0.167$ sq. cm./sec.

Equation (2.23) shows $D$ varying substantially as $T^{3/2}$ and inversely as the pressure, which will serve for extrapolation at least over moderate ranges of temperature and pressure. The effect of varying conditions may also be followed through the dimensionless Schmidt number, $Sc = \mu/\rho D$, which remains substantially constant. The experimental evidence respecting the effect of concentration on $D$ for a binary gas mixture is meager and indicates substantially negligible concentration dependence. Hirschfelder et al.[5] show the effect rarely to be greater than about 3 per cent.

The coefficient of self-diffusion, or $D$ for a gas diffusing through itself, is a quantity that can be determined experimentally only by very special techniques involving, for example, the use of radioactive tracers. It can be estimated from Eq. (2.23) by setting $A = B$.

## MOLECULAR DIFFUSION IN LIQUIDS

Applications of the basic expression, Eq. (2.1), to the liquid phase are based largely on treatment paralleling that for gases. The kinetic theory is not readily extended to the liquid phase, and our knowledge of the variations of properties with concentration are less well developed than with gases. The resulting expressions are consequently much less reliable.

If $N$ is again defined as the number of moles of solute diffusing through the solution per unit time per unit cross section,

$$N = cu \qquad (2.27)$$

Equation (2.1) therefore becomes

$$-dc_A = \beta(c_A u_A c_B - c_A u_B c_B) \, dz \qquad (2.28)$$
$$-dc_A = \beta(N_A c_B - N_B c_A) \, dz \qquad (2.29)$$

1. *Steady-state Equimolal Counterdiffusion.* $N_A$ and $N_B$ are constant; $N_A = -N_B$. Assuming that $\beta$ and $c_A + c_B$ are constant with changing composition, or with $z$, Eq. (2.29) becomes

$$-dc_A = \beta N_A(c_A + c_B) \, dz \qquad (2.30)$$

Defining the diffusivity for liquids as

$$D_{AB} = \frac{1}{\beta(c_A + c_B)} \tag{2.31}$$

then

$$-\int_{c_{A1}}^{c_{A2}} dc_A = \frac{N_A}{D_{AB}} \int_{z_1}^{z_2} dz \tag{2.32}$$

$$N_A = \frac{D_{AB}}{z}(c_{A1} - c_{A2}) \tag{2.33}$$

which is Fick's law. If $c_A + c_B = c$, then $c_A = x_A c$, etc., and Eq. (2.33) in terms of mole-fraction compositions $x$ becomes

$$N_A = \frac{D_{AB}c}{z}(x_{A1} - x_{A2}) \tag{2.34}$$

2. *Steady-state Diffusion of A through Stagnant (Nondiffusing) B.* $N_A = $ const., $N_B = 0$. Equation (2.29) becomes

$$-dc_A = \beta N_A c_B \, dz = \frac{N_A c_B}{D_{AB}(c_A + c_B)} \, dz \tag{2.35}$$

Assuming

$$D_{AB}(c_A + c_B) = D_{AB}c = \text{const.} \tag{2.36}$$

Equation (2.35) integrates in the same fashion as the corresponding case for gases,

$$N_A = \frac{D_{AB}c(c_{A1} - c_{A2})}{c_{BM}z} = \frac{D_{AB}c(x_{A1} - x_{A2})}{x_{BM}z} \tag{2.37}$$

where $c_{BM}$ and $x_{BM}$ are the average concentrations of $B$ at positions 1 and 2. Moderate variations of $c$ at the two positions can be taken care of by use of an average value, $c = (c_1 + c_2)/2$. There is some question of the usefulness of a relationship such as Eq. (2.37) in preference to Eq. (2.33) for this case, since $D_{AB}$ and $c_A + c_B$ will be constant only for dilute solutions. Under these circumstances, $c \doteq c_{BM}$, and Eq. (2.33) can be used for both.

**Illustration 4.** Calculate the rate of diffusion of acetic acid $(A)$ across a film of water $(B)$ solution 0.1 cm. thick at 17°C. when the concentrations on opposite sides of the film are, respectively, 9 and 3 wt. %. The diffusivity of acetic acid in the solution may be taken as $0.95 \times 10^{-5}$ sq. cm./sec.

*Solution.* Use Eq. (2.37). $z = 0.1$ cm. Mol. wt. acetic acid = 60.03, mol. wt. water = 18.02. At 17°C., the density of the 9% solution is 1.0120 gm./cu. cm. Therefore,

$$c_{A1} = \frac{1.0120(0.09)}{60.03} = 0.001515 \text{ gm. mole acetic acid/cu. cm.}$$

$$c_{B1} = \frac{1.0120(0.91)}{18.02} = 0.0455 \text{ gm. mole water/cu. cm.}$$

$$c_1 = c_{A1} + c_{B1} = 0.0470 \text{ gm. mole/cu. cm.}$$

The density of the $3\%$ solution is $1.0032$ gm./cu. cm. Therefore,

$$c_{A2} = \frac{1.0032(0.03)}{60.03} = 0.000501 \text{ gm. mole acetic acid/cu. cm.}$$

$$c_{B2} = \frac{1.0032(0.97)}{18.02} = 0.0540 \text{ gm. mole acetic acid/cu. cm.}$$

$$c_2 = c_{A2} + c_{B2} = 0.0545 \text{ gm. mole/cu. cm.}$$

$$c_{BM} = \frac{c_{B2} - c_{B1}}{\ln (c_{B2}/c_{B1})} = \frac{0.0540 - 0.0455}{\ln (0.0540/0.0455)} = 0.0497 \text{ gm. mole/cu. cm.}$$

$$c = \frac{c_1 + c_2}{2} = \frac{0.0470 + 0.0545}{2} = 0.0508 \text{ gm. mole/cu. cm.}$$

$$N_A = \frac{D_{ABC}(c_{A1} - c_{A2})}{c_{BM}z} = \frac{0.95(10^{-5})(0.0508)(0.001505 - 0.000501)}{0.0497(0.1)}$$

$$= 9.85(10^{-8}) \text{ gm. mole/(sq. cm.)(sec.)}$$

**Diffusivity of Liquids.** The dimensions for diffusivity in the liquid phase are the same as those for gases, $(\text{length})^2/\text{time}$. Unlike the case for gases, however, the diffusivity varies appreciably with concentration. A few typical data are listed in Table 2.3. Estimations of the diffusivity

TABLE 2.3. LIQUID DIFFUSIVITIES[6]

| Solute | Solvent | Temp., °C. | Solute concn., gm. moles/liter | Diffusivity,† sq. cm./sec. $\times 10^5$ |
|---|---|---|---|---|
| $Cl_2$..................... | Water | 16 | 0.12 | 1.26 |
| HCl................... | Water | 0 | 9 | 2.7 |
| | | | 2 | 1.8 |
| | | 10 | 9 | 3.3 |
| | | | 2.5 | 2.5 |
| | | 16 | 0.5 | 2.44 |
| $NH_3$................... | Water | 5 | 3.5 | 1.24 |
| | | 15 | 1.0 | 1.77 |
| $CO_2$.................. | Water | 10 | 0 | 1.46 |
| | | 20 | 0 | 1.77 |
| NaCl.................. | Water | 18 | 0.05 | 1.26 |
| | | | 0.2 | 1.21 |
| | | | 1.0 | 1.24 |
| | | | 3.0 | 1.36 |
| | | | 5.4 | 1.54 |
| Methanol............... | Water | 15 | 0 | 1.28 |
| Acetic acid............. | Water | 12.5 | 1.0 | 0.82 |
| | | | 0.01 | 0.91 |
| | | 18.0 | 1.0 | 0.96 |
| Ethanol................ | Water | 10 | 3.75 | 0.50 |
| | | | 0.05 | 0.83 |
| | | 16 | 2.0 | 0.90 |
| $n$-Butanol.............. | Water | 15 | 0 | 0.77 |
| $CO_2$.................. | Ethanol | 17 | 0 | 3.2 |
| Chloroform............. | Ethanol | 20 | 2.0 | 1.25 |

† For example, $D$ for $Cl_2$ in water is $0.0000126$ sq. cm./sec.

for nonelectrolytes in dilute solution in the absence of experimental data can be made by the methods of Wilke,[16] which were developed as empirical extensions of the theory of absolute rates.[4]   The quantity†

$$\frac{T}{D_{AB}\mu_B} = F \tag{2.38}$$

where $T$ = abs. temp., °K.

$D_{AB}$ = diffusivity of solute $A$ through solvent $B$, sq. cm./sec.

$\mu_B$ = viscosity of solvent $B$, centipoises

correlated as a function of the molal volume of the solute (Fig. 2.4). The parameter $\phi$ takes into account differences in solvent properties.

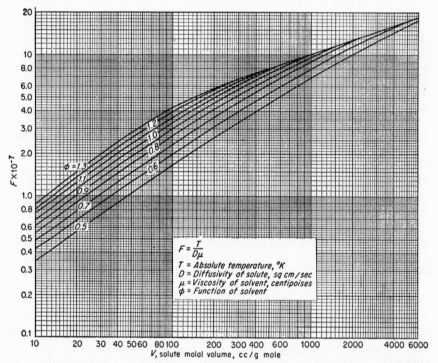

FIG. 2.4. Diffusivity correlation for dilute solutions of nonelectrolytes.[16]   (Reproduced with the permission of the American Institute of Chemical Engineers.)

For solute molal volumes less than 150 cu. cm./gm. mole, $\phi$ equals the ratio of $F$ for diffusion in the solvent to $F$ for diffusion in water at constant solute molal volume.   Values of $\phi$ for water, methanol, and benzene are 1.0, 0.82, and 0.70, respectively.   For other solvents, $\phi$ may be obtained by plotting all the available diffusion data for the solvent on the figure and drawing the best line through the plotted points.   If such data are

† The listed units must be used in Eq. (2.38).

lacking, $\phi$ may be taken as 0.9. In using Fig. 2.4, the value of $v_A$, solute molal volume, must be obtained empirically in the manner used in establishing the figure. It must be calculated by Kopp's law, which states that the molal volume is an additive function of the atomic volumes of the constituents of a molecule, and the contributions for each atom are listed in Table 2.4. For the smaller molecules the table lists directly the value to be used, and for more complex molecules the values for con-

TABLE 2.4. ATOMIC AND MOLECULAR VOLUMES

| *Atomic vol.* | | *Mol. vol.* | |
|---|---|---|---|
| Carbon | 14.8 | $H_2$ | 14.3 |
| Hydrogen | 3.7 | $O_2$ | 25.6 |
| Chlorine | 24.6 | $N_2$ | 31.2 |
| Bromine | 27.0 | Air | 29.9 |
| Iodine | 37.0 | CO | 30.7 |
| Sulfur | 25.6 | $CO_2$ | 34.0 |
| Nitrogen | 15.6 | $SO_2$ | 44.8 |
| Nitrogen in primary amines | 10.5 | NO | 23.6 |
| Nitrogen in secondary amines | 12.0 | $N_2O$ | 36.4 |
| Oxygen | 7.4 | $NH_3$ | 25.8 |
| Oxygen in methyl esters | 9.1 | $H_2O$ | 18.9 |
| Oxygen in higher esters | 11.0 | $H_2S$ | 32.9 |
| Oxygen in acids | 12.0 | COS | 51.5 |
| Oxygen in methyl ethers | 9.9 | $Cl_2$ | 48.4 |
| Oxygen in higher ethers | 11.0 | $Br_2$ | 53.2 |
| Benzene ring: subtract | 15 | $I_2$ | 71.5 |
| Naphthalene ring: subtract | 30 | | |

stituent atoms are added together. Thus, for toluene, $C_7H_8$, $v = 7(14.8) + 8(3.7) - 15 = 118.2$. It was further observed that $F$ for a given solution is relatively independent of temperature, which thus provides a means of estimating the effect of temperature on $D$.

**Illustration 5.** Estimate the diffusivity of mannitol, $CH_2OH(CHOH)_4CH_2OH$, $C_6H_{14}O_6$, in dilute water solution at 20°C. Compare with the observed value, $0.56(10^{-5})$ sq. cm./sec.

*Solution.* From the data of Table 2.4,

$$v_A = 14.8(6) + 3.7(14) + 7.4(6) = 185.0$$

For water as solvent, $\phi = 1.0$. From Fig. 2.4, $F = 4.80(10^7)$. At 20°C., the viscosity of water is 1.005 centipoises; $T = 293°K$.

$$D_{AB} = \frac{T}{\mu_B F} = \frac{293}{1.005(4.80)(10^7)} = 0.605(10^{-5}) \text{ sq. cm./sec.}$$

**Illustration 6.** Estimate the diffusivity of mannitol in dilute water solution at 70°C., and compare with the observed value, $1.56(10^{-5})$ sq. cm./sec.

*Solution.* At 20°C., the observed value of $D$ is $0.56(10^{-5})$ sq. cm./sec., and the viscosity of water is 1.005 centipoises. At 70°C., the viscosity of water is 0.4061 centipoise.

$$F = \left(\frac{T}{\mu_B D_{AB}}\right)_{20°C.} = \left(\frac{T}{\mu_B D_{AB}}\right)_{70°C.}$$

$$\frac{273 + 20}{1.005(0.56)(10^{-5})} = \frac{273 + 70}{0.4061 D_{AB}}$$

$$D_{AB} \text{ at } 70°C. = 1.62(10^{-5}) \text{ sq. cm./sec.}$$

With the calculated value of $F = 4.80(10^7)$ from Illustration 5, the estimated $D$ at 70°C. is $1.76(10^{-5})$ sq. cm./sec.

The diffusivity for concentrated solutions differs from that for dilute solutions because of changes in viscosity with concentration and also because of changes in the degree of ideality of the solution. In the case of solutions of strong electrolytes in water, the diffusion rates are those of the individual ions, which move more rapidly than the larger undissociated molecules. Estimation of these effects may be made by methods beyond the scope of this book.[14]

## TRANSFER OF MOMENTUM AND HEAT IN LAMINAR FLOW

We have seen that in most diffusional operations the diffusing substance must pass by a process of molecular diffusion through a layer of fluid in laminar flow. At the same time there will necessarily be a transfer of momentum from one position in the fluid to the other, and very frequently a transfer of heat. The three processes are so intimately connected, and our understanding of any of the three so greatly assisted by knowledge of the others, that it is now necessary briefly to consider the problems of momentum and heat transfer under conditions of laminar flow.

**Momentum Transfer.** When a fluid flows parallel to a flat solid surface, extensive study of the velocity within the laminar layer adjacent to the wall has established that the velocity is zero at the surface and increases linearly with distance from the wall, as in Fig. 2.5. If the flow as a whole is in well-developed turbulence, the thickness of the laminar film is very small, of the order of a fraction of a millimeter. Within the film, the fluid may be imagined as being made up of very thin layers sliding over one another at increasing velocities as the distance from the surface increases. In order to maintain the velocity of each layer, a force must be applied to the layers. The force per unit area parallel to the surface, or shearing stress $\tau$, is proportional to the velocity gradient,

$$\tau g_c = -\mu \frac{dU}{dz} \qquad\qquad (2.39)$$

where $\mu$ is the viscosity coefficient, or simply viscosity. This may be written as

$$\tau g_c = -\frac{\mu}{\rho}\frac{d(U\rho)}{dz} = -\nu\frac{d(U\rho)}{dz} \tag{2.40}$$

where $\nu$ = kinematic viscosity = $\mu/\rho$

$\quad U\rho$ = momentum per unit vol.

The kinematic viscosity has the same dimensions as diffusivity, (length)$^2$/ time, while the quantity $U\rho$ may be looked upon as a "momentum concentration."[11]    The force $\tau g_c$ is the rate of transfer of momentum per unit area.    Equation (2.40) is therefore a rate equation giving the rate of

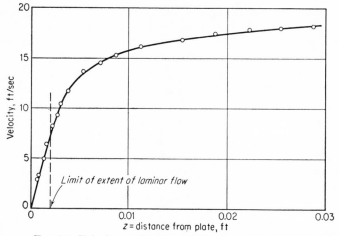

FIG. 2.5. Velocity profile, flow of air along a flat plate.[10]

momentum transfer as a function of the "momentum concentration," analogous to Eq. (2.13) or (2.32) for diffusion.

In the transfer of momentum in this manner there is, of course, no bulk flow of fluid from one layer to the other in the $z$ direction.    Instead, molecules in one layer, in the course of traveling their mean-free-path distance in random directions, will move from one layer to an adjacent layer, thereby transmitting momentum. Diffusion in the $z$ direction occurs by the same mechanism.    At high molecular concentrations, such as in gases at elevated pressures or even more so in liquids, the molecular diameter becomes appreciable in comparison to the mean free path, and momentum will be transmitted directly through the molecules themselves at high rates.[1]    Visualize, for example, a number of billiard balls arranged in a group in close contact with one another on a table.    A moving cue ball, colliding with one of the outermost balls of the packed group, will transmit its momentum very rapidly to one of the balls on the opposite side of the group, which will then be propelled from its original position. On the other hand, a cue ball would be able to move bodily through a group of even loosely packed billiard balls only very slowly because of the large number of collisions it would experience. Thus at high molecular concentrations the direct parallelism between molecular diffusivity and momentum transfer (or kinematic viscosity) breaks down: diffusion is much the slower process. It is interesting, however, that for gases at low pressures a simplified kinetic theory predicts that both the coefficient of self-diffusion and kinematic viscosity are given by the same expression,

$$D_{AA} = \frac{\mu_A}{\rho_A} = \frac{w\lambda}{3} \qquad (2.41)$$

where $w$ = av. mol. velocity

$\lambda$ = mean free path of a molecule

The Schmidt number for a pure gas, $Sc = \mu_A/\rho_A D_{AA}$, should by this theory equal unity. More advanced calculations give values from 0.67 to 0.83, which is precisely the range found experimentally at moderate pressures. Considerations of this sort lead to the use of viscosity data such as those of Table 2.2 for the estimation of gas diffusivities. For liquids, as would be expected, $\mu_A/\rho_A D_{AA}$ is considerably larger, approximately 297 for water at 77°F., for example.[15]

**Heat Transfer.** When a temperature gradient is superimposed upon a stagnant fluid, the rate of heat transfer will be

$$q = -k\frac{dt}{dz} \qquad (2.42)$$

where $k$ is the thermal conductivity of the fluid and $dt/dz$ the temperature gradient. This may also be written as

$$q = -\frac{k}{C_p\rho}\frac{d(tC_p\rho)}{dz} = -\alpha\frac{d(tC_p\rho)}{dz} \qquad (2.43)$$

where $C_p$ is the heat capacity at constant pressure. The quantity $tC_p\rho$ may be looked upon as a volumetric thermal concentration, and $\alpha = k/C_p\rho$ is the thermal diffusivity, which like momentum and mass diffusivities has the dimensions (length)$^2$/time. Equation (2.43) is therefore a rate equation analogous to the corresponding equations for momentum and mass transfer.

In a gas at relatively low pressures the heat energy is transferred from one position to another by the molecules traveling a distance equal to their mean free path. A simplified kinetic theory, in the manner used for kinematic viscosity, leads to the expression

$$\alpha = \frac{k}{C_p\rho} = \frac{1}{3}w\lambda\frac{C_v}{C_p} \qquad (2.44)$$

Combining Eqs. (2.41) and (2.44) would give the dimensionless ratio $\nu/\alpha = C_p\mu/k$ equal to $C_p/C_v$. A more advanced kinetic theory modifies the value of the ratio, which is known as the Prandtl number Pr, and experimentally it has the range of values 0.65 to 0.9 for gases at low pressures, depending upon the molecular complexity of the gas. At higher molecular concentrations, the molecular diameter is relatively large in comparison with the mean free path, and the energy is transferred to some extent directly across the molecule itself. The process is then more rapid, and the ratio may be considerably different. Thus, for most liquids Pr is larger (Pr = 7.02 for water at 68°F., for example).

The dimensionless group formed by dividing the thermal diffusivity by the diffusion coefficient, $\alpha/D$, has not yet been given a formal name. As will be seen later, it plays an important part in problems of simultaneous heat and mass transfer.

We may summarize this discussion of the similarity between momentum, heat, and mass transfer as follows. An elementary consideration of the three processes leads to the conclusion that in certain simplified situations, such as the case of simple gases at low molecular concentrations, Sc = Pr = $\alpha/D$ = 1. In so far as this is true, direct analogies between the processes may be possible. Significant differences between the various diffusivities exist, however, and consequently only limited parallelism can be expected. Furthermore, we can expect that a change in nature of the flow regime, such as the appearance of turbulence, or simultaneous appearance of more than one process, will have an influence on the situation.

## NOTATION FOR CHAPTER 2

Generally, consistent units in either the c.g.s. or the English system may be used. It has become the custom to express pressures in the diffusion equations as atmospheres, in either system. Certain empirical equations may be used with specific units only, and these are marked in the text and in the following list:

$c$ = concentration, gm. moles/cu. cm. or lb. moles/cu. ft.

$C_p$ = heat capacity at constant pressure, cal./(gm.)(°C.) or B.t.u./(lb.)(°F.)

$C_v$ = heat capacity at constant volume, cal./(gm.)(°C.) or B.t.u./(lb.)(°F.)

$d$ = differential operator

$D$ = diffusivity, sq. cm./sec. or sq. ft./hr. In Eqs. (2.23) and (2.38), only sq. cm./sec.

$D'$ = effective diffusivity, sq. cm./sec. or sq. ft./hr.

$f$ = a function

$F$ = a quantity defined by Eq. (2.38)

$g_c$ = conversion factor, 980 gm. mass (cm.)/(gm. force)(sec.)$^2$ or 4.17(10$^8$) lb. mass (ft.)/(lb. force)(hr.)$^2$

$k$ = thermal conductivity, cal. (cm.)/(sec.)(sq. cm.)(°C.) or B.t.u. (ft.)/(hr.)(sq. ft.)(°F.)

$k$ = Boltzmann constant = $1.38(10^{-16})$ erg/°K.    [Eqs. (2.23) to (2.25), Table 2.2, Fig. 2.3]

ln = natural logarithm

$M$ = molecular weight, gm./gm. mole or lb./lb. mole

$N$ = rate of diffusion, gm. moles/(sec.)(sq. cm.) or lb. moles/(hr.)(sq. ft.)

$p$ = partial pressure, atm.

$P$ = total pressure, atm.

Pr = Prandtl number (dimensionless) = $C_p\mu/k$

$q$ = rate of heat transfer, cal./(sec.)(sq. cm.) or B.t.u./(hr.)(sq. ft.)

$r$ = molecular separation at collision, A [Eqs. (2.23) and (2.26), Table 2.2]

$R$ = universal gas constant, 82.06 cu. cm. (atm.)/(gm. mole)(°K.) or 0.729 cu. ft. (atm.)/(lb. mole)(°R.)

Sc = Schmidt number (dimensionless) = $\mu/\rho D$

$t$ = temperature, °C. or °F.

$T$ = absolute temperature, °K. or °R.   In Eqs. (2.23) and (2.38) and Fig. 2.3, only °K.

$T_{\text{crit}}$ = critical temperature, °K. [Eq. (2.24)]

$T_{nbp}$ = normal boiling point, °K. [Eq. (2.25)]

$u$ = linear velocity of diffusion, cm./sec. or ft./hr.

$U$ = linear velocity, cm./sec. or ft./hr.

$v$ = liquid molal volume, cu. cm./gm. mole (Fig. 2.4)

$v_{\text{crit}}$ = critical molal volume, cu. cm./gm. mole [Eq. (2.26)]

$w$ = average molecular velocity, cm./sec. or ft./hr.

$x$ = concentration in a liquid solution, mole fraction

$Y$ = concentration in a gas, solute-free basis, mole fraction

$z$ = distance in the direction of diffusion, cm. or ft.

$\alpha$ = thermal diffusivity, sq. cm./sec. or sq. ft./hr.

$\beta$ = proportionality factor for interdiffusion

$\partial$ = partial differential operator

$\epsilon$ = energy of molecular interaction, ergs [Eqs. (2.23) to (2.25), Table 2.2, Fig. 2.3]

$\theta$ = time, sec. or hr.

$\lambda$ = mean free path of a molecule, cm. or ft.

$\mu$ = viscosity, gm./(cm.)(sec.) (= poises) or lb./(ft.)(hr.).   In Eq. (2.38), only centipoises (= 100 × poises)

$\nu$ = kinematic viscosity = $\mu/\rho$, sq. cm./sec. or sq. ft./hr.

$\rho$ = density, gm./cu. cm. or lb./cu. ft.

$\tau$ = shearing stress, gm. force/sq. cm. = (dynes/sq. cm.)($\frac{1}{980}$) or lb. force/sq. ft.

$\phi$ = ratio of $F$ for solvent to $F$ for water

Subscripts:

$A$ = component $A$

$B$ = component $B$

$C$ = component $C$

$D$ = component $D$

$i$ = inert or nondiffusing component

$M$ = mean

1 = position 1

2 = position 2

## REFERENCES

1. Bosworth, R. C. L.: "Physics in Chemical Industry," Macmillan & Co., Ltd., London, 1950.
2. Chapman, S., and T. G. Cowling: "Mathematical Theory of Non-uniform Gases," Cambridge University Press, London, 1939.
3. Gilliland, E. R.: *Ind. Eng. Chem.*, **26**, 681 (1934).
4. Glasstone, S., K. J. Laidler, and H. Eyring: "The Theory of Rate Processes," McGraw-Hill Book Company, Inc., New York, 1941.
5. Hirschfelder, J. O., R. R. Bird, and E. L. Spotz: *Trans. A.S.M.E.*, **71**, 921 (1949); *Chem. Rev.*, **44**, 205 (1949).
6. "International Critical Tables," vol. V, McGraw-Hill Book Company, Inc., New York, 1929.
7. Lewis, W. K., and K. C. Chang: *Trans. Am. Inst. Chem. Engrs.*, **21**, 127 (1928).
8. Maxwell, J. C.: *Phil. Trans. Roy. Soc.*, **157**, 49 (1866).
9. ———: "Scientific Papers," vol. 2, p. 343, Cambridge University Press, London, 1890.
10. Page, F., W. G. Schlinger, D. K. Breaux, and B. H. Sage: *Ind. Eng. Chem.*, **44**, 424 (1952).
11. Sherwood, T. K.: *Ind. Eng. Chem,.* **42**, 2077 (1950).
12. ———: "Absorption and Extraction," 1st ed., McGraw-Hill Book Company, Inc., New York, 1937.
13. Stefan, J.: *Wien. Sitzber.*, **63**, 63 (1871).
14. Treybal, R. E.: "Liquid Extraction," McGraw-Hill Book Company, Inc., New York, 1951.
15. Wang, J. H.: *J. Am. Chem. Soc.*, **73**, 510, 4181 (1951).
16. Wilke, C. R.: *Chem. Eng. Progr.*, **45**, 218 (1949).
17. ———: *Chem. Eng. Progr.*, **46**, 95 (1950).
18. Wintergerst, E.: *Ann. Physik*, **4**, 323 (1930).

## PROBLEMS

**1.** In an oxygen-nitrogen gas mixture at 1 atm., 25°C., the concentrations of oxygen at two planes 0.2 cm. apart are 10 and 20 vol. %, respectively. Calculate the rate of diffusion of the oxygen, expressed as gm. moles oxygen/(sq. cm.)(sec.) for the case where

*a.* The nitrogen is nondiffusing.

*b.* There is equimolar counterdiffusion of the two gases.

**2.** Repeat the calculations of Prob. 1 for a total pressure of 10 atm.

**3.** Estimate the following gas diffusivities:

*a.* Ethyl alcohol–air, 1 atm., 0°C.

*b.* Nitrogen–carbon dioxide, 1 atm., 25°C.

*c.* Hydrogen chloride–air, 2 atm., 25°C.

*d.* Toluene-air, 1 atm., 25°C.

*e.* Hydrogen-methane, 1 atm., 25°C.

**4.** Ammonia is diffusing through a stagnant gas mixture consisting of one-third nitrogen, two-thirds hydrogen, by volume. The total pressure is 30 lb./sq. in. abs. and the temperature 130°F. Calculate the rate of diffusion of the ammonia, expressed as lb./(hr.)(sq. ft.), through a film of gas 0.5 mm. thick, when the concentration change across the film is 10 to 5% ammonia by volume.

**5.** Estimate the following liquid diffusivities:

*a.* Ethyl alcohol in dilute water solution, 10°C.

*b.* Carbon tetrachloride in dilute solution in methyl alcohol, 15°C. (obsvd. value = $1.69 \times 10^{-5}$ sq. cm./sec.).

*c.* Self-diffusion in water, 25°C.

**6.** Calculate the rate of diffusion of NaCl at 18°C. through a stagnant film of water 0.1 cm. thick, when the concentrations are 20 and 10%, respectively, on either side of the film.

**7.** At 14.7 lb./sq. in. abs. and 212°F., the density of air is 0.0592 lb./cu. ft., the viscosity 0.0218 centipoise, the thermal conductivity 0.0183 B.t.u.(ft.)/(hr.)(sq. ft.)(°F.), and the specific heat at constant pressure 0.250 B.t.u./(lb.)(°F.).    At 77°F., the viscosity is 0.0179 centipoise.

*a.* Calculate the kinematic viscosity at 212°F., sq. ft./hr.

*b.* Calculate the thermal diffusivity at 212°F., sq. ft./hr.

*c.* Calculate the Prandtl number at 212°F.

*d.* Assume that for air at 1 atm. Pr = Sc and that Sc is constant with changing temperature.    From this, calculate $D$ for air at 77°F., sq. ft./hr.    Compare with the value of $D$ for the system $O_2$-$N_2$ at 1 atm., 77°F., from the data of Table 2.1.

CHAPTER 3

# DIFFUSION IN TURBULENT FLOW

We have seen that when a fluid flows past a surface under conditions such that turbulence generally prevails, there is a thin film of fluid in laminar flow immediately adjacent to the surface. This is followed by a transition, or buffer, zone where the flow gradually changes to the turbulent condition existing in the outer regions of the fluid. We have noted also that the rate of transfer of dissolved substance through the three regions will necessarily depend upon the nature of the fluid motion prevailing in each region.

In the turbulent region, particles of fluid no longer flow in the orderly manner found in the laminar film. Instead, relatively large portions of the fluid, called eddies, move rapidly from one position to the other with an appreciable component of their velocity in the direction perpendicular to the surface past which the fluid is flowing. These eddies bring with them dissolved material, and the eddy motion thus contributes considerably to the mass-transfer process. Since the eddy motion is rapid, mass transfer in the turbulent region is also rapid, much more so than that resulting from molecular diffusion in the laminar film. Because of the rapid eddy motion, the concentration gradients existing in the turbulent region will be smaller than those in the film, and Fig. 3.1 shows concentration gradients of this sort. In the experiment for which these are the data, air in turbulent motion flowed past a water surface, and water evaporated into the air. Samples of the air were taken at various distances from the surface, and the water-vapor concentration was determined by analysis. At the water surface, the water concentration in the gas was the same as the vapor pressure of pure water at the prevailing temperature. It was not possible to sample the gas very close to the water surface, but the rapid change in concentration in the laminar film, and the slower change in the outer turbulent region, are nevertheless unmistakable. It is important also to note the general similarity of data of this sort to the velocity distribution shown in Fig. 2.5.

It is also useful to compare the data for mass transfer with similar data for heat transfer. Thus, in Fig. 3.2 are plotted the temperatures at various distances from the surface when air flowed past a heated plate.

35

The large temperature gradient in the laminar film and the lesser gradient
in the turbulent region are again evident.   It will generally be convenient
to keep the corresponding heat-transfer process in mind when the mass-
transfer process is discussed, since in many instances the methods of

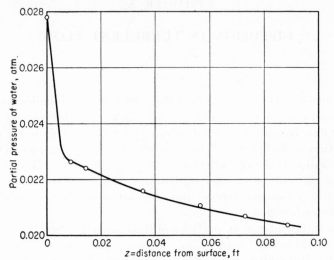

FIG. 3.1. Evaporation of water into air.[16]

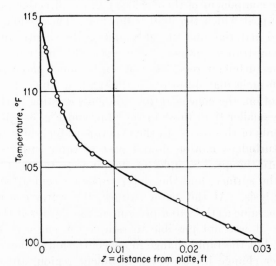

FIG. 3.2. Heat transfer, flow of air past a heated plate.[9]

reasoning used to describe the latter are borrowed directly from those
found to be successful with the former.

**Mass-transfer Coefficients.**   The mechanism of the flow process
involving the movements of the eddies in the turbulent region is not

thoroughly understood.   On the other hand, the mechanism of molecular diffusion, at least for gases, is fairly well known since it can be described in terms of a kinetic theory to give results which agree well with experience.   It is natural therefore to attempt to describe the rate of mass transfer through a combination of laminar film and turbulent zone, including the intervening buffer zone, in the same manner found useful for the laminar film alone.   Refer to Fig. 3.3, which might represent the concentration gradients existing in a gas flowing past a surface while

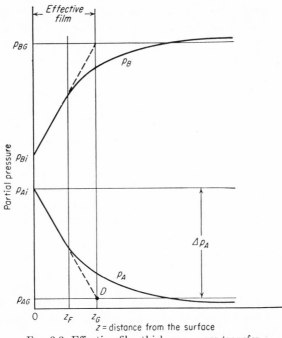

FIG. 3.3. Effective film thickness, mass transfer.

there is an equimolal counterdiffusion of component $A$ of the gas from the surface and of component $B$ to the surface.   The laminar film, whose thickness $z_F$ depends upon the general degree of turbulence, contains the majority of the concentration gradients for both $A$ and $B$.   If all the gas flowing past the surface were thoroughly mixed, the resulting concentrations would be $p_{AG}$ and $p_{BG}$, which are then average concentrations of the gas stream.   If the movement of $A$ followed only the laws of molecular diffusion, the concentration $p_{AG}$ would be reached at some point such as $D$, at a distance $z_G$ from the interface.   Equation (2.14) applied to this situation then becomes

$$N_A = \frac{D_{AB}}{RTz_G} (p_{Ai} - p_{AG}) \qquad (3.1)$$

Since for a given set of circumstances $D_{AB}/RTz_G$ is constant, these quantities may be combined in a new term $k'_G$, the mass-transfer film coefficient for the gas,

$$k'_G = \frac{D_{AB}}{RTz_G} \tag{3.2}$$

and

$$N_A = k'_G(p_{Ai} - p_{AG}) = k'_G \, \Delta p_A \tag{3.3}$$

The quantity $z_G$ is then a fictitious or effective laminar-film thickness whose resistance to molecular diffusion is the same as that offered to mass transfer by the real laminar film, buffer zone, and turbulent region all combined. Similarly had the mass transfer involved diffusion of $A$ through nondiffusing $B$, Eq. (2.21) would apply,

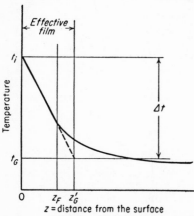

$$N_A = \frac{D_{AB}P}{RTz_G p_{BM}} (p_{Ai} - p_{AG})$$
$$= k_G(p_{Ai} - p_{AG}) = k_G \, \Delta p_A \tag{3.4}$$

where $k_G$ is now defined as $D_{AB}P/RTz_G p_{BM}$ and $p_{BM}$ is the logarithmic average of $p_{BG}$ and $p_{Bi}$.

We may write similar expressions for the liquid phase. Thus, for equimolar counterdiffusion of $A$ and $B$,

Fig. 3.4. Effective film thickness, heat transfer.

$$N_A = \frac{D_{AB}}{z_L} (c_{AL} - c_{Ai})$$
$$= k'_L(c_{AL} - c_{Ai}) = k'_L \, \Delta c_A \tag{3.5}$$

where $k'_L$, the liquid-film mass-transfer coefficient, is $D_{AB}/z_L$, $z_L$ the effective liquid-film thickness, and $c_{AL}$ the average or bulk concentration of $A$ in the liquid as a whole.

We may note also that the same device is ordinarily used for heat transfer, and the rate of heat transfer for a situation such as that described in Fig. 3.4 is written as

$$q = \frac{k}{z'_G} (t_i - t_G) = h(t_i - t_G) = h \, \Delta t \tag{3.6}$$

where $t_G$ is the average or bulk fluid temperature, $h$ the heat-transfer film coefficient, and $z'_G$ the effective film thickness whose resistance to heat transfer by conduction equals that due to the laminar film, buffer zone, and turbulent region combined.

The mass-transfer film coefficients have the dimensions moles transferred/(time)(area)(concentration difference). Some confusion can arise because the units for expressing the concentrations in the rate equations

TABLE 3.1. RELATION BETWEEN MASS-TRANSFER COEFFICIENTS

| | Gases | | | Liquids | | |
|---|---|---|---|---|---|---|
| | Rate equation | | Units of coefficient | Rate equation | | Units of coefficient |
| | Equimolal counterdiffusion | Diffusion of A through non-diffusing B | | Equimolal counterdiffusion | Diffusion of A through non-diffusing B | |
| | $N_A = k_G' \, \Delta p_A$ | $N_A = k_G \, \Delta p_A$ | $\dfrac{\text{Moles transferred}}{\text{Time(area)(pressure)}}$ | $N_A = k_L' \, \Delta c_A$ | $N_A = k_L \, \Delta c_A$ | $\dfrac{\text{Moles transferred}}{\text{Time(area)(moles/vol.)}}$ |
| | $N_A = k_y' \, \Delta y_A$ | $N_A = k_y \, \Delta y_A$ | $\dfrac{\text{Moles transferred}}{\text{Time(area)(mole fraction)}}$ | $N_A = k_x' \, \Delta x_A$ | $N_A = k_x \, \Delta x_A$ | $\dfrac{\text{Moles transferred}}{\text{Time(area)(mole fraction)}}$ |
| | $N_A = k_c' \, \Delta c_A$ | $N_A = k_c \, \Delta c_A$ | $\dfrac{\text{Moles transferred}}{\text{Time(area)(moles/vol.)}}$ | $k_L' = \dfrac{k_x'}{c}$ | $k_L = \dfrac{k_x}{c}$ | |
| | | $W_A = k_Y \, \Delta Y_A'$ | $\dfrac{\text{Mass transferred}}{\text{Time(area)(mass } A/\text{mass } B)}$ | $k_L' = k_L \dfrac{c_{BM}}{c} = k_L x_{BM}$ $k_x' = k_x x_{BM}$ | | |
| | $k_G' = \dfrac{k_y'}{P} = \dfrac{k_c'}{RT}$ | $k_G = \dfrac{k_y}{P}$ $= \dfrac{k_c}{RT}$ $= \dfrac{k_Y}{p_{BM} M_B}$ | | | | |
| | $k_G' = k_G \dfrac{p_{BM}}{P}$ $k_y' = k_y \dfrac{p_{BM}}{P} = k_y(y_{BM})$ $k_c' = k_c \dfrac{p_{BM}}{P} = k_c \dfrac{c_{BM}}{c}$ | | | | | |

39

have unfortunately not been standardized. The mass-transfer coefficients have therefore been used with a variety of units on different occasions. Table 3.1 will be helpful in reconciling these.

As written in Eqs. (3.3) to (3.5), the mass-transfer coefficients are "local" coefficients, i.e., they apply to the particular situation existing at the point where they are used. Consider, for example, a gas flowing up a long vertical pipe, down the inside surface of which a film of liquid water flows, with evaporation of the water into the flowing gas. Under steady-state conditions, where rates of flow and concentrations do not change with time, the concentrations of Fig. 3.3 might be expected to apply at a particular elevation along the pipe. But since the gas is accumulating water vapor in its flow through the pipe, the bulk concentration $p_G$ and hence the driving force $\Delta p$ will change; and since the properties of the gas-water vapor mixture change, the degree of turbulence and hence the effective film thickness may change from one end of the pipe to the other. The local mass-transfer film coefficient, therefore, will vary from one end of the apparatus to the other, and if the entire system is to be described by a single coefficient, some sort of averaging of conditions must be done.

The total resistance to mass transfer in a situation such as that described in Fig. 3.3 is clearly made up of two parts: that residing in the laminar film and that represented by the buffer zone and turbulent region. The thickness of the laminar film and consequently its diffusional resistance is a function of the degree of turbulence of the fluid as a whole, which can be described by the Reynolds number Re. Similarly the resistance offered by the turbulent region can be related to the Reynolds number. The molecular diffusivity will be necessary to describe the rate of diffusion across the laminar film but will be relatively unimportant in considering the turbulent region. The mass-transfer film coefficient, therefore, can be expected to depend upon the diffusivity $D$ and the quantities making up the Reynolds number: the average fluid velocity $U_{av}$, the density $\rho$, viscosity $\mu$, and some dimension of the apparatus $d$, as perhaps the diameter of a pipe,

$$k'_c = RTk'_G = \phi(D,U_{av},d,\mu,\rho) \qquad (3.7)$$

or, if arranged in terms of dimensionless groups,

$$\frac{k'_c d}{D} = \frac{RTk'_G}{D} = \frac{d}{z_G} = \phi'\left(\frac{dU_{av}\rho}{\mu}, \frac{\mu}{\rho D}\right) = \phi'(Re,Sc) \qquad (3.8)$$

The group $k'_c d/D$ corresponds in mass transfer to the Nusselt number $hd/k$ in heat transfer.

Dimensional analysis, which leads to Eq. (3.8), will not establish the nature of the unspecified function. There have been several methods of attack on the problem of developing this function, all of which have been most useful: (1) developments relating mass transfer to flow conditions which parallel similar successful work in heat transfer; (2) work on the mechanism of eddy diffusion in the turbulent region; (3) experimental studies with empirical treatment of the resulting data.

## MASS-, HEAT-, AND MOMENTUM-TRANSFER ANALOGIES

As in the case of laminar flow, there are certain similarities among the processes of mass, heat, and momentum transfer for fluids in turbulent flow the study of which have led to very useful results. It is important,

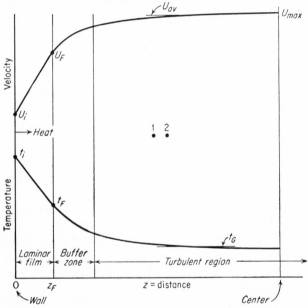

FIG. 3.5. Heat transfer to a gas in turbulent flow.

therefore, to examine these, at least to a limited extent, and to establish their limitations.

Keeping in mind that we wish ultimately to establish the nature of the mass-transfer process through both the laminar and turbulent zones of a fluid in motion, let us first consider a typical case of heat transfer with turbulent flow of a gas through a circular pipe, as in Fig. 3.5. The velocity is zero at the wall, $U_i = 0$, and increases to a maximum value $U_{max}$ at the center of the pipe. $U_{av}$ is the average velocity, obtained by dividing the volumetric rate of flow by the pipe cross section. Assume also that heat is being transferred from the pipe wall to the gas but that the heat transfer does not influence the velocity distribution in the fluid.

Consider two places, points 1 and 2 in the turbulent region.[5]  Here the velocity gradient is small, and the velocity at any point fluctuates with time in a direction both parallel to and perpendicular to the wall of the pipe.  If we imagine an interchange of a mass of fluid $W$ per unit time per unit area between points 1 and 2 owing to the fluctuations in a direction perpendicular to the wall, then the net interchange of momentum between the points, as measured by the shearing force per unit area, is

$$\tau g_c = W \, \Delta u \tag{3.9}$$

where $\Delta u$ is some measure of the fluctuating velocity in the direction parallel to the pipe wall.  If there is a temperature gradient between the two points, then there is also a transfer of heat,

$$q = W C_p \, \Delta t \tag{3.10}$$

Eliminating $W$,

$$\frac{\tau g_c}{\Delta u} = \frac{q}{C_p \, \Delta t} \tag{3.11}$$

Equation (3.11) for turbulence may be compared with the result obtained by eliminating $z_F$ between Eqs. (2.39) and (2.42) when these are applied to the laminar film,

$$\frac{\tau_i g_c}{U_F - 0} = \frac{\mu q}{k(t_i - t_F)} \tag{3.12}$$

It is clear that the same mechanism relates heat and momentum transfer for both laminar and turbulent flow only if $\mu/k = 1/C_p$, or if $C_p \mu/k = \mathrm{Pr} = 1$.  This is nearly so for most gases at ordinary pressure.  This principle is the basis of the Reynolds heat transfer–pipe friction analogy developed in 1874,[11] which states that, for a fluid flowing in a heated pipe in turbulent flow, Eq. (3.11) may be written to cover conditions from the turbulent zone through the laminar film to the pipe wall.  Stated in words, this becomes the same as equating the following ratios:

$$\frac{\text{Loss in momentum to pipe wall as represented by skin friction}}{\text{Loss in momentum if all fluid were brought to velocity at pipe wall}} = \frac{\text{ht. actually supplied to fluid}}{\text{ht. supplied to fluid if it were all brought to pipe-wall temp.}}$$

For fluids whose Prandtl number does not equal unity, the Reynolds analogy ignores the differences in heat-transfer mechanisms existing in the laminar film, turbulent core, and intervening buffer zone.

Prandtl[10] and Taylor[15] modified the Reynolds analogy by applying Eq. (3.11) to the turbulent and buffer zones and Eq. (3.12) for the laminar film, thus obtaining the following expression for a heat-transfer film coefficient.†

---

† The derivation of Eq. (3.13) follows closely the form of the derivation of Eq. (3.21) below.

$$h = \frac{\tau_i g_c C_p / U_{\mathrm{av}}}{1 - U_F/U_{\mathrm{av}} + (U_F/U_{\mathrm{av}}) \, \mathrm{Pr}} \tag{3.13}$$

Since the shear stress at the wall $\tau_i$ can be related to the familiar Fanning friction factor $f$,

$$\tau_i g_c = \tfrac{1}{2} f U_{\mathrm{av}}^2 \tag{3.14}$$

Equation (3.13) becomes

$$\frac{1}{2} f = \frac{h}{C_p U_{\mathrm{av}} \rho} \left( 1 - \frac{U_F}{U_{\mathrm{av}}} + \frac{U_F}{U_{\mathrm{av}}} \, \mathrm{Pr} \right) \tag{3.15}$$

which is designed to permit computation of the film coefficient for heat transfer at a given value of Re from the friction-factor correlation for pressure drop in flow through pipes. The relationship still does not adequately account for conditions in the buffer zone, and perhaps for this reason it correlates friction and heat transfer well only for gases for which Pr is not far removed from unity. It was later found that an empirical modification was an improvement,[4]

$$\frac{1}{2} f = \left( \frac{h}{C_p U_{\mathrm{av}} \rho} \, \mathrm{Pr}^{2/3} = j_H \right) \tag{3.16}$$

**Mass and Momentum Transfer.** Similar reasoning can be applied to the problem of mass transfer. Consider again a gas flowing in a pipe in turbulent flow, where at the same time there is a mass transfer of substance $A$ from the pipe wall into the gas stream (Fig. 3.6). This might be the case if, for example, the pipe wall were wet with a liquid which evaporated into the gas. It is assumed, however, that the mass transfer does not influence the velocity gradients existing in the fluid. The partial pressures $p_A$ of the diffusing substance are indicated on the diagram at the appropriate places. In the turbulent region between points 1 and 2, interchange of mass $W$ per unit time per unit area brings about a net transfer of momentum, given by Eq. (3.9). Similarly there will be a net transfer of substance $A$,

$$N_A = \frac{W \, \Delta p_A}{M_{\mathrm{av}} P} \tag{3.17}$$

Combining Eqs. (3.9) and (3.17),

$$\frac{\tau g_c}{\Delta u} = \frac{N_A M_{\mathrm{av}} P}{\Delta p_A} \tag{3.18}$$

which gives the general relation between shear stress and mass transfer in turbulence. For the laminar film, we can eliminate $z_F$ between Eqs.

(2.14) and (2.39),

$$z_F = \frac{D_{AB}(p_{Ai} - p_{AF})}{RTN_A} = \frac{\mu(U_F - 0)}{\tau_i g_c} \tag{3.19}$$

$$\frac{\tau_i g_c}{U_F - 0} = \frac{N_A \mu RT}{D_{AB}(p_{Ai} - p_{AF})} \tag{3.20}$$

Comparison of Eqs. (3.18) and (3.20) shows that the mechanism of momentum and mass transfer will be alike for both laminar and turbulent flow provided $M_{av}P = \mu RT/D_{AB}$, or if $\mu RT/D_{AB}M_{av}P = \mu/\rho D_{AB} = Sc = 1$. Assuming that we may use the form of Eq. (3.18) for the

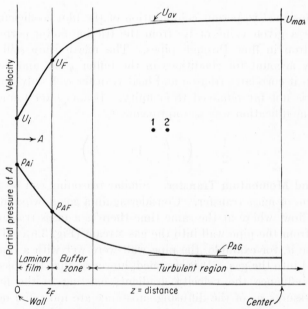

FIG. 3.6. Mass transfer to a gas in turbulent flow.

average velocities of the turbulent and buffer regions, and assuming that $\tau = \tau_i$ at $z = z_F$ since the film is very thin,

$$\frac{\tau_i g_c}{U_{av} - U_F} = \frac{N_A M_{av} P}{p_{AF} - p_{AG}} \tag{3.20a}$$

Further

$$N_A = k_G'(p_{Ai} - p_{AG}) = k_G'[(p_{Ai} - p_{AF}) + (p_{AF} - p_{AG})] \tag{3.20b}$$

If Eqs. (3.20) and (3.20a) are solved for their partial-pressure differences and these substituted in Eq. (3.20b), there results[3]

$$k_G' = \frac{\tau_i g_c/U_{av} M_{av} P}{1 - U_F/U_{av} + (U_F/U_{av})Sc} \tag{3.21}$$

or, substituting Eq. (3.14),

$$\frac{1}{2}f = \frac{k_G' M_{av} P}{U_{av}\rho}\left(1 - \frac{U_F}{U_{av}} + \frac{U_F}{U_{av}}\,\text{Sc}\right) \tag{3.22}$$

which of course exactly parallels Eq. (3.15) for heat transfer. Equation (3.22) was found to give poor results for cases where Sc differed greatly from unity, and it was modified by Chilton and Colburn[2] in the manner used previously,

$$\frac{1}{2}f = \left(\frac{k_G' M_{av} P}{U_{av}\rho}\,\text{Sc}^{2/3} = \frac{k_G' P}{G_M}\,\text{Sc}^{2/3} = j_D\right) \tag{3.23}$$

Equation (3.23) can now be put in the form of the function which it was desired to establish, Eq. (3.8),

$$\frac{k_c' d}{D} = \frac{RT k_G' d}{D} = \frac{1}{2}f\,\text{Re}\,\text{Sc}^{1/3} \tag{3.24}$$

For mass-transfer coefficients involving other units, substitutions may be made from Table 3.1.

Equations (3.23) and (3.24) and their companion, Eq. (3.16), have been used so much in chemical-engineering work that it is important to point out a few of their limitations in a general way. We shall see later how well they describe some of our observed data. It will be recalled that they stem originally from the Reynolds analogy, that they therefore relate heat- and mass-transfer rates to skin friction in flow through pipes, and that the friction factor for flow through pipes is commonly measured by determination of the pressure drop. If, therefore, the equations are used to predict the rates of heat and mass transfer for flow through or past objects of other shapes, it must be certain that the friction factor which is used relates to skin friction only. When a fluid flows past a sphere, at right angles to a cylinder, through a bed of packed solids, or generally past bluff objects, the total drag includes, in addition to the skin friction, the pressure loss due to impact and to formation of eddies in the wake behind the object. Friction factors based on total drag are therefore not suitable for use in the equations. In these cases, we may find correlations of $RT k_G' d/D$ with Re at a fixed value of Sc, that $RT k_G' d/D$ varies as $\text{Sc}^{1/3}$ or more generally $\text{Sc}^n$, or even that $j_H = j_D$, but that generally $j_D$ will not equal $\frac{1}{2}f$. On the other hand, we may expect direct usefulness of friction factors when the fluid flows over a flat plane, or axially outside a cylinder, or past streamlined shapes generally. In addition it is assumed that the three processes of mass, heat, and momentum transfer are occurring separately, for example, that the transfer of mass by diffusion in a direction normal to the general flow has no influence on the shear stress involved.[1]   The equations are useful, of course, only for turbulent flow.

The quantity in the parentheses of Eq. (3.22) may be looked upon as being made up of two parts.   The first, which could be written as $(1 - U_F/U_{av})Sc^0$, presumably applies to the turbulent core where molecular diffusivity as represented by the Schmidt number enters to the zero power and is unimportant.   The second, $(U_F/U_{av})Sc$, presumably applies to the laminar film where molecular diffusivity enters to the first power. The ratio $U_F/U_{av}$ depends upon the velocity distribution and the degree of turbulence, and hence the Reynolds number.   The empirical modification, Eq. (3.23), where $Sc^{2/3}$ is used, presumably combines the two effects by using the diffusivity to a power between zero and unity.   The $2/3$ power can be looked upon as an average value applicable to a wide range of Reynolds numbers.   By using more detailed descriptions of the velocity distribution through the various zones of flow, it is possible to arrive at more complicated and perhaps more exact expressions to replace $Sc^{2/3}$ in Eq. (3.23).   These are beyond the scope of this book, but they are conveniently summarized and discussed elsewhere.[14]   In cases not involving flow through pipes, powers other than $2/3$ may be more suitable for general averaging purposes, and for these situations it may be better to define the $j_H$ and $j_D$ expressions more generally as

$$j_H = \frac{h}{C_p G}\,\psi(\mathrm{Pr}) = \psi'(\mathrm{Re}) \tag{3.25}$$

$$j_D = \frac{k_G' P}{G_M}\,\psi(\mathrm{Sc}) = \psi'(\mathrm{Re}) \tag{3.26}$$

## EDDY DIFFUSION

Consider again the case of turbulent flow of a fluid flowing through a circular pipe.   In the central portion of the pipe, where turbulence exists, the flow is characterized by motion of the fluid particles, or eddies, which is irregular with respect both to direction and to time.   At a particular point in the cross section, the time-average velocity in a direction parallel to the pipe axis may be $U$, but at any instant the velocity may be expressed as $U \pm u$, where $u$ is the *deviating velocity*.   Similarly, in a radial direction, there will be a time-average component of the velocity $V$, which at any instant may be $V \pm v$.   Since the deviating velocities may at various instances be either positive or negative, we may for convenience use instead $u' = \sqrt{\bar{u}^2}$ and $v' = \sqrt{\bar{v}^2}$.

Now consider two parallel planes in the turbulent zone a distance $L$ apart, where the velocities are $U$ and $U + u'$, as in Fig. 3.7.[12]   If $u'$ is small,

$$u' = L \frac{dU}{dz} \tag{3.27}$$

where $L$ is the "Prandtl mixing length." An eddy which moves at a velocity $u'$ faster than the average velocity $U$ blends into a stream traveling at velocity $U + u'$ and disappears after traveling a distance $L$. $L$ is thus one measure of the size of an eddy. Knowledge of the velocity gradient $dU/dz$ permits calculation of $L$ at any position in the pipe cross section, and it has been found that $L$ varies from zero at the pipe wall to about 15 per cent of the pipe radius at the center.

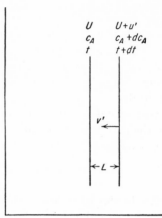

Suppose eddies move between the planes of Fig. 3.7. The transfer of momentum from the fast- to the slow-moving plane results in a shear stress between the planes,

$$\tau g_c = -\rho(uv) = -\rho v' L' \frac{dU}{dz} \tag{3.28}$$

$z = $ distance

Fig. 3.7. Eddy diffusion of momentum, heat, and mass.

where $(uv)$ is the time average of the product of $u$ and $v$, $L' = rL$, and $r$, a coefficient relating the deviating velocities, $= (uv)/u'v'$. $L'$ is then a measure of turbulence. The total shear stress, due both to molecular motion and to eddy motion, is then

$$\tau g_c = -(\mu + \rho v' L') \frac{dU}{dz} = -(\mu + \rho E_v) \frac{dU}{dz} = -(\nu + E_v) \frac{d(U\rho)}{dz} \tag{3.29}$$

where $E_v$ is the eddy viscosity or eddy momentum diffusivity, with dimensions (length)$^2$/time. While $\nu$ or $\mu$ is a constant for each fluid depending only upon the temperature, $E_v$ will depend on the degree of turbulence as indicated by the Reynolds number and should be otherwise independent of fluid properties. In the various regions of flow, $\nu$ and $E_v$ contribute differently to the total shearing stress: in the laminar film $\nu$ is large in comparison with $E_v$, in the buffer zone they are of the same order of magnitude, and in the turbulent zone $E_v$ is large in comparison with $\nu$.

The eddies bring about a transfer of mass as well as momentum, as we have seen before. If the concentration of dissolved substance is expressed as $c_A$ moles/unit volume, then $-v' \, dc_A$ is the net transfer of dissolved substance per unit time per unit area of the planes of Fig. 3.7. Assuming that this rate can also be described in terms of a concentration gradient

$dc_A/dz$,

$$-v' \, dc_A = -E_D \frac{dc_A}{dz} \tag{3.30}$$

where $E_D$ is the eddy mass diffusivity, (length)$^2$/time. The total mass transfer due both to molecular and to eddy diffusion then becomes

$$N_A = -(D_{AB} + E_D) \frac{dc_A}{dz} \tag{3.31}$$

As in the case of momentum transfer, $D$ is a constant for a particular fluid mixture at a given temperature, while $E_D$ depends upon the extent of turbulence and should be independent of fluid properties. In the laminar film $E_D$ is much smaller than $D$, in the turbulent zone $E_D$ is much larger than $D$, while in the buffer zone they are of the same order of magnitude.

The corresponding rate of heat transfer resulting from the eddy movement in the turbulent zone will be $-v'\rho C_p \, dt$, and if this can be written in terms of a temperature gradient $dt/dz$, then

$$-v'\rho C_p \, dt = -E_H \rho C_p \frac{dt}{dz} \tag{3.32}$$

where $E_H$ is the eddy thermal diffusivity, (length)$^2$/time. The total heat-transfer rate due to conduction and eddy motion becomes

$$q = -(k + E_H \rho C_p) \frac{dt}{dz} = -(\alpha + E_H) \frac{d(t\rho C_p)}{dz} \tag{3.33}$$

As before, $\alpha$ for a given fluid is a function of temperature, but $E_H$ varies with degree of turbulence and should be independent of fluid properties.

The foregoing equations indicate that

$$E_v = v'L' \qquad E_D = v' \, dz \qquad E_H = v' \, dz \tag{3.34}$$

The theory would therefore indicate a simple relationship among $E_v$, $E_D$, and $E_H$, or between the turbulent Schmidt number $E_v/E_D$ and the turbulent Prandtl number $E_v/E_H$. The eddy diffusivities can be determined experimentally by measuring the various gradients which may exist in a pipe or duct during fluid flow: velocity gradients to obtain $E_v$, temperature gradients to give $E_H$, and concentration gradients for $E_D$. For example, measurements by Sherwood and his coworkers[16,17] of $E_D$ for $H_2$ and CO in air and of $H_2O$ in He, $CO_2$, and air gave values of the order of 100 times as great as the corresponding values of $D$. $E_D$ would correlate for different mixtures with Re only if multiplied by $\rho$ (despite theoretical indication that physical properties should be unimportant except in so far as Re is concerned), and the ratio $E_v/E_D$ was constant at 0.63, independent of Reynolds number and substance diffusing. Recent measurements in heated air streams[9] gave values of $E_v/E_H$ in the turbulent region in the range 0.7 to 0.9, depending on the Reynolds number and the position in the duct cross section. Eddy diffusion of HCl in liquid water[6] gave values of $E_v/E_D$ equal approximately to unity, with $E_D$ roughly $10^{12}$ times as great as $D$.

Comparison of Eqs. (3.29) and (3.31) for extreme conditions of turbulence can now be made.[12] If for highly developed turbulence $D$ and $\nu$ are considered negligible in comparison with $E_D$ and $E_v$, respectively, then these equations can be integrated from the turbulent zone to the wall of the conduit to give

$$k_c' = \frac{N_A}{\Delta c_A} = \frac{E_D \tau_i g_c}{E_v U_{av} \rho} = \frac{f E_D U_{av}}{2 E_v} \tag{3.35}$$

On the other hand, if in laminar flow $E_D$ and $E_v$ are negligible in comparison with $D$ and $\nu$, respectively, there is obtained

$$k_c' = \frac{N_A}{\Delta c_A} = \frac{f D_{AB} U_{av}}{2\nu} = \frac{f}{2} \frac{1}{Sc} U_{av} \tag{3.36}$$

This suggests that a general relationship might be

$$\frac{2k_c'}{f U_{av}} = \phi'' \left( Sc, \frac{E_v}{E_D} \right) \tag{3.37}$$

Provided $E_v/E_D$ were not dependent upon Reynolds number, then this reduces to an equation of the form of Eq. (3.23). Similar treatment of Eqs. (3.29) and (3.33) leads to

$$\frac{2h}{f \rho C_p U_{av}} = \phi''' \left( Pr, \frac{E_v}{E_H} \right) \tag{3.38}$$

which is of the form of Eq. (3.16) if $E_v/E_H$ is independent of Re. Elaboration of the functions of Eqs. (3.37) and (3.38) requires detailed knowledge of the ratios $E_v/E_D$ and $E_v/E_H$ and of their dependence upon flow conditions, all of which have not yet been firmly established. Tentative treatments of this sort are summarized in detail by Sherwood and Pigford.[14]

## MASS-TRANSFER DATA FOR SIMPLE SITUATIONS

Over the past twenty years a considerable amount of experimental data has been accumulated in an attempt to establish the nature of the function of Eq. (3.8) for various situations and to establish as far as possible the validity of the theoretical studies which have been made. We can now consider some of these experiments and compare the observed results with the theoretical principles.

**Turbulent Flow through Pipes.**    Mass-transfer rates for fluids flowing through pipes have been studied more completely than other cases.    The rates of diffusion into gases flowing through pipes have been studied with the help of the wetted-wall tower, shown diagrammatically in Fig. 3.8. A volatile liquid is permitted to flow down the inside surface of a circular pipe, while a gas is blown upward or downward through the center of the pipe.    Measurement of the rate of evaporation of liquid into the gas stream over the known surface permits calculation of the mass-transfer coefficients for the diffusion of the vapor into the gas stream.    Since the liquids may be pure liquids, the concentration gradient for the diffusion exists entirely within the gas stream and coefficients $k_G$ or their equivalent may be obtained directly from the data. Sherwood and Gilliland[13] conducted a series of experiments of this sort, using a variety of volatile liquids with air in turbulent flow. Typical of the data obtained are those giving the lowest line of Fig. 3.9.    Here the mass-transfer coefficients in the form of a dimensionless group are plotted against the Reynolds number[†] of the gas for the system air–water (Sc = 0.60).    Similar data were obtained for such volatile liquids as butyl alcohol, toluene, ethyl acetate, and others, and some of the resulting lines are shown (without the data, to avoid confusion) in the lower part of Fig. 3.9.    Values of Re from 2,000 to 35,000 were covered, as well as values of Sc from 0.6 to 2.5 and gas pressures from 0.1 to 3 atm.

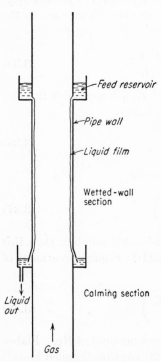

Feed reservoir

Pipe wall

Liquid film

Wetted-wall section

Calming section

Liquid out

Gas

FIG. 3.8. Wetted-wall tower.

In a later series of tests, Linton and Sherwood[7] caused water to flow through pipes made by casting molten benzoic acid in pipe form.    The rate of solution of the pipe wall was measured, giving rise to the data uppermost in Fig. 3.9.    Similar experiments were made with pipes of other materials such as cinnamic acid, and $\beta$-naphthol, resulting in the lines shown in the upper section of Fig. 3.9 (the data scatter somewhat and are omitted for the sake of clarity; as a result of the scattering, the Schmidt numbers marked on the lines do not follow the same orderly progression as in the case of the gases).

† Re is calculated relative to the stationary pipe wall rather than to the surface of the moving liquid film.

The average slope of the lines on Fig. 3.9 is 0.83, so that the groups $(k_c d/D)(p_{BM}/P)$ and $k_L d/D$ vary as $Re^{0.83}$. On Fig. 3.10, the intercepts of these lines at $Re = 10,000$ are plotted against the corresponding value of Sc, on logarithmic coordinates. The principal line of Fig. 3.10 has a slope of $\frac{1}{3}$, and its ordinate is 48.5 at Sc = 1.0. Since $48.5/10,000^{0.83} =$

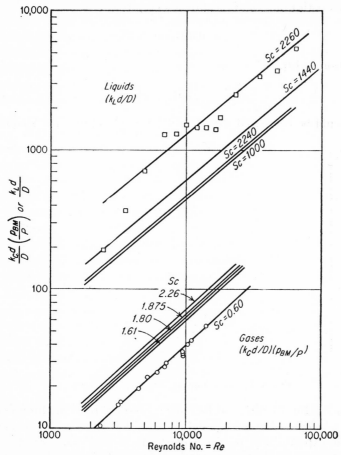

Fig. 3.9. Mass transfer, flow through pipes.

0.023, the equation which describes all the data, for both liquid and gas flow, is therefore

$$\frac{k_c d}{D}\frac{p_{BM}}{P} = \frac{k_L d}{D} = 0.023\ Re^{0.83}\ Sc^{\frac{1}{3}} \tag{3.39}$$

This empirical equation is truly remarkable in the manner in which it generally confirms the relationship between heat, mass, and momentum transfer developed theoretically. For example, in the case of fluids flowing in turbulent flow inside circular pipes, the heat-transfer coefficient is given empirically by[8]

$$\frac{hd}{k} = 0.023 \ \mathrm{Re}^{0.8} \ \mathrm{Pr}^{0.3} \tag{3.40}$$

and the striking similarity between the two expressions is evident. Further, over the range of Re = 5,000 to 200,000, the friction factor for flow through smooth pipes can be expressed empirically as

$$\frac{f}{2} = 0.023 \ \mathrm{Re}^{-0.20} \tag{3.41}$$

Substitution in Eq. (3.39) gives

$$\frac{k_L d}{D} = \frac{1}{2} f \ \mathrm{Re}^{1.03} \ \mathrm{Sc}^{\frac{1}{3}} \tag{3.42}$$

which should be compared with Eq. (3.24). Generally, the inequalities

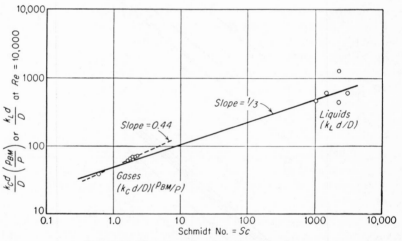

FIG. 3.10. Mass transfer, flow through pipes.

between $j_H$ of Eq. (3.16), $j_D$ of Eq. (3.23), and $f/2$ for flow through pipes within the range of Reynolds numbers considered in Fig. 3.9 seem to be within the experimental precision of the heat- and mass-transfer data. It should be noted that the evaporation of the volatile liquids in a wetted-wall tower results in cooling of the liquids and consequent simultaneous heat transfer between liquid and gas. The heat-transfer rates obtained are somewhat higher than those given by Eq. (3.40) for dry tubes, owing possibly to ripples and waves on the liquid surface. It should also be noted that the data of Fig. 3.9 and 3.10 for gases only (Sc = 0.6 to 2.5) are correlated empirically better by the relation

$$\frac{k_c d}{D} \frac{p_{BM}}{P} = 0.023 \ \mathrm{Re}^{0.83} \ \mathrm{Sc}^{0.44} \tag{3.43}$$

corresponding to the broken line on Fig. 3.10.

**Flow past Other Shapes.** The data for flow past other shapes are generally not so extensive as those for flow through pipes, but the more important correlations can be summarized as in Fig. 3.11. In many cases, the effect of diffusivity may be accounted for by use of the Schmidt number to the $\frac{2}{3}$ power in the $j_D$ expression, but deviations from this are necessary in others. Generally, the larger the range of Sc investigated, the more firmly is the correlation established. In the case of flow over flat plates, the same curve can describe friction, heat transfer, and mass transfer. For flow past spheres or cylinders or through beds of packed solids, on the other hand, it was anticipated that pressure drop would not correlate with the heat- and mass-transfer processes. Indeed, in the last-mentioned situation, it is presently impossible to correlate even the mass-transfer data alone by a single curve for both liquids and gases. Merely changing the power on the Schmidt number will not bring about an over-all correlation, since different functions of Re are also required. Further investigation and gathering of additional data will doubtless eventually reconcile these difficulties.

For situations not covered by the curves of Fig. 3.11, it seems reasonable to assume that the mass-transfer coefficients can be estimated as functions of Re from the corresponding heat-transfer data, if available, by placing the latter in the form of a $j_H$ function, replacing Pr by Sc and the group $h/C_pG$ by $k_G'P/G_M$ or its equivalent. If only an isolated heat-transfer measurement is available, it may be put in the form of Eq. (3.16) and the corresponding mass-transfer rate at the same Reynolds number estimated by Eq. (3.23), on the assumption that $j_D = j_H$. Special correlations for use in specific unit operations are considered in the appropriate later chapters.

**Illustration 1.** Estimate the rate of evaporation of water from a reservoir in the bottom of a large duct carrying air at 20 ft./sec. The reservoir is 1 ft. square, and the surface of the water is at 90°F. The air is at 140°F., 1 atm., and has a partial pressure of water vapor equal to 0.0315 atm.

*Solution.* The average molecular weight of the gas is 28.7. The density is therefore

$$\frac{28.7}{359} \frac{492}{460 + 140} = 0.0655 \text{ lb./cu. ft.}$$

The viscosity = 0.0195 centipoise = 0.0195(2.42) = 0.0471 lb./(ft.)(hr.). The length of the water surface = $l$ = 1 ft.

$$\text{Re}''' = \frac{lU\rho}{\mu} = \frac{1(20)(3,600)(0.0655)}{0.0471} = 100,000$$

For air-water vapor, $D$ at 25.9°C. (78.6°F.) = 0.258 sq. cm./sec. (Table 2.1).

$$\therefore D \text{ at } 140°F. = 0.258 \left( \frac{140 + 460}{78.6 + 460} \right)^{3/2} = 0.306 \text{ sq. cm./sec.}$$

$$= 0.306(3.87) = 1.184 \text{ sq. ft./hr.}$$

$$\text{Sc} = \frac{\mu}{\rho D} = \frac{0.0471}{0.0655(1.184)} = 0.608$$

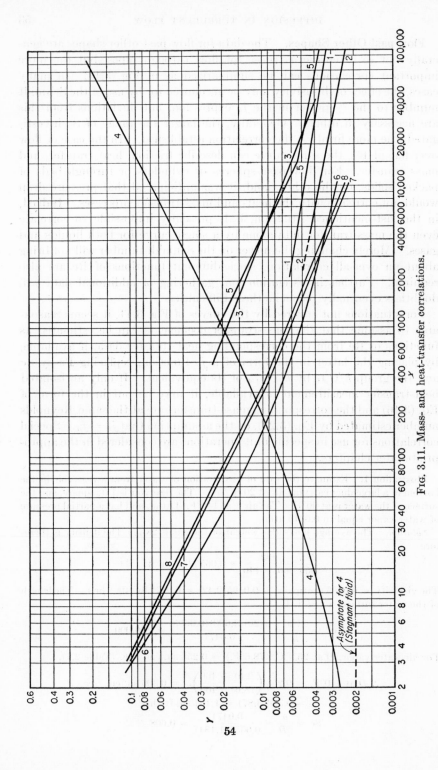

FIG. 3.11. Mass- and heat-transfer correlations.

| Curve | Situation | Operation | X | Y | Sc range |
|---|---|---|---|---|---|
| 1 | Flow inside pipes | Mass transfer | Re | $j_D = \dfrac{k_G' P}{G_M}(Sc)^{2/3} = \dfrac{k_x}{L_M}(Sc)^{2/3}$ | 0.6–3,000 |
| 2 | Flow inside pipes | Heat transfer, friction | Re | $\dfrac{f}{2} = j_H = \dfrac{h}{C_p G}(Pr)^{2/3}$ | |
| 3 | Flow of gases transverse to cylinders | Mass transfer | Re' | $j_D = \dfrac{k_G' P}{G_M}(Sc)^{0.56}$ | 0.6–2.6 |
|   |   | Heat transfer | Re' | $j_H = \dfrac{h}{C_p G}(Pr)^{0.56}$ | |
| 4 | Flow of gases past single spheres | Mass transfer | Re''$(Sc)^{2/3}$ | $\dfrac{k_c d_p}{D}(10^{-3})$ | 0.6–2.7 |
|   |   | Heat transfer | Re''$(Pr)^{2/3}$ | $\dfrac{h d_p}{k}(10^{-3})$ | |
| 5 | Flow of gases parallel to plates | Mass transfer | Re''' | $j_D = \dfrac{k_G' P}{G_M}(Sc)^{2/3}$ | 0.6–2.1 |
|   |   | Heat transfer, friction | Re''' | $j_H = \dfrac{h}{C_p G}(Pr)^{2/3} = \dfrac{f}{2}$ | |
| 6 | Flow of liquids through packed solids | Mass transfer | Re''/$\epsilon$ | $j_D(10^{-1}) = \dfrac{k_x}{L_M}(Sc)^{0.58}(10^{-1})$ | 164–10,690 |
| 7 | Flow of gases through packed solids | Mass transfer | Re'' | $j_D(10^{-1}) = \dfrac{k_y}{G_M}(Sc)^{2/3}(10^{-1})$ | 0.6 |
| 8 | Flow of gases through packed solids | Heat transfer | Re'' | $j_H(10^{-1}) = \dfrac{h}{C_p G}(Pr)^{2/3}(10^{-1})$ | |

From Fig. 3.11, $j_D = 0.0037$. For this case, $k_G$ is required since the water vapor diffuses through the nondiffusing air.

$$\therefore j_D = 0.0037 = \frac{k_G p_{BM}}{G_M} \text{Sc}^{\frac{2}{3}}$$

$$G_M = \frac{U\rho}{M} = \frac{20(3,600)(0.0655)}{28.7} = 164.2 \text{ lb. moles/(hr.)(sq. ft.)}$$

$p_{Ai}$ = partial pressure water vapor at liquid surface
= vapor pressure water at 90°F. = 0.0475 atm.
$p_{AG}$ = partial pressure vapor in gas stream = 0.0315 atm.
$p_{Bi}$ = $1 - 0.0475 = 0.9525$ atm.     $p_{BG} = 1 - 0.0315 = 0.9685$ atm.

$$p_{BM} = \frac{0.9685 + 0.9525}{2} = 0.961 \text{ atm.}$$

$$k_G = \frac{0.0037 G_M}{p_{BM} \text{Sc}^{\frac{2}{3}}} = \frac{0.0037(164.2)}{0.961(0.608)^{\frac{2}{3}}} = 0.884 \text{ lb. mole/(hr.)(sq. ft.)(atm.)}$$

$$N_A = k_G \, \Delta p_A = 0.884(0.0475 - 0.0315) = 0.1414 \text{ lb. mole/(hr.)(sq. ft.)}$$

Rate of evaporation = $0.1414(1)(18.02) = 2.55$ lb./hr.    *Ans.*

**Illustration 2.**  Gaffney and Drew [*Ind. Eng. Chem.*, **42**, 1120 (1950)] passed an unsaturated acetone–succinic acid solution through a bed of succinic acid pellets in a 3.02-in. I.D. pipe (their run 8).  The pellets each had the shape of a cylinder 0.504 in. diameter, 0.180 in. long, surmounted on each end by a spherical segment 0.150 in. high, and were packed in the bed at a density of 13,420 pellets per cubic foot.  The solution flowed at a rate of 369 lb./hr. at 24.57°C., and its average concentration was 1.427 mole % acid.  At this temperature and concentration, the viscosity of the solution is 0.318 centipoise, density 0.7975 gm./cu. cm., and the diffusivity of succinic acid $2.38 \times 10^{-6}$ sq. cm./sec.  Estimate the mass-transfer coefficient to be expected.

*Solution.*  The surface of the cylindrical portion of each pellet is $\pi(0.504)(0.180)$ sq. in.  The surface of the two spherical segments, assuming the sphere radius to be $0.504/2 = 0.252$ in., is $2(2)\pi(0.252)(0.150)$ sq. in.  The total surface is therefore 0.7605 sq. in., or 0.00529 sq. ft. per pellet.  The diameter of a sphere of this surface is $d_p = \sqrt{(0.00529)/\pi} = 0.0408$ ft.  The interfacial surface $a = 13,420(0.00529) = 71.0$ sq. ft./cu. ft.

Fractional void vol. = $\epsilon = 1 - d_p a/6 = 1 - 0.0408(71.0)/6$
$= 0.517$

$U_{av}\rho$ = av. mass velocity based on empty-tower cross section
$$= \frac{(369 \text{ lb./hr.})(4)(144)}{\pi(3.02)^2} = 7,440 \text{ lb./(hr.)(sq. ft.)}$$

$\mu = 0.318$ centipoise $(2.42) = 0.770$ lb./(ft.)(hr.)

$$\frac{\text{Re}''}{\epsilon} = \frac{d_p U_{av}\rho}{\mu\epsilon} = \frac{0.0408(7,440)}{0.770(0.517)} = 761$$

Fig. 3.11:
$$j_D(10^{-1}) = 0.0053$$

$$j_D = 0.053 = \frac{k_x}{L_M} \text{Sc}^{0.58}$$

$M$ of succinic acid = 118.09     $M$ of acetone = 58.08
$M_{av} = 58.08(0.01427) + 118.09(1 - 0.01427) = 117.3$
$L_M = 7,440/117.3 = 63.4$ lb. moles/(hr.)(sq. ft.)

$$\text{Sc} = \frac{\mu}{\rho D} = \frac{0.00318}{0.7975(2.38 \times 10^{-6})} = 167$$

$$k_x = \frac{j_D L_M}{\text{Sc}^{0.58}} = \frac{0.053(63.4)}{167^{0.58}} = 0.172 \text{ lb. mole/(hr.)(sq. ft.)(mole fraction)}$$

(Gaffney and Drew found $k_x = 0.176$.)

**Illustration 3.** Powell [*Trans. Inst. Chem. Engrs. (London)*, **18**, 36 (1940)] reports that the rate of evaporation of water into air from wetted circular disks of various diameters facing upwind (evaporation from the upwind surface only) is given by the expression

$$\frac{wd}{p_w - p_a} = 3.3(10^{-7})(Ud)^{0.56}$$

where  $w$  = rate of evaporation, gm. water/(sec.)(sq. cm.)

$p_w$ = vapor pressure water at surface temp. mm. Hg

$p_a$ = partial pressure water in air stream, mm. Hg

$U$ = air velocity, cm./sec.

$d$ = disk diam., cm.

The air temperature was approximately 25°C., and the total pressure atmospheric. Transform this empirical expression into the $j_D$ form on the assumption that Sc enters to the $\frac{2}{3}$ power, thus making it useful for estimating evaporation of other liquids from similarly placed disks.

*Solution*

$$p_w - p_a, \text{ mm. Hg} = \Delta p \text{ atm. (760)}$$

$$w \text{ gm. H}_2\text{O}/(\text{sec.})(\text{sq. cm.}) = [N_A \text{ gm. moles H}_2\text{O}/(\text{sec.})(\text{sq. cm.})](18.02)$$

$$\therefore \frac{N_A(18.02)d}{\Delta p(760)} = 3.3(10^{-7})(Ud)^{0.56}$$

$$N_A = k_G \,\Delta p$$

$$\therefore k_G = \frac{3.3(10^{-7})(760)(Ud)^{0.56}}{18.02d} = \frac{1.39(10^{-5})(Ud)^{0.56}}{d}$$

$$j_D = \frac{k_G M_{\text{av}} p_{BM}}{U\rho} \text{Sc}^{2/3} = \frac{1.39(10^{-5})(Ud)^{0.56} \text{Sc}^{2/3} \, M_{\text{av}} p_{BM}}{dU\rho}$$

$$= \frac{1.39(10^{-5}) \text{Sc}^{2/3} \, M_{\text{av}} p_{BM}(\rho/\mu)^{0.44}}{\rho(dU\rho/\mu)^{0.44}}$$

For the conditions of the experiment, $M_{\text{av}} = 29$; $\mu$ for air $= 0.00018$ poise; Sc $= 0.60$; $\rho$ for air $= 0.001186$ gm./cu. cm.; $p_{BM} \doteq 0.95$ atm.

$$\therefore j_D = \frac{k_G M_{\text{av}} p_{BM}}{U\rho} \text{Sc}^{2/3}$$

$$= \frac{1.39(10^{-5})(0.60)^{2/3}(29)(0.95)(0.001186/0.00018)^{0.44}}{(0.001186) \text{ Re}^{0.44}}$$

$$= 0.527/\text{Re}^{0.44}$$

## NOTATION FOR CHAPTER 3

Consistent units in either the c.g.s. or the English system may be used. Pressures in diffusion equations are ordinarily expressed in atmospheres in either system.

$a$ = interfacial surface per unit volume, sq. cm./cu. cm. or sq. ft./cu. ft.

$c$ = concentration, gm. moles/cu. cm. or lb. moles/cu. ft.

$C_p$ = heat capacity at constant pressure, cal./(gm.)(°C.) or B.t.u./(lb.)(°F.)

$d$ = pipe diameter, cm. or ft.

= differential operator

$d_c$ = cylinder diameter, cm. or ft.

$d_p$ = diameter of a sphere of the same surface area as a particle, cm. or ft.

$D$ = molecular diffusivity, sq. cm./sec. or sq. ft./hr.

$E_D$ = eddy mass diffusivity, sq. cm./sec. or sq. ft./hr.

$E_H$ = eddy thermal diffusivity, sq. cm./sec. or sq. ft./hr.

$E_v$ = eddy viscosity, sq. cm./sec. or sq. ft./hr.

$f$ = friction factor (dimensionless), defined by Eq. (3.14)

$g_c$ = conversion factor, 980 gm. mass (cm.)/(gm. force)(sec.)$^2$ or 4.17 $\times$ 10$^8$ lb. mass (ft.)/(lb. force)(hr.)$^2$

$G$ = mass velocity of a gas (based on total cross section in the case of flow through packed beds) = $U_{av}\rho$, gm./(sec.)(sq. cm.) or lb./(hr.)(sq. ft.)

$G_M$ = molar mass velocity of a gas, gm. moles/(sec.)(sq. cm.) or lb. moles/(hr.)(sq. ft.)

$h$ = film coefficient for heat transfer, cal./(sec.)(sq. cm.)(°C.) or B.t.u./(hr.)(sq. ft.)(°F.)

$j_D$ = $(k'_G P/G_M)\psi$ (Sc), dimensionless

$j_H$ = $(h/C_p G)\psi$(Pr), dimensionless

$k$ = thermal conductivity, cal. (cm.)/(sec.)(sq. cm.)(°C.) or B.t.u.(ft.)/(hr.)(sq. ft.)(°F.)

$k_G$, $k'_G$, $k_x$, etc. = mass-transfer coefficients; for dimensions, see Table 3.1

$l$ = distance from upstream edge of a plate to downstream edge of heated or wetted section, cm. or ft.

$L$ = Prandtl mixing length, cm. or ft.

$L'$ = a scale of turbulence = $rL$

$L_M$ = superficial molal mass velocity of a liquid, gm. moles/(sec.)(sq. cm.) or lb. moles/(hr.)(sq. ft.)

$M$ = molecular weight, gm./gm. mole or lb./lb. mole

$n$ = a constant

$N$ = rate of mass transfer, gm. moles/(sec.)(sq. cm.) or lb. moles/(hr.)(sq. ft.)

$p$ = partial pressure, atm.

$P$ = total pressure, atm.

Pr = Prandtl number (dimensionless) = $C_p\mu/k$

$q$ = rate of heat transfer, cal./(sec.)(sq. cm.) or B.t.u./(hr.)(sq. ft.)

$r$ = a correlation coefficient = $(uv)/u'v'$

$R$ = universal gas constant, 82.06 cu. cm. (atm.)/(gm. mole)(°K.) or 0.729 cu. ft. (atm.)/(lb. mole)(°R.)

Re = Reynolds number (dimensionless) = $dU_{av}\rho/\mu$

Re' = Reynolds number (dimensionless) for flow past a cylinder = $d_c U_{av}\rho/\mu$

Re'' = Reynolds number (dimensionless) for flow past particles = $d_p U_{av}\rho/\mu$

Re''' = Reynolds number (dimensionless) for flow past plates = $l U_{av}\rho/\mu$

Sc = Schmidt number (dimensionless) = $\mu/\rho D$

$t$ = temperature, °C. or °F.

$T$ = absolute temperature, °K. or °R.

$u$, $v$ = deviating velocity; cm./sec. or ft./hr.

$u'$, $v'$ = root-mean-square deviating velocity; cm./sec. or ft./hr.

$U$ = fluid velocity in principal direction of flow, cm./sec. or ft./hr.

$U_m$ = maximum fluid velocity in principal direction of flow, cm./sec. or ft./hr.

$V$ = velocity normal to the principal direction of flow, cm./sec. or ft./hr.

$W$ = mass transferred/time area, gm./(sec.)(sq. cm.) or lb./(hr.)(sq. ft.)

$x$ = liquid concentration, mole fraction

$y$ = gas concentration, mole fraction

$Y'$ = gas concentration, mass ratio of components

$z$ = distance in direction of diffusion, cm. or ft.

$z_G$ = effective film thickness, diffusion in gases, ft.

$z_G'$ = effective film thickness, heat transfer, cm. or ft.

$z_L$ = effective film thickness, diffusion in liquids, cm. or ft.

$\alpha$ = thermal molecular diffusivity, sq. cm./sec. or sq. ft./hr.

$\Delta$ = difference

$\epsilon$ = fractional void volume = $1 - d_p a / 6$

$\mu$ = viscosity, gm./(cm.)(sec.)(= poises) or lb./(ft.)/(hr.)

$\nu$ = kinematic viscosity or momentum molecular diffusivity, $\mu/\rho$, sq. cm./sec. or sq. ft./hr.

$\rho$ = density, gm./cu. cm. or lb./cu. ft.

$\tau$ = shearing stress, gm. force/sq. cm. or lb. force/sq. ft.

$\phi$, $\phi'$, etc. = functions

$\psi$, $\psi'$ = functions

Subscripts:

$A, B$ = component $A$, component $B$

av = average

$F$ = film

$G$ = gas

$i$ = interface or wall

$L$ = liquid

$M$ = logarithmic average

1, 2 = positions 1, 2

## REFERENCES

1. Bedingfield, C. H., and T. B. Drew: *Ind. Eng. Chem.*, **42**, 1164 (1950).
2. Chilton, T. H., and A. P. Colburn: *Ind. Eng. Chem.*, **26**, 1183 (1934).
3. Colburn, A. P.: *Ind. Eng. Chem.*, **22**, 967 (1930).
4. ———: *Trans. Am. Inst. Chem. Engrs.*, **29**, 174 (1933).
5. Eckert, E. R. G.: "Introduction to the Transfer of Heat and Mass," McGraw-Hill Book Company, Inc., New York, 1950.
6. Kalinske, A. A., and C. L. Pien: *Ind. Eng. Chem.*, **36**, 220 (1944).
7. Linton, W. H., and T. K. Sherwood: *Chem. Eng. Progr.*, **46**, 258 (1950).
8. McAdams, W. H.: "Heat Transmission," 2d. ed, McGraw-Hill Book Company, Inc., New York, 1942.
9. Page, F., W. G. Schlinger, D. K. Breaux, and B. H. Sage: *Ind. Eng. Chem.*, **44**, 424 (1952).
10. Prandtl, L.: *Z. Physik*, **11**, 1072 (1910); **29**, 487 (1928).
11. Reynolds, O.: "Scientific Papers of Osborne Reynolds," vol. II, Cambridge University Press, New York, 1901.
12. Sherwood, T. K.: *Ind. Eng. Chem.*, **42**, 2077 (1950).
13. ——— and E. R. Gilliland: *Ind. Eng. Chem.* **26**, 516 (1934).

14. ——— and R. L. Pigford: "Absorption and Extraction," 2d ed., McGraw-Hill Book Company, Inc., New York, 1952.
15. Taylor, G. I.: *Rept. Mem., Brit. Advisory Comm. Aeronaut.*, **272**, 423 (1916).
16. Towle, W. L., and T. K. Sherwood: *Ind. Eng. Chem.*, **31**, 457 (1939).
17. Woertz, B. B., and T. K. Sherwood: *Trans. Am. Inst. Chem. Engrs.*, **35**, 517 (1939).

## PROBLEMS

**1.** Calculate the effective film thickness for the mass transfer of Illustration 1.

**2.** Show the algebraic steps leading from Eq. (3.23) to Eq. (3.24).

**3.** Estimate the mass-transfer coefficient and effective film thickness to be expected in the absorption of ammonia from air by a 2 *N* sulfuric acid solution in a wetted-wall tower under the following circumstances:

Air flow = 41.4 gm./min. (air only)
Av. partial pressure ammonia in air = 30.8 mm. **Hg**
Total pressure = 760 mm. Hg
Av. gas temp. = 25°C.
Av. liquid temp. = 25°C.
Diam. tower = 1.46 cm. I.D.

For absorption of ammonia in sulfuric acid of this concentration, the entire mass-transfer resistance lies within the gas, and the partial pressure of ammonia at the liquid interface is negligible. [NOTE: The circumstances correspond to run 47 of Chambers and Sherwood, *Trans. Am. Inst. Chem. Engrs.*, **33**, 579 (1937), who observed $d/z_G$ = 16.6.]

**4.** Toluene flows in a thin film down the outside surface of a vertical circular cylinder, 2 in. diameter, 2 ft. long. Dry air at 110°F., 1 atm., flows at right angles to the wetted cylinder at a velocity of 25 ft./sec. The liquid temperature is 70°F. Calculate the rate at which the liquid should be supplied to the top of the cylinder so that evaporation will just prevent it from reaching the bottom of the cylinder.

**5.** Powell [*Trans. Inst. Chem. Engrs. (London)*, **18**, 36 (1940)] evaporated water from the outside surface of cylinders into an air stream flowing parallel to the axes of the cylinders. The conditions were those described in Illustration 3, and the results are given by the following expression:

$$\frac{wl}{p_w - p_a} = 3.17(10^{-8})(Ul)^{0.8}$$

where $w$ = gm. water evaporated/(sec.)(sq. cm.)
$p_w$ = vapor pressure water at temp. of surface, mm. Hg
$p_a$ = partial pressure water in air stream, mm. Hg
$U$ = velocity air stream, cm./sec.
$l$ = length cylinder, cm.

*a.* Transform the equation into the form $j_D = \phi(\text{Re}''')$.

*b.* Calculate the rate of sublimation from a cylinder of naphthalene, 3 in. in diameter, 24 in. long, into a stream of pure carbon dioxide flowing parallel to the cylinder at a velocity of 20 ft./sec., at 1 atm., 100°C. The vapor pressure of naphthalene at the surface temperature may be taken as 10 mm. Hg, and its diffusivity in carbon dioxide as 0.0515 sq. cm./sec. (at 0°C.). Express the results as grams naphthalene evaporated per hour.

**6.** The free-fall terminal velocity of waterdrops in air at atmospheric pressure is given by the following table of data:[14]

| Diam., mm | 0.05 | 0.2 | 0.5 | 1.0 | 2.0 | 3.0 |
|---|---|---|---|---|---|---|
| Velocity, ft./sec | 0.18 | 2.3 | 7.0 | 12.7 | 19.2 | 23.8 |

*a.* Calculate the time and distance of free fall for a waterdrop of initial diameter 1.0 mm. to evaporate to a diameter of 0.2 mm., in quiet dry air at 1 atm., 100°F.   The water temperature may be taken as 58°F.   Assume the drop remains spherical and that the atmospheric pressure remains constant at 1 atm. throughout the fall.

*b.* Calculate the time for the above evaporation, assuming that the drop is suspended without motion (as from a fine thread) in still air.

# CHAPTER 4

# DIFFUSION IN SOLIDS

It was indicated in Chap. 1 that certain of the diffusional operations such as leaching, drying, adsorption, and the "membrane" operations of dialysis and gaseous effusion involve contact of fluids with solids. In such operations the diffusion must involve the solid phase and may proceed according to several mechanisms. Diffusion through a solid when the solute is dissolved to form a homogeneous solid solution may be termed "structure-insensitive" diffusion, and this form is most nearly similar to diffusion through fluids. A porous or granular solid, however, may permit flow of a liquid or gas through the interstices and capillaries, and diffusion by this mechanism may be termed "structure-sensitive." Diffusion may occur even along the surface of a solid with nothing but superficial penetration of the solute into the solid itself, which may be important in certain adsorption operations.

## STRUCTURE-INSENSITIVE DIFFUSION

This type of diffusion may occur when the diffusing substance dissolves in the solid to form a homogeneous solution. The actual mechanisms of the diffusion may be quite complex and very different for diverse substances. For example, in the diffusion of hydrogen through palladium metal the hydrogen molecules evidently dissociate and enter the metal crystal lattice as atoms. On the other hand, nitrogen or oxygen when diffusing through metals forms compounds, and it is the progressive decomposition of these nitrides or oxides which results in the passage of the gas. Helium and hydrogen may diffuse through the anionic network of a glass, while gases such as argon and air diffuse along faults in the structure. The diffusion of metals into each other such as the diffusion of gold through silver follows a different mechanism from that of the diffusion of gases through membranes of rubber and other polymers or of ammonia and water through certain zeolitic crystals.

**Steady-state Diffusion.** When the concentration gradient remains unchanged with passage of time, so that the rate of diffusion is constant, Fick's law may be applied in the form used in Chap. 2 for cases where the diffusivity is independent of concentration. Thus $N_A$, the rate of diffusion of substance $A$ per unit cross section of solid, is proportional to the concentration gradient in the direction of diffusion, $-dc_A/dz$,

$$N_A = -D_{AB}\frac{dc_A}{dz} \tag{4.1}$$

where $D_{AB}$ is the diffusivity of $A$ through $B$. If $D_{AB}$ is constant, integration of Eq. (4.1) for *diffusion through a flat slab* of thickness $z$ results in

$$N_A = \frac{D_{AB}(c_{A1} - c_{A2})}{z} = k_S\,\Delta c_A \tag{4.2}$$

which parallels the expressions obtained for fluids in a similar situation. Here $c_{A1}$ and $c_{A2}$ are the concentrations at opposite sides of the slab. For other solid shapes, the rate is given by

$$w = N_A S_{av} = \frac{D_{AB}S_{av}(c_{A1} - c_{A2})}{z} \tag{4.3}$$

with appropriate values of the average cross section for diffusion, $S_{av}$, to be applied. Thus, for *radial diffusion through a solid cylinder* of inner and outer radii $a_1$ and $a_2$, respectively, and of length $l$,

$$S_{av} = \frac{2\pi l(a_2 - a_1)}{\ln\,(a_2/a_1)} \tag{4.4}$$

and
$$z = a_2 - a_1 \tag{4.5}$$

For *radial diffusion through a spherical shell* of inner and outer radii $a_1$ and $a_2$,

$$S_{av} = 4\pi a_1 a_2 \tag{4.6}$$
$$z = a_2 - a_1 \tag{4.7}$$

**Illustration 1.** Hydrogen gas at 2 atm. pressure, 25°C., is flowing through a pipe made of a vulcanized neoprene rubber, whose inner and outer diameters are 1 and 2 in., respectively. The solubility of the hydrogen is 0.053 cu. cm. $H_2$ at standard conditions per cubic centimeter rubber per atmosphere, and the diffusivity of the hydrogen through the rubber is $0.18 \times 10^{-5}$ sq. cm./sec. Estimate the rate of loss of hydrogen by diffusion per foot of pipe length.

*Solution.* At 2 atm. hydrogen pressure, the solubility is $0.053(2) = 0.106$ cu. ft. $H_2$ at standard conditions per cubic foot rubber. Therefore concentration $c_{A1}$ at the inner surface of the pipe $= 0.106/359 = 0.000295$ lb. mole $H_2$/cu. ft.

At the outer surface, $c_{A2} = 0$ (assuming that the resistance to diffusion of the $H_2$ away from the surface is negligible).

$$D_{AB} = (0.18 \times 10^{-5})(3.87) = 0.696 \times 10^{-5} \text{ sq. ft./hr.}$$
$$z = a_2 - a_1 = (2 - 1)/2(12) = 0.0417 \text{ ft.}$$
$$l = 1 \text{ ft.}$$

Eq. (4.4): $\quad S_{av} = \dfrac{2\pi(1)(1 - 0.5)}{12\ln\,(1/0.5)} = 0.377$ sq. ft.

Eq. (4.3): $\quad w = \dfrac{D_{AB}S_{av}(c_{A1} - c_{A2})}{z} = \dfrac{0.696(10^{-5})(0.377)(0.000295 - 0)}{0.0417}$

$$= 1.86(10^{-8}) \text{ lb. mole } H_2/\text{hr.} \quad \textit{Ans.}$$

**Unsteady-state Diffusion.**    Since solids are not so readily transported through equipment as are fluids, the application of batch and semibatch processes and consequent unsteady-state diffusional conditions arise much more frequently than in the case of fluids.    Even in continuous operation, as in the case of a continuous drier, the history of each solid piece as it passes through the equipment is representative of the unsteady state. These cases are therefore of considerable importance.

Consider the bar-shaped solid of Fig. 4.1, and assume that the diffusion is occurring in the $z$ direction only, under unsteady-state conditions through unit cross section.    The quantity of solute entering the

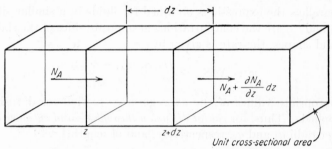

Fig. 4.1. Unsteady-state unidimensional diffusion.

section at $z$ is different from that leaving the section at $z + dz$ because some solute is retained by the volume of solid between the sections.    The quantity of solute in the small volume between the sections is $c_A\,dz$, and the rate of loss of solute from the section is therefore $-\partial(c_A\,dz)/\partial\theta$.    This rate of loss must equal the difference in rates of diffusion to and from the small volume.    If $N_A$ is the rate of diffusion of solute to the volume and the rate of diffusion away from it is $N_A + (\partial N_A/\partial z)\,dz$, then the net rate of loss is the difference, or $(\partial N_A/\partial z)\,dz$.

$$-\frac{\partial(c_A\,dz)}{\partial\theta} = \frac{\partial N_A}{\partial z}\,dz \tag{4.8}$$

$$-\frac{\partial c_A}{\partial\theta} = \frac{\partial N_A}{\partial z} \tag{4.9}$$

But, from Eq. (4.1),

$$\frac{\partial N_A}{\partial z} = -D_{AB}\frac{\partial^2 c_A}{\partial z^2} \tag{4.10}$$

$$\frac{\partial c_A}{\partial\theta} = D_{AB}\frac{\partial^2 c_A}{\partial z^2} \tag{4.11}$$

This is the expression for linear diffusion; for diffusion in two or three dimensions, analogous equations may be written.    These can be applied to the problems of unsteady-state diffusion by integration with appropriate boundary conditions, and Newman[4] has summarized the resulting expressions most conveniently:

1. *Diffusion from a slab with sealed edges.* Consider a slab of thickness $2a$, with sealed edges on four sides, so that diffusion can take place only toward and from the flat parallel faces, a cross section of which is shown in Fig. 4.2. Suppose initially the concentration of solute throughout the slab is uniform, $c_{A0}$, and that the slab is immersed in a medium so that the solute will diffuse out of the slab. Let the concentration at the surfaces be $c_{A\infty}$, invariant with passage of time. If the diffusion were

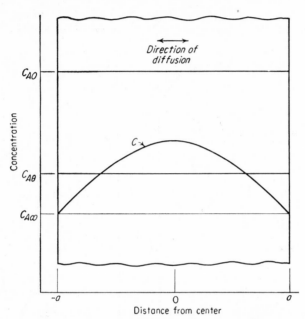

FIG. 4.2. Unsteady-state diffusion from a slab.

allowed to continue indefinitely, the concentration would fall to the uniform value $c_{A\infty}$, and $c_{A0} - c_{A\infty}$ is a measure of the amount of solute removed. On the other hand, if diffusion from the slab were stopped at time $\theta$, the distribution of solute would be given by the curve marked $c$, which by internal diffusion would level off to the uniform concentration $c_{A\theta}$, where $c_{A\theta}$ is the average concentration at time $\theta$. The quantity $c_{A\theta} - c_{A\infty}$ is a measure of the amount of solute still unremoved. The fraction unremoved, $E$, is given by integration of Eq. (4.11),

$$E = \frac{c_{A\theta} - c_{A\infty}}{c_{A0} - c_{A\infty}} = f\left(\frac{D\theta}{a^2}\right)$$

$$= \frac{8}{\pi^2}\left(e^{-D\theta\pi^2/4a^2} + \frac{1}{9}e^{-9D\theta\pi^2/4a^2} + \frac{1}{25}e^{-25D\theta\pi^2/4a^2} + \cdots\right) = E_a \qquad (4.12)$$

The function is shown graphically in Fig. 4.3.

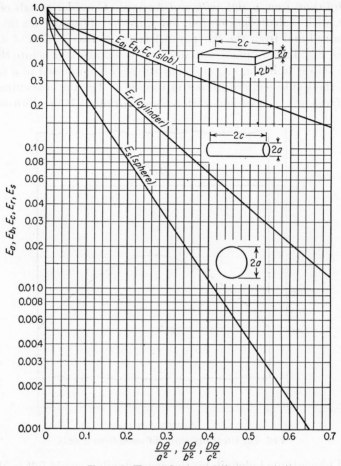

FIG. 4.3. Unsteady-state diffusion.

2. *Diffusion from a rectangular bar with sealed ends.* For a rectangular bar of thickness 2a and width 2b, with sealed ends,

$$E = f\left(\frac{D\theta}{a^2}\right) f\left(\frac{D\theta}{b^2}\right) = E_a E_b \tag{4.13}$$

3. *Diffusion for a rectangular parallelepiped.* For a brick-shaped bar, of dimensions 2a, 2b, and 2c, with diffusion from all six faces,

$$E = f\left(\frac{D\theta}{a^2}\right) f\left(\frac{D\theta}{b^2}\right) f\left(\frac{D\theta}{c^2}\right) = E_a E_b E_c \tag{4.14}$$

4. *Diffusion from a sphere.* For a sphere of radius a,

$$E = f'\left(\frac{D\theta}{a^2}\right) = E_s \tag{4.15}$$

5. *Diffusion from a cylinder with sealed ends.* For a cylinder of radius $a$, with plane ends sealed,

$$E = f'' \left( \frac{D\theta}{a^2} \right) = E_r \qquad (4.16)$$

6. *Diffusion from a cylinder.* For a cylinder of radius $a$ and length $2c$, with diffusion from both ends as well as from the cylindrical surface,

$$E = f \left( \frac{D\theta}{c^2} \right) f'' \left( \frac{D\theta}{a^2} \right) = E_c E_r \qquad (4.17)$$

The functions $f'(D\theta/a^2)$ and $f''(D\theta/a^2)$ are also shown graphically in Fig. 4.3.

For solid shapes where the diffusion takes place from one rather than two opposite faces, the functions are calculated as if the thickness were twice the true value. For example, if diffusion occurs through only one face of a flat slab of thickness $2a$, edges sealed, the calculation is made with $D\theta/4a^2$. The equations may also be used for diffusion into, as well as out of, the various shapes.

It is important to note that Eqs. (4.12) to (4.17) assume constant diffusivity and constancy of the edge concentration $c_{A\infty}$. The latter is the same as assuming no resistance to diffusion in the medium surrounding the solid. Van Arsdel[7] has considered integrations of Eq. (4.11) involving varying $D$, and Barrer,[1] Jost,[2] and Newman[4] have shown the effects of added diffusional resistances and interfacial reactions.

**Illustration 2.** A 5% agar gel containing a uniform concentration of 5 gm. urea/-100 cu. cm. was molded in the form of a 3-cm. cube. One face of the cube was exposed to a running supply of fresh water into which the urea diffused. The other faces were protected by the mold. The temperature was 5°C. At the end of 68 hr., the average urea concentration in the gel had fallen to 3 gm./100 cu. cm. The resistance to diffusion may be considered as residing wholly within the gel.

*a.* Calculate the diffusivity of the urea in the gel.

*b.* How long would it have taken for the average concentration to fall to 1 gm./100 cu. cm.?

*c.* Repeat (b) for the case where two opposite faces of the cube are exposed.

*Solution.* *a.* $c_A$ can be calculated in terms of gm./100 cu. cm. $c_{A0} = 5$ gm./100 cu. cm.; $c_{A\theta} = 3$, $c_{A\infty} = 0$ since pure water was the leaching agent. $a = \frac{3}{2} = 1.5$ cm.; $\theta = 68(3,600) = 245,000$ sec.

$$\frac{c_{A\theta} - c_{A\infty}}{c_{A0} - c_{A\infty}} = \frac{3}{5} = 0.6 = E$$

The abscissa read from Fig. 4.3, which is $D\theta/4a^2$ for diffusion from only one exposed face, is 0.128.

$$D = \frac{0.128(4)a^2}{\theta} = \frac{0.128(4)(1.5)^2}{245,000} = 4.70(10^{-6}) \text{ sq. cm./sec.}$$

*b.* For $c_{A\theta} = 1$ gm./100 cu. cm.,

$$\frac{c_{A\theta} - c_{A\infty}}{c_{A0} - c_{A\infty}} = \frac{1}{5} = 0.20 \qquad \frac{D\theta}{4a^2} = 0.568 \qquad \text{from Fig. 4.3}$$

$$\theta = \frac{0.568(4)a^2}{D} = \frac{0.568(4)(1.5)^2}{4.70(10^{-6})} = 1,087,000 \text{ sec., or } 302 \text{ hr.}$$

*c.* For two opposite faces exposed, $a = 1.5$ cm., $c_{A\theta}/c_{A0} = 0.2$, and $D\theta/a^2 = 0.568$.

$$\theta = \frac{0.568a^2}{D} = \frac{0.568(1.5)^2}{4.70(10^{-6})} = 222,000 \text{ sec., or } 61.5 \text{ hr.}$$

**Diffusivity and Permeability.** While a great many measurements of diffusivity have been made, these are largely in connection with systems not of immediate interest here. The diffusivity in metals, for example, is of great interest to the metallurgist in problems of carburizing, nitriding, or powder metallurgy, but of little value in the diffusional operations of the chemical engineer. A great many data on the diffusivity of gases through membranes have been gathered, a few typical values of which are listed in Table 4.1 in order to indicate order of magnitude. In con-

TABLE 4.1. DIFFUSIVITY OF GASES IN VULCANIZED RUBBER,[1] 25°C.

| Diffusing substance $(A)$ | $D_{AB}$, sq. cm./sec. | Solubility, cu. cm. gas, 0°C., 1 atm. (cu. cm. rubber)(atm.) |
|---|---|---|
| H$_2$ | $0.85 \times 10^{-5}$ | 0.040 |
| O$_2$ | $0.21 \times 10^{-5}$ | 0.070 |
| N$_2$ | $0.15 \times 10^{-5}$ | 0.035 |
| CO$_2$ | $0.11 \times 10^{-5}$ | 0.90 |

nection with diffusion through membranes particularly, it is common to cite the so-called permeability $P$, rather than the diffusivity. Permeability is defined as

$$P = \frac{V}{-dp/dz} \qquad (4.18)$$

where $V$ is the volume of gas (at some specified temperature and pressure, frequently 1 atm., 0°C.) diffusing per unit time (area) under the pressure gradient $-dp/dz$. The maximum concentration of solute gas in the solid is its solubility, which varies with the pressure of the gas in contact with the membrane.

**Illustration 3.** From the data of Table 4.1, calculate the rate of diffusion of carbon dioxide, CO$_2$, through a membrane of the rubber 1 mm. thick at 25°C., if the partial pressure of the CO$_2$ is 1 cm. Hg on one side and zero on the other. Calculate also the permeability of the membrane.

*Solution.* At a pressure of 1 cm. Hg ($\frac{1}{76}$ atm.) the solubility of CO$_2$ in the rubber is 0.90/76 = 0.01184 cu. cm. gas (measured at 0°C., 1 atm.) per cu. cm. rubber, or

0.01184/22,400 gm. mole $CO_2$/cu. cm. On the downstream face of the membrane the $CO_2$ concentration is zero. The thickness $z = 0.1$ cm. Therefore

$$V = 22{,}400N_A = 22{,}400D_{AB}\,\Delta c/z = 0.11(10^{-5})(0.01184)/0.1$$
$$= 0.13(10^{-6})\ \text{cu. cm. (0°C., 1 atm.) per sec. sq. cm.}$$

Eq. (4.18): $\quad P = \dfrac{V}{-dp/dz} = \dfrac{0.13(10^{-6})}{(\frac{1}{6})/0.1}$

$$= 0.99(10^{-6})\ \text{cu. cm. (0°C., 1 atm.) per sec. sq. cm. (atm./cm.)}$$

Note that $P = D_{AB}$ (solubility) $= 0.11(10^{-5})(0.90) = 0.99(10^{-6})$.

Diffusivities in solids may vary very rapidly with temperature, much more so than with liquids or gases. For example, $D$ for nitrogen through a vulcanized chloroprene polymer membrane is cited as $0.019 \times 10^{-5}$ sq. cm./sec. at 27.1°C. and $0.450 \times 10^{-5}$ sq. cm./sec. at 84.3°C.[1] Usually, log $D$ is linear with reciprocal absolute temperature for solid diffusion. The diffusivity may vary considerably with concentration; it may be anisotropic, for example, the diffusivity through crystals may vary depending upon the direction with respect to the various crystallographic axes. Observations such as these make it understandable that it is now impossible to predict the diffusivity in solids, as we did for liquids or gases, and it is necessary in practice to measure the diffusivity experimentally under the desired conditions.

## STRUCTURE-SENSITIVE DIFFUSION

This is a most complex subject, owing to the great variety of solid structures and diffusing solutes which may have to be studied. Only a few of the situations can be considered in any detail.

**Diffusion through a Uniformly Porous Solid.** Consider a rigid solid which is uniformly porous throughout, i.e., where the nature and percentage of voids are constant in all directions and in every part of the solid, as might be the case with an idealized clay brick. Suppose the pores and interstices of such a solid are filled with a solution, such as a solution of salt in water. If the solid is now immersed in water, one may imagine a continuous liquid path leading from the depths within the solid to the surrounding liquid through the myriad interstices formed by the rigid solid structure. Since a concentration gradient of dissolved salt exists within the liquid path, diffusion occurs and in time the salt will completely diffuse from the solid into the surrounding fresh water.

To such a system the previous equations applicable to solid solutions may be applied. Since the liquid path along which the diffusion takes place is relatively very long and in general not known, one may characterize the operation by use of an effective diffusivity to be used in the equations of the preceding section, which could be expected to be smaller than the ordinary diffusivities for the solute in the solvent in the absence of a constraining solid structure. As an alternative,[3,5] one may define a "pore-shape factor" $K$, characteristic of the number, size, and nature of the pores in the solid, which when multiplied by the ordinary solid thickness provides a measure of the true length of the diffusion path. The factor is independent of solute and solvent, concentration, time, or any other variable affecting the rate of diffusion. Use of the preceding equations then requires, as before, constancy of the diffusivity, or the use of a correct average or integral diffusivity, over the concentration range experienced.

Under certain limited conditions, the previous relations may also be used to describe the change in average moisture content of a solid during drying: under conditions such that internal diffusion of moisture controls the rate of drying, and in cases where the solid structure contains very fine interstices. Coarse sands do not fall into the latter category, and the drying of wood on occasions may be complicated by the variation of diffusivity with direction, i.e., with or across the grain. These matters are considered in greater detail in Chap. 12. Applications to leaching are discussed in Chap. 13.

**Illustration 4.** Porous alumina spheres, 1 cm. diameter, 25% voids, were thoroughly impregnated with an aqueous potassium chloride, KCl, solution, concentration 0.25 gm./cu. cm. When immersed in pure running water, they lost 90% of their salt content in 4.75 hr. The temperature was 25°C. At this temperature the average diffusivity of KCl in water over the indicated concentration range is $1.84 \times 10^{-5}$ sq. cm./sec.

Estimate the time for removal of 90% of the dissolved solute if the spheres had been impregnated with potassium chromate, $K_2CrO_4$, solution at a concentration 0.28 gm./cu. cm., when immersed in a running stream of water containing 0.02 gm. $K_2CrO_4$/cu. cm. The average diffusivity of $K_2CrO_4$ in water at 25°C. is $1.14 \times 10^{-5}$ sq. cm./sec.

*Solution.* For these spheres, $a = 0.5$ cm., and, for the KCl diffusion, $\theta = 4.75(3,600) = 17,000$ sec. When the spheres are surrounded by pure water, the ultimate concentration in the spheres, $c_{A\infty} = 0$.

$$\therefore \frac{c_{A\theta} - c_{A\infty}}{c_{A0} - c_{A\infty}} = 0.1 \qquad \text{for } 90\% \text{ removal of KCl}$$

From Fig. 4.3, $D\theta/(Ka)^2 = 0.18$, where $K$ is the pore-shape factor.

$$K^2 = \frac{D\theta}{a^2(0.18)} = \frac{1.84(10^{-5})(17,000)}{0.5^2(0.18)} = 6.95$$

For the $K_2CrO_4$ diffusion, $c_{A0} = 0.28$ gm./cu. cm.; $c_{A\infty} = 0.02$, and $c_{A\theta} = 0.1(0.28) = 0.028$.

$$\therefore E = \frac{c_{A\theta} - c_{A\infty}}{c_{A0} - c_{A\infty}} = \frac{0.028 - 0.02}{0.28 - 0.02} = 0.0308 = E_s$$

From Fig. 4.3, $D\theta/(Ka)^2 = 0.30$.

$$\theta = \frac{0.30(Ka)^2}{D} = \frac{0.30(6.95)(0.5)^2}{1.14(10^{-5})} = 45{,}800 \text{ sec., or } 12.2 \text{ hr.} \quad Ans.$$

**Illustration 5.** A slab of wood, 15.2 by 15.2 by 1.90 cm., of initial uniform moisture content 39.7% water, was exposed to relatively dry air.[6] The thin edges were sealed, and drying took place from the two large flat faces by internal diffusion of liquid water to the surface and evaporation at the surface. The moisture content at the surface remained constant at 8.0%. At the end of 7 hr. 40 min., the average moisture content had fallen to 24.0%.

*a.* Calculate the effective diffusivity, sq. cm./sec.

*b.* Assuming $D$ remains constant and is the same for diffusion in all directions, what average water content would have resulted had the slab been dried from one face only, and from all six faces, for the same length of time?

*c.* What average water content would be had for a cylinder 1 ft. long, 6 in. diameter. drying from all surfaces for a period of 7 days?

*Solution.* *a.* Let $\rho$ = dry density of wood, lb. dry wood/cu. ft., assumed constant. If $X$ is mass fraction of water, concentration in lb. moles/cu. ft. $= \rho \dfrac{X}{1-X} \dfrac{1}{18.02}$. Since the factor $\rho/18.02$ then appears in all such concentrations, $E$ may be computed in terms of lb. water/lb. dry wood, $X/(1-X)$.

$$c_{A0} = \frac{0.397}{1-0.397} = 0.658 \text{ lb. water/lb. dry wood}$$

$$c_{A\infty} = \frac{0.08}{1-0.08} = 0.087 \text{ lb. water/lb. dry wood}$$

$$c_{A\theta} = \frac{0.240}{1-0.240} = 0.316 \text{ lb. water/lb. dry wood}$$

At $\theta = 7.67(3{,}600) = 27{,}600$ sec.,

$$E = \frac{c_{A\theta} - c_{A\infty}}{c_{A0} - c_{A\infty}} = \frac{0.316 - 0.087}{0.658 - 0.087} = 0.40 = E_a$$

From Fig. 4.3, $D\theta/a^2 = 0.287$. Since $a = 1.90/2 = 0.95$ cm.,

$$\text{Effective diffusivity} = D = \frac{0.287a^2}{\theta} = \frac{0.287(0.95)^2}{27{,}600}$$
$$= 9.38(10^{-6}) \text{ sq. cm./sec.}$$

*b.* For diffusion through one face only,

$$\frac{D\theta}{4a^2} = \frac{9.38(10^{-6})(27{,}600)}{4(0.95)^2} = 0.0718$$

From Fig. 4.3, $E = E_a = 0.7$.

$$\therefore\ 0.7 = \frac{c_{A\theta} - 0.087}{0.658 - 0.087}$$
$$c_{A\theta} = 0.487 \text{ lb. water/lb. dry wood}$$

corresponding to

$$\frac{0.487}{1.487}(100) = 32.8\% \text{ water}$$

For diffusion through six faces, $a = 0.95$ cm., $b = c = 15.2/2 = 7.6$ cm.

$$\frac{D\theta}{a^2} = \frac{9.38(10^{-6})(27,600)}{0.95^2} = 0.287$$

$$\frac{D\theta}{b^2} = \frac{D\theta}{c^2} = \frac{9.38(10^{-6})(27,600)}{7.6^2} = 0.00448$$

From Fig. 4.3, $E_a = 0.4$, $E_b = E_c = 0.94$.

Eq. (4.14):          $E = E_a E_b E_c = 0.4(0.94)(0.94) = 0.353$

$$0.353 = \frac{c_{A\theta} - 0.087}{0.658 - 0.087}$$

$c_{A\theta} = 0.291$ lb. water/lb. dry wood (22.5% water)

c. For 7 days, $\theta = 7(24) = 168$ hr.

$$D = 9.38(10^{-6})(3.87) = 36.3(10^{-6}) \text{ sq. ft./hr.}$$
$$a = 0.5/2 = 0.25 \text{ ft.}    c = \tfrac{1}{2} = 0.5 \text{ ft.}$$
$$\frac{D\theta}{a^2} = \frac{36.3(10^{-6})(168)}{0.25^2} = 0.0975    E_r = 0.405$$
$$\frac{D\theta}{c^2} = \frac{36.3(10^{-6})(168)}{0.5^2} = 0.0244    E_c = 0.82$$

Eq. (4.17):          $E = E_c E_r = 0.82(0.405) = 0.332$

$$0.332 = \frac{c_{A\theta} - 0.087}{0.658 - 0.087}$$

$c_{A\theta} = 0.277$ lb. water/lb. dry wood (21.7% water)

**Flow of Gases through Porous Solids.**    If there exists a concentration difference, i.e., a pressure difference, for a gas across a porous solid, a flow of the gas through the solid will take place.   Under ordinary conditions, this is not a diffusional flow in the usual sense; yet since it may be described according to the methods of diffusion, it is sometimes so considered.   Let us for the moment simplify the structure of the porous solid and consider it to be a series of straight capillary tubes of constant diameter $d$, and of length $l$, reaching from the high-pressure to the low-pressure side of the solid.   At ordinary pressures, the flow of the gas in the capillaries may be either streamline or turbulent, depending upon whether the dimensionless Reynolds number, $du\rho/\mu$, is below or above 2,100.   For the present purposes, where the diameter of the capillaries is small, and the pressure difference and hence the velocity are small, flow will be streamline and is described by Poiseuille's law for a compressible fluid obeying the perfect-gas law,

$$N_A = \frac{d^2 g_c}{32\mu l R T} \, p_{\text{av}}(p_1 - p_2) \tag{4.19}$$

where          $$p_{\text{av}} = \frac{p_1 + p_2}{2} \tag{4.20}$$

This assumes that the entire pressure difference is due to friction in the capillaries and ignores entrance and exit losses and kinetic-energy effects, which is satisfactory for present purposes. The capillaries leading through the porous solid are not of constant diameter, and their length is on the average some multiple of the solid thickness $z$. Only a fraction of the surface of the solid is open to the gas. The equation may then be written

$$RTN_A = \frac{kp_{av}(p_1 - p_2)}{z} \tag{4.21}$$

If the rate of flow is measured in terms of a gas volume $V$ at the average pressure flowing per unit time per unit cross section of the solid, then Eq. (4.21) becomes

$$p_{av}V = \frac{Pp_{av}(p_1 - p_2)}{z} \tag{4.22}$$

where $P$ is the permeability of the solid to gas flow by Poiseuille's law. It is possible to compute average capillary sizes in membranes and porous barriers by measurements made according to this equation.

Under certain conditions, a different type of flow will occur, however. If the capillary diameters are small in comparison with the mean free path of the gas molecules $\lambda$ (say $d \leqq 0.1\lambda$), flow takes place by molecular effusion, following Knudsen's law. For a single straight capillary, this becomes

$$N_A = k' \sqrt{\frac{g_c}{2\pi MRT}} \frac{d}{l} (p_1 - p_2) \tag{4.23}$$

where $k'$ is a correction to take care of reflection of the molecule from the capillary wall. This may be written

$$RTN_A = k' \sqrt{\frac{g_c RT}{2\pi M}} \frac{d}{l} (p_1 - p_2) \tag{4.24}$$

or since, as before, the capillaries are of variable diameter nor is their length the same as the thickness of the solid,

$$p_{av}V = \frac{P'(p_1 - p_2)}{z} \tag{4.25}$$

where $P'$ is now the permeability of the solid to molecular streaming. The mean free path of the molecules can be estimated from the relation

$$\lambda = \frac{3.2\mu}{p} \sqrt{\frac{RT}{2\pi g_c M}} \tag{4.26}$$

Flow according to Knudsen's law is a function of the molecular weight of the gas, and consequently the components of a gas mixture will pass through a porous solid barrier at different rates. This has been used as a method for analyzing gas mixtures and is the basis of the separation process of gaseous effusion.

In a given capillary, flow will occur according to both laws: at very low pressures or in extremely fine capillaries Knudsen flow predominates, while at higher pressures Poiseuille flow predominates. In a porous solid with capillaries of various diameters, the different types may predominate in different capillaries within the same solid. In any case, the equations show that the rate of flow as measured by the quantity $p_{av}V$ is proportional to the pressure difference and inversely proportional to the thickness, as in true diffusion in solution. The effect of temperature on the permeability may be used to indicate which type of flow predominates.[1] For flow according to Poiseuille's law, the permeability varies inversely as the gas viscosity, which in turn increases with temperature; $P$ then decreases with increased temperature. For Knudsen flow, $P'$ varies as $\sqrt{T}$ and therefore increases with increased temperature. Further, it will be remembered that, should diffusion in solid solution occur, the temperature dependence of $P$ depends upon those of $D$ and the solubility. All these effects may occur at once, and the resulting temperature dependence may therefore be very complex.

Finally it should be remembered that, should the pressure difference become very large, the possibility of turbulent flow exists, which follows still a different law.

**Illustration 6.** A porous carbon diaphragm 1 in. thick, of average pore diameter 100 microns, permitted the flow of nitrogen at the rate of 9.0 cu. ft. (measured at 1 atm., 80°F.) per square foot per minute with a pressure difference across the diaphragm of 2 in. of water. The temperature was 80°F., and the downstream pressure was 1 atm. Calculate the flow to be expected at 250°F., with the same pressure difference.

*Solution.* At 80°F., 1 atm., the viscosity of nitrogen is 0.018 centipoise.

$$\mu = 0.018(\tfrac{1}{100}) = 0.00018 \text{ gm./(cm.)(sec.)}$$
$$p = 1(1{,}033.2) = 1{,}033.2 \text{ gm./sq. cm.}$$
$$T = (80 + 460)(1/1.8) = 300°K.$$
$$R = 84{,}780 \text{ gm.(cm.)/(°K.)(gm. mole)}$$
$$g_c = 980 \text{ cm./sec.}^2$$
$$M = 28.02$$

Eq. (4.26): 
$$\lambda = \frac{3.2\mu}{p}\sqrt{\frac{RT}{2\pi g_c M}} = \frac{3.2(0.00018)}{1{,}033.2}\sqrt{\frac{84{,}780(300)}{2(\pi)(980)(28.02)}}$$
$$= 0.00000557 \text{ cm., or } 0.0557 \text{ micron}$$

With capillary diameters of 100 microns, flow is therefore according to Poiseuille's law. For the first condition,

$$V_2 = 9.0 \text{ cu. ft./(sq. ft.)(min.)} \qquad \text{at } 80°F., 1 \text{ atm.}$$
$$p_2 = 1 \text{ atm.} = 14.7(144) = 2{,}120 \text{ lb./sq. ft.}$$
$$p_1 - p_2 = \tfrac{2}{12}(62.2) = 10.4 \text{ lb./sq. ft.}$$
$$p_{av} = 2{,}120 + 10.4/2 = 2{,}125 \text{ lb./sq. ft.}$$

Eq. (4.22): 
$$\frac{P}{z} = \frac{p_2 V_2}{p_{av}(p_1 - p_2)} = \frac{2{,}120(9.0)}{2{,}125(10.4)}$$
$$= 0.864 \text{ cu. ft./(min.)(sq. ft.) (lb./sq. ft.)}$$

for 1 in. thickness at 80°F.

At 250°F., the viscosity of nitrogen is 0.022 centipoise, and the new permeability becomes

$$\frac{P}{z} = 0.864 \frac{0.018}{0.022} = 0.706$$

$$\therefore V_2 = \frac{P p_{av}(p_1 - p_2)}{z p_2} = \frac{0.706(2,125)(10.4)}{2,120}$$

$$= 7.36 \text{ cu. ft./(min.)(sq. ft.)} \qquad \text{measured at 250°F., 1 atm.}$$

## NOTATION FOR CHAPTER 4

Consistent units in either the c.g.s. or the English system may be used throughout.

$a$ = one-half thickness or radius, cm. or ft.

$b$ = one-half width, cm. or ft.

$c$ = concentration, gm. moles/cu. cm. or lb. moles/cu. ft.

= one-half length, cm. or ft.

$d$ = diameter of a capillary, cm. or ft.

= differential operator

$D$ = diffusivity, sq. cm./sec. or sq. ft./hr.

$e$ = 2.7183

$E$ = fraction of solute unremoved, dimensionless

$f, f', f''$ = functions

$g_c$ = conversion factor, 980 gm. mass (cm.)/(gm. force)(sec.)$^2$ or $4.17 \times 10^8$ lb. mass (ft.)/(lb. force)(hr.)$^2$

$k_s$ = mass-transfer coefficient, gm. moles/(sec.)(sq. cm.) $\Delta c$ or lb. moles/(hr.) (sq. ft.) $\Delta c$

$k, k'$ = constants

$K$ = pore-shape factor, dimensionless

$l$ = length, cm. or ft.

ln = natural logarithm

$M$ = molecular weight, gm./gm. mole or lb./lb. mole

$N$ = rate of diffusion, gm. moles/(sec.)(sq. cm.) or lb. moles/(hr.)(sq. ft.)

$p$ = pressure, gm./sq. cm. or lb./sq. ft. (unless otherwise indicated)

$P$ = permeability = rate of diffusion per unit pressure gradient, cu. cm./ (sec.)(sq. cm.)(gm./sq. cm./cm.) or cu. ft./(hr.)(sq. ft.)(lb./sq. ft./ft.) (frequently also in other pressure units)

$R$ = universal gas constant, 84,780 gm.(cm.)/(gm. mole)(°K.) or 1,543 ft.-lb./(lb. mole)(°R.)

$S$ = cross-sectional area, sq. cm. or sq. ft.

$T$ = absolute temperature, °K. or °R.

$u$ = linear velocity, cm./sec. or ft./hr.

$V$ = volumetric rate of flow, cu. cm./(sec.)(sq. cm.) or cu. ft./(hr.)(sq. ft.)

$w$ = rate of diffusion, gm. moles/sec. or lb. moles/hr.

$z$ = distance in the direction of diffusion, cm. or ft.

$\partial$ = partial differential operator

$\Delta$ = difference

$\theta$ = time, sec. or hr.

$\lambda$ = molecular mean free path, cm. or ft.

$\mu$ = viscosity, gm./(cm.)(sec.)(= poises) or lb./(ft.)(hr.)

$\pi$ = 3.1416

$\rho$ = density, gm./cu. cm. or lb./cu. ft.

Subscripts:

$A$, $B$ = components $A$, $B$
av = average
0 = initial (at time zero)
$\theta$ = at time $\theta$
$\infty$ = at time $\infty$; at equilibrium
1, 2 = positions 1, 2

## REFERENCES

1. Barrer, R. M.: "Diffusion in and through Solids," Cambridge University Press, London, 1941.
2. Jost, W.: "Diffusion in Solids, Liquids, and Gases," Academic Press, Inc., New York, 1952.
3. McBain, J. W., and T. H. Liu: *J. Am. Chem. Soc.*, **53**, 59 (1931).
4. Newman, A. B.: *Trans. Am. Inst. Chem. Engrs.*, **27**, 203, 310 (1931).
5. Piret, E. L., R. A. Ebel, C. T. Kiang, and W. P. Armstrong: *Chem. Eng. Progr.*, **47**, 405, 628 (1951).
6. Sherwood, T. K.: *Ind. Eng. Chem.*, **21**, 12, 976 (1929).
7. Van Arsdel, W. B.: *Chem. Eng. Progr.*, **43**, 13 (1947).

## PROBLEMS

**1.** Removal of soybean oil impregnating a porous clay plate by contact with a solvent for the oil has been shown to be a matter of internal diffusion of the oil through the solid [Boucher, Brier, and Osburn, *Trans. Am. Inst. Chem. Engrs.*, **38**, 967(1942)]. Such a clay plate, $\frac{1}{16}$ in. thick by 1.80 in. long by 1.08 in. wide, thin edges sealed, was impregnated with soybean oil to a uniform concentration of 0.229 lb. oil/lb. dry clay. It was immersed in a flowing stream of pure tetrachloroethylene at 120°F., whereupon the oil content of the plate was reduced to 0.048 lb. oil/lb. dry clay in 1 hr. The resistance to diffusion may be taken as residing wholly within the plate and the final ultimate oil content of the clay as zero when contacted with pure solvent.

*a.* Calculate the effective diffusivity.

*b.* A cylinder of the same clay, 0.5 in. diameter, 1 in. long, both ends sealed, contains an initial uniform concentration of 0.17 lb. oil/lb. clay. When immersed in a flowing stream of pure tetrachloroethylene at 120°F., to what concentration will the oil content fall in 10 hr.?

*c.* Recalculate (*b*) for the cases where only one end of the cylinder is sealed and where neither end is sealed.

*d.* How long will it take for the concentration to fall to 0.01 lb. oil/lb. clay for the cylinder of (*b*) with neither end sealed?

**2.** A slab of clay, such as that used to make brick, 2 in. thick, was dried from both flat surfaces with the four thin edges sealed, by exposure to dry air. The initial uniform moisture content was 15%. The drying took place by internal diffusion of the liquid water to the surface, followed by evaporation at the surface. The diffusivity may be assumed to be constant with varying water concentration, and uniform in all directions. The surface moisture content was 3%. In 5 hr. the average moisture content had fallen to 10.2%.

*a.* Calculate the diffusivity, sq. ft./hr.

*b.* Under the same drying conditions, how much longer would it have taken to reduce the average water content to 6%?

*c.* How long would it require to dry a sphere of 6 in. radius from 15 to 6% under the same drying conditions?

*d.* How long would it require to dry a cylinder 1 ft. long, 6 in. diameter, drying from all surfaces, to a moisture content of 6%?

**3.** An unglazed porcelain plate 0.5 cm. thick has an average pore diameter of 0.2 micron. Pure oxygen gas at an absolute pressure of 2 cm. Hg, 100°C., on one side of the plate passed through at a rate of 0.093 cu. cm. (at 2 cm. Hg, 100°C.) per second per square centimeter when the pressure on the downstream side was so low as to be considered negligible. Estimate the rate of passage of hydrogen gas at 25°C. and a pressure of 1 cm. Hg abs., with negligible downstream pressure.

CHAPTER 5

# INTERPHASE MASS TRANSFER

In most of the diffusional operations two insoluble phases are brought into contact in order to permit diffusion of constituent substances between them. The phases may both be fluid, i.e., gaseous or liquid, or one may be a solid, and we are now concerned with the simultaneous application of the diffusional mechanisms for each phase as described in the previous chapters to the combined system. We have seen that the rate at which a diffusing substance is transferred from one of the phases to the other is in every case dependent upon the concentration gradient existing in each phase. At the same time the concentration gradients are a measure of the departure from equilibrium which exists between the phases. Should equilibrium be established, the concentration gradients and hence the rates of diffusion will fall to zero. It is necessary, therefore, to consider both the diffusional mechanism and the equilibria in order to describe the various situations fully.

**Equilibrium.** It is convenient first to consider the equilibrium established in a particular operation and to generalize the results for others. As an example, we may choose the gas-absorption operation which occurs when ammonia is dissolved from an ammonia-air mixture by liquid water. Suppose a fixed amount of pure liquid water is placed in a closed container together with a gaseous mixture of ammonia and air, the whole arranged so that the system can be maintained at constant temperature and total pressure. Ammonia is very soluble in water, and consequently ammonia molecules will instantly start to diffuse from the gas into the liquid, crossing the interfacial surface separating the two phases. The concentration of ammonia in the gas, as measured by its partial pressure, will therefore fall. Ammonia molecules which enter the liquid will diffuse by virtue of their molecular motion into the main body of the liquid and eventually permeate the entire liquid phase. A portion of the ammonia molecules escape into the gas phase and the rate at which they do so is proportional to their concentration in the liquid at the surface. As more ammonia enters the liquid, with consequent increase in concentration within the liquid, the rate at which ammonia returns to the gas increases, until eventually the rate at which ammonia enters

78

the liquid exactly equals that at which it leaves. At the same time, through the mechanism of diffusion, the concentrations throughout each phase become uniform, but not necessarily the same in each phase. A dynamic equilibrium now exists, and while ammonia molecules continue to move back and forth from one phase to the other, the concentrations within each phase no longer change, no matter how long the phases are kept in contact. To the observer who cannot see the individual molecular motions, the diffusion has apparently stopped.

If we now inject additional pure ammonia into the container, a new set of equilibrium concentrations will eventually be established, with higher concentrations in each phase than were at first obtained. By adding more and more ammonia in this manner, we can eventually obtain a complete relationship between the equilibrium concentrations in both phases. If the ammonia is designated as substance $A$, its concentration in the gas phase measured in terms of partial pressure $p_A$, and its concentration in the liquid as $c_A$, we may plot the equilibrium values so obtained against each other to give a curve of the type shown in Fig. 5.1. This curve results irrespective of the relative proportions of water and air that we start with and is influenced

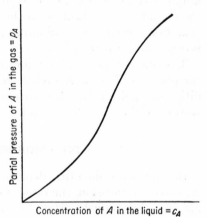

FIG. 5.1. Equilibrium distribution of a solute between a gas and a liquid phase, at constant temperature.

only by the conditions, such as temperature and pressure, imposed upon the three-component system. For example, had we started with an aqueous ammonia solution and pure air in the closed container, the same curve would describe the equilibrium concentrations ultimately obtained. The curve of Fig. 5.1 does not of course show all the equilibrium concentrations existing within the system. For example, the water will partially vaporize into the gas phase, the components of the air will also dissolve to a small extent in the liquid, and equilibrium concentrations for these substances will also be obtained. For the moment we need not consider these equilibria, since they are of minor importance to the discussion at hand.

Generally speaking, whenever a substance is distributed between two insoluble phases, a dynamic equilibrium of this type can be established. The various equilibria, it must be emphasized, are peculiar to the particular systems considered. For example, replacement of the water in the example described above with another liquid such as benzene or with a solid adsorbent such as activated carbon or replacement of the ammonia with another solute such as sulfur dioxide will each result in new curves not at all related to the first. The equilibrium resulting for a two-liquid-phase system bears no relation to that for a liquid-solid system. A discussion of the characteristic shapes of the equilibrium curves for the various situations and the influence of conditions such as temperature and pressure must be left for the studies of the individual unit operations. Nevertheless the following principles are common to all systems involving the distribution of a substance between two insoluble phases:

1. At a fixed set of conditions, referring to temperature and pressure, there exists a set of equilibrium relationships which may be shown graphically in the form of an equilibrium-distribution curve by plotting the equilibrium concentrations in the two phases one against the other.

2. For a system in equilibrium, there is no net diffusion of the components between the phases.

3. For a system not in equilibrium, diffusion of the components between the phases will occur in such a manner as to bring the system to a condition of equilibrium. If sufficient time is available, equilibrium concentrations will eventually prevail.

## DIFFUSION BETWEEN PHASES

Having established that departure from equilibrium provides the driving force for diffusion, the rates of diffusion in terms of the driving forces may now be studied. Many of the mass-transfer operations are carried out in steady-flow fashion, with continuous and invariant flow of the contacted phases, and under circumstances such that concentrations at any position in the equipment used do not change with time. It will be convenient to use one of these as an example with which to establish the principles and to generalize respecting other operations later. For this purpose, let us consider the absorption of a soluble gas such as ammonia (substance $A$), from a mixture such as air and ammonia, by liquid water as the absorbent, in one of the simplest of apparatus, the wetted-wall tower previously described in Chap. 3 (Fig. 3.8). The ammonia-air mixture may enter at the bottom and flow upward while the water flows downward around the inside of the pipe. The gas mixture changes its composition from a high- to a low-solute concentration as it flows upward, while the water dissolves the ammonia and leaves at the bottom as an aqueous ammonia solution. Under steady-state conditions, the concentrations at any point in the apparatus do not change with passage of time.

**Two-film Theory.** Let us investigate the situation at a particular level along the tower, for example, at a point midway between top and bottom. Since the solute is diffusing from the gas phase into the liquid, there must be concentration gradients in the direction of diffusion within each phase. In the gas phase, the diffusional resistance which the concentration gradient overcomes lies largely within a thin laminar film at the interface between the two phases, but partly also within the turbulent main core of the gas. As explained in Chap. 3, the entire diffusional resistance may be described in terms of a fictitious or effective film whose resistance to molecular diffusion is the same as the true molecular and eddy diffusional resistances actually present. A similar situation exists

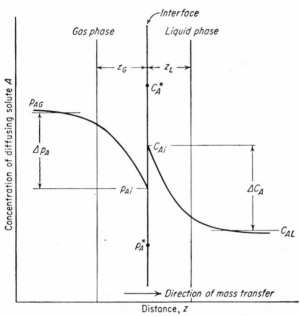

Fig. 5.2. The two-film theory of interphase diffusion.

within the liquid phase. These concentration gradients may be shown graphically in terms of the distance through the phases as in Fig. 5.2, where a section through the two phases in contact is shown. The average concentration of $A$ in the gas phase in terms of its partial pressure is $p_{AG}$, and the concentration falls to $p_{Ai}$ at the interface largely within the effective film thickness $z_G$. In the liquid phase, the concentration falls from $c_{Ai}$ at the interface to $c_{AL}$, the average concentration. The bulk, or average, concentrations $p_{AG}$ and $c_{AL}$ are clearly not equilibrium values, since otherwise diffusion of the solute would not occur. This picture of the diffusional mechanism for a two-phase system was first drawn by Whitman and Lewis,[4,7] who also suggested that there is no resistance to the transfer of the diffusing solute across the interface itself. The last proposition is tantamount to assuming that the concentrations within each phase at the interface $(p_{Ai}, c_{Ai})$ are equilibrium concentrations, values which are the same as if the surfaces had been in contact for an indefinitely long period of time.[†]

It might at first seem from Fig. 5.2 that the apparent concentration rise at the interface $p_{Ai}$ to $c_{Ai}$ would represent a barrier to diffusion, a sort of concentration hurdle which would prevent diffusion in the direction gas to liquid. It must be kept in mind, however, that even should equilibrium exist throughout both phases, so that the concentrations would be represented by horizontal lines at $p_{Ai}$ in the gas and at $c_{Ai}$ in the liquid, the apparent concentration rise at the interface would still exist and yet the net diffusion would have stopped. The break in continuity of the concentration curve as we pass from one phase to the other is partly due to the use of two different concentration units. The situation is analogous to one of heat transfer by conduction through two solids in series: if a curve of temperature against distance were plotted for such a case with a change of temperature scale from centigrade to Fahrenheit degrees as we passed from one solid to the next, a discontinuity similar to that of Fig. 5.2 would result even though actually no temperature rise would exist. But even the use of the same concentration unit for both phases in the case of mass transfer will not alter the situation unless a measure of concentration is employed which provides equality of numerical values at equilibrium. Fugacity and activity of the dissolved solute are such quantities, and these will provide a continuous curve, but they are rarely convenient to use. It is also clear that the discontinuity, especially if the concentrations in the two phases are expressed in units such as mole fractions, may be in the form of a drop rather than a rise, depending upon the equilibrium relationship.

The various concentrations may also be shown graphically as in Fig. 5.3, whose coordinates are the same as those of Fig. 5.1. The coordinates of point $P$ are those of the average solute concentrations within the two phases, those of point $M$ the values at the interface, with the

---

[†] The two-film theory as outlined has been in the main successful in interpreting the results of most two-phase mass-transfer operations of industrial importance. Alternatively, Higbie[3] has shown, in the case of a liquid in the wetted-wall tower under discussion and also in other situations of practical importance, that it is unnecessary and perhaps incorrect to assume the presence of a laminar film at the interface whose solute content is negligible. He has applied instead a concept of unsteady-state penetration of a solute into a fluid during its time of exposure to a diffusing solute, and this theory, too, has had successful application. The possibilities of an interfacial diffusional resistance or its equivalent have also been suggested, as, for example, in the orientation of a molecule into the crystalline lattice of a solid during crystal growth[1] or the blocking of an interface for passage of a solute by a locally high concentration of a surface-active agent.[2] Measurements of the interfacial resistance in special cases have been made and found not to be negligible.[6] Nevertheless, most data have been interpreted in terms of the two-film theory, and it will be emphasized here.

point $M$ on the equilibrium-distribution curve for the system under consideration.  The thicknesses of the effective films are so small that the solute content of the films themselves may be considered negligible. Under steady-state conditions, for every mole of solute $A$ which diffuses from the body of the gas to the interface there is also a mole of $A$ which

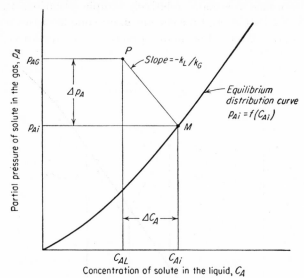

Fig. 5.3. Driving forces in a two-phase system.

diffuses into the body of the liquid, where it is carried away.   The appropriate mass-transfer-rate equations may then be written, one for each phase, and equated.

$$N_A = k_G(p_{AG} - p_{Ai}) = k_L(c_{Ai} - c_{AL}) \tag{5.1}$$
$$N_A = k_G\,\Delta p_A = k_L\,\Delta c_A \tag{5.2}$$

The driving forces $\Delta p_A$ and $\Delta c_A$ are shown in the figures.   Rearrangement of Eq. (5.1),

$$\frac{p_{AG} - p_{Ai}}{c_{AL} - c_{Ai}} = -\frac{k_L}{k_G} \tag{5.3}$$

provides the slope of the line $PM$.   If then the mass-transfer coefficients are known, the values of $c_{Ai}$ and $p_{Ai}$, the driving forces, and hence the rate $N_A$ may be determined for a given situation, either graphically by plotting the line $PM$ or analytically by solving Eq. (5.3) simultaneously with the algebraic expression for the equilibrium-distribution curve,

$$p_{Ai} = f(c_{Ai}) \tag{5.4}$$

It is important at this time to emphasize that the conditions depicted by Figs. 5.2 and 5.3 are so-called "point" conditions, those existing at one particular level of the wetted-wall tower or other device in which phase contact takes place.   At different places in the equipment, for example, at the top or bottom of the wetted-wall tower, the coordinates of point $P$ would be very different.

**Over-all Mass-transfer Coefficients.**   The mass-transfer coefficients may be determined for many relatively simple situations through the correlations of Chap. 3, and for certain more complex cases by methods to be considered later.   For many practical circumstances, however,

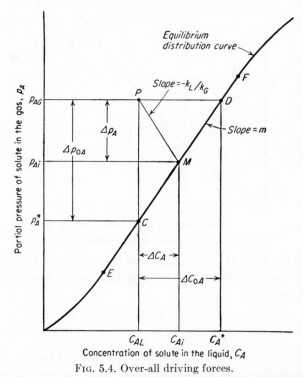

FIG. 5.4. Over-all driving forces.

adequate correlations of the individual mass-transfer coefficients do not exist.   An experimental approach whereby an actual sampling of the fluids at the interface is attempted for determination of the values of $p_{Ai}$ and $c_{Ai}$ also fails since any ordinary sampling device will be so large in comparison with the film thickness that it is impossible to approach the interface sufficiently closely.   Sampling and analysis will provide compositions $p_{AG}$ and $c_{AL}$, but not the interfacial values.   Under such circumstances we may avoid some of the difficulty provided the equilibrium relationship is sufficiently simple.

Consider a system whose equilibrium-distribution curve is straight over the range of compositions which need be considered, as in Fig. 5.4.

Over the linear portion of the curve, the equilibrium concentrations can be represented by

$$p_{Ai} = mc_{Ai} + b \qquad (5.5)$$

As long as the ratio $-k_L/k_G$ remains constant and within the linear portion of the equilibrium curve, $\Delta c_A$ is proportional to $\Delta p_A$. Point $C$, on the equilibrium curve at concentration $c_{AL}$, provides a partial pressure $p_A^*$ such that

$$p_A^* = mc_{AL} + b \qquad (5.6)$$

and the difference $p_{AG} - p_A^* = \Delta p_{oA}$ is also proportional to $\Delta p_A$. The rate equation [Eq. (5.1)] can therefore be rewritten as

$$N_A = k_G(p_{AG} - p_{Ai}) = K_G(p_{AG} - p_A^*) = K_G \, \Delta p_{oA} \qquad (5.7)$$

where $K_G$ is an *over-all* mass-transfer coefficient accounting for the entire diffusional resistance present in both phases in terms of a partial-pressure driving force. The composition $p_A^*$ does not exist physically at the particular position in the equipment under consideration but represents a gas-phase composition which would be in equilibrium with the average liquid composition at this point. It may be imagined as existing at the point marked $p_A^*$ on Fig. 5.2. In similar fashion a point $D$ on Fig. 5.4 might be chosen on the equilibrium curve such that

$$p_{AG} = mc_A^* + b \qquad (5.8)$$

where $c_A^*$ is in equilibrium with $p_{AG}$ (see also Fig. 5.2). Since $\Delta c_{oA}$ is proportional to $\Delta c_A$ and $\Delta p_A$,

$$N_A = k_L(c_{Ai} - c_{AL}) = K_L(c_A^* - c_{AL}) = K_L \, \Delta c_{oA} \qquad (5.9)$$

and $K_L$ is an *over-all* mass-transfer coefficient accounting for the diffusional resistances in both phases expressed in terms of the liquid concentration gradient. Since the concentration gradients are proportional to the mass-transfer resistances, then

$$\frac{\text{Resistance in gas phase}}{\text{Total resistance, both phases}} = \frac{\Delta p_A}{\Delta p_{oA}} = \frac{1/k_G}{1/K_G} \qquad (5.10)$$

$$\frac{\text{Resistance in liquid phase}}{\text{Total resistance, both phases}} = \frac{\Delta c_A}{\Delta c_{oA}} = \frac{1/k_L}{1/K_L} \qquad (5.11)$$

It is clear that should the ratio $k_L/k_G$ change in passing from one position to another in a piece of equipment where the phases are contacted, or should the equilibrium curve not be straight over the concentrations considered, the relative resistances of the two fluid films will change and the use of over-all coefficients except as representative of point conditions becomes unsound.

From the geometry of Fig. 5.4,

$$\Delta p_{oA} = \frac{k_L}{k_G} \Delta c_A + m \, \Delta c_A = \left(\frac{k_L}{k_G} + m\right) \Delta c_A \tag{5.12}$$

Further,    $$N_A = K_G \, \Delta p_{oA} = K_G \left(\frac{k_L}{k_G} + m\right) \Delta c_A = k_L \, \Delta c_A \tag{5.13}$$

$$\therefore \; K_G \left(\frac{k_L}{k_G} + m\right) = k_L \tag{5.14}$$

$$\frac{1}{K_G} = \frac{1}{k_G} + \frac{m}{k_L} \tag{5.15}$$

Similarly,    $$\frac{1}{K_L} = \frac{1}{mk_G} + \frac{1}{k_L} \tag{5.16}$$

Each term of the right-hand sides of Eqs. (5.15) and (5.16) represents the relative resistances to diffusion within the individual phases.  Assuming that the numerical values of $k_G$ and $k_L$ are approximately equal, the importance of the term $m$ in establishing the position of the major diffusional resistance can then be demonstrated.  If $m$ is small, so that at equilibrium only a small concentration of $A$ in the gas phase will provide a very large concentration in the liquid (solute $A$ is very soluble in the liquid), the term $m/k_L$ of Eq. (5.15) becomes minor and the major resistance is represented by the term $1/k_G$.  The major resistance to diffusion lies within the gas phase, and it is said that the *gas film controls*. In the extreme, this becomes

$$\frac{1}{K_G} \doteq \frac{1}{k_G} \tag{5.17}$$

or    $$\Delta p_{oA} \doteq \Delta p_A \tag{5.18}$$

a situation which may be shown graphically as in Fig. 5.5.  Under such circumstances, even fairly large percentage changes in $k_L$ will not change the value of $K_G$ significantly.  If therefore in an unfamiliar system we observe that conditions known to change the value of $k_L$ considerably, such as vigorous agitation of the liquid, produce only minor changes in the rate of mass transfer, we conclude that the gas film controls.  Reasoning in a similar manner sometimes assists in the choice of equipment or in predicting the relative performance of two types of equipment.  For example, in the absorption of a very soluble gas in a liquid, it would generally be expected that showering a rain of liquid droplets down through a continuum of the gas would be more effective than bubbling the gas upward through a continuum of the liquid.  This follows from the fact that the fluid inside a small gas droplet is relatively stagnant, with transfer occurring largely through the mechanism of molecular diffusion.  It will therefore be desirable to decrease the gas-phase resistance as much as possible by permitting it to be agitated vigorously by the rain of liquid drops; the resistance of the latter to diffusion is relatively small anyway by virtue of the value of $m$. Such reasoning must sometimes be tempered by other considerations, such as the desirability of creating a large interfacial surface and consequently dispersing the fluid which flows in the largest amount. These matters as they pertain to the particular unit operations will be considered in detail at the appropriate time.

Conversely, consider the case where $m$ is very large (solute $A$ relatively insoluble in the liquid) with $k_G$ and $k_L$ nearly equal. Here the first term of the right-hand sides of Eq. (5.16) becomes minor, the major

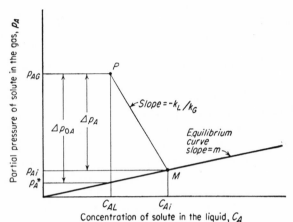

FIG. 5.5. Driving forces for a small value of $m$.

resistance to diffusion resides within the liquid, and it is said that the *liquid film controls*. Ultimately we obtain

$$\frac{1}{K_L} \doteq \frac{1}{k_L} \tag{5.19}$$

and
$$\Delta c_{OA} \doteq \Delta c_A \tag{5.20}$$

shown graphically in Fig. 5.6. In such a case, efforts to effect large changes in the rate of mass transfer are best directed to conditions influencing the liquid-film coefficient $k_L$. Figure 5.6, incidentally, shows a situation where in the same system major control may pass from the liquid to the gas film, as it will for a point $P'$, for example. This emphasizes again the limitations on the use of over-all coefficients to systems of linear equilibrium curves.

For cases where $k_L$ and $k_G$ are not nearly equal, Eq. (5.12) indicates that the ratio of $k_L/k_G$ to $m$ is of importance in setting the position of the major controlling resistance, since the first term within the parentheses represents the relative gas-phase resistance, the second term that due to the liquid. Since the film coefficients are functions of flow rates, for example (see Chap. 3), it is clear that the controlling resistance can be influenced by conditions other than the distribution coefficient $m$.

The use of over-all mass-transfer coefficients as described above is in many ways similar to the use of over-all heat-transfer coefficients in the case of heat-exchange design. Following the procedure which has proved so successful in the latter case, much effort is currently being spent in establishing correlations of the mass-transfer coefficients involving operating conditions, such as those described in Chap. 3 for the simpler situations, so that appropriate over-all coefficients may be computed for

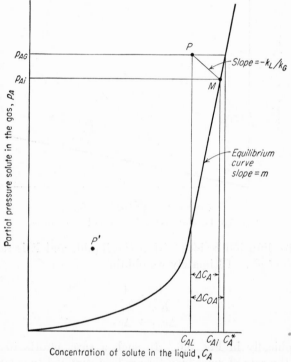

FIG. 5.6. Driving forces for a large value of $m$.

design purposes. As in heat transfer, where there is a substantial difference in the resistance offered by the several films and the over-all coefficient is customarily calculated in terms of the film exhibiting the larger resistance, so in mass transfer the over-all coefficient is ordinarily described in terms of the concentration gradients of the film offering the largest resistance to diffusion. For example, in a case where the gas film controls in a gas-absorption process, $K_G$ is ordinarily used, whereas if the liquid film controls, $K_L$ is used.

For the purpose of establishing the nature of the two-film theory and the over-all-coefficient concept, an operation of gas absorption was chosen as an example, involving the diffusion of a solute substance through a nondiffusing carrier gas in the gas phase and through a nondiffusing solvent within the liquid. The principles are by no means limited to this one operation but may be applied to the others, with appropriate film mass-transfer coefficients combining to provide the over-all coefficient. For example, in the case of distillation, where it will be shown that an equimolal counterdiffusion of the substances is ordinarily encountered, the coefficients $k'_G$ and $k'_L$, rather than $k_G$ and $k_L$, would be used for the vapor and liquid phases to give over-all coefficients $K'_G$ and $K'_L$. In liquid extraction, two liquid-film coefficients would be combined. In each case, furthermore, concentration units other than those in the example described above may be more convenient, as listed in Table 3.1. Because of the lack of convective or turbulent movement within a solid phase, however, these concepts have not been extensively applied to operations involving fluid-solid contact. In all cases, the equilibrium-solubility coefficient $m$ must be appropriately expressed in terms of the concentrations as given by the following consistent expressions:

*Linear equilibrium relation:*

$$\text{Concn. in phase } E = m \text{ (concn. in phase } R) + \text{const.} \qquad (5.21)$$

*Resistance relations:*

$$\frac{1}{K_E} = \frac{1}{k_E} + \frac{m}{k_R} \qquad (5.22)$$

$$\frac{1}{K_R} = \frac{1}{mk_E} + \frac{1}{k_R} \qquad (5.23)$$

$$K_R = mK_E \qquad (5.24)$$

Here the $K$'s and the $k$'s are generalized mass-transfer coefficients, to be expressed in terms of the concentration units employed in Eq. (5.21). It is also possible that both heat and mass transfer between two phases may occur simultaneously, in which case the heat-transfer film resistances may be combined to give the over-all heat-transfer resistance.

**Illustration 1.** In the absorption of ammonia, $NH_3$, into water from an air-ammonia mixture in a certain apparatus at 2 atm. total pressure, 60°F., the average value of $k_y$ is estimated to be 0.40 lb. moles/(hr.)(sq. ft.)(mole fraction) and that of $k_L$ to be 1.10 lb. moles/(hr.)(sq. ft.)(mole/cu. ft.). For dilute solutions of ammonia in water at 60°F., the equilibrium partial pressure of ammonia is given by

$$p' = 645x$$

where $p'$ = partial pressure ammonia, mm. Hg, and $x$ = mole fraction ammonia in the liquid. Compute the over-all gas mass-transfer coefficient expressed as lb. moles/(hr.)(sq. ft.)(atm.) and the relative size of the resistance of the gas and liquid phases.

*Solution.*  In Eq. (5.21), let $E$ represent the gas phase, $R$ the liquid phase. If $K_E$ is to be calculated in terms of lb. moles/(hr.)(sq. ft.)(atm.), then the concentrations in the gas phase must be in terms of atmospheres.  Since $k_L$ is in terms of moles/cu. ft., the concentrations in the liquid must also be in these terms.  Therefore the equilibrium equation must be transformed into

$$p = mc$$

where $p$ = atm., $c$ = lb. moles/cu. ft.

$$p' \text{ mm. Hg} = p \text{ atm. (760)}$$

For dilute solutions,

$$\frac{x \text{ moles NH}_3}{\text{Mole solution}} = \frac{x \text{ moles NH}_3}{\text{Mole H}_2\text{O}} = \frac{(x \text{ moles NH}_3)(62.2 \text{ lb./cu. ft.})}{18 \text{ lb. H}_2\text{O}} = c$$

$$x = c/3.45$$
$$p(760) = 645(c/3.45)$$
$$p = 0.246c$$

and $m = 0.246$ atm./(mole/cu. ft.).

The coefficient $k_y$ must be converted to $k_G$ lb. moles/(hr.)(sq. ft.)(atm.) (see Table 3.1).

$$k_G = \frac{k_y}{P} = \frac{0.40}{2} = 0.20 \text{ lb. moles/(hr.)(sq. ft.)(atm.)}$$

Eq. (5.22) in terms of the present quantities:

$$\frac{1}{K_G} = \frac{1}{k_G} + \frac{m}{k_L} = \frac{1}{0.20} + \frac{0.246}{1.10} = 5.0 + 0.224 = 5.224$$
$$K_G = 0.1913 \text{ lb. moles/(hr.)(sq. ft.)(atm.)}$$

The relative resistance of the gas phase is $5.0(100)/5.224 = 95.5\%$; that of the liquid phase $100 - 95.5 = 4.5\%$.

## MATERIAL BALANCES AND STAGES

The concentration-difference driving forces discussed above are, as has been pointed out, those existing at one position in the equipment used to contact the immiscible phases.  In the case of a steady-state process, because of the transfer of solute from one phase to the other, the concentration within each phase changes as it moves through the equipment.  Similarly, in the case of a batch process, the concentration in each phase changes with time.  These changes produce corresponding variations in the driving forces, and it is necessary to follow the variations that may occur with the help of material balances.

**Steady-state Cocurrent Processes.**  Consider any mass-transfer operation whatsoever conducted in a steady-state cocurrent fashion as in Fig. 5.7, in which the apparatus used is represented simply as a rectangular box.  Let the two insoluble phases be identified as phase $E$ and phase $R$, and for the present consider only the case where a single substance $A$

diffuses from phase $R$ to phase $E$ during their contact. The other constituents of the phases, solvents for the diffusing solutes, are then considered not to diffuse.

At the entrance to the device in which the phases are contacted, phase $R$ contains $R_1$ moles per unit time of total substances, consisting of nondiffusing solvent $R_s$ moles per unit time and diffusing solute $A$, whose concentration is $x_1$ mole fraction. As phase $R$ moves through the equipment, $A$ diffuses to phase $E$ and consequently the total quantity of $R$

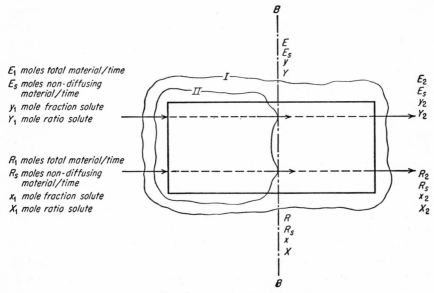

$E_1$ moles total material/time
$E_s$ moles non-diffusing material/time
$y_1$ mole fraction solute
$Y_1$ mole ratio solute

$R_1$ moles total material/time
$R_s$ moles non-diffusing material/time
$x_1$ mole fraction solute
$X_1$ mole ratio solute

FIG. 5.7. Steady-state cocurrent processes.

falls to $R_2$ moles per unit time at the exit, although the rate of flow of nondiffusing solvent $R_s$ is the same as at the entrance. The concentration of $A$ has fallen to $x_2$ mole fraction. Similarly, phase $E$ at the entrance contains $E_1$ moles per unit time total substances, of which $E_s$ moles is nondiffusing solvent, and an $A$ concentration of $y_1$ mole fraction. Owing to the accumulation of $A$ to a concentration $y_2$ mole fraction, phase $E$ increases in amount to $E_2$ moles per unit time at the exit, although the solvent content $E_s$ has remained constant.

Envelope I, the closed, irregular line drawn about the equipment, will help to establish a material balance for substance $A$, since an accounting for substance $A$ must be made wherever the envelope is crossed by an arrow representing a flowing stream. The $A$ content of the entering $R$ phase is $R_1x_1$, that of the $E$ phase is $E_1y_1$. Similarly the $A$ content of the leaving streams is $R_2x_2$ and $E_2y_2$, respectively.

Thus,                    $R_1x_1 + E_1y_1 = R_2x_2 + E_2y_2$                    (5.25)

or                       $R_1x_1 - R_2x_2 = E_2y_2 - E_1y_1$                    (5.26)

But                      $R_1x_1 = R_S \dfrac{x_1}{1 - x_1} = R_S X_1$          (5.27)

where $X_1$ is the mole-ratio concentration of $A$ at the entrance, moles $A$/mole non-$A$. The other terms may be similarly described, and Eq. (5.26) becomes

$$R_S(X_1 - X_2) = E_S(Y_2 - Y_1)$$                                             (5.28)

The last is the equation of a straight line on $(X,Y)$ coordinates, of slope $-R_S/E_S$, passing through two points whose coordinates are $(X_1,Y_1)$ and $(X_2,Y_2)$, respectively.

At any section $B$-$B$ through the apparatus, the mole fractions of $A$ are $x$ and $y$, and the mole ratios $X$ and $Y$, in phases $R$ and $E$, respectively, and if an envelope II is drawn so as to include all the device from the entrance to section $B$-$B$, the $A$ balance becomes

$$R_S(X_1 - X) = E_S(Y - Y_1)$$                                                (5.29)

This is also the equation of a straight line on $(X,Y)$ coordinates, of slope $-R_S/E_S$, through the points $(X_1,Y_1)$ and $(X,Y)$. Since the two straight lines have the same slope and a point in common, they are the same straight line and Eq. (5.29) is therefore a general expression relating the compositions of the phases in the equipment at any distance from the entrance.†

Since $X$ and $Y$ represent concentrations in the two phases, the equilibrium relationship may also be expressed in terms of these coordinates. Figure 5.8 shows a representation of the equilibrium relationship as well as the straight line $QP$ of Eqs. (5.28) and (5.29). The line $QP$, called an *operating line*, should not be confused with the driving-force lines of the earlier discussion. At the entrance to the apparatus, for example, the mass-transfer coefficients in the two phases may give rise to the driving-force line $KP$, where $K$ represents the interface compositions at the entrance and the distances $KM$ and $MP$ represent, respectively, the driving forces in phase $E$ and phase $R$. Similarly, at the exit, point $L$ may represent the interface composition and $LQ$ the line representative of the driving forces. If the apparatus were longer than that indicated in Fig. 5.7, so that eventually an equilibrium between the two phases were established, the corresponding equilibrium compositions $X_e$ and $Y_e$ are given by an extension of the operating line to intersection with the equilibrium curve at $T$. The driving forces, and therefore the diffusion rate, at this point will have fallen to zero. Should the diffusion be in

† Masses, mass fractions, and mass ratios may be substituted consistently for moles, mole fractions, and mole ratios in Eqs. (5.25) to (5.29).

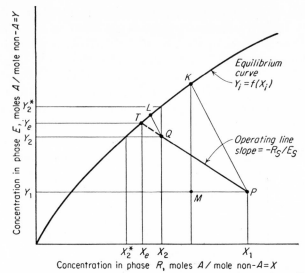

FIG. 5.8. Steady-state cocurrent process, transfer of solute from phase $R$ to phase $E$.

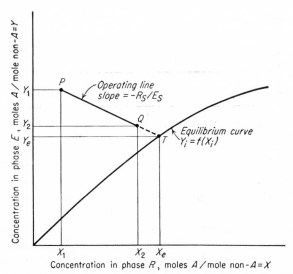

FIG. 5.9. Steady-state cocurrent process, transfer of solute from phase $E$ to phase $R$.

the opposite direction, i.e., from phase $E$ to phase $R$, the operating line will fall on the opposite side of the equilibrium curve, as in Fig. 5.9.

It must be emphasized that the graphical representation of the operating line as a *straight* line is greatly dependent upon the units in which the concentrations of the material balance are expressed. The representations of Figs. 5.8 and 5.9 are straight lines because the mole-ratio concentrations are based on the unchanging quantities $E_s$ and $R_s$. If Eq. (5.26) is plotted on mole-fraction coordinates, or if any concentration unit proportional to mole fractions such as partial pressure is used, for example, Fig. 5.10 indicates the nature of the operating *curve* obtained. The slope of this curve is $-R/E$ at any point, and since the quantities $R$ and $E$ change, the slope changes. Extrapolation to locate the ultimate equilibrium conditions at $T$ is of course much more difficult than for mole-ratio coordinates. On the other hand, in any operation where the total quantities of each of the phases $E$ and $R$ remain constant while the compositions change owing to diffusion of several components, a diagram in

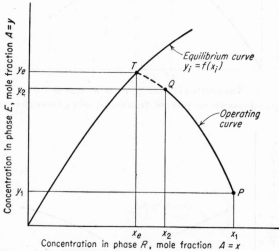

FIG. 5.10. Steady-state cocurrent process, transfer of solute from phase $R$ to phase $E$.

terms of mole fractions will provide a straight-line operating line, as Eq. (5.26) indicates (let $E_2 = E_1 = E$; $R_2 = R_1 = R$). If all the components diffuse so that the total quantities of each phase do not remain constant, the operating line will generally be curved.

**The Stage.** The cocurrent process of Fig. 5.7, which produces as its ultimate possible result two effluent streams in equilibrium, is called a *single-stage* process (see Chap. 1). An *ideal*, or *theoretical*, stage is one where the time of contact between phases is sufficient so that the effluents are indeed in equilibrium, as at point $T$ on Fig. 5.8. The approach to equilibrium attained in an actual stage is then the *stage efficiency*, which may be expressed in a variety of ways, as, for example, the fraction which the line $QP$ represents of the line $TP$. The most frequently used expression is, however, the Murphree stage efficiency **E**, the fractional approach of one leaving stream to equilibrium with the actual concentration in the other leaving stream.[5] Referring to Fig. 5.8, this may be expressed in terms of the concentrations in phase $E$ or in phase $R$,

$$\mathbf{E}_E = \frac{Y_2 - Y_1}{Y_2^* - Y_1} \qquad \mathbf{E}_R = \frac{X_1 - X_2}{X_1 - X_2^*} \qquad (5.30)$$

These definitions of stage efficiency are somewhat arbitrary since, for example, in the case of a truly parallel-flow operation such as that of Fig. 5.8 it would be impossible to obtain a leaving concentration in phase $E$ higher than $Y_e$ or one in phase $R$ lower than $X_e$.

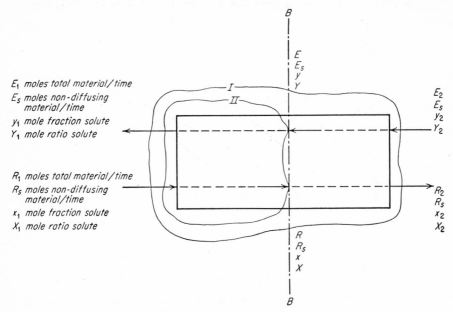

$E_1$ moles total material/time
$E_s$ moles non-diffusing material/time
$y_1$ mole fraction solute
$Y_1$ mole ratio solute

$R_1$ moles total material/time
$R_s$ moles non-diffusing material/time
$x_1$ mole fraction solute
$X_1$ mole ratio solute

FIG. 5.11. Steady-state countercurrent processes.

**Steady-state Countercurrent Processes.** If the same process as previously considered is carried out in countercurrent fashion, as in Fig. 5.11, where the subscripts 1 indicate that end of the apparatus where phase $R$ enters and 2 that end where phase $R$ leaves, the material balances become, by envelope I,†

$$E_2 y_2 + R_1 x_1 = E_1 y_1 + R_2 x_2 \qquad (5.31)$$

and

$$R_S(X_1 - X_2) = E_S(Y_1 - Y_2) \qquad (5.32)$$

and, for envelope II,

$$E y + R_1 x_1 = E_1 y_1 + R x \qquad (5.33)$$

and

$$R_S(X_1 - X) = E_S(Y_1 - Y) \qquad (5.34)$$

† Masses, mass ratios, and mass fractions may be substituted consistently for moles, mole ratios, and mole fractions in Eqs. (5.31) to (5.34).

Equations (5.33) and (5.34) give the general relationship between concentrations in the phases at any section, while Eqs. (5.31) and (5.32) establish the entire material balance. Equation (5.32) is that of a straight line on $(X,Y)$ coordinates, of slope $R_S/E_S$, through points of coordinates $(X_1,Y_1)$, $(X_2,Y_2)$ as shown in Fig. 5.12. The line will lie above the equilibrium-distribution curve if diffusion proceeds from phase $E$ to phase $R$, below for diffusion in the opposite direction. For the former case, at a point where the concentrations in the phases are given by the point $P$, the driving-force line may be indicated by line $PM$, whose

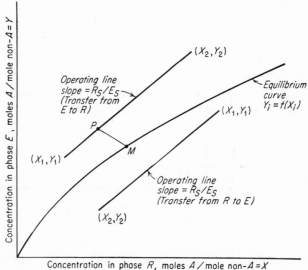

FIG. 5.12. Steady-state countercurrent processes.

slope depends upon the relative diffusional resistances of the phases. The driving forces obviously change in magnitude from one end of the equipment to the other. If the operating line should touch the equilibrium curve anywhere so that the contacted phases are in equilibrium, the driving force and hence the rate of diffusion would become zero, and the time required for a finite material transfer infinite. This may be interpreted in terms of a limiting ratio of flow rates of the phases for the concentration changes specified.

As in the cocurrent case, linearity of the operating line depends upon the method of expressing the concentrations. The operating lines of Fig. 5.12 are straight because the mole-ratio concentrations $X$ and $Y$ are based on the quantities $R_S$ and $E_S$, which were stipulated to be constant. If for this situation mole fractions (or quantities such as partial pressures, which are proportional to mole fractions) are used, the operating lines are curved as indicated in Fig. 5.13 and of slope $R/E$ at any point.

However, for some operations should the total quantity of each of the phases $E$ and $R$ be constant while the compositions change, the mole-fraction diagram will provide the straight-line operating lines, as Eq. (5.31) would indicate (let $E = E_1 = E_2$; $R = R_1 = R_2$). As in the

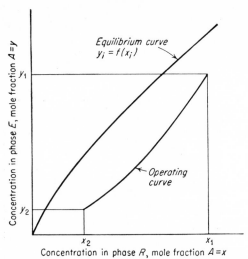

FIG. 5.13. Steady-state countercurrent process, transfer of solute from phase $R$ to phase $E$.

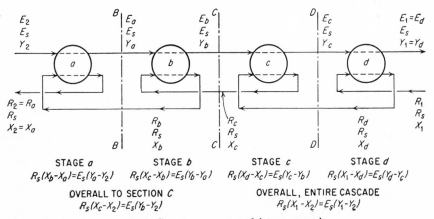

STAGE $a$      STAGE $b$      STAGE $c$      STAGE $d$

$$R_s(X_b-X_a)=E_s(Y_a-Y_2) \quad R_s(X_c-X_b)=E_s(Y_b-Y_a) \quad R_s(X_d-X_c)=E_s(Y_c-Y_b) \quad R_s(X_1-X_d)=E_s(Y_d-Y_c)$$

OVERALL TO SECTION $C$      OVERALL, ENTIRE CASCADE

$$R_s(X_c-X_2)=E_s(Y_b-Y_2) \qquad R_s(X_1-X_2)=E_s(Y_1-Y_2)$$

FIG. 5.14. Countercurrent multistage cascade.

cocurrent case, however, the operating line will generally be curved if all components diffuse so that the total quantities of each phase do not remain constant.

The countercurrent process may be carried out either by continuous contact of the phases as they flow through a single piece of equipment or by repeated contact and separation in a cascade of stages each operating essentially in cocurrent fashion. Consider the cascade of four ideal stages shown in Fig. 5.14, for example. Each stage, such as $a$, $b$, etc., is identical in its action to the cocurrent process of Fig. 5.7; yet the cascade as a whole has the characteristics of the countercurrent process of Fig. 5.11. The cocurrent operating line for each stage is written beneath it on the figure, and since the stages are each ideal, the effluents are in equilibrium ($Y_b$ in equilibrium with $X_b$, $Y_c$ with $X_c$, etc.). The graphical relations are shown on Fig. 5.15. Line $PQ$ is the operating line for

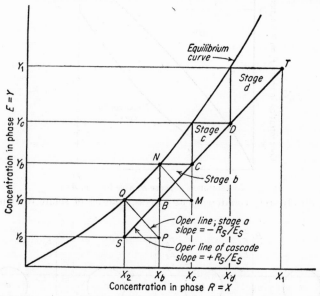

Fig. 5.15. Countercurrent multistage cascade, solute transfer from $R$ to $E$.

stage $a$, $NM$ for stage $b$, etc., and the coordinates $(X_b, Y_b)$ fall on the equilibrium curve because stage $b$ is ideal. Points such as $Q$ or $N$ on the figure represent, therefore, streams leaving a stage. Line $ST$ is the operating line for the entire cascade [Eq. (5.32)], and points such as $B$, $C$, and $D$ represent compositions at any level or section in the cascade, as at section $B$, $C$, and $D$, respectively, of Fig. 5.14. We may therefore determine the number of ideal stages required for a countercurrent process by drawing the stairlike construction $SQBNC \cdots T$ (Fig. 5.15) between the cascade operating line and the equilibrium curve. If anywhere the equilibrium curve and cascade operating line should touch, the steps become *pinched* and an infinite number are required to bring about the required change in composition.

Each stage in the cascade will have its individual stage efficiency, which is not necessarily constant from one stage to another. The fractional *over-all* stage efficiency for the entire cascade is simply the ratio of the number of ideal stages to the number of actual stages for the specified composition change.

**Unsteady-state Processes.** It is characteristic of *batch* operations that while there is no flow of the phases into and out of the equipment used, the concentrations within each phase change with time. When initially brought into contact, the phases will not be of equilibrium compositions, but they will approach equilibrium with passage of time. The material-balance equation for the cocurrent steady-state operations [Eq. (5.29)] then shows the relation between the concentrations $X$ and $Y$ in the phases which coexist at any time after the start of the operation and Figs. 5.8 and 5.9 the graphical representation of these compositions. Point $T$ on these figures represents the ultimate compositions which are obtained at equilibrium. The batch operation is a single stage.

In *semibatch* operations, the stationary phase undergoes a concentration change with time, approaching equilibrium with the entering moving phase. The composition of the latter is constant as it enters the equipment but changes as it passes through; the effluent composition changes with time. These relations cannot readily be shown graphically in the manner of the other processes but will be considered in detail for each operation as it occurs.

**Stages and Mass-transfer Rates.** It is clear from the previous discussion that each process may be considered either in terms of the number of stages it represents or in terms of the appropriate mass-transfer rates. A batch or continuous cocurrent operation, for example, is a single-stage operation, but the stage efficiency realized in the available contact time will depend upon the average mass-transfer rates prevailing. A change of composition greater than that possible with one stage may be brought about by repetition of the cocurrent process, where one of the effluents from the first stage is brought again into contact with fresh treating phase. Alternatively a countercurrent multistage cascade can be arranged. If, however, the countercurrent operation is carried out in continuous contact fashion without repeated separation and recontacting of the phases in a stepwise manner, it is still possible to describe the operation in terms of the number of stages to which it is equivalent. But in view of the differential changes in composition which occur in such cases, it is more correct to characterize them in terms of average mass-transfer coefficients or equivalent. Integration of the point mass-transfer-rate equations must be delayed until the characteristics of each operation can be considered, but the computation of the number of ideal stages requires only the equilibrium and material-balance relationships.

**Illustration 2.** When a certain sample of moist soap is exposed to air at 120°F., 1 atm. pressure, the equilibrium distribution of moisture between the air and soap is as follows:

| Wt. % moisture in soap | 0 | 2.40 | 3.76 | 4.76 | 6.10 | 7.83 | 9.90 | 12.63 | 15.40 | 19.02 |
|---|---|---|---|---|---|---|---|---|---|---|
| Partial pressure water in air, mm. Hg | 0 | 9.66 | 19.20 | 28.4 | 37.2 | 46.4 | 55.0 | 63.2 | 71.9 | 79.5 |

*a.* Ten pounds of wet soap containing 16.7% moisture by weight is placed in a vessel containing 150 cu. ft. moist air whose initial moisture content corresponds to a water-vapor partial pressure of 12 mm. Hg. After the soap has reached a moisture content of 13.0%, the air in the vessel is entirely replaced by fresh air of the original moisture content and the system is then allowed to reach equilibrium. The total pressure and temperature are maintained at 1 atm. and 120°F., respectively. What will be the ultimate moisture content of the soap?

*b.* It is desired to dry the soap from 16.7 to 4% moisture continuously in a counter-current stream of air whose initial water-vapor partial pressure is 12 mm. Hg. The pressure and temperature will be maintained throughout at 1 atm. and 120°F. Per 1 lb. initial wet soap per hour, what is the minimum amount of air required per hour?

*c.* If 30% more air than that determined in (*b*) is used, what will be the moisture content of the air leaving the drier? To how many ideal stages will the process be equivalent?

*Solution.* *a.* The process is a batch operation. Since air and soap are mutually insoluble, with water distributing between them, Eq. (5.28) applies. Let the $E$ phase be air-water and the $R$ phase be soap-water. Define $Y$ as lb. water/lb. dry air and $X$ as lb. water/lb. dry soap. It will be necessary to convert the equilibrium data to these units.

For a partial pressure of moisture $= p$ mm. Hg and a total pressure of 760 mm. Hg, $p/(760 - p)$ is the mole ratio of water to dry air. Multiplying this by the ratio of molecular weights of water to air then gives $Y$: $Y = [p/(760 - p)](18.02/29)$. Thus, at $p = 71.9$ mm. Hg,

$$Y = \frac{71.9}{760 - 71.9} \frac{18.02}{29} = 0.0650 \text{ lb. water/lb. dry air}$$

In similar fashion the per cent moisture content of the soap is converted to units of $X$. Thus, at 15.40% moisture,

$$X = \frac{15.40}{100 - 15.40} = 0.182 \text{ lb. water/lb. dry soap}$$

In this manner all the equilibrium data are converted to these units and the data plotted as the equilibrium curve of Fig. 5.16.

*First operation*

Initial air, $p = 12$ mm. Hg:

$$Y_1 = \frac{12}{760 - 12} \frac{18.02}{29} = 0.00996 \text{ lb. water/lb. dry air}$$

Initial soap, 16.7% water:

$$X_1 = \frac{16.7}{100 - 16.7} = 0.20 \text{ lb. water/lb. dry soap}$$

Final soap, 13% water:

$$X_2 = \frac{13.0}{100 - 13.0} = 0.1493 \text{ lb. water/lb. dry soap}$$
$$R_S = 10(1 - 0.167) = 8.33 \text{ lb. dry soap}$$

$E_S$, the mass of dry air, is found by use of the perfect-gas law,

$$E_S = 150 \frac{760 - 12}{760} \frac{492}{460 + 120} \frac{29}{359} = 10.1 \text{ lb. dry air}$$

Slope of operating line $= -R_S/E_S = -8.33/10.1 = -0.825$

From point $P$, coordinates $(X_1, Y_1)$, on Fig. 5.16, the operating line of slope $-0.825$ is drawn, to reach the abscissa $X_2 = 0.1493$ at point $Q$. The conditions at $Q$ correspond to the end of the first operation.

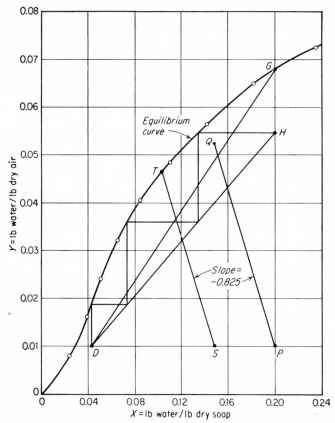

Fig. 5.16. Solution to Illustration 2.

*Second operation.* $X_1 = 0.1493$, $Y_1 = 0.00996$, which locate point $S$ on the figure. The operating line is drawn parallel to the line $PQ$ since the ratio $-R_S/E_S$ is the same as in the first operation. Extension of the line to the equilibrium curve at $T$ provides the final value of $X_2 = 0.103$ lb. water/lb. dry soap.

Final moisture content of soap $= (0.103/1.103)100 = 9.33\%$

*b.* Equation (5.32) and Fig. 5.11 apply.

$$R_S = 1(1 - 0.167) = 0.833 \text{ lb. dry soap/hr.}$$

Entering soap: $X_1 = 0.20$ lb. water/lb. dry soap
Leaving soap: $X_2 = 0.04/(1 - 0.04) = 0.0417$ lb. water/lb. dry soap
Entering air:   $Y_2 = 0.00996$ lb. water/lb. dry air

$$\text{Slope of operating line} = \frac{R_S}{E_S} = \frac{\text{lb. dry soap/hr.}}{\text{lb. dry air/hr.}}$$

Point $D$ [coordinates $(X_2, Y_2)$] is plotted on Fig. 5.16.   The operating line of least slope giving rise to equilibrium conditions will indicate the least amount of air usable. Such a line is $DG$, which provides equilibrium conditions at $X_1 = 0.20$.   The corresponding value of $Y_1 = 0.068$ lb. water/lb. dry air is read from the figure at $G$.

Eq. (5.32):          $0.833(0.20 - 0.0417) = E_S(0.068 - 0.00996)$
$$E_S = 2.27 \text{ lb. dry air/hr.}$$
This corresponds to

$$\frac{2.27}{29}(359)\frac{760}{760 - 12}\frac{460 + 120}{492} = 33.6 \text{ cu. ft. air per 1 lb. soap.}$$

   c. $E_S = 1.30(2.27) = 2.95$ lb. dry air/hr.

Eq. (5.32):          $0.833(0.20 - 0.0417) = 2.95(Y_1 - 0.00996)$
$$Y_1 = 0.0547 \text{ lb. water/lb. dry air}$$

This corresponds to operating line $DH$, where $H$ has the coordinates $X_1 = 0.20$, $Y_1 = 0.0547$.   The ideal stages are marked on the figure and total three.

## NOTATION FOR CHAPTER 5

   Consistent units in either the c.g.s. or the English system may be used.   It is customary to express pressures in the diffusion equations as atmospheres, in either system.

   $A$ = substance $A$, the diffusing solute
   $b$ = a constant
   $c$ = liquid-phase concentration, gm. moles/cu. cm. or lb. moles/cu. ft.
   $c_{Ai}$ = liquid-phase concentration of $A$ at the interface, gm. moles/cu. cm. or lb. moles/cu. ft.
   $c_{AL}$ = average liquid-phase concentration of $A$, gm. moles/cu. cm. or lb. moles/cu. ft.
   $c_A^*$ = liquid-phase concentration of $A$, in equilibrium with $p_{AG}$, gm. moles/cu. cm. or lb. moles/cu. ft.
   $E$ = phase $E$; total moles per unit time in phase $E$, gm. moles/sec. or lb. moles/hr.
   $\mathbf{E}$ = fractional Murphree stage efficiency, defined by Eq. (5.30)
   $E_S$ = moles nondiffusing solvent per unit time in phase $E$, gm. moles/sec. or lb. moles/hr.
   $f$ = a function
   $k_E$ = generalized mass-transfer film coefficient for phase $E$, gm. moles/(sec.)(sq. cm.)(concentration difference) or lb. moles/(hr.)(sq. ft.)(concentration difference)
   $k_G$ = mass-transfer gas-film coefficient, for $A$ diffusing through a stagnant gas, gm. moles/(sec.)(sq. cm.)(atm.) or lb. moles/(hr.)(sq. ft.)(atm.)

$k_L$ = mass-transfer liquid-film coefficient, for $A$ diffusing through a stagnant liquid, gm. moles/(sec.)(sq. cm.)(gm. moles/cu. cm.) or lb. moles/(hr.)(sq. ft.)(lb. moles/cu. ft.)

$k_R$ = generalized mass-transfer film coefficient for phase $R$, gm. moles/(sec.)(sq. cm.)(concentration difference) or lb. moles/(hr.)(sq. ft.)(concentration difference)

$K_G$ = over-all gas mass-transfer coefficient for $A$ diffusing through stagnant solvents, gm. moles/(sec.)(sq. cm.)(atm.) or lb. moles/(hr.)(sq. ft.)(atm.)

$K_E$ = generalized over-all mass-transfer coefficient based on concentrations in phase $E$, gm. moles/(sec.)(sq. cm.)(concentration difference) or lb. moles/(hr.)(sq. ft.)(concentration difference)

$K_L$ = over-all liquid mass-transfer coefficient for $A$ diffusing through stagnant solvents, gm. moles/(sec.)(sq. cm.)(gm. moles/cu. cm.) or lb. moles/(hr.)(sq. ft.)(lb. moles/cu. ft.)

$K_R$ = generalized over-all mass-transfer coefficient based on concentrations in phase $R$, gm. moles/(sec.)(sq. cm.)(concentration difference) or lb. moles/(hr.)(sq. ft.)(concentration difference)

$m$ = slope of equilibrium-distribution curve, $\Delta$ concentration in phase $E$/$\Delta$ concentration in phase $R$, units to be chosen in accordance with Eq. (5.21)

$N$ = rate of diffusion, gm. moles/(sec.)(sq. cm.) or lb. moles/(hr.)(sq. ft.)

$p$ = partial pressure, atm.

$p_{AG}$ = average partial pressure of $A$ in the gas, atm.

$p_{Ai}$ = partial pressure of $A$ in the gas at the interface, atm.

$p_A^*$ = partial pressure of $A$ in equilibrium with $c_{AL}$, atm.

$R$ = phase $R$; total moles per unit time in phase $R$, gm. moles/sec. or lb. moles/hr.

$R_S$ = moles nondiffusing solvent per unit time in phase $R$, gm. moles/sec. or lb. moles/hr.

$x$ = concentration of $A$ in phase $R$, mole fraction

$X$ = concentration of $A$ in phase $R$, mole ratio, moles $A$/moles non-$A$

$y$ = concentration of $A$ in phase $E$, mole fraction

$Y$ = concentration of $A$ in phase $E$, mole ratio, moles $A$/moles non-$A$

$z$ = effective film thickness, cm. or ft.

$\Delta$ = difference

Subscripts:

$A$ = substance $A$

$e$ = equilibrium

$E$ = phase $E$

$G$ = gas stream

$i$ = interface

$L$ = liquid stream

$O$ = over-all

$R$ = phase $R$

$1$ = position 1

$2$ = position 2

## REFERENCES

1. Badger, W. L., and W. L. McCabe: "Elements of Chemical Engineering," 2d ed., p. 241, McGraw-Hill Book Company, Inc., New York, 1936.
2. Chu, J. C., C. C. Taylor, and D. J. Levy: *Ind. Eng. Chem.*, **42**, 1157 (1950).

3. Higbie, R.: *Trans. Am. Inst. Chem. Engrs.*, **31**, 365 (1935).
4. Lewis, W. K., and W. G. Whitman: *Ind. Eng. Chem.*, **16**, 1215 (1924).
5. Murphree, E. V.: *Ind. Eng. Chem.*, **17**, 747 (1925).
6. Tung, L. H., and H. G. Drickamer: *J. Chem. Phys.*, **20**, 6, 10 (1952).
7. Whitman, W. G.: *Chem. Met. Eng.*, **29**, 147 (1923).

## PROBLEMS

**1.** In the absorption of Illustration 1, at one point in the equipment the average gas concentration is 1% ammonia by volume, and the water is pure.

*a.* Calculate the interfacial compositions for both phases.

*b.* Draw to scale a graph of $p$ vs. $c$, plot the equilibrium curve, the point representing the gas and liquid compositions, and the point representing the interface compositions. Mark the driving forces in each phase and the over-all gas-phase driving force.

*c.* Compute the rate of absorption, as lb. moles ammonia/(hr.)(sq. ft.), using $k_G$, $k_L$, and $K_G$.

**2.** In a certain apparatus used for the absorption of sulfur dioxide, $SO_2$, from air by means of water, at one point in the equipment the gas contained 10% $SO_2$ by volume and was in contact with liquid containing 0.4% $SO_2$ by weight (density = 61.8 lb./cu. ft.). The temperature was 50°C. and the total pressure 1 atm. The over-all mass-transfer coefficient based on gas concentrations was $K_G = 0.055$ lb. mole $SO_2$ absorbed/(hr.)(sq. ft.)(atm.). Forty-seven per cent of the diffusional resistance lay in the gas phase, 53% in the liquid. Equilibrium data at 50°C. are as follows:

| Gm. $SO_2$/100 gm. water............ | 0.2 | 0.3 | 0.5 | 0.7 |
|---|---|---|---|---|
| Partial pressure $SO_2$, mm. Hg....... | 29 | 46 | 83 | 119 |

*a.* Calculate the over-all coefficient based on liquid concentrations in terms of lb. moles/cu. ft.

*b.* Calculate the individual film coefficients for the gas film [expressed as $k_G$ lb. moles/(hr.)(sq. ft.)(atm.), $k_y$ lb. moles/(hr.)(sq. ft.) (mole fraction), and $k_c$ lb. moles/(hr.)(sq. ft.)(lb. moles/cu. ft.)] and for the liquid film [expressed as $k_L$ lb. moles/(hr.) (sq. ft.)(lb. moles/cu. ft.) and $k_x$ lb. moles/(hr.)(sq. ft.)(mole fraction)].

*c.* Determine the interfacial compositions in both phases.

**3.** The equilibrium partial pressure of water vapor in contact with a certain silica gel on which water is adsorbed is, at 25°C., as follows:

| Partial pressure of water, mm. Hg.... | 0 | 2.14 | 4.74 | 7.13 | 9.05 | 10.9 | 12.6 | 14.3 | 16.7 |
|---|---|---|---|---|---|---|---|---|---|
| Lb. water/100 lb. dry gel........... | 0 | 5 | 10 | 15 | 20 | 25 | 30 | 35 | 40 |

*a.* Plot the equilibrium data as $p$ = partial pressure of water vapor, mm. Hg, against $x$ = wt. fraction water in the gel.

*b.* Plot the equilibrium data as $X$ = lb. moles water/lb. dry gel, $Y$ = lb. moles water vapor/lb. moles dry air, for a total pressure of 1 atm.

*c.* Ten pounds of silica gel containing 5 wt. % adsorbed water is placed in a flowing air stream containing a partial pressure of water vapor of 12 mm. Hg. The total pressure is 1 atm. and the temperature 25°C. When equilibrium is reached, how many pounds of additional water will the gel have adsorbed? Air is not adsorbed.

*d.* One pound of silica gel containing 5 wt. % adsorbed water is placed in a vessel in which there are 400 cu. ft. moist air whose partial pressure of water is 15 mm. Hg.

The total pressure and temperature are kept at 1 atm. and 25°C., respectively. At equilibrium, what will be the moisture content of the air and gel and the weight of water adsorbed by the gel?

*e.* Write the equation of the operating line for (*d*) in terms of $X$ and $Y$. Convert this into an equation in terms of $p$ and $x$, and plot the operating curve on the $p$, $x$ coordinates.

*f.* One pound of silica gel containing 18% adsorbed moisture is placed in a vessel containing 500 cu. ft. dry air. The temperature and pressure are maintained at 1 atm. and 25°C., respectively. Compute the final equilibrium moisture content of the air and gel.

*g.* Repeat (*f*) for a total pressure of 2 atm. (Note that the equilibrium curve in terms of $X$ and $Y$ previously used is not applicable.)

**4.** The equilibrium adsorption of benzene vapor on a certain activated charcoal at 33.3°C. is as follows:

| Cu. cm. benzene vapor adsorbed (measured at standard conditions)/gm. C. ................ | 15 | 25 | 40 | 50 | 65 | 80 | 90 | 100 |
|---|---|---|---|---|---|---|---|---|
| Partial pressure benzene, mm. Hg | 0.0010 | 0.0045 | 0.0251 | 0.115 | 0.251 | 1.00 | 2.81 | 7.82 |

*a.* One hundred cubic feet per minute of a nitrogen-benzene vapor mixture containing 1.0% benzene by volume is to be passed countercurrently in contact with a moving stream of the activated charcoal so as to remove 95% of the benzene from the gas in a continuous process. The entering charcoal contains 15 cu. cm. benzene vapor (at standard conditions) adsorbed per gram charcoal. The temperature and total pressure are to be maintained at 33.3°C. and 1 atm., respectively, throughout. The nitrogen is not adsorbed. What is the least amount of charcoal which may be used per hour? If twice as much is used, what will be the concentration of adsorbed benzene upon the charcoal leaving?

*b.* Repeat (*a*) for a cocurrent flow of gas and charcoal.

*c.* One hundred pounds charcoal per hour which has adsorbed upon it 100 cu. cm. (at standard conditions) benzene vapor per gram charcoal is to be stripped of its benzene to a concentration of 55 cu. cm. adsorbed benzene/gm. charcoal by continuous countercurrent contact with a stream of pure nitrogen gas at 1 atm. The temperature will be maintained at 33.3°C. What is the minimum rate of nitrogen flow, cu. ft./hr.? What will be the benzene content of the exit gas if twice as much nitrogen is fed? What will be the number of ideal stages?

**5.** Assuming the equilibrium curve of Fig. 5.8 is straight and of slope $m$, derive a relation between the Murphree efficiencies $E_E$ and $E_R$.

# PART II

# GAS-LIQUID OPERATIONS

The operations which include humidification and dehumidification, gas absorption and desorption, and distillation in its various forms all have in common the requirement that a gas and a liquid phase be brought into contact for the purpose of a diffusional interchange between them.

The order listed above is in many respects that of increasing complexity of the operations, and this is therefore the order in which they will be considered. Since in humidification the liquid is a pure substance, concentration gradients exist and diffusion of matter occurs only within the gas phase. In absorption, concentration gradients exist within both the liquid and the gas, and diffusion of at least one component occurs within both. In distillation, all the substances comprising the phases diffuse. These operations are also characterized by an especially intimate relationship between heat and mass transfer. The evaporation or condensation of a substance introduces consideration of latent heats of vaporization, sometimes heats of solution as well. In distillation, the new phase necessary for mass-transfer separation is created from the original by addition or withdrawal of heat. Our discussion must necessarily include considerations of these important heat quantities and their effects.

In the case of all these operations, the equipment used has as its principal function the contact of the gas and liquid in as efficient a fashion as possible. For the improvement of the diffusion rates, it will in every case be desirable to create as much interfacial surface between the phases and as much turbulence in the fluids as possible, commensurate with the cost. In principle at least, any type of equipment satisfactory for one of these operations is also satisfactory for the others, and the major types are indeed used in all. For these reasons, our discussion begins with equipment. Certain types of equipment, however, for reasons of cost, corrosion resistance, special adaptability, and custom, have been used only in one or another of these operations, and in our discussion these will be described in their appropriate places.

CHAPTER 6

# EQUIPMENT FOR GAS-LIQUID OPERATIONS

It is the purpose of the equipment used for the gas-liquid operations to provide intimate contact of the two fluids in order to permit interphase diffusion of the constituents. The rate of mass transfer is directly dependent upon the interfacial surface exposed between the phases, and the nature and degree of dispersion of one fluid in the other are therefore of prime importance. The equipment may be classified in a general way according to whether the gas or the liquid is the dispersed phase.

### I. GAS DISPERSED

In this group are included those devices, such as agitated vessels and the various types of tray towers, in which the gas phase is dispersed into bubbles or drops. The most important of the group is the bubble-cap tray tower.

**Agitated Vessels.** The simplest method of dispersing the gas into a batch of liquid is to discharge it through a perforated pipe or sparger beneath the liquid surface. The gas bubbles from such a sparger are relatively large, and the interfacial surface is correspondingly small therefore. The degree of dispersion may be increased by forcing the gas through smaller openings such as those in porous ceramic or metallic plates, but the small openings require high gas pressures and are subject to clogging. It is preferable to increase the degree of dispersion by use

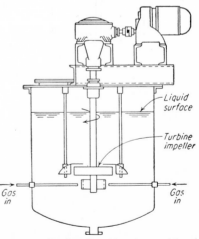

Fig. 6.1. Turbo Gas Absorber. (*Courtesy of General American Transportation Corporation.*)

of a mechanical agitator, as in Fig. 6.1. Here the agitation is brought about by a turbine-type impeller. The gas is introduced through submerged pipes against a "target," an open sleeve, which leads the gas into the bottom of the impeller at a position about halfway from the center to the periphery.   This prevents formation of a large gas bubble at the center of the impeller and assists in the shearing of the gas into bubbles of small sizes by the impeller.   The hooded ring surrounding the impeller aids in projecting the stream downward and provides therefore a longer time of contact between gas and liquid.   Figure 6.2 shows an agitated vessel with an additional impeller near the liquid surface which will draw gas down into the liquid.   Such a vessel is used, for example, in the absorption of hydrogen into vegetable oils in hydrogenation processes.

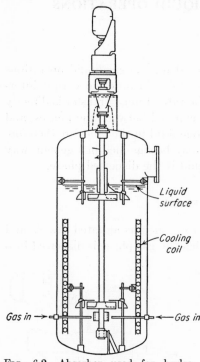

Impellers of the type shown will finely subdivide gas introduced at superficial linear velocities less than 0.1 ft./sec. based on vessel cross sections.   Agitated vessels are therefore primarily useful for dispersing small quantities of gases into liquids, on a batch, semibatch, or continuous basis.   They are also especially useful for cases where the liquid contains a suspended solid, as, for example, in the precipitation of calcium carbonate by the absorption of carbon dioxide from flue gas into a lime slurry or in the hydrogenation of a liquid in the presence of a suspended solid catalyst.

Fig. 6.2. Absorber used for hydrogenation. (*Courtesy of General American Transportation Corporation.*)

Since a well-designed turbine impeller provides very thorough mixing of the liquid, it may reasonably be assumed that the concentration throughout the liquid phase in such devices is quite uniform.   The benefits of countercurrent flow for continuous operation cannot therefore be had with a single tank and agitator.   Multistage arrangements, with counterflow of gas and liquid, require multiple vessels and agitators, piped to lead the gas from the top of one tank to the bottom of the next and the liquid from vessel to vessel in the opposite direction.

**Bubble-cap Tray Towers.**   Bubble-cap tray towers are vertical cylinders in which the liquid and gas are contacted countercurrently in stepwise fashion on trays or plates, in a manner shown schematically in Fig. 6.3.   The vapor or gas rises through openings in the trays (vapor

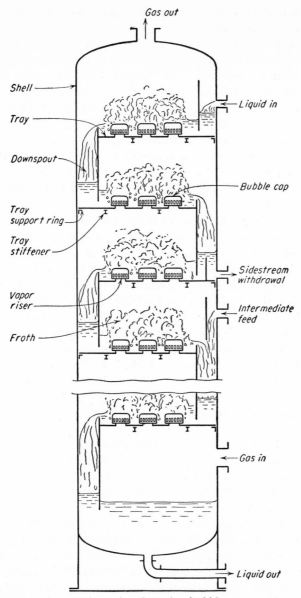

FIG. 6.3. Schematic section through a bubble-cap tray tower.

risers, or upcomers) into the bubble caps which surmount each riser. The periphery of each cap is pierced with a number of openings (slots) through which the gas bubbles into the liquid.   The liquid flows downward from tray to tray through downspouts, crosses each tray, and contacts the gas issuing from the bubble-cap slots.

The number of trays in a column or tower is dependent upon the difficulty of the mass-transfer operation to be carried out. The diameter of the tower and the distance between trays, on the other hand, depend upon the quantities of liquid and gas flowing through the tower per unit time. Once the number of trays required has been determined, the principal problem in the design of the tower is to choose dimensions and arrangements which will represent the best compromise among several opposing tendencies, for it is generally found that conditions leading to high mass-transfer efficiency will ultimately lead to operation difficulties.

Each tray of the tower is essentially a stage, since on the tray the fluids are brought into intimate contact, interphase diffusion occurs, and the fluids are physically separated. In order that stage efficiencies or tray efficiencies be high, therefore, the time of contact must be as long as possible to permit the diffusion to occur, the interfacial surface between phases must be made as large as possible, and every portion of each fluid must be contacted with the other fluid. In order to provide long contact time, the liquid pool on each tray should be as deep as possible so that bubbles of gas will require a relatively long time to rise through the liquid. When the gas bubbles only slowly through the slot openings of the caps, the bubbles are large and the interfacial surface per unit of gas volume is small, the liquid is relatively quiescent, and much of it may pass over the tray without having contacted the gas. On the other hand, when the gas velocity is relatively high, it is dispersed very thoroughly into the liquid, which in turn is agitated into a froth or foam. This provides large interfacial surface areas. For high tray efficiency, therefore, we require deep pools of liquid and relatively high velocities for the gas.

These conditions, however, lead to difficulties with entrainment of droplets of liquid in the rising gas stream and to high pressure drop for the gas. Too extensive liquid foaming or frothing may cause the foam to reach considerable heights above the tray level, and when the gas is finally disengaged from the bulk of the liquid, small droplets of the latter will be carried by the gas to the tray above. Liquid which is carried up the tower in this manner will tend to reduce the concentration change which is brought about by the mass transfer and consequently will adversely affect the tray efficiency. It will then be necessary to maintain relatively great distances between trays in order to minimize the entrainment, thereby increasing the cost of the tower considerably. Furthermore, great liquid depths on the tray and high gas velocities both result in high pressure drop for the gas in flowing through the tray, and this in turn leads to a number of difficulties. In the case of absorbers and humidifiers, high pressure drop results in high fan power to blow or draw the gas through the tower, and consequently high operating cost.

In the case of distillation, high pressures at the bottom of the tower result in high boiling temperatures, which in turn may lead to heating difficulties and possibly damage to heat-sensitive compounds.

High pressure drop may also lead to a condition of *flooding*. With a large pressure difference in the spaces between trays, the level of liquid leaving a tray at relatively low pressure and entering one of high pressure must necessarily assume an elevated position in the downspouts, as shown in Fig. 6.3. As the pressure difference is increased owing to increased rate of flow of either gas or liquid, the level of the liquid in the downspout will rise further in order to permit the liquid to enter the lower tray. Ultimately the liquid level may reach that on the tray above. Further increase in either flow rate then aggravates the condition rapidly, and the liquid will fill the entire space between trays. The tower is then flooded; the tray efficiency falls to a very low value, the flow of gas is erratic, and liquid may be forced out of the gas exit pipe at the top of the tower (priming).

We may summarize these opposing tendencies as follows: Great depths of liquid on the trays lead to high tray efficiency through long time of contact, but also high pressure drops per tray. High gas velocities, within limits, provide good vapor-liquid contact through excellence of dispersion but lead to excessive entrainment and high pressure drop. The various arrangements and dimensions chosen for design are those which experience has proved to be reasonably good compromises. The general design procedure involves application of these somewhat empirically, followed by computational check to ensure that pressure drop and flexibility, i.e., ability of the tower to handle more than the immediately expected fluid quantities, are satisfactory.

*Shell and Trays.* The tower may be made of any of a number of materials, depending upon the corrosion conditions encountered. Glass, glass-lined metal, impervious carbon, plastics, even wood, but most frequently metals are used. For metal towers, the shells are usually cylindrical for reasons of cost. If made in one piece, they are fitted with handholes or manholes to permit installation of trays and cleaning. Alternatively, they may be made of a number of flanged sections bolted together.

The trays may be cast iron, in which case the risers for the gas may be made integral with the trays. From the point of view of cost, thinner gauge metal is usually preferable even if special alloys are required, and the thickness chosen is governed by the corrosion rate. In any case, the trays must be stiffened by supporting beams as in Fig. 6.3, and they must be fastened to the shell to prevent movement due to surges of gas, with allowance for thermal expansion. This can be arranged by use of tray support rings with slotted boltholes, to which the trays are bolted.

Large trays are made in sections for ease in installation. They should be installed level.

*Tray Spacing.* Tray spacing is usually chosen first on the basis of expediency in construction, maintenance, and cost and later checked to be certain that adequate insurance against flooding is present. For special work where headroom is a most important consideration, tray spacings as low as 2 in. have been used, but it is recommended that ordinarily, for reasons of flexibility in flow-handling capacity, tray spacings be not less than 6 in. For all except the smallest tower diameters, 18 in. would seem a more workable minimum from the point of view of cleaning the trays. Most petroleum-refinery installations use 18 to 20 in. for tower diameters up to 4 ft., and increased spacing for greater diameters in order to facilitate cleaning and removal of trays through manholes in the shell.[9] See Table 6.1 for a summary of recommended values.

*Tower Diameter.* From considerations of entrainment, the tray spacing is intimately connected with depth of liquid on the tray and the gas velocity through the tower. The tower diameter and consequently its cross section must be sufficiently large to handle the gas and liquid at reasonable velocities. The superficial linear gas velocity through the tower, $V$ (cu. ft. gas/sec. divided by empty tower cross section, sq. ft.), is chosen through Eq. (6.1),

$$V = K \left( \frac{\rho_L - \rho_G}{\rho_G} \right)^{1/2} \tag{6.1}$$

where $\rho_G$ is the gas density in lb./cu. ft. based on the ideal-gas law and $K$ is an empirical constant chosen with the help of Fig. 6.4. These constants are taken from the data of Carey[5] and represent both the results of experimental study and good commercial practice to ensure against excessive entrainment. Liquid seal $h_s$ is the depth of clear liquid over the top of the bubble-cap slots ($= h_1 + h_2$, to be defined later), chosen in accordance with the total pressure in the tower (see Table 6.1).

The tower cross section and consequently its diameter are then fixed by the volumetric rate of gas flow and the calculated superficial gas velocity. For most circumstances, the diameter so chosen will be adequate for handling the liquid flow to be expected, although occasionally the latter will be the controlling consideration. A well-designed single-pass crossflow tray can ordinarily be expected to handle up to 100 gal./min. of liquid per foot of diameter [$q/d = 0.22$ cu. ft./(sec.)(ft.)] without excessive liquid gradient. For most installations, considerations of cost make it impractical to vary the tower diameter to accommodate variations in liquid or gas flow from one end of the tower to the other, and the maximum flow quantities are used to set the design. When the variation in flow is considerable and especially when expensive alloys are used in construction, two diameters are sometimes used.

The tower diameter may clearly be decreased by use of increased tray spacing so that the tower cost, which depends on height as well as diameter, passes through a minimum at some optimum tray spacing.

*Bubble Caps and Risers.* The caps are ordinarily circular, 3 to 6 in. diameter, sometimes rectangular (tunnel caps), 3 to 6 in. wide by 12 in. or more long. They are most frequently made of metal by casting, or

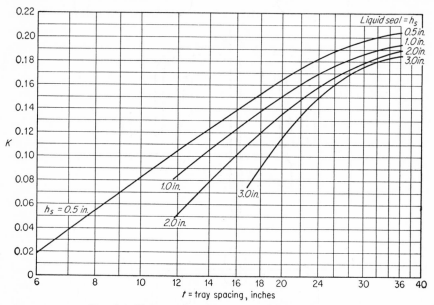

FIG. 6.4. Tray-spacing constants. (*Data of Carey.*[5])

punched or spun from sheet metal, but also from other materials such as glass, plastic, or carbon. Figure 6.5 shows some typical designs. The caps must be held to the tray preferably by bolts, sometimes by bars which hold down many caps in a row. The latter arrangement interferes with liquid flow and is not recommended. The slots are arranged around the periphery of the cap and are either of saw-tooth design or cut so that they do not extend to the edge of the cap. The slots may be rectangular or triangular; the shape does not seem particularly important in influencing the tray efficiency.

Once the cap design has been chosen, the number of caps used per tray is governed by the permissible gas velocity through the slots. If the slot velocity is too small, the tray efficiency is reduced because of inadequate dispersion. If too great, the liquid may be blown away from the cap, and tray efficiency will again be poor. At the best velocity, the liquid is

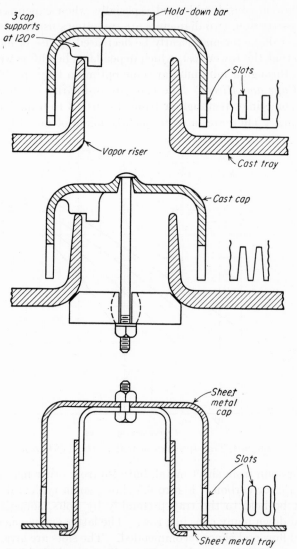

FIG. 6.5. Typical bubble-cap designs. (*With permission of American Petroleum Institute and The Pressed Steel Co.*)

agitated into a froth which offers a large interfacial surface for mass transfer. The superficial slot velocity (linear gas velocity, ft./sec., through the slots, assuming the entire slot area to be utilized) should not exceed[9] about $12/\rho_G^{0.5}$ or be less than $3.4/\rho_G^{0.5}$. The former criterion may be used as a tentative design figure to establish the number of caps, subject to correction for pressure drop and the available space for them.

The caps are arranged on the trays in rows so that the liquid is ade-

quately contacted, as in Fig. 6.6.    The gas issuing from the slots is usually not projected more than about 1 in. from the cap, so that the distance
between caps should be between 1 and 3 in., and for the same reason the
clearance between caps and shell should be kept small.    The bottom edge
of the caps may be placed directly on the tray or raised from 0.5 to 1.5 in.
(skirt clearance).    At least 0.5 in. clearance is desirable to prevent accumulation of sediment from the liquid.

The vapor risers under each cap are chosen of such diameter that the
linear gas velocity in the riser-cap system is as nearly constant as practicable in order to reduce expansion and contraction pressure losses for the

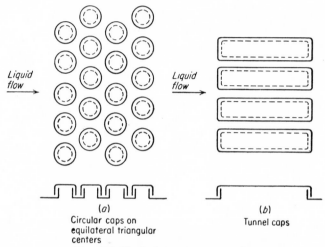

(a)
Circular caps on
equilateral triangular
centers

(b)
Tunnel caps

FIG. 6.6. Typical cap arrangements.

gas.    The risers should extend above the top of the slots to reduce the
tendency to back trap (flow of liquid through the riser).

*Downspouts.*    The liquid is led from one tray to the next by means of
downspouts, or downcomers.    These may be circular pipes or, as in the
simple arrangement shown in Fig. 6.3, simply portions of the tower cross
section set aside for liquid flow by vertical plates.    Since the liquid is
agitated into a froth on the tray, adequate residence time must be allowed
in the downspout to permit disengaging of the gas from the liquid so that
only clear liquid enters the tray below.    A minimum residence, or holdup,
time for the liquid of 5 sec. (= total volume of downspout in cu. ft./cu. ft.
liquid per sec.) will ordinarily ensure this.[9]    The downspout must be
brought sufficiently close to the tray below so as to seal into the liquid
on that tray ($\frac{1}{2}$ to 1 in. below the outlet weir level), thus preventing
gas bubbles from rising up the downspout to short-circuit the caps on
the tray above.    Seal pots and seal-pot dams (inlet weirs) may be used,
as in Fig. 6.7, but not if there is any tendency to accumulate sediment.

*Weirs.* The depth of liquid on the tray required to seal the bubble-cap slots is maintained by an overflow weir, which may or may not be a continuation of the downspout plate. The weir may be straight rectangular or notched; circular weirs which are extensions of circular pipe downspouts are not recommended. In order to ensure reasonably uni-

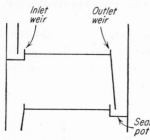

form distribution of liquid flow on single-pass trays, a weir length of 60 to 80 per cent of the tower diameter is used. To assist the weir action, the last row of caps should be set at least 3 to 5 in. from the weir, so that some vapor disengaging space is provided before the liquid flows over the weir. Alternatively the slots of the caps facing the weir may be blanked off.

Fig. 6.7. Seal-pot arrangement.

Inlet weirs (see Fig. 6.7) are sometimes used to assist in sealing the downspout and also to provide for more uniform liquid flow across the tray.

*Liquid Flow.* An increase in liquid depth from the outlet to the inlet of the tray, the liquid gradient, results from the resistance offered to flow of liquid by the caps and risers (see Fig. 6.8). If the liquid gradient is excessive, the gas will tend to flow through those caps which are only shallowly covered owing to their smaller pressure drop. Caps near the

| | | | |
|---|---|---|---|
| Back-trapping | Row of caps not bubbling | Normal operation | Gas blowing beneath cap skirt |

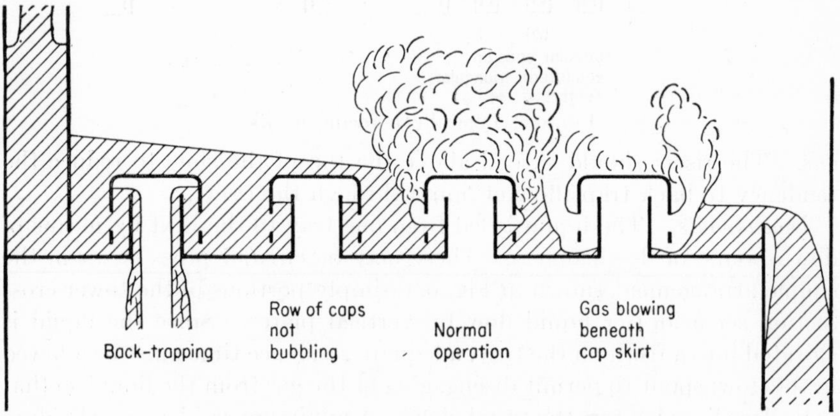

Fig. 6.8. Effect of excessive liquid gradient.

liquid inlet will stop bubbling, and the effectiveness of the tray is materially reduced. In severe cases, liquid may even flow through the gas risers (back-trapping or dumping).

The liquid gradient may be minimized by reducing the number of rows of caps through which the liquid must flow. For large-diameter towers, radial or split flow may be substituted for the simple crossflow thus far described (see Fig. 6.9). For very large diameters, cascade trays of several levels, each with its own weir, can be used, although their cost is considerable. For towers up to 4 ft. in diameter, simple crossflow is probably best. In any case, the liquid gradient should be kept to about 0.5 in., with 1.0 in. as a maximum.

In order to provide for drainage of liquid from the trays when operation of the tower is shut down, a few very small holes (weep holes) are usually drilled in the tray near the weir. At ordinary vapor velocities, substantially no liquid will flow through these holes.

*Plate Stability.* A plate is stable provided all caps are bubbling, and it has been demonstrated that the best tray efficiencies result when each row of caps is handling as nearly as possible the same amount of gas. The effect of liquid gradient may be partially offset by providing for high velocity of gas on the average through all caps, but some unevenness in the gas distribution will still result. In severe cases the caps of different rows may be set at different elevations from the tray floor so as to follow the liquid level,

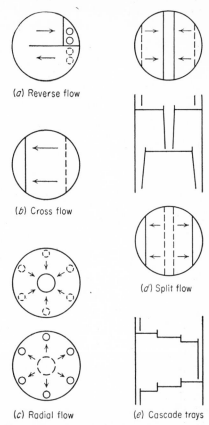

(*a*) Reverse flow

(*b*) Cross flow

(*c*) Radial flow

(*d*) Split flow

(*e*) Cascade trays

FIG. 6.9. Tray arrangements. Arrows show direction of liquid flow.

or some of the slots of caps in the downstream rows may be blanked off in order to increase the pressure drop through these rows.

*Bubble-cap Tray Hydraulics.* It has been shown that the stability and efficiency of a bubble-cap tray as well as its tendency to flood are influenced by the pressure drop suffered by the gas in its flow through the tray and the various levels assumed by the liquid surface. Refer to Fig. 6.10, where there is shown a schematic sectional representation of a simple crossflow tray. Only one bubble cap is shown, but it is understood that there may be many rows of caps normal to the direction of liquid flow. Despite the fact that the liquid is in reality agitated into a froth, in all computations involving pressure drop and liquid gradient it is assumed that only clear liquid is present, for lack of adequate information on the depth and density of the froth.

*Gas-pressure drop.* For convenience, all gas-pressure drops will be expressed as equivalent heads, in inches, of clear liquid of density $\rho_L$ lb./cu. ft. on the tray. The average pressure drop $h$ experienced by the gas will be the sum of the liquid depths through which the gas must rise and the losses incurred in passing through risers, caps, and slots. Assuming an approximately linear variation of liquid gradient with distance across the tray,

$$h = h_1 + h_2 + h_3 + 0.5\,\Delta \tag{6.2}$$

where $h_1$ = head on the weir, in.

$h_2$ = static submergence of the slots (assuming no liquid flow), in.

$h_3 = h_c + h_{slot}$ = pressure drop owing to flow through caps and slots, in.

$\Delta$ = hydraulic gradient, in.

### TABLE 6.1. RECOMMENDED CONDITIONS AND DIMENSIONS FOR BUBBLE-CAP TRAYS

1. *Tray spacing*

| $d$ = tower diam. | $t$ = tray spacing |
|---|---|
| | 6 in. min. |
| 4 ft. or less | 18–20 in. |
| 4–10 ft. | 24 in. |
| 10–12 ft. | 30 in. |
| 12–24 ft. | 36 in. |

2. *Liquid seal*

| Pressure | $h_s$ |
|---|---|
| Vacuum | 0.5 in. |
| Atm. | 1 in. |
| 500 lb./sq. in. | 3 in. |

3. *Liquid flow*    a. Not over 0.22 cu. ft./(sec.)(ft. diam.) for single-pass crossflow trays

       b. Not over 0.35 cu. ft./(sec.)(ft. weir length) for others

4. *Superficial slot velocity*    $3.4/\rho_G^{0.5}$ ft./sec. minimum; $12/\rho_G^{0.5}$ ft./sec. max.

5. *Skirt clearance*    0.5 in. min.; 1.5 in. for dirty liquids

6. *Cap spacing*    1 in. min. (low slot velocities); 3 in. max. (high slot velocities)

7. *Downspout holdup*    5 sec. minimum

8. *Downspout seal*    0.5 in. min. at no liquid flow

9. *Weir length*    Straight rectangular weirs for crossflow trays, $0.6d$–$0.8d$

10. *Liquid gradient*    0.5 in. (1 in. max.)

11. *Pressure drop per tray*

| Pressure | Pressure drop |
|---|---|
| 35 mm. Hg abs. | 3 mm. Hg or less |
| Atm. | 0.07–0.12 lb./sq. in. |
| 300 lb./sq. in. | 0.15 lb./sq. in. |

*Weir head $h_1$.* This discussion is limited to straight weirs. For rectangular, sharp-edged straight weirs, the flow rate and depth of liquid are related by a modification of the familiar Francis formula,

$$\frac{q}{W_{eff}} = 3.33\left(\frac{h_1}{12k_w}\right)^{3/2} \tag{6.3}$$

where $q$ = rate of liquid flow, cu. ft./sec.

$W_{eff}$ = effective length of weir, ft.

$h_1$ = liquid head, in.

$k_w$ = correction to allow for velocity with which liquid approaches weir

Owing to the fact that the weir action is hampered by the curved sides of the circular tower, it is recommended[10] that $W_{eff}$ be represented as a chord of the circle of diameter $d$, a distance $h_1$ farther from the center than the actual weir, as in Fig. 6.11.

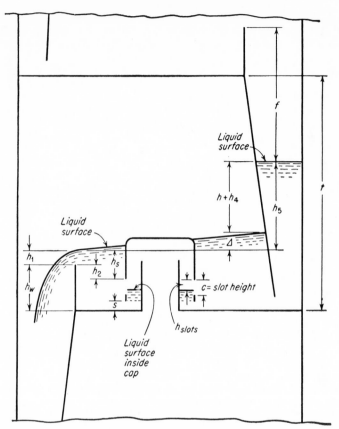

FIG. 6.10. Schematic diagram of crossflow tray.

Equation (6.3) may then be rearranged to

$$h_1 = 5.38 k_w \left(\frac{W}{W_{eff}}\right)^{2/3} \left(\frac{q}{W}\right)^{2/3} \tag{6.4}$$

The lengths of effective weirs have been calculated from the geometry of Fig. 6.11, and the correction $(W/W_{eff})^{2/3}$ is given by Fig. 6.12. The approach-velocity correction was calculated by standard methods[18] and is given by Fig. 6.13.

*Pressure drop through caps, $h_c$.* This drop in pressure is primarily the result of expansion and contraction losses incurred as the gas flows through the various cross sections represented by the riser, the reversal area (the area for flow between the top of the riser and the underneath surface of the cap), and the annulus between cap and riser. The results of many measurements showed this to be adequately represented by six

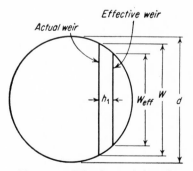

FIG. 6.11. Effective weir length.

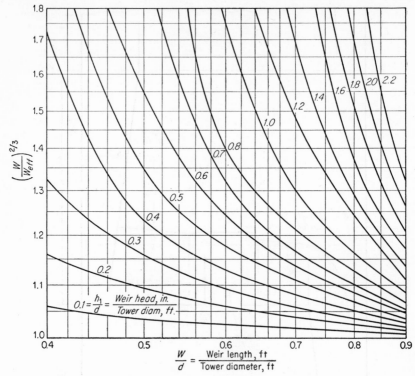

FIG. 6.12. Correction for effective weir length.

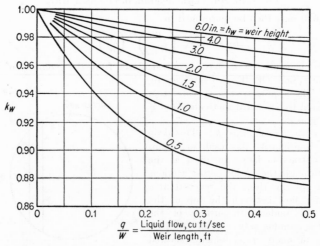

FIG. 6.13. Weir correction for approach velocity of liquid.

velocity heads[20] for the gas,

$$h_c = \frac{12(6)V_m^2}{2g_c} \frac{\rho_G}{\rho_L} = \frac{1.1V_m^2\rho_G}{\rho_L} \tag{6.5}$$

where $V_m$ = max. linear velocity of gas, ft./sec., based on smallest cross section for flow among the following: riser, reversal area, annulus

*Pressure drop through the slots, $h_{slots}$.* In order that the gas may issue from the bubble-cap slots, the liquid level under the cap must be depressed vertically below the top of the slot by a distance $h_{slot}$. This represents the drop in pressure for the gas in passing from inside the cap to the outside at the level of the top of the slots. At low rates of gas flow, bubbles of gas issue intermittently from the slots, and the necessary depression of the liquid level is dependent only upon the surface tension and geometry of the slot opening. At high rates of flow, the gas issues in a steady stream as through an orifice, and the liquid depression increases as gas rate increases. These effects have been thoroughly studied by Cross and Ryder,[7] whose results for the average slot opening may be expressed in convenient units as follows:

1. For triangular-shaped slots, of height $c$ and base $b$, inches,

$$h_{slot} = \alpha \qquad \text{for } Q_s < \left(\frac{\alpha}{\beta}\right)^{5/2} \tag{6.6}$$

$$h_{slot} = \beta Q_s^{2/5} \qquad \text{for } Q_s > \left(\frac{\alpha}{\beta}\right)^{5/2} \tag{6.7}$$

where

$$\alpha = 0.1404 \left[ \sigma \left(\frac{2c}{b} + 1\right) \right]^{1/2} \tag{6.8}$$

$$\beta = 11.1 \left[ \frac{c}{b} \sqrt{\frac{\rho_G}{\rho_L - \rho_G}} \right]^{2/5} \tag{6.9}$$

2. For rectangular slots of height $c$ and width $b$, inches,

$$h_{slot} = \alpha \qquad \text{for } Q_s < \left(\frac{\alpha}{\beta}\right)^{3/2} \tag{6.10}$$

$$h_{slot} = \beta Q_s^{2/3} \qquad \text{for } Q_s > \left(\frac{\alpha}{\beta}\right)^{3/2} \tag{6.11}$$

where

$$\alpha = 0.986 \frac{\sigma}{100b\rho_L} + \left[ 0.974 \left(\frac{\sigma}{100b\rho_L}\right)^2 + 1.971 \left(\frac{\sigma}{100\rho_L}\right) \right]^{1/2} \tag{6.12}$$

$$\beta = 29.7 \left(\frac{1}{b} \sqrt{\frac{\rho_G}{\rho_L - \rho_G}}\right)^{2/3} \tag{6.13}$$

In these expressions

$$Q_s = \text{cu. ft. gas/sec. through each slot}$$
$$\sigma = \text{surface tension of liquid, dynes/cm.}$$

The calculations are valid only for values of $h_{slot}$ less than the slot height $c$. Owing to the smaller density of the froth in comparison with that of the clear liquid, and to provide for the wider slot opening for the last row of caps, $h_{slot}$ ought not to be much larger than $0.5c$.

*Liquid gradient $\Delta$.* The most generally and readily applicable expressions for estimation of the liquid gradient appear to be those of Davies,[8] which are, however, limited to cases where the tops of the caps are either not covered with liquid or

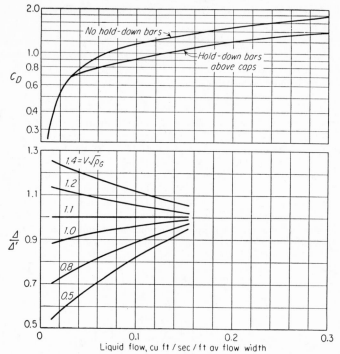

FIG. 6.14. Hydraulic-gradient constant, and correction. [*Ind. Eng. Chem.*, **39**, 774 (1947), *with permission.*]

covered to a depth not greater than 1 in. These may be written as follows,

$$(\Delta')^{1.5} + (\Delta')^{0.5} \frac{y}{x} = \frac{z}{x} \tag{6.14}$$

where                    $\Delta'$ = liquid gradient, in., for $V\rho_G^{0.5} = 1.1$

$$y = 3r \left[ h_1 + h_w + s \left( \frac{l_2}{l_1} - 1 \right) \right] \tag{6.15}$$

For caps arranged on equilateral-triangle centers,

$$x = 1.5r - 1.4 \tag{6.16}$$

$$z = \frac{209r^{1.5}q}{C_D l_1} \tag{6.17}$$

For caps arranged on square centers (and approximately for tunnel caps),

$$x = 1.5r - 1.0 \tag{6.18}$$

$$z = \frac{187r^{1.5}q}{C_D l_1} \tag{6.19}$$

where $r$ = number of rows of caps perpendicular to direction of flow

   $l_1$ = av. total free distance between caps, measured perpendicular to direction of liquid flow, in.

   $l_2$ = av. total free distance between risers, measured perpendicular to direction of liquid flow, in.

   $s$ = skirt clearance, in.

   $C_D$ = a const. taken from Fig. 6.14

For purposes of obtaining $l_1$ and $l_2$, the distances are calculated for each row of caps and averaged for all the rows. Figure 6.15, which covers the most likely ranges of the variables, will permit solution of Eq. (6.14) without trial and error. $\Delta'$ is converted to $\Delta$, the actual gradient, with the help of Fig. 6.14. For data on caps covered by liquid to depths greater than 1 in., the work of Kemp and Pyle[13] should be consulted.

The average pressure drop $h$ may now be computed [Eq. (6.2)].

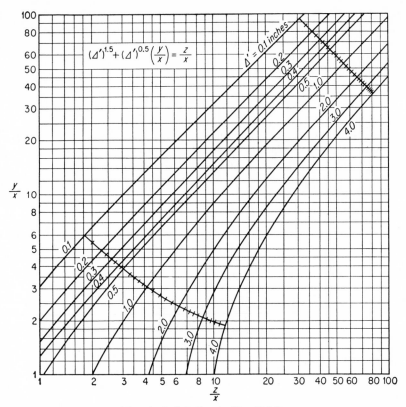

$$(\Delta')^{1.5} + (\Delta')^{0.5}\left(\frac{y}{x}\right) = \frac{z}{x}$$

FIG. 6.15. Solution to Eq. (6.14).

*Plate stability.* The first row of caps, i.e., the first row following the liquid inlet, will stop bubbling vapor when $\Delta/h_3$ exceeds unity. Even if $\Delta/h_3$ is less than unity, however, there will be more gas passing through the last row of caps than the first. It is even possible that the total slot opening in the last row is insufficient to pass all the gas through this row, and gas may issue from underneath the cap skirt. As a guide, in order to maintain as even a distribution of vapor as practicable, it is recommended that:[9]

1. The liquid gradient be kept to about 0.5 in., never to exceed 1 in.
2. The value of $h_3$ be kept as high as practicable to ensure more uniform vapor flow
3. The ratio $\Delta/h_3$ be kept to less than 0.4
4. The value of $h_{slot}$ (based on average gas flow $Q_s$) be kept to $0.5c$ as a maximum

*Flooding.* Flooding will not occur so long as there exists some free space $f$ (Fig. 6.10) between the level of the liquid in the downspout and the weir of the tray above.

From the figure,

$$f = t - h_5 - h_1 \tag{6.20}$$

and since the liquid in the downspout may actually include froth whose average density is less than $\rho_L$, it is recommended that $h_5 + h_1$ be less than $0.5t$, where

$$h_5 = h + h_4 + \Delta \tag{6.21}$$

and $h_4$ is the head loss owing to resistance to flow of liquid through the downspout and onto the tray. The friction for liquid flow in the downspout is generally negligible unless excessive foam disengaging occurs, and the loss is largely due to flow through the constriction between the tray floor and the bottom edge of the downspout. It may be estimated as three velocity heads for the liquid,[6]

$$h_4 = \frac{3(12)}{2g_c} \left(\frac{q}{A_d}\right)^2 = 0.558 \left(\frac{q}{A_d}\right)^2 \tag{6.22}$$

where $A_d$ = min. free cross-sectional area for flow for the liquid, sq. ft.

**Illustration 1.** A dilute aqueous solution of methanol and water is to be stripped with steam in a bubble-cap tray tower. The conditions chosen for design are (1) vapor, 700 moles/hr., 18 mole % methanol; (2) liquid, 2,100 lb. moles/hr., 5 wt. % (2.9 mole %) methanol; (3) temperature 95°C., pressure 1 atm. Design a suitable bubble-cap tray.

*Solution.* Mol. wt. methanol = 32, mol. wt. water = 18. Av. mol. wt. gas = $0.18(32) + 0.82(18) = 20.5$ lb./lb. mole.

$$\rho_G = \frac{20.5}{359} \frac{273}{273 + 95} = 0.0424 \text{ lb./cu. ft.}$$

$$Q = \frac{700}{3,600} (359) \frac{273 + 95}{273} = 94 \text{ cu. ft./sec. vapor rate}$$

$$\rho_L = 60 \text{ lb./cu. ft.}$$

Av. mol. wt. liquid = $100/(\frac{5}{32} + \frac{95}{18}) = 18.43$ lb./lb. mole

$$q = 2,100(18.43) \frac{1}{60} \frac{1}{3,600} = 0.1794 \text{ cu. ft. liquid/sec.}$$

*Tower diameter.* Tentatively take $h_s = 1$ in. liquid seal, $t = 20$ in. tray spacing. From Fig. 6.4, $K = 0.15$.

Eq. (6.1): $\quad V = K \left(\frac{\rho_L - \rho_G}{\rho_G}\right)^{0.5} = 0.15 \left(\frac{60 - 0.04}{0.0424}\right)^{0.5} = 5.64$ ft./sec.

Tower cross section = $Q/V = 94/5.64 = 16.7$ sq. ft.
Diam. = $d = [4(16.7)/\pi]^{0.5} = 4.61$ ft. Make $d = 4$ ft. 8 in., or 4.67 ft., and use a crossflow tray (Figs. 6.9b and 6.16).

$$\text{Corrected } V = 94(4)/\pi(4.67)^2 = 5.50 \text{ ft./sec.}$$

*Weir.* Make $W = 0.7d = 0.7(4.67) = 3.27$ ft.

Distance from center to weir = $[(d/2)^2 - (W/2)^2]^{0.5} = [(4.67/2)^2 - (3.27/2)^2]^{0.5}$
$\qquad\qquad\qquad\qquad\qquad = 1.665$ ft. = 20 in.

(This provides 1.82 sq. ft. downspout area, a superficial liquid velocity in the downspout of 0.0985 ft./sec., and a residence time in the downspout of 17 sec., which is amply large.)

*Caps.* The cap design of Fig. 6.16 will be used, with standard 2½-in. pipe nipples as risers. The caps are to be bolted to the tray without hold-down bars (not shown in the figure). Slot area = $0.25(1.5)(24)/144 = 0.0625$ sq. ft. per cap.

The superficial slot velocity should be between $12/\rho_G^{0.5} = 58.3$ ft./sec. and $3.4/\rho_G^{0.5}$ = 16.5 ft./sec.   With the arrangement of caps on the figure, 66 caps on 5¼-in. equi-lateral-triangle centers (1¼ in. between caps) provides a superficial slot velocity of 94/66(0.0625) = 22.8 ft./sec.

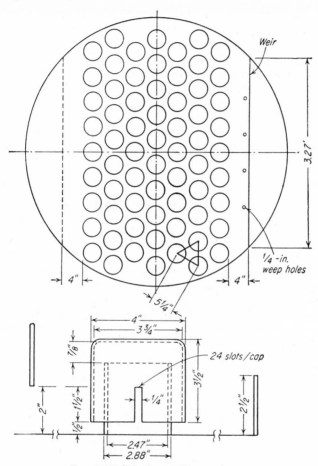

FIG. 6.16. Solution to Illustration 1.

Take $h_w$ = 2.5 in. and skirt clearance = 0.5 in.

*Weir head.*   $q/W = 0.1794/3.27 = 0.0550$ cu. ft. liquid/sec.(ft.).   From Fig. 6.13, $k_w = 0.99$.   Tentatively assume $W/W_{eff} = 1$.

Eq. (6.4):        Tentative $h_1 = 5.38k_w(q/W)^{2/3} = 5.38(0.99)(0.0550)^{2/3}$
$$= 0.77 \text{ in.}$$
$$W/d = 0.7, \qquad h_1/d = 0.77/4.67 = 0.165 \text{ in./ft.}$$
Fig. 6.12:                $(W/W_{eff})^{2/3} = 1.03$
Corrected $h_1 = 0.77(1.03) = 0.793$ in.

$h_s = 0.5 + 0.793 = 1.293$ in. (previously assumed as 1 in.).   This will not affect the choice of tower diameter.

*Pressure drop*

$$\text{Riser cross section} = \pi(2.47)^2/4 = 4.80 \text{ sq. in. per cap}$$
$$\text{Reversal area} = \tfrac{7}{8}(\pi)(2.47) = 6.80 \text{ sq. in. per cap}$$
$$\text{Annulus area} = \frac{\pi}{4}[(3.75)^2 - (2.88)^2] = 4.61 \text{ sq. in. per cap}$$

The last is the smallest.

$$V_m = \frac{94(144)}{4.61(66)} = 44.5 \text{ ft./sec.}$$

Eq. (6.5): $\qquad h_c = \dfrac{1.1 V_m^2 \rho_G}{\rho_L} = \dfrac{1.1(44.5)^2(0.0424)}{60} = 1.54$ in. liquid

$$b = 0.25 \text{ in.} \qquad \sigma = 50 \text{ dynes/cm.}$$

Eq. (6.12):

$$\alpha = 0.986 \frac{50}{100(0.25)(60)} + \left\{ 0.974 \left[ \frac{50}{100(0.25)(60)} \right]^2 + 1.971 \left[ \frac{50}{100(60)} \right] \right\}^{\frac{1}{2}}$$
$$= 0.1759$$

Eq. (6.13):

$$\beta = 29.7 \left[ \frac{1}{0.25} \left( \frac{0.0424}{60 - 0.04} \right)^{0.5} \right]^{\frac{2}{3}} = 6.40$$
$$\left( \frac{\alpha}{\beta} \right)^{\frac{3}{2}} = \left( \frac{0.1759}{6.40} \right)^{\frac{3}{2}} = 0.00455$$

This is smaller than

$$Q_s = \frac{94}{24(66)} = 0.0594 \text{ cu. ft./sec. (slot)}$$

Eq. (6.11): $\qquad h_{slot} = \beta Q_s^{\frac{2}{3}} = 6.40(0.0594)^{\frac{2}{3}} = 0.972$ in. liquid
$$h_3 = h_c + h_{slot} = 1.54 + 0.972 = 2.51 \text{ in. liquid}$$

*Liquid gradient.* $r = 7$ rows of caps, $s = 0.5$ in., $h_1 = 0.793$ in., $h_w = 2.50$ in.

| Row No. | No. caps | Total length, in. | In. between caps | In. between risers |
|---------|----------|-------------------|------------------|--------------------|
| 1 | 9 | 49 | $49 - 9(4) = \quad 13$ | $49 - 9(2.88) = \quad 23.1$ |
| 2 | 10 | 53.3 | 13.3 | 24.5 |
| 3 | 9 | 55.5 | 19.5 | 29.6 |
| 4 | 10 | 56 | 16 | 27.2 |
| 5 | 9 | 55.5 | 19.5 | 29.6 |
| 6 | 10 | 53.3 | 13.3 | 24.5 |
| 7 | 9 | 49 | 13 | 23.1 |
| Total | 66 | 371.6 | 107.6 | 181.6 |

$$l_1 = \frac{107.6}{7} = 15.37 \text{ in.} \qquad l_2 = \frac{181.6}{7} = 25.94 \text{ in.}$$

Eq. (6.15): $\qquad y = 3(7) \left[ 0.793 + 0.5 \left( \frac{25.94}{15.37} - 1 \right) \right] = 76.5$

Eq. (6.16): $\qquad x = 1.5(7) - 1.4 = 9.1$

$$\text{Av. flow width} = 371.6/7 = 53.1 \text{ in.} = 4.42 \text{ ft.}$$
$$\text{Liquid flow} = 0.1794/4.42 = 0.0406 \text{ cu. ft./sec.(ft.) (av.)}$$

Fig. 6.14: $\qquad C_D = 0.8$

Eq. (6.17): $\qquad z = \dfrac{209(7)^{1.5}(0.1794)}{0.8(15.37)} = 56.5$

$y/x = 76.5/9.1 = 8.42 \qquad z/x = 56.5/9.1 = 6.21$

Fig. 6.15: $\qquad \Delta' = 0.45$ in.

$V\rho_G^{0.5} = 5.50(0.0424)^{0.5} = 1.13$

Fig. 6.14: $\qquad \Delta/\Delta' = 1.03$

$\Delta = 1.03(0.45) = 0.46$ in.

Eq. (6.2): $\qquad h = h_1 + h_2 + h_3 + 0.5\Delta = 0.793 + 0.5 + 2.51 + 0.5(0.46)$

$= 4.03$ in.

$\dfrac{\Delta}{h_3} = \dfrac{0.46}{2.51} = 0.184$

and the vapor distribution should be fairly uniform.

$A_d$ (at bottom of downspout) $= 3.27(\frac{2}{12}) = 0.545$ sq. ft.

Eq. (6.22): $\qquad h_4 = 0.558 \left(\dfrac{0.1794}{0.545}\right)^2 = 0.061$ in. liquid

Eq. (6.21): $\qquad h_5 = 4.03 + 0.061 + 0.46 = 4.551$ in.

Eq. (6.20): $\qquad f = 20 - 4.551 - 0.793 = 14.66$ in.

and $\qquad h_5 + h_1 = 4.551 + 0.793 = 5.344$ in. (less than $0.5t$)

Unless foaming is unexpectedly heavy, the tray spacing is therefore satisfactory.

The tray has been provided with four $\frac{1}{4}$-in. weep holes (see Fig. 6.16) for drainage of the trays during shutdown periods.

**Sieve-tray (Perforated-plate) Towers.** The cost of construction of bubble-cap trays in recent years has become sufficiently great so that there has been increasing interest in simpler devices of the tray type. The sieve tray, or perforated plate, is one such device. This has actually been known for many years but used relatively little; interest in it has recently revived. A sieve tray is basically the same as a bubble-cap tray with the exception that in the area normally devoted to vapor risers and bubble caps there is instead a plate with many perforations through which the gas bubbles into the liquid. When properly designed, the sieve tray has stability over a wide range of flow rates and tray efficiencies and gas-pressure drops comparable with those of bubble-cap trays.

The mass-transfer rates should be greater for smaller perforations, but the gas-pressure drop will be larger. A $\frac{3}{16}$-in. hole size has been found very satisfactory, and the holes may be drilled or punched in metal trays on a $\frac{3}{4}$-in. triangular pitch.[17] The gas-pressure drop is the sum of that due to flow through the dry plate and that due to the depth of the liquid-gas foam on the tray. The dry-plate pressure drop $h_p$ may be computed with standard orifice equations, using an orifice coefficient of 0.85,

$$\frac{Q}{A_s} = 0.85 \left(2g_c \frac{h_p}{12} \frac{\rho_L}{\rho_G}\right)^{0.5} = 1.978 \left(\frac{h_p \rho_L}{\rho_G}\right)^{0.5} \qquad (6.23)$$

In the absence of information respecting the foam density, the depth of clear liquid over the perforations, $h_w + h_1$, may be used, so that[1,17]

$$h = h_p + h_w + h_1 \qquad (6.24)$$

The liquid gradient on the trays is negligible. There must be a sufficient gas-pressure drop, and consequently gas velocity, so that liquid does not "weep," or leak, through the perforations but instead flows over the weir. At least for air-water and for liquid depths up to 6 in., this has been shown[17] to be the case provided

$$(h_p)_{min} = 0.067(h_w + h_1) + 0.2 \qquad (6.25)$$

To be certain of stable operation (no liquid weeping), it is desirable to use a value of $h_p$ at least three to four times the minimum value. For values of $h$ in the neighborhood of 4 to 5 in., tray spacings of 18 in. have been used.

**Illustration 2.** For the stripper of the previous illustration, indicate the general dimensions of a perforated-plate tray using $3/16$-in.-diameter perforations on $3/4$-in. triangular pitch centers.

*Solution.* Assuming the same value for $h_w + h_1$ as used in Illustration 1 ($h_w + h_1$ = 2.5 + 0.793 = 3.29 in.) [Eq. (6.25)],

$$(h_p)_{min} = 0.067(3.29) + 0.2 = 0.42 \text{ in. liquid}$$

Take $h_p$ = 4 times min. value = 4(0.42) = 1.68 in.

$$h = h_p + h_w + h_1 = 1.68 + 3.29 = 4.97 \text{ in. liquid pressure drop per tray}$$

Eq. (6.23):
$$\frac{94}{A_s} = 1.978 \left[ \frac{1.68(60)}{0.0424} \right]^{0.5}$$
$$A_s = 0.975 \text{ sq. ft. total perforations per tray}$$
$$\text{Area each perforation} = (\pi/4)(3/16)^2/144 = 0.000192 \text{ sq. ft.}$$
$$\text{No. perforations required} = 0.975/0.000192 = 5,080 \text{ per tray}$$

Each $3/4$-in. equilateral triangle (0.244 sq. in.) will contain $1/2$ perforation, so that the tray area devoted to perforations will be 5,080(0.244)(2)/144 = 17.2 sq. ft.

Assuming a weir length of $0.7d$, the central area between inlet and outlet weirs can be shown by simple geometry to be $0.647d^2$, and hence

$$d = (17.2/0.647)^{0.5} = 5.15 \text{ ft. tower diam.}$$

The weir length is then 0.7(5.15) = 3.61 ft., and the weir height for the available liquid flow can be computed to give the assumed liquid depth on the tray, 3.29 in., using Eq. (6.4) and a trial-and-error procedure. This calculates to be $h_w$ = 2.55 in. and $h_1$ = 0.737 in.

**Grid Tray.** In Fig. 6.17 there is shown another simple tray-type contacting device which has recently been proved to be very effective.[3,12,23] This design requires no liquid downcomers, the liquid flowing directly through the same openings used by the gas. Pressure drops are lower than for bubble-cap trays, while flow capacities are larger. These trays

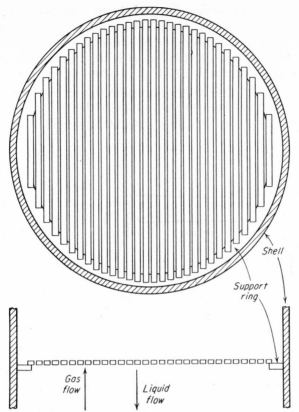

FIG. 6.17. "Turbo-grid" tray.    (*With permission of Shell Development Co.*)

are especially useful for liquids containing small amounts of suspended solids.

## II. LIQUID DISPERSED

In this group are included those devices in which the liquid is dispersed into pools, thin films, or drops, such as wetted-wall towers, tourills, sprays and spray towers, and the various packed towers.    The packed towers are the most important of the group.

**Tourills.**    In some gas-absorption operations, the absorption of hydrogen chloride into water, for example, the evolution of heat is considerable, and it has been the custom in the past to retard the absorption so that the heat could be adequately dissipated.    The gas and liquid flowed countercurrently through a series of large, stoneware bottle-shaped vessels (tourills), which were often submerged in tanks of water for purposes of removing the heat evolved.    Rather than retard the mass-transfer process, it is better to provide for more rapid heat removal.    One of the more efficient tourills designed especially for this purpose is the fused silica S bend, shown in Fig. 6.18. The cascade is frequently cooled by trickling a spray of water over the outside of the vessels.

**Wetted-wall Towers.** A thin film of liquid falling down the inside of a vertical pipe, up through which the gas flows, constitutes a wetted-wall tower. By surrounding the pipe with rapidly flowing cooling water, any heat evolved can be removed so rapidly that the size of the absorption equipment can be very much smaller than the tourills described

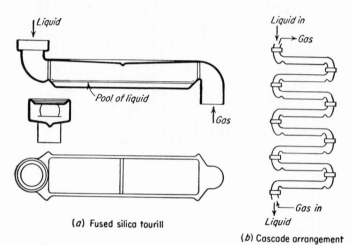

(a) Fused silica tourill

(b) Cascade arrangement

FIG. 6.18. Tyler S bends. (*With permission of the American Institute of Chemical Engineers.*)

above. Such devices have made successful absorbers for hydrochloric acid. Wetted-wall towers have also been used for theoretical studies of mass transfer, as described in Chap. 3, because the interfacial surface between the phases is readily kept under control and is measurable.

The height of a wetted-wall tower required for many mass-transfer operations is excessive, and consequently this has not been a widely used device. Where large quantities of gas or liquid would have to be handled, it would be necessary to arrange many vertical pipes operated in parallel and this leads to difficulties in distribution of the liquid onto the inner surface of the tubes. The gas-pressure drop for this type of equipment is very low, however, since it is almost entirely confined to skin-friction effects, with few or no expansion or contraction losses.

**Spray Towers, Spray Chambers.** The liquid may be sprayed into a gas stream by means of a nozzle which disperses the liquid into a fine spray of drops. The flow may be countercurrent as in vertical towers with the liquid sprayed downward or parallel as in horizontal spray chambers (see Chap. 7). These devices have the advantage of very low gas-pressure drop but also have a number of disadvantages.  There is a relatively high pumping cost for the liquid owing to the pressure drop through the spray nozzle.  The tendency for entrainment of liquid by the gas leaving is considerable, and entrainment eliminators will almost always be necessary.  Unless the diameter/length ratio is very small, the gas will be fairly thoroughly mixed by the spray, and consequently the full advantage of countercurrent flow cannot be had.  The diameter/-length ratio, however, cannot ordinarily be made very small since then the spray will quickly reach the walls of the tower and become ineffective as a spray.

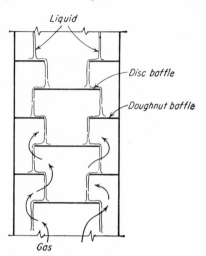

**Baffle Towers.**  In a tower of the design shown in Fig. 6.19, the gas flows upward through showers of liquid falling from the edges of the baffles. The liquid dispersion is not so good as with sprays, but countercurrent contact is more readily maintained.  Pressure drop for the gas is very low.

**Packed Towers.**  Packed towers, used for continuous countercurrent contact of liquid and gas, are vertical columns which have been filled with packing or devices of large surface, as in Fig. 6.20.  The liquid is distributed over and trickles down through the

Fig. 6.19. Section through disk-and-doughnut baffle column.

packed bed, thus exposing a large surface to contact the gas.

*Packing.*  The tower packing, or fill, should offer the following characteristics.

1. Provide for large interfacial surface between liquid and gas.  The surface of the packing per unit volume of packed space, $a_p$, should be large, but not in a microscopic sense.  Lumps of coke, for example, have a large surface owing to their porous structure, but most of this would be covered by the trickling film of liquid.  The specific packing surface $a_p$ in any event is almost always larger than the interfacial liquid-gas surface.

2. Possess desirable fluid-flow characteristics.  This ordinarily means that the fractional void volume, or fraction of empty space, in the packed bed, $\epsilon$, should be large.  The packing must permit passage of large volumes of fluid through small tower cross sections without loading or flooding (see below) and with low pressure drop for the gas.  Furthermore, gas-pressure drop should be largely the result of skin friction if possible, since this is more effective than that resulting from multiple expansions and contractions in promoting high values of the mass transfer coefficients.

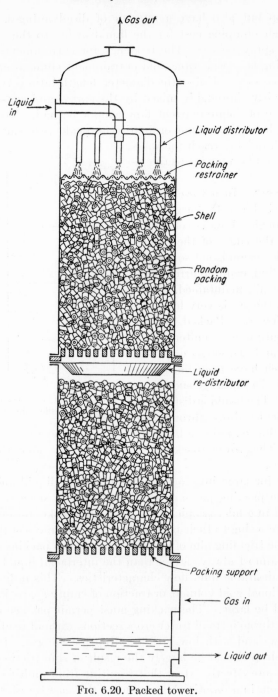

FIG. 6.20. Packed tower.

3. Chemical inertness to fluids being processed.

4. Structural strength to permit easy handling and installation.

5. Low cost.

Packings are of two major types, random and regular.

*Random Packings.* Random packings are those which are simply dumped into the tower during installation and allowed to fall at random. In the past such readily available materials as broken stone, gravel, or lumps of coke were used, but although inexpensive, these are not desirable for reasons of small surface and poor fluid-flow characteristics. Random

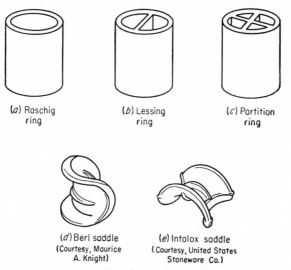

(a) Raschig ring     (b) Lessing ring     (c) Partition ring

(d) Berl saddle (Courtesy, Maurice A. Knight)     (e) Intalox saddle (Courtesy, United States Stoneware Co.)

FIG. 6.21. Random tower packings.

packings most frequently used at present are manufactured, and the common types are shown in Fig. 6.21. Raschig rings are hollow cylinders as shown, of diameters ranging from $\frac{1}{4}$ to 4 in. or more. They may be made of chemical stoneware or porcelain, which is useful in contact with most liquids except alkalies and hydrofluoric acid, or of carbon, which is useful except in strongly oxidizing atmospheres, of metals, or of plastics. Thin-walled metal rings offer the advantage of lightness in weight. Lessing rings and rings with internal partitions are less frequently used. The saddle-shaped packings, Berl saddles and Intalox saddles, are available in sizes from $\frac{1}{2}$ to 2 in., ordinarily made of chemical stoneware although they may be made of any material which can be stamped into shape. Generally the random packings offer larger specific surface (and larger gas-pressure drop) in the smaller sizes but cost less in the larger sizes. For industrial work the 1- to 2-in. sizes are most popular. During installations the packings are poured into the tower to fall at random, and in order to prevent breakage of the more fragile packings the tower may be first filled with water so as to reduce the velocity of fall.

*Regular Packings.*  Packings of the type shown in Fig. 6.22 offer the advantage of lower pressure drop and greater possible throughput of fluids, usually at the expense at least of more costly installation than random packings.  The larger sizes of Raschig rings (3 in. or larger)

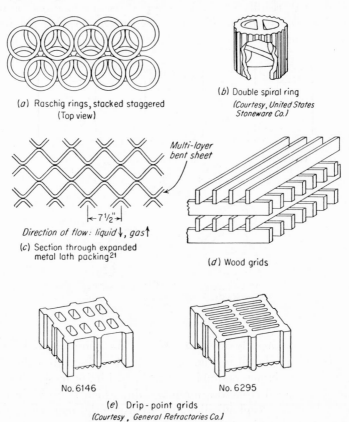

(*a*) Raschig rings, stacked staggered
(Top view)

(*b*) Double spiral ring
*(Courtesy, United States
Stoneware Co.)*

Multi-layer
bent sheet

|← 7½″ →|

*Direction of flow: liquid↓, gas↑*

(*c*) Section through expanded
metal lath packing[21]

(*d*) Wood grids

No. 6146                No. 6295

(*e*)  Drip-point grids
*(Courtesy, General Refractories Co.)*

Fig. 6.22. Regular, or stacked, tower packings.

may be carefully stacked as in Fig. 6.22*a*.  Raschig rings are also available with internal single, double, or even triple spirals as in Fig. 6.22*b*, and these may be stacked one on top of the other to provide continuous passages for the gas.  The packing of Fig. 6.22*c*[21] has recently been proved very satisfactory.  It is made of sheets of several layers of expanded metal lath which have been formed into wave-shaped surfaces, and these are installed in the towers in the manner shown.  Wood grids (Fig. 6.22*d*) are inexpensive, and the arrangement shown, as well as variants of this, is used, especially in filling water-cooling towers (see Chap. 7).    Drip-point ceramic grid tiles are large and easily stacked; they provide very effective contact at low gas-pressure drop.

The packings shown in Figs. 6.21 and 6.22 are by no means the only ones used but are probably the most popular.    Many others are available which offer particular advantages, such as especially low pressure drop or every effective contact.    Among these are Stedman packing,[4] a specially shaped wire gauze; McMahon packing,[16] a sort of Berl saddle made of wire gauze; packing made of Fiberglas;[24] and small helices of wire or glass.

*Tower Shells.*    These may be made of wood, metal, chemical stoneware, acidproof brick, glass, or other material, depending upon the corrosive conditions to be encountered. For ease of construction they are usually circular in cross section.

*Packing Support.*    Some of the regular packings are supported on the bottom of the tower itself. Random packing, however, is generally supported above the gas inlet in order to provide opportunity for satisfactory distribution of the gas. The support should contain ample free space for flow of liquid and gas, at least equal to that of the packing itself.    Perforated plates may be used, but the bar-grid type shown in

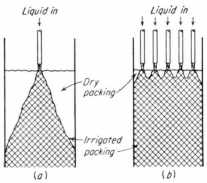

FIG. 6.23. Liquid distribution and packing irrigation.    (*a*) Inadequate; (*b*) adequate.

Fig. 6.20[19] is more easily made stronger for the necessary large free space. Special risers for conducting the gas through the support plate may be used, or the packing may rest upon bricks in an open checkerwork construction.

*Liquid Distribution.*    The importance of adequate initial distribution of the liquid at the top of the packing is indicated in Fig. 6.23.    Unirrigated packing is of course completely ineffective, and various devices of the sort shown in Fig. 6.24 are used.    It is generally considered necessary to provide at least five points of introduction of liquid for each square foot of tower cross section.    In the case of random packings, the packing density, i.e., the number of packing pieces per cubic foot, is ordinarily less in the immediate vicinity of the tower walls, and there is consequently a tendency for the liquid to segregate toward the walls. This tendency is very much less pronounced provided the diameter of individual packing pieces is smaller than one-eighth the diameter of the tower,[2] and it is recommended that this criterion always be followed. Even so it is customary to provide for redistribution of the liquid in random-packed towers at intervals of 10 to 15 ft. as in Fig. 6.20.[19]

It was pointed out that the liquid-gas interfacial surface, which is a major factor influencing the rate of mass transfer, is not the same as the specific surface of the dry packing. It is probable that incomplete wetting of most random packings exists at all liquid rates up to near the flooded condition (see later), and at low liquid rates the interfacial surface may be as small as 30 per cent of the dry packing surface. The wetted surface is practically uninfluenced by the rate of gas flow but

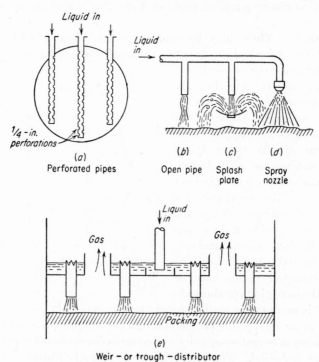

Fig. 6.24. Liquid distributors.

depends strongly on that of the liquid. It is desirable, therefore, to use a superficial liquid velocity of at least 800 lb./(hr.)(sq. ft. tower cross section). If process requirements call for less, part of the liquid effluent from the bottom of the tower may sometimes be recirculated to the top. This will, however, always result in lower concentration-difference driving forces for mass transfer and increase the necessary height of the packed bed.

*Entrainment Eliminators.* Especially at high gas velocities and where spray or splash liquid distributors are used, the gas leaving the top of the packing may carry off droplets of liquid as a mist (entrainment). This may be removed by mist eliminators through which the gas must pass: a layer of wire mesh several inches thick, 2 or 3 ft. of dry random packing above the liquid distributor, or thin slats arranged in the manner of a partly opened venetian blind may be used.  The liquid droplets impinge upon these surfaces, coalesce, and fall back into the tower.

*Flow of Fluids through Packings.*  For most random packings, the pressure drop suffered by the gas is influenced by the gas and liquid flow rates in a manner similar to that shown in Fig. 6.25.  The slope of the line for the dry packing is usually in the range 1.8 to 2.0, indicating turbulent flow for most practical gas velocities.

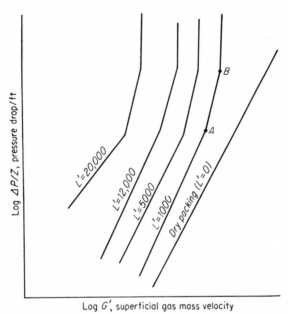

FIG. 6.25. Typical gas-pressure drop for counterflow of liquid and gas in random packings.

At a fixed gas velocity, the gas-pressure drop increases with increased liquid rate, owing principally to the reduced free cross section available for the flow of gas resulting from irrigation by the liquid.  At moderate gas rates, the curve for each rate of liquid flow is nearly parallel to that for dry packing, but two changes of slope occur at higher gas rates.  The lower break in each curve, as at point $A$ (Fig. 6.25), which may not always be distinct, represents conditions known as the "initial load point," or simply "loading."  The appearance of the irrigated packing when observed in transparent glass towers is not greatly changed at loading, and the condition is more easily characterized by the greater rise in pressure drop with increased gas flow than by any other criterion. As the gas rate is increased beyond the first break in the curve, the liquid holdup (i.e., the quantity of liquid contained by the packed bed) increases at first slowly, suddenly more rapidly, and one of a number of visible changes occurs: (1) a layer of liquid, through which the gas bubbles, may appear at the top of the packing, (2) liquid may fill the tower, starting at the bottom, so that there is a change from the gas-continuous liquid-dispersed condition to one of liquid-continuous gas-dispersed, or (3) slugs of foam may rise rapidly upward through the packing. At the same time, entrainment of drops of liquid by the gas leaving the packing at the top increases rapidly, and the tower is said to be "flooded." The diverse

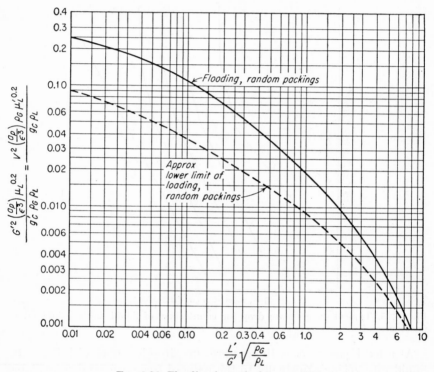

FIG. 6.26. Flooding in packed towers.[15,22]

phenomena observed under different circumstances may be the result of differences in physical properties of the fluids, free void space in the packing, and restrictions in the packing support. The pressure-drop curves (Fig. 6.25) show a second higher break (point $B$), usually at a slightly greater gas rate, and it is more satisfactory to use this as an indication of the flooded condition because of its greater reproducibility. For each liquid rate, there is a gas rate at which flooding occurs, higher for low liquid rates, and vice versa.

It is not practical to operate a packed tower in a flooded condition, and because of the high pressure drop and greater sensitivity of pressure drop to flow rates it is usually considered desirable to provide sufficient tower cross section to produce rates of flow below the loading point. Loading, however, is the more difficult condition to define, and it has therefore become the practice to design for gas velocities 40 to 70 per cent of those which cause flooding; this will ordinarily ensure a condition below loading.

*Flooding.* Flooding velocities in random packings are well correlated by the upper curve of Fig. 6.26,[15,22] which represents measurements made with 15 different liquids and 3 gases on a variety of packings, including Raschig rings, saddle packings, spheres, wire helices, and ribbed rings. It has been firmly established that accurate values of the group $a_p/\epsilon^3$ are

TABLE 6.2. TOWER-PACKING CHARACTERISTICS
For use in the absence of experimental data

| Nominal size, in. | Stoneware Raschig rings | | | Carbon Raschig rings | | | Berl saddles | | | Intalox saddles | |
|---|---|---|---|---|---|---|---|---|---|---|---|
| | $\epsilon$ | $a_p/\epsilon^3$† | | $\epsilon$ | $a_p/\epsilon^3$ | | $\epsilon$ | $a_p/\epsilon^3$ | | $\epsilon$ | $a_p/\epsilon^3$ |
| | | Dry-packed | Wet-packed‡ | | Dry-packed | Wet-packed | | Dry-packed | Wet-packed | | |
| ¼ | ..... | 768 | 719 | ..... | 2,770 | 1,869 | ..... | 4,225 | | | |
| ⅜ | ..... | 494 | 566 | | | | | | | | |
| ½ | 0.568 | 570 | 547 | 0.707 | 373 | 357 | ..... | 574 | 481 | | |
| ⅝ | ..... | 282 | 281 | | | | | | | | |
| ¾ | 0.742 | 199 | 218 | ..... | 336 | 329 | 0.71 | 190 | | | |
| 1 | 0.685 | 159 | 164 | 0.745 | 170 | 169 | 0.764 | 229 | 208 | 0.74§ | 100§ |
| 1¼ | ..... | 83.7 | 92.2 | | | | | | | | |
| 1½ | 0.711 | 108.4 | 115.5 | 0.67 | 92.3 | 98.7 | 0.76 | 79 | ... | 0.80§ | 52§ |
| 2 | 0.734 | 46.3 | 50.2 | 0.73 | 55.9 | 56.8 | | | | | |

† $a_p/\epsilon^3$ from Lobo *et al.*[15]
‡ "Wet-packed" = av. of "wet-shaken" and "wet-unshaken."
§ Value from Leva.[14]

essential to the correlation. The number of packing pieces per unit packed volume will vary considerably depending upon whether the tower is packed dry or whether the packing is allowed to settle through water. Settling of the packing after installation owing to the flow of the liquid and gas may occur, and the fraction voids and surface area may be influenced considerably. In using the correlation, it is therefore essential that these quantities be known for the conditions prevailing. In the absence of experimental data which are preferable, Table 6.2 may be used as a guide.

Flooding velocities for regular or stacked packings will generally be considerably greater than those for random packing.

**Illustration 3.** Fifteen thousand cubic feet per hour of a gas containing 15% sulfur dioxide, 6% oxygen, 79% nitrogen is to be scrubbed countercurrently in a packed tower with 20,000 lb./hr. of water to remove substantially all the sulfur dioxide. The temperature is 70°F., and the pressure 1 atm. One-inch stoneware Raschig rings, packed by dumping into water, will be used. Specify the diameter of tower required.

*Solution.* The largest quantities of gas and liquid will be at the bottom of the tower, and these will be used for design (entering gas and leaving liquid).

$$\text{Gas entering} = 15,000(^{492}\!/_{530})(^1\!/_{359}) = 38.8 \text{ lb. moles/hr.}$$
$$\text{Av. mol. wt. gas} = 0.15(64) + 0.06(32) + 0.79(28)$$
$$= 33.6 \text{ lb./lb. mole}$$
$$\text{Gas entering} = 38.8(33.6) = 1,303 \text{ lb./hr.}$$
$$\rho_G = \frac{1,303}{15,000} = 0.0869 \text{ lb./cu. ft.}$$

Assuming complete absorption, sulfur dioxide, $SO_2$, absorbed $= 38.8(0.15)64 = 373$ lb./hr. Liquid leaving $= 20,000 + 373 = 20,373$ lb./hr.

The solution leaving is sufficiently dilute so that its properties may be taken as those of water: $\rho_L = 62.3$ lb./cu. ft., $\mu_L' = 0.982$ centipoise.

$$\frac{L'}{G'}\left(\frac{\rho_G}{\rho_L}\right)^{0.5} = \frac{20,373}{1,303}\left(\frac{0.0869}{62.3}\right)^{0.5} = 0.583$$

Fig. 6.26: At flooding,    $\dfrac{G'^2(a_p/\epsilon^3)\mu_L'^{0.2}}{g_c\rho_G\rho_L} = 0.032$

From Table 6.2, for 1-in. stoneware Raschig rings, $a_p/\epsilon^3 = 164$.

$$\frac{G'^2(164)(0.982)^{0.2}}{4.17(10^8)(0.0869)(62.3)} = 0.032$$
$$G' \text{ at flooding} = 665 \text{ lb./(hr.)(sq. ft.)}$$

Use $G' = 0.5(665) = 338$ lb./(hr.)(sq. ft.). (This provides a value of the ordinate on Fig. 6.26 below the line for loading.)

$$\text{Tower cross section} = 1,303/338 = 3.86 \text{ sq. ft.}$$
$$\text{Tower diam.} = [(4/\pi)(3.86)]^{0.5} = 2.2 \text{ ft.}$$

*Pressure Drop in Dry Packing.* The pressure drop suffered by the gas in flowing through a bed of packed solids is the result of viscous-energy losses and kinetic-energy losses. Ergun,[11] by considering both sources of energy loss, has successfully correlated the pressure drop for any single fluid flowing through a packed bed, including the flow of gases through dry, random packing of the type considered here, by the relation

$$\frac{\Delta P}{Z}\frac{g_c'\epsilon^3 d_p\rho_G}{(1-\epsilon)G'^2} = \frac{150(1-\epsilon)}{\text{Re}} + 1.75 \tag{6.26}$$

The first term on the right represents the fractional viscous-energy loss, the second the fractional kinetic-energy loss. Ordinarily the former is relatively small, the latter large. $\text{Re} = d_pG'/\mu_G$, and $d_p$ is the effective diameter of the particles, the diameter of a sphere of the same surface/-

volume ratio as the packing. If the packing surface is $a_p$ sq. ft./cu. ft., the surface per unit volume of the particles is then $a_p/(1 - \epsilon)$ and, from the properties of a sphere,

$$d_p = \frac{6(1 - \epsilon)}{a_p} \qquad (6.27)$$

The pressure drop is very sensitive to values of $a_p$ and $\epsilon$, both of which may vary considerably for a given packing with the method of installation, as previously indicated. Reliable experimental values for the existing conditions are always preferred, but in the complete absence of data Table 6.2 provides some typical values.

**Illustration 4.** Estimate the pressure drop to be expected for air flowing through dry ½-in. stoneware Raschig rings at a superficial mass velocity of 1,000 lb./(hr.)(sq. ft.), at 75°F. and 1 atm. total pressure.

*Solution.* At 75°F., 1 atm., the density of air $= \rho_G = 0.0745$ lb./cu. ft., and the viscosity is 0.018 centipoise. $\mu_G = 0.018(2.42) = 0.0435$ lb./(ft.)(hr.). In the absence of more specific information, the packing characteristics will be taken from Table 6.2: $\epsilon = 0.568$, $a_p/\epsilon^3 = 547$, $a_p = 547(0.568)^3 = 100$ sq. ft./cu. ft. $G' = 1,000$ lb./(hr.)(sq. ft.).

Eq. (6.27): $\qquad d_p = 6(1 - 0.568)/100 = 0.0259$ ft.

$\qquad\qquad\qquad$ Re $= d_p G'/\mu_G = 0.0259(1,000)/0.0435 = 595$

Eq. (6.26): $\dfrac{\Delta P}{Z} \dfrac{4.17(10^8)(0.568)^3(0.0259)(0.0745)}{(1 - 0.568)(1,000)^2} = \dfrac{150(1 - 0.568)}{595} + 1.75$

$\qquad\qquad \dfrac{\Delta P}{Z} = 5.47$ lb./(sq. ft.)(ft. packed depth)

[NOTE: Observed values are 5.9, Sarchet, *Trans. Am. Inst. Chem. Engrs.*, **38**, 283 (1942); 7.8, Schoenborn and Dougherty, *ibid.*, **40**, 51 (1944). The differences are very probably the result of differences in packing density.]

*Pressure Drop in Irrigated Packing.* For simultaneous countercurrent flow of liquids and gas, the pressure-drop data of various investigators show wide discrepancies, sometimes as much as 60 per cent for the same type of packing and rates of flow, presumably owing to differences in packing density. Most of the data available were taken with air and water as the fluids, and the effects of liquid properties are not well established. Liquids of high viscosity cause greater gas-pressure drop at equal mass-flow rates than liquids of low viscosity, but the data are too scanty to permit thorough evaluation.

Leva[14] has shown that an empirical relation of the following type applies reasonably well *below the loading point:*

$$\frac{\Delta P}{Z} = m(10^{-8})(10^{nL'/\rho_L}) \frac{G'^2}{\rho_G} \qquad (6.28)$$

Considering the variations in the existing data, nothing more elaborate seems warranted at this time. Leva's values of the constants have been adjusted for the units used in Eq. (6.28), and these and others for a few additional packings are listed in Table 6.3.   They should not be used for towers packed with particles of diameter greater than one-eighth that of the tower, nor for liquid rates outside the range indicated, nor for $\Delta P/Z$ beyond that at the loading point.   At the loading point, $\Delta P/Z$ for random packings is of the order of 2.6 lb./(sq. ft.)(ft. packed depth), while at flooding it is in the range 10 to 15 lb./(sq. ft.)(ft.).   Values for regular or stacked packings may be very different from this.

TABLE 6.3. PRESSURE-DROP CONSTANTS FOR TOWER PACKING

| Packing | Nominal size, in. | $m$ | $n$ | Range of $L'$, lb./(hr.)(sq. ft.) | Range of $\Delta P/Z$, lb./(sq. ft.)(ft.) |
|---|---|---|---|---|---|
| Raschig rings .. | ½ | 139 | 0.00720 | 300– 8,600 | 0–2.6 |
|  | ¾ | 32.9 | 0.00450 | 1,800–10,800 | 0–2.6 |
|  | 1 | 32.1 | 0.00434 | 360–27,000 | 0–2.6 |
|  | 1½ | 12.08 | 0.00398 | 720–18,000 | 0–2.6 |
|  | 2 | 11.13 | 0.00295 | 720–21,600 | 0–2.6 |
| Berl saddles.... | ½ | 60.4 | 0.00340 | 300–14,100 | 0–2.6 |
|  | ¾ | 24.1 | 0.00295 | 360–14,400 | 0–2.6 |
|  | 1 | 16.01 | 0.00295 | 720–28,800 | 0–2.6 |
|  | 1½ | 8.01 | 0.00225 | 720–21,600 | 0–2.6 |
| Intalox saddles. | 1 | 12.44 | 0.00277 | 2,520–14,400 | 0–2.6 |
|  | 1½ | 5.66 | 0.00225 | 2,520–14,400 | 0–2.6 |
| Drip-point grid tiles | No. 6146: |  |  |  |  |
|  | Continuous flue | 1.045 | 0.00214 | 3,000–17,000 | 0–0.5 |
|  | Cross flue | 1.218 | 0.00227 | 300–17,500 | 0–0.5 |
|  | No. 6295: |  |  |  |  |
|  | Continuous flue | 1.088 | 0.00224 | 850–12,500 | 0–0.5 |
|  | Cross flue | 1.435 | 0.00167 | 900–12,500 | 0–0.5 |

**Illustration 5.**   Air at 75°F. is to be blown at the rate of 200 lb./hr. upward through a 12-in.-diam. tower packed to a depth of 10 ft. with 1-in. Berl saddles.   The gas is to discharge at 1 atm. pressure.   The packing is irrigated with 12,000 lb./hr. of water flowing countercurrent to the air.   Estimate the power required to overcome the gas-pressure drop in the packing.

*Solution.*   The pressure drop will be small, so that the density of air at the exit conditions will suffice.   $\rho_G = 0.0745$ lb./cu. ft., $\rho_L = 62.3$ lb./cu. ft.   Cross-section area of tower $= \pi(1)^2/4 = 0.785$ sq. ft.   $G' = 200/0.785 = 255$ lb./(hr.)(sq. ft.).   $L' = 12,000/0.785 = 15,300$ lb./(hr.)(sq. ft.).   From Table 6.3, $m = 16.01$, $n = 0.00295$.

Eq. (6.28):   $$\frac{\Delta P}{Z} = 16.01(10^{-8})(10^{0.00295(15,300)/62.3})\frac{255^2}{0.0745} = 0.742 \text{ lb./(sq. ft.)(ft.)}$$

$$\Delta P = 10(0.742) = 7.42 \text{ lb./sq. ft.}$$

Pressure at gas inlet $= 1 + 7.42/14.7(144) = 1.0035$ atm., and inlet density of air $= 0.0746$ lb./cu. ft.

Power output of blower, for packing pressure drop only,

$$7.42 \frac{200}{0.0746} \frac{1}{3,600} = 5.53 \text{ ft.-lb./sec., or } 0.01 \text{ hp.}$$

## PACKED TOWERS VS. PLATE TOWERS

While a number of equipment types are useful for countercurrent continuous contact of gas and liquid, the great majority of industrial installations are either of the bubble-cap-tray or packed-tower type, since these devices have proved to be reliable and effective. Each has its special field of usefulness.

Packed towers will generally show smaller pressure drops than tray types and are consequently particularly useful for vacuum operations. At least up to moderate diameters, they can be made for service with corrosive fluids more cheaply. Except for very open packings, such as the wood-grid types used for cooling towers, packings are not useful when suspended solids are present in the fluid streams owing to clogging and the impracticability of cleaning the fouled packing. Packed towers are not generally favored for large diameters owing to the difficulty of redistribution of the liquid at frequent intervals and to the higher cost in the larger sizes.

Plate towers, on the other hand, can handle wide variations in liquid- and gas-flow rates; permit easy withdrawal of intermediate gas or liquid streams, installation of cooling coils, cleaning through manholes or handholes; are relatively free from liquid- and gas-distribution difficulties; but show relatively high pressure drops. In the larger sizes they are more economical than packed towers.

## NOTATION FOR CHAPTER 6

$a_p$ = specific surface of dry packing, **sq. ft./cu. ft.**

$A_d$ = minimum area for flow in or out **of a downspout**, sq. ft.

$A_s$ = area of slots or perforations, sq. ft. per tray

$b$ = slot width, in.

$c$ = slot height, in.

$C_D$ = liquid-gradient constant [Eqs. (6.17), (6.19)]

$d$ = tower diameter, ft.

$d_p$ = diameter of a sphere whose surface/volume ratio is the same as that of a packing particle, ft.

$f$ = height of clear space from top of liquid in downspout to top of weir, in.

$g_c$ = 32.2 lb. mass (ft.)/(lb. force)(sec.)$^2$

$g_c'$ = 4.17 ($10^8$) lb. mass (ft.)/(lb. force) **(hr.)$^2$**

$G'$ = superficial mass velocity of gas (based on empty tower cross section), lb./(hr.)(sq. ft.)

$h$ = pressure drop for the gas, expressed as head of liquid on a tray, in. liquid

$h_c$ = gas-pressure drop through riser, reversal area, and annulus under a bubble cap, in. liquid

$h_p$ = gas-pressure drop for flow through a dry perforation, in. liquid

$(h_p)_{min}$ = minimum value of $h_p$ to prevent weeping of liquid through perforation, in. liquid

$h_s = h_1 + h_2$, in. liquid

$h_{slot}$ = depression of liquid inside cap below top of slot, in.

$h_w$ = height of weir above tray floor, in.

$h_1$ = head on a weir; height of liquid surface over the weir, in.

$h_2$ = static submergence; vertical distance, top of slot to top of weir, in.

$h_3 = h_c + h_{slot}$, in.

$h_4$ = pressure drop due to flow of liquid through downspout constriction, in. liquid

$h_5$ = height of liquid in downspout above weir crest, in.

$k_w$ = correction for weir approach velocity [Eq. (6.4)]

$K$ = tray-spacing constant [Eq. (6.1)]

$l_1$ = average total free distance between caps in a direction perpendicular to the liquid flow, in.

$l_2$ = average total free distance between risers in a direction perpendicular to the liquid flow, in.

$L'$ = superficial mass velocity of liquid (based on empty-tower cross section), lb./(hr.)(sq. ft.)

$\Delta P$ = pressure drop, lb./sq. ft.

$q$ = volumetric liquid rate, cu. ft./sec.

$Q$ = volumetric gas rate, cu. ft./sec.

$Q_s$ = volumetric gas rate through a slot, cu. ft./sec. per slot

$r$ = number of rows of caps, perpendicular to direction of liquid flow

Re = Reynolds number for a particle, based on superficial gas velocity = $d_p G'/\mu_G$, dimensionless

$s$ = skirt clearance, vertical distance between bottom of cap and tray floor, in.

$t$ = tray spacing or distance between trays, in.

$V$ = superficial linear gas velocity (based on empty-tower cross section), ft./sec.

$V_m$ = maximum linear gas velocity in the riser, reversal area, or annulus under a cap, ft./sec.

$W$ = length of weir (actual), ft.

$W_{eff}$ = effective weir length, ft.

$x, y, z$ = quantities defined by Eqs. (6.15) to (6.19) for hydraulic gradient

$Z$ = height of packing, ft.

$\alpha, \beta$ = quantities defined by Eqs. (6.8), (6.9), (6.12), (6.13) for slot pressure drop

$\Delta$ = hydraulic gradient for entire tray, in. liquid

$\Delta'$ = hydraulic gradient for $V\rho_G^{0.5} = 1.1$, in. liquid

$\epsilon$ = fraction voids in a packed bed, dimensionless

$\mu_G$ = gas viscosity, lb./(ft.)(hr.)

$\mu_L'$ = liquid viscosity, centipoises

$\rho_G$ = gas density, lb./cu. ft.

$\rho_L$ = liquid density, lb./cu. ft.

$\sigma$ = surface tension, dynes/cm.

## REFERENCES

1. Arnold, D. S., C. A. Plank, and E. M. Schoenborn: *Chem. Eng. Progr.*, **48**, 633 (1952).
2. Baker, T., T. H. Chilton, and H. C. Vernon: *Trans. Am. Inst. Chem. Engrs.*, **31**, 296 (1935).
3. Barnes, K. B.: *Oil Gas J.*, **51**(19), 72 (1952).
4. Bragg, L. B.: *Trans. Am. Inst. Chem. Engrs.*, **37**, 21 (1941).
5. Carey, J. S.: In J. H. Perry, ed., "Chemical Engineers' Handbook," 3d ed., p. 598, McGraw-Hill Book Company, Inc., New York, 1950.
6. Cicalese, J. J., J. A. Davies, P. J. Harrington, G. S. Houghland, A. J. L. Hutchinson, and T. J. Walsh: *Proc. Am. Petroleum Inst.*, **26**, sec. III, 180 (1946).
7. Cross, C. A., and H. Ryder: *J. Appl. Chem.*, **2**, 51 (1952).
8. Davies, J. A.: *Ind. Eng. Chem.*, **39**, 774 (1947).
9. ———: *Petroleum Refiner*, **29**(8), 93, (9), 121 (1950).
10. Edmister, W. C.: *Petroleum Engr.*, 1948, no. 12, p. 193.
11. Ergun, S.: *Chem. Eng. Progr.*, **48**, 89 (1952).
12. Hull, W. Q.: *Ind. Eng. Chem.*, **44**(9), 13A (1952).
13. Kemp, H. S., and C. Pyle: *Chem. Eng. Progr.*, **45**, 435 (1949).
14. Leva, M.: *Chem. Eng. Progr. Symposium Ser.*, **50**(10), 51 (1954).
15. Lobo, W. E., L. Friend, F. Hashmall, and F. Zenz: *Trans. Am. Inst. Chem. Engrs.*, **41**, 693 (1945).
16. McMahon, H. O.: *Ind. Eng. Chem.*, **39**, 712 (1947).
17. Mayfield, F. D., W. L. Church, A. C. Green, D. C. Lee, and R. W. Rassmussen: *Ind. Eng. Chem.*, **44**, 2238 (1952).
18. Perry, J. H., ed.: "Chemical Engineers' Handbook," 3d ed., p. 409, McGraw-Hill Book Company, Inc., New York, 1950.
19. Pratt, H. R. C.: *Ind. Chemist*, **26**, 291, 470 (1950); **27**, 3, 51, 152 (1951).
20. Robinson, C. S., and E. R. Gilliland: "Elements of Fractional Distillation," 4th ed., McGraw-Hill Book Company, Inc., New York, 1950.
21. Scofield, R. C.: *Chem. Eng. Progr.*, **46**, 405 (1950).
22. Sherwood, T. K., G. H. Shipley, and F. A. L. Holloway: *Ind. Eng. Chem.*, **30**, 765 (1938).
23. Staff, Shell Development Co.: *Chem. Eng. Progr.*, **50**, 57 (1954).
24. Williams, G. C., R. B. Akell, and C. P. Talbott: *Chem. Eng. Progr.*, **43**, 585 (1947).

## PROBLEMS

**1.** For the finished design of Illustration 1, compute the maximum capacity of the tray as follows:

*a.* Maximum liquid flow at constant gas rate
*b.* Maximum gas flow at constant liquid rate
*c.* Maximum total flow at constant liquid/gas ratio

**2.** A gas containing methane, propane, and butane is to be scrubbed countercurrently in a bubble-tray tower with a hydrocarbon oil to absorb the propane and butane. It is agreed to design the trays for the circumstances existing at the bottom of the tower, where the conditions are:

Pressure = 50 lb./sq. in. abs.
Temp. = 100°F.

Gas, 1,750 lb. moles/hr., containing 85% methane, 10% propane, and 5% butane by volume

Liquid, 1,800 lb. moles/hr., av. mol. wt. = 150, density = 53.0 lb./cu. ft., surface tension = 25 dynes/cm., viscosity = 1.60 centipoises

The bubble caps to be used are of the same general design as those in Fig. 6.16, but the dimensions are as follows: O.D. = 6.0 in., metal thickness 0.125 in., height 4.0 in. There are 40 slots per cap, each 0.25 in. wide by 1.5 in. high, cut to the cap skirt as in Fig. 6.16.

The liquid/gas flow ratio is high for this absorber, so that care must be taken to determine whether the gas flow or liquid flow controls the tower diameter. The special conditions described below are suggested in order to keep the liquid gradient low. For each design, check stability, pressure drop, and flooding.

*a.* Design a crossflow tray, using a square-pitch arrangement for the caps.

*b.* Design a pair of split-flow trays, using a triangular-pitch cap arrangement.

**3.** A bubble-cap tray tower is to be designed for stripping carbon dioxide, $CO_2$, from an aqueous ethanolamine solution with steam. The conditions for design may be taken as follows:

Temp. = 230°F.
Pressure = 5 lb./sq. in. gauge
Liquid = 600 gal./min., density = 60 lb./cu. ft.
Gas = 25 lb. moles/min., containing 85 mole % steam, 15 mole % $CO_2$

The tower will require 12 trays. It will be constructed of a medium chrome steel (sp. gr. 7.7), trays and bubble caps of gauge metal, shell and heads $\frac{1}{4}$ in. thick. Completed trays will weigh 20 lb./sq. ft. (0 to 4 ft. diam.), 22 lb./sq. ft. (4 to 8 ft. diam.), 26 lb./sq. ft. (8 to 12 ft. diam.) and will cost $0.70 per pound. The shell and heads will cost $0.40 per pound, which may be assumed to include the cost of nozzles, manholes, etc., when computed simply as a shell. The foundation will be assumed not to vary in cost with diameter. Regardless of diameter and general tray spacing, the space above the top tray will be kept at not less than 3 ft., that below the bottom tray at 6 ft. It is agreed to design for a 1-in. liquid seal, for tray spacings not less than 12 in., and for liquid-flow rates not over 0.22 cu. ft./(sec.)(ft. diameter).

Calculate the diameter and tray spacing for the tower which will have the smallest initial cost.

**4.** A packed tower is to be designed for the countercurrent contact of a benzene-nitrogen gas mixture with kerosene to wash out the benzene from the gas. The circumstances are:

Gas in = 20 cu. ft./sec., containing 5 mole % benzene, 800 mm. Hg abs., 75°F.
Gas out = substantially pure nitrogen
Liquid in = 3.0 lb./sec., benzene-free. Sp. gr. = 0.80, viscosity = 2.3 centipoises

The packing will be 1-in. carbon Raschig rings, and the gas velocity is to be 50% of the flooding value.

*a.* Calculate the diameter of the tower to be used.

*b.* Assume that, for the diameter chosen, the irrigated packed depth will be 20 ft. and that 3 ft. of unirrigated packing will be placed above the liquid inlet to act as an entrainment separator. The blower-motor combination used at the gas inlet will have an over-all efficiency of 60%. Calculate the power required to blow the gas through the packing.

# CHAPTER 7

# HUMIDIFICATION OPERATIONS

The operations considered in this chapter are concerned with the interphase transfer of mass and of energy which result when a gas is brought into contact with a pure liquid in which it is essentially insoluble. While the term "humidification operations" is used to characterize these in a general fashion, the purpose of such operations may include not only humidification of the gas but dehumidification and cooling of the gas, measurement of its vapor content, and cooling of the liquid as well. The matter transferred between phases in such cases is the substance comprising the liquid phase, which either vaporizes or condenses. As in all mass-transfer problems, it is necessary for a complete understanding of the operation to be familiar with the equilibrium characteristics of the systems. But since the mass transfer in these cases will invariably be accompanied by a simultaneous transfer of heat energy as well, some consideration must also be given to the enthalpy characteristics of the systems.

## VAPOR-LIQUID EQUILIBRIUM AND ENTHALPY FOR A PURE SUBSTANCE

As indicated above, the substance undergoing interphase transfer in these operations is the material comprising the liquid phase, which diffuses in the form of a vapor. The equilibrium vapor-pressure characteristics of the liquid are therefore of importance.

**Vapor-pressure Curve.** Every liquid exerts an equilibrium pressure, the vapor pressure, to an extent depending upon the temperature. When the vapor pressures of a liquid are plotted against the corresponding temperatures, a curve such as $TBDC$ (Fig. 7.1) results. The vapor-pressure curve for each substance is unique, but each exhibits characteristics generally similar to that in the figure. The curve separates two areas of the plot, representing, respectively, conditions where the substance exists wholly in the liquid state and wholly in the vapor state. If the conditions imposed upon the substance are in the liquid-state area, such as at point $A$, the substance will be entirely liquid. Under all conditions in the lower area, such as those at point $E$, the substance is entirely a vapor. At all conditions corresponding to points on the curve $TBDC$, however, liquid and vapor may coexist in any proportions indefinitely. The vapor-pressure curve has two abrupt end points, at $T$ and $C$. Point $T$, from which originate curves $LT$ and $ST$, which separate the conditions for the solid state from those for the liquid and vapor, is the *triple point* at which all three states of aggregation may coexist. Point $C$ is the *critical point*, or *state*, whose coordinates are the *critical pressure* and *critical temperature*. At the critical point, distinction between the liquid and vapor phases disappears, and all the properties of the liquid such as density, viscosity, refractive index, etc., are identical with those of the

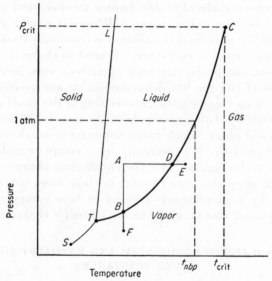

FIG. 7.1. Vapor pressure of a pure liquid.

vapor. The substance at a temperature above the critical is called a *gas*, and it will then not be liquefied regardless of how high a pressure may be imposed. This distinction between a gas and a vapor is, however, not always strictly adhered to, and the term gas is frequently used to designate merely a condition relatively far removed from the vapor-pressure curve. The temperature corresponding to each pressure on the curve is termed the boiling point of the liquid at the pressure in question, and that corresponding to 1 atm. in particular is known as the *normal boiling point*, as at $t_{nbp}$ on Fig. 7.1.

Imagine a portion of the substance contained in a cylinder fitted with a frictionless piston, so that the pressure on the substance may be varied at will by placing weights upon the piston, as in Fig. 7.2. If the pressure and temperature correspond to point $A$ (Fig. 7.1), the substance will be entirely a liquid as in Fig. 7.2a, with no vapor space underneath the piston whatsoever. Suppose heat is now added to the substance, keeping the weights on the piston and consequently the pressure unchanged, and allowing the piston to rise as the volume of the substance increases. The path of such a process on Fig. 7.1 is given by the line $ADE$. Addition of heat to the liquid at $A$ raises its temperature, but so long as the temperature is less than that at $D$, the substance remains entirely liquid. Such heat is called *sensible heat*, since it brings about a change which can be detected by the sense of touch, i.e., a temperature rise. Heat added

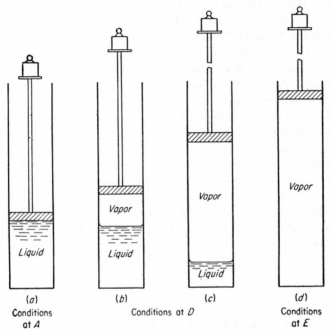

(a)                (b)                (c)                (d)
Conditions      Conditions at $D$                  Conditions
at $A$                                                  at $E$

Fig. 7.2. Vaporization of a pure liquid.

to the liquid at $D$, however, converts it to the vapor state without change of temperature, giving rise to situations such as those shown in Fig. 7.2b and c. As more heat is added, more of the liquid is converted to vapor and the conditions of both liquid and vapor and indeed the entire cylinder contents correspond all the while to point $D$ (Fig. 7.1). Liquid and vapor thus represented by points on the equilibrium curve are called *saturated liquid* and *saturated vapor*, respectively. Eventually all the liquid is converted isothermally to saturated vapor, and the heat required for the conversion is the *latent heat of vaporization*. Further addition of heat now raises the temperature of the vapor (sensible heat), and the path of the process continues on Fig. 7.1 from $D$ toward $E$, corresponding to conditions shown in Fig. 7.2d. Such vapor at a temperature higher than that corresponding to the vapor pressure is termed *superheated*.

Complete reversal of the process, by removal of heat at constant pressure from the superheated vapor at $E$, will eventually bring the conditions back to those at $A$, with the reappearance of all the phenomena described in reverse order. Similar changes in phase may also be observed by carrying out the isothermal process following path $ABF$ on Fig. 7.1 by reducing the pressure. At $B$, both saturated liquid and vapor will be present in the cylinder until complete conversion at constant pressure occurs. Whenever a path is followed which crosses the equilibrium curve, a change of phase will result which will manifest itself by the appearance of an interface separating the less dense vapor from the more dense liquid.

**Interpolation between Data.** For the common liquids such as water, the ordinary refrigerants such as ammonia, and others, the vapor pressure–temperature coordinates of the equilibrium curve have been carefully established at many points. For most liquids, however, relatively few points have been measured, and it therefore frequently becomes necessary to interpolate between the measured data, or even to extrapolate the curve into regions where it is not known. On rectangular coordinates, the curvature of the vapor-pressure curve is such that it is exceedingly difficult to carry out either of these with precision. On the other hand, if coordinate scales can be devised so that the vapor-pressure curve is straight or nearly so, then interpolation and extrapolation with a minimum of data become simple. Most of the common methods are based upon consideration of the Clausius-Clapeyron equation, which relates the slope of the vapor-pressure curve to the latent heat of vaporization,

$$\frac{dP}{dT} = \frac{\lambda'}{T(v_G - v_L)} \tag{7.1}$$

where $v_G$ and $v_L$ are the molal specific volumes of saturated vapor and liquid, respectively, and $\lambda'$ is the molal latent heat of vaporization in units consistent with the rest of the equation. The equation is frequently put in a form which is readily integrable by neglecting $v_L$ in comparison with $v_G$ and expressing the latter in terms of the ideal-gas law,

$$d \ln P = \frac{dP}{P} = \frac{\lambda' \, dT}{RT^2} \tag{7.2}$$

On the assumption that $\lambda'$ is constant over modest temperature ranges, on integration between conditions 1 and 2 this becomes

$$\ln P_2 - \ln P_1 = \frac{\lambda'}{R}\left(\frac{1}{T_1} - \frac{1}{T_2}\right) \tag{7.3}$$

Equation (7.3) has been used for calculating the vapor pressure $P_2$ at temperature $T_2$ provided $P_1$ and $T_1$ and $\lambda'$ are known. Practically, the assumptions of the validity of the ideal-gas law for a saturated vapor and the constancy of $\lambda'$ make this calculation generally very approximate. It does suggest, however, that a plot of vapor-pressure data as $\log P$ against $1/T$ will be nearly straight, thus simplifying interpolation and extrapolation over short temperature ranges. Such plots will not be straight over very considerable temperature ranges, however. The equation is useful as a guide in interpolating between data points listed in tables of vapor pressures where it is not desired to plot a curve.

**Illustration 1.** A table lists the vapor pressure of benzene to be 100 mm. Hg at 26.1°C. and 400 mm. Hg at 60.6°C. At what temperature is the vapor pressure 200 mm. Hg?

*Solution.* At 26.1°C., $1/T = 1/299.1$ reciprocal °K.; at 60.6°C., $1/T = 1/333.6$.

$$\frac{1/299.1 - 1/T}{1/299.1 - 1/333.6} = \frac{\log 100 - \log 200}{\log 100 - \log 400}$$

$$T = 315.4°K., \text{ corresponding to } 42.4°C.$$

The correct value is 42.2°C. Linear interpolation would have given 34.7°C.

**Reference-substance Plots.** Equation (7.2) may be rewritten for a second substance, called a *reference substance*, at the same temperature,

$$d \ln P_r = \frac{\lambda_r' \, dT}{RT^2} \tag{7.4}$$

where $P_r$ is the vapor pressure of the reference substance and $\lambda_r'$ its molal latent heat. Dividing Eq. (7.2) by Eq. (7.4), there is obtained

$$\frac{d \ln P}{d \ln P_r} = \frac{\lambda'}{\lambda_r'} = \frac{\lambda M}{\lambda_r M_r} \tag{7.5}$$

which gives, on integration,

$$\log P = \frac{\lambda M}{\lambda_r M_r} \log P_r + \text{const.} \tag{7.6}$$

Equation (7.6) suggests that a linear plot will result if $\log P$ as ordinate is plotted against $\log P_r$ for the reference substance as abscissa, where for each plotted point the vapor pressures of the two substances are taken at the same temperature. Othmer[14] has shown the great utility of this method and has pointed out that such lines of vapor pressure are quite straight over large temperature ranges except near the critical temperature for either substance, owing to the fact that while both $\lambda$ and $\lambda_r$ vary considerably with temperature the ratio is reasonably constant. As reference substance, it is convenient to choose one whose vapor pressure is tabulated in detail, such as water, although frequently more successful results are obtained if chemically similar substances are compared. Logarithmic graph paper avoids the necessity of using logarithms, and the vapor-pressure scale for the reference substance may be marked directly with temperatures after it has been established. The slope of the line is the ratio of the molal latent heats of vaporization at the same temperature. Othmer has extended the principle of this method considerably, and it will be found useful in later chapters for dealing with other properties.

**Illustration 2.** (*a*) Plot the vapor pressure of benzene over the range 15 to 180°C. using water as reference substance according to the method of Othmer. (*b*) Determine the vapor pressure of benzene at 100°C. (*c*) Determine the latent heat of vaporization of benzene at 25°C.

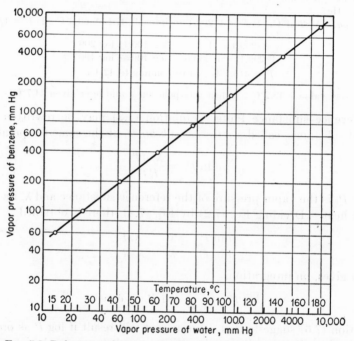

Fig. 7.3. Reference-substance plot for the vapor pressure of benzene.

*Solution.* *a.* Logarithmic graph paper is marked with scales for the vapor pressure of benzene and for water, as in Fig. 7.3. The vapor pressure of benzene at 15.4°C. is 60 mm. Hg, and that for water at this temperature is 13.1 mm. Hg. These pressures provide the coordinates of the lowest point on the plot. In similar fashion, additional data for benzene are plotted with the help of a steam table, thus providing the curve shown. The line is very nearly straight over the temperature range used.

*b.* At 100°C., the vapor pressure of water is 760 mm. Hg. Entering the plot at this value for the abscissa, the vapor pressure of benzene is read as 1,400 mm. Hg. Alternatively the abscissa can be marked with the temperatures corresponding to the vapor pressures of water, as shown, thus eliminating the necessity of referring to the steam table.

*c.* The slope of the curve at 25°C. is 0.775. (NOTE: This is most conveniently determined with a millimeter rule. If the coordinates are used, the slope will be

$\Delta \log P / \Delta \log P_r$.) At 25°C., the latent heat of vaporization of water is 1049.8 B.t.u./lb. From Eq. (7.6),

$$\frac{\lambda M}{\lambda_r M_r} = \frac{\lambda(78.05)}{1,049.8(18.02)} = 0.775$$
$$\lambda = 187.5 \text{ B.t.u./lb.} \qquad \text{for benzene at 25°C.}$$

(The accepted value is 186.5 B.t.u./lb.)

**Enthalpy.** The internal energy $U$ of a substance is the total energy residing in the substance owing to the motion and relative position of the constituent atoms and molecules. Absolute values of internal energy are not known, but numerical values relative to some arbitrarily defined standard state for the substance can be computed. The sum of the internal energy and the product of pressure and volume of the substance, when both quantities are expressed in the same units, is defined as the *enthalpy* of the substance,

$$H = U + (Pv) \tag{7.7}$$

In a batch process at constant pressure, where work is done only in expansion against the pressure, the heat absorbed by the system is the gain in enthalpy,

$$Q = \Delta H = \Delta[U + (Pv)] \tag{7.8}$$

In a steady-state continuous-flow process, the net transfer of energy to the system as heat and work will be the sum of its gains in enthalpy and potential and kinetic energies. It frequently happens that the changes in potential and kinetic energies are insignificant in comparison with the enthalpy change and that there is no mechanical work done. In such cases, Eq. (7.8) can be used to compute the heat added to the system, and such a calculation is termed a *heat balance*. In *adiabatic* operations, where no exchange of heat between the system and its surroundings occurs, the heat balance becomes simply an equality of enthalpies in the initial and final condition.

Absolute values of the enthalpy of a substance, like the internal energy, are not known. However, by arbitrarily setting the enthalpy of a substance at zero when it is in a convenient reference state, relative values of enthalpy at other conditions may be calculated. To define the reference state, the temperature, pressure, and state of aggregation must be established. For the substance water, the ordinary steam tables list the relative enthalpy at various conditions referred to the enthalpy of the substance at 32°F., the equilibrium vapor pressure at this temperature, and in the liquid state. For other substances, other reference conditions may be more convenient.

Figure 7.4 is a graphical representation of the relative enthalpy of a typical substance where the liquid, vapor, and gaseous states are shown.

The data are most conveniently shown on lines of constant pressure. The curves marked "saturated liquid" and "saturated vapor," however, cut across the constant-pressure lines and show the enthalpies for these conditions at temperatures and pressures corresponding to the equilibrium vapor-pressure relationship for the substance. The vertical distance between the saturated-vapor and -liquid curves, such as the distance $BC$,

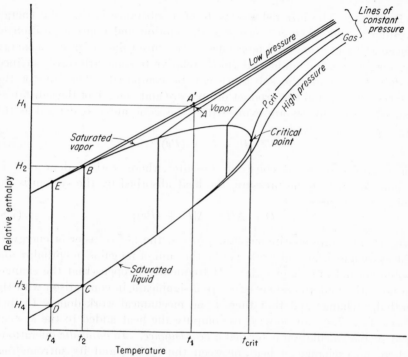

FIG. 7.4. Typical enthalpy-temperature diagram for a pure substance.

represents the latent heat of vaporization at the corresponding temperature. The latent heat thus decreases with increased temperature, becoming zero at the critical point. In the vapor state at low pressures, the enthalpy is essentially a function of temperature; at all pressures where the ideal-gas law may be used to describe the $Pvt$ relation, the lines of constant pressure are superimposed and the enthalpy is independent of pressure. Except near the critical temperature, the enthalpy of the liquid is also substantially independent of pressure until exceedingly high pressures are reached.

The change in enthalpy between two conditions, such as those at $A$ and $D$, may be taken simply as the difference in ordinates corresponding to the points. Thus, to calculate the enthalpy of the substance in the superheated condition at point $A$ relative to the saturated liquid at $D$, or $H_1 - H_4$, we may add the enthalpy change $H_1 - H_2$, the sensible heat of the vapor from the saturation temperature $t_2$ at the same pressure to the superheated condition at $A$; $H_2 - H_3$, the latent heat of vaporization at $t_2$; and $H_3 - H_4$, the sensible heat of the liquid from the final condition at $D$ to the boiling point at the prevailing pressure, $t_2$. For a liquid or vapor, the slope of the constant-pressure lines at any temperature is termed the *heat capacity*. The lines are not strictly straight, so that the heat capacity changes with temperature. By use of an average heat capacity or average slope, however, sensible heats are readily calculated. Thus, referring again to Fig. 7.4,

$$H_1 - H_2 = C(t_1 - t_2) \tag{7.9}$$

where $C$ is the average heat capacity of the vapor at constant pressure over the indicated temperature range.

**Illustration 3.** Compute the heat evolved when 10 lb. of benzene as a superheated vapor at 94 mm. Hg, 100°C., is cooled and condensed to a liquid at 10°C. The average heat capacity for the vapor may be taken as 0.30 and for the liquid 0.36 B.t.u./(lb.) (°F.).

*Solution.* Refer to Fig. 7.3. When the pressure is 94 mm. Hg, the saturation temperature for benzene is 25°C. The latent heat of vaporization at this temperature is 186.5 B.t.u./lb. (Illustration 2). The initial condition corresponds to a point such as $A$ on Fig. 7.4, the final condition to point $D$, the path of the process to $ABCD$. Using the notation of Fig. 7.4,

$$H_1 - H_2 = C(t_1 - t_2) = 0.30(100 - 25)(1.8) = 40.5 \text{ B.t.u./lb.}$$
$$H_2 - H_3 = 186.5 \text{ B.t.u./lb.}$$
$$H_3 - H_4 = C(t_2 - t_4) = 0.36(25 - 10)(1.8) = 9.7 \text{ B.t.u./lb.}$$
$$\therefore H_1 - H_4 = 40.5 + 186.5 + 9.7 = 236.7 \text{ B.t.u./lb.}$$
$$\therefore \text{Heat evolved for 10 lb. benzene} = 10(236.7) = 2367 \text{ B.t.u.}$$

## VAPOR-GAS MIXTURES

In what follows, the term *vapor* will be applied to that substance, designated as substance $A$, in the vaporous state which is relatively near its condensation temperature at the prevailing pressure. The term *gas* will be applied to substance $B$, which is a relatively highly superheated gas.

**Concentration Terms.** In dealing with vapor-gas mixtures, it is necessary to be able to express the concentrations of the two substances in convenient terms. For all conditions where the ideal-gas law may be applied, to which the present discussion is limited, the common concentration terms can easily be interrelated.

1. *Partial Pressure.* This is the pressure which one component of a gaseous mixture would exhibit if it were present alone in a container of the same volume as the mixture, at the same temperature. The sum of

the partial pressures of the vapor $p_A$ and of the gas $p_B$ in a vapor-gas mixture equals the total pressure $P$.

$$p_A + p_B = P \tag{7.10}$$

The fraction of the total pressure due to the presence of component $A$ is then $p_A/P$.

2. *Mole Fraction.* The ratio of the number of moles $n_A$ of a constituent to the total number of moles of mixture $n_A + n_B$ is the mole fraction of component $A$, $y_A$,

$$y_A = \frac{n_A}{n_A + n_B} \tag{7.11}$$

3. *Volume Fraction.* The partial volume of a constituent of a gas mixture is the volume which it would exhibit if it alone were at the temperature and total pressure of the mixture. The volume fraction of the constituent is then the ratio of its partial volume to the total volume of mixture. Inasmuch as the molar volumes of all gases are equal at the same temperature and pressure, it follows that the mole fraction, volume fraction, and pressure fraction for a constituent are all identical.

4. *Absolute Humidity.* The ratio of mass of vapor $w_A$ to the mass of gas $w_B$ in a mixture is the absolute humidity $Y'$. If the quantities of the components are expressed in terms of moles, the ratio is termed the *molal* absolute humidity $Y$.

$$Y = \frac{n_A}{n_B} = \frac{y_A}{y_B} = \frac{p_A}{p_B} = \frac{p_A}{P - p_A} \qquad \frac{\text{moles } A}{\text{moles } B} \tag{7.12}$$

$$Y' = \frac{w_A}{w_B} = Y\frac{M_A}{M_B} = \frac{p_A}{P - p_A}\frac{M_A}{M_B} \qquad \frac{\text{mass } A}{\text{mass } B} \tag{7.13}$$

In many respects the molal ratio is the more convenient, owing to the ease with which moles and volumes may be interrelated through the gas law, for example, but the mass ratio has nevertheless become firmly established in the humidification literature. The mass absolute humidity was first introduced by Grosvenor[6] and is sometimes called the Grosvenor humidity.

5. *Mass of Vapor per Unit Volume of Mixture.* Of the several units of these dimensions possible, the most frequently used quantity is the relatively inconvenient term, grains vapor/cu. ft. mixture. It is related to the more conventional terms through the gas law,

$$\frac{\text{Grains vapor}}{\text{Cu. ft. mixture}} = y_A M_A \frac{7{,}000}{359}\frac{492}{t + 460} P \tag{7.14}$$

where 7,000 is the number of grains per pound, $t$ the temperature in degrees Fahrenheit, $P$ the total pressure in atmospheres, and 359 the molar volume in cu. ft./lb. mole at standard conditions.

**Illustration 4.** In a mixture of benzene vapor $(A)$ and nitrogen gas $(B)$ at a total pressure of 800 mm. Hg and temperature 60°C., the partial pressure of benzene, $p_A$, is 100 mm. Hg. Express the benzene concentration in other terms.

*Solution.* The partial pressure of nitrogen $= p_B = P - p_A = 800 - 100 = 700$ mm. Hg.

*a.* Mole fraction. Since the pressure fraction and mole fraction are identical, $y_A = p_A/P = {}^{100}\!/_{800} = 0.125$ mole fraction benzene. The mole fraction nitrogen $= y_B = 1 - 0.125 = {}^{700}\!/_{800} = 0.875$.

*b.* Volume fraction of benzene equals the mole fraction 0.125.

*c.* Absolute humidity

$$Y = y_A/y_B = p_A/p_B$$
$$= 0.125/0.875 = {}^{100}\!/_{700} = 0.143 \text{ mole benzene/mole nitrogen}$$
$$Y' = Y(M_A/M_B) = 0.143(78.05/28.02) = 0.398 \text{ lb. benzene/lb. nitrogen}$$

*d.* $\dfrac{\text{Grains benzene}}{\text{Cu. ft. mixture}} = 0.125(78.05)\dfrac{7,000}{359}\dfrac{273}{60 + 273}\dfrac{800}{760}$
$$= 164.0$$

**Illustration 5.** A mixture of benzene vapor $(A)$ and nitrogen gas $(B)$ at 10 lb./sq. in. abs. total pressure and 100°F. contains 100 grains benzene/cu. ft. Compute the molal absolute humidity and partial pressure of benzene.

*Solution.* One cubic foot mixture contains 100 grains or $100/7,000(78.05) = 0.0001832$ lb. mole benzene. The total number of moles in 1 cu. ft. mixture is

$$1\dfrac{492}{100 + 460}\dfrac{10}{14.7}\dfrac{1}{359} = 0.001665 \text{ lb. mole}$$

$y_A = 0.0001832/0.001665 = 0.110$ mole fraction benzene
$Y = 0.110/(1 - 0.110) = 0.1237$ mole benzene/mole nitrogen
$p_A = y_A P = YP/(1 + Y)$
$\qquad = 0.110(10) = 0.1237(10)/1.1237 = 1.10$ lb./sq. in. abs.

## Saturated Vapor-gas Mixtures.

If an insoluble dry gas $B$ is brought into contact with sufficient liquid $A$, molecules of the liquid will enter the gas as vapor, thus creating a concentration of the vapor in the gas space. As the concentration of vapor increases, the rate at which vapor molecules return to the liquid and condense also increases, until eventually a dynamic equilibrium is established when the rate of evaporation equals that of condensation, at which time the partial pressure of the vapor in the mixture will be its equilibrium vapor pressure $P_A$ at the prevailing temperature. So long as the gas can be considered insoluble in the liquid, the partial pressure of vapor in the saturated mixture is independent of the nature of the gas and the total pressure and is dependent only upon the temperature and identity of the liquid. However, the saturated molal absolute humidity $Y_s = P_A/(P - p_A)$ will be additionally dependent upon the total pressure and the saturated absolute humidity $Y'_s = Y_s M_A/M_B$ upon the total pressure and identity of the gas. Both saturated-humidity terms become infinite at the boiling point of the liquid at the prevailing total pressure.

**Illustration 6.**  A gas $(B)$–benzene $(A)$ mixture is saturated at 1 atm., 50°C.  Calculate the absolute humidity if $(a)$ $B$ is nitrogen and $(b)$ if $B$ is oxygen.

*Solution.*  Since the mixture is saturated, the partial pressure of benzene $p_A$ equals the equilibrium vapor pressure $P_A$ of benzene at 50°C.  From Fig. 7.3, $P_A = 275$ mm. Hg, or 0.362 atm.

    $a.$  $Y_s = P_A/(P - P_A) = 0.362/(1 - 0.362) = 0.568$ mole benzene/mole nitrogen
        $Y_s' = Y_s M_A/M_B = 0.568(78.05)/28.02 = 1.583$ lb. benzene/lb. nitrogen
    $b.$  $Y_s = P_A/(P - P_A) = 0.362/(1 - 0.362) = 0.568$ mole benzene/mole oxygen
        $Y_s' = Y_s M_A/M_B = 0.568(78.05)/32.00 = 1.387$ lb. benzene/lb. oxygen

**Unsaturated Vapor-gas Mixtures.**  If the partial pressure of the vapor in a vapor-gas mixture is for any reason less than the equilibrium vapor pressure of the liquid at the same temperature, the mixture is unsaturated.

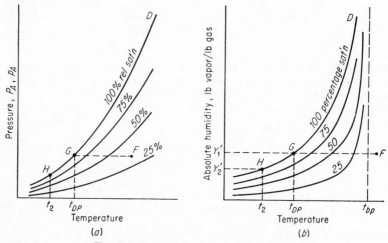

Fig. 7.5. Forms of psychrometric charts.

1. *Dry-bulb Temperature.*  This is the temperature of a vapor-gas mixture as ordinarily determined by immersion of a thermometer in the mixture.

2. *Relative Saturation.*  *Relative saturation,* also called *relative humidity,* expressed as a percentage is defined as $100p_A/P_A$, where $P_A$ is the vapor pressure at the dry-bulb temperature of the mixture.  For any vapor, the graphical representation of conditions of constant relative saturation may be easily constructed on a vapor pressure–temperature chart, as in Fig. 7.5a, by dividing the ordinates of the vapor-pressure curve into appropriate intervals.  Thus the curve for 50 per cent relative saturation shows a vapor partial pressure equal to one-half the equilibrium vapor pressure at any temperature.  A reference-substance plot, such as Fig. 7.3, could also be used for this.

3. *Percentage Saturation.*  *Percentage saturation,* or *percentage absolute humidity,* is defined as $100Y/Y_s$ and $100Y'/Y_s'$, where the saturated values

are computed at the dry-bulb temperature of the mixture. Graphical representation of the quantity for any vapor may be made on a chart of $Y$ vs. $t$ (in which case the chart must be limited to a single total pressure) or one of $Y'$ vs. $t$ (for a single total pressure and a specific gas), as in Fig. 7.5b. On this chart, the saturation humidities are plotted from vapor-pressure data with the help of Eq. (7.13), to give curve $GD$. The curve for humidities at 50 percentage saturation is plotted at half the ordinate of curve $GD$, etc. All the curves of constant percentage saturation reach infinity at the boiling point of the liquid at the prevailing pressure.†

4. *Dew Point.* This is the temperature at which a vapor-gas mixture becomes saturated when cooled at constant total pressure out of contact with a liquid. For example, if an unsaturated mixture such as that at $F$ (Fig. 7.5) is cooled at constant pressure out of contact with liquid, the path of the cooling process follows the line $FG$, the mixture becoming more nearly saturated as the temperature is lowered, and fully saturated at $t_{DP}$, the dew-point temperature. All mixtures of absolute humidity $Y_1'$ on this figure have the same dew point. If the temperature is reduced only an infinitesimal amount below $t_{DP}$, vapor will condense as a liquid dew. This is used as a method of humidity determination: a shiny metal surface is cooled in the presence of the gas mixture, and the appearance of a fog which clouds the mirrorlike surface indicates that the dew point has been reached.

If the mixture is cooled to a lower temperature, the vapor-gas mixture will continue to precipitate liquid, itself always remaining saturated, until at the final temperature $t_2$ (Fig. 7.5) the residual vapor-gas mixture will be at point $H$. The mass of vapor condensed per unit mass of dry gas will be $Y_1' - Y_2'$. Except under specially controlled circumstances supersaturation will not occur, and no vapor-gas mixture whose coordinates lie to the left of curve $GD$ will result.

5. *Humid Volume.* The humid volume $v_H$ of a vapor-gas mixture is the volume in cubic feet of 1 lb. of dry gas and its accompanying vapor at the prevailing temperature and pressure. For a mixture of absolute humidity $Y'$ at $t°F$. and $P$ atm., the ideal-gas law gives the humid volume as

$$v_H = \left(\frac{1}{M_B} + \frac{Y'}{M_A}\right) 359 \frac{t + 460}{492} \frac{1}{P} = 0.730 \left(\frac{1}{M_B} + \frac{Y'}{M_A}\right) \frac{t + 460}{P} \quad (7.15)$$

The humid volume of a saturated mixture is computed with $Y' = Y_s'$ and that for a dry gas with $Y' = 0$. These values may then be plotted

---

† For this reason curves of constant relative saturation are sometimes drawn on absolute humidity–temperature charts. Since relative saturation and percentage saturation are not numerically equal for an unsaturated mixture, the position of such curves must be computed by the methods of Illustration 7.

against temperature on a psychrometric chart. For partially saturated mixtures, $v_H$ may be interpolated between values for zero and 100 percentage saturation at the same temperature according to percentage saturation. When the mass of *dry* gas in a mixture is multiplied by the humid volume, the volume of *mixture* results.

6. *Humid Heat.* The humid heat $C_S$ is the heat required to raise the temperature of 1 lb. of gas and its accompanying vapor 1°F. at constant pressure. For a mixture of absolute humidity $Y'$,

$$C_S = C_B + Y'C_A \tag{7.16}$$

Provided neither vaporation nor condensation occurs, the heat in B.t.u. required to raise the temperature of $W_B$ lb. dry gas *and* its accompanying vapor $\Delta t$°F. will be

$$Q = W_B C_S \, \Delta t \tag{7.17}$$

7. *Enthalpy.* The (relative) enthalpy of a vapor-gas mixture is the sum of the (relative) enthalpies of the gas and of the vapor content. Imagine 1 lb. of a gas containing $Y'$ lb. vapor at dry-bulb temperature $t$°F. If the mixture is unsaturated, the vapor is in a superheated state and we may calculate the enthalpy relative to the reference states gas and saturated liquid at $t_0$°F. The enthalpy of the gas alone is $C_B(t - t_0)$. The vapor at $t$ is at a condition corresponding to point $A$ on Fig. 7.4, and its reference state corresponds to point $D$. If $t_{DP}$ is the dew point of the mixture ($t_2$ on Fig. 7.4) and $\lambda_{DP}$ the latent heat of vaporization of the vapor at that temperature, the enthalpy per pound of vapor will be $C_A(t - t_{DP}) + \lambda_{DP} + C_{AL}(t_{DP} - t_0)$. Then the total enthalpy for the mixture, per pound of dry gas, is

$$H' = C_B(t - t_0) + Y'[C_A(t - t_{DP}) + \lambda_{DP} + C_{AL}(t_{DP} - t_0)] \tag{7.18}$$

Refer again to Fig. 7.4. For the low pressures ordinarily encountered in humidification work, the point $A$ which actually lies on a line of constant pressure corresponding to the partial pressure of the vapor in the mixture may, for all practical purposes, be considered as lying on the line whose pressure is the saturation pressure of the vapor at the reference temperature, or at $A'$. The vapor enthalpy may then be computed by following the path $A'ED$ and becomes, per pound of vapor, $C_A(t - t_0) + \lambda_0$, where $\lambda_0$ is the latent heat of vaporization at the reference temperature. The enthalpy of the mixture, per pound of dry gas, is then

$$H' = C_B(t - t_0) + Y'[C_A(t - t_0) + \lambda_0] = C_S(t - t_0) + Y'\lambda_0 \tag{7.19}$$

Occasionally different reference temperatures are chosen for the dry gas and for the vapor. Note that the enthalpy $H'$ for a mixture may be increased by increasing the temperature at constant humidity, by increasing the humidity at constant temperature, or by increasing both. Alternatively, under certain conditions $H'$ may remain constant as $t$ and $Y'$ vary in opposite directions.

By substitution of $Y'_s$ and the appropriate humid heat in Eq. (7.19), the enthalpy of saturated mixtures $H'_s$ may be computed and plotted against temperature on the psychrometric chart. Similarly $H$ for the dry gas may be plotted. Enthalpies for unsaturated mixtures may then be interpolated between the saturated and dry values at the same temperature according to the percentage saturation.

**The System Air–Water.** While psychrometric charts for any vapor-gas mixture may be prepared when circumstances warrant, the system air–water vapor occurs so frequently that unusually complete charts for this mixture are available. Figure 7.6 is one such chart prepared for a total pressure of 1 atm. For convenient reference, the various equations representing the curves are listed in Table 7.1. It should be noted that

TABLE 7.1. PSYCHROMETRIC RELATIONS FOR THE SYSTEM AIR $(B)$–WATER $(A)$ AT 1 ATM. PRESSURE

$M_A = 18.02$, mol. wt. water
$M_B = 28.97$, mol. wt. air

$$Y' = 0.622 \frac{p_{H_2O}}{1 - p_{H_2O}} \quad \text{lb. water vapor/lb. air}$$

$$Y'_s = 0.622 \frac{p_{H_2O}}{1 - P^*_{H_2O}} \quad \text{lb. water vapor/lb. air at saturation}$$

$v_H = (0.0252 + 0.0405Y')(t + 460) \quad$ cu. ft. mixture/lb. air
$C_S = 0.24 + 0.45Y' \quad$ B.t.u. for mixture/(lb. air)(°F.)
$t_0 = 32°F.$
$\lambda_0 = 1075.2$ B.t.u./lb., latent heat of vaporization of water, 32°F.
$H' = (0.24 + 0.45Y')(t - 32) + 1{,}075.2Y'$, relative enthalpy, B.t.u. for mixture/lb. air, referred to gaseous air and saturated liquid water at 32°F.

all the quantities (absolute humidity, enthalpies, humid volumes) are plotted against temperature. In the case of the enthalpies, gaseous air and saturated liquid water at 32°F. were the reference conditions used so that the chart may be used in conjunction with the steam tables. The data for enthalpy of saturated air were then plotted with two enthalpy scales to provide for the large range of values necessary. The series of curves marked "adiabatic-saturation curves" on the chart were plotted according to Eq. (7.27), to be considered later. For most purposes these may be considered as curves of constant enthalpy for the vapor-gas mixture per pound of gas.

**Illustration 7.** An air $(B)$–water vapor $(A)$ sample has a dry-bulb temperature of 135°F. and an absolute humidity 0.030 lb. water/lb. dry air at 1 atm. pressure. Tabulate its characteristics.

*Solution.* The point of coordinates $t = 135°F.$, $Y' = 0.030$ is located on the psychrometric chart (Fig. 7.6), a schematic version of which is shown in Fig. 7.7. This is point $D$ on Fig. 7.7.

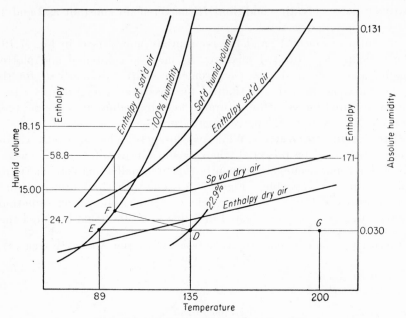

FIG. 7.7. Solution to Illustrations 7 and 8.

*a.* By vertical interpolation between the adjacent curves of constant per cent humidity, the sample has a per cent humidity of 22.9%. Alternatively, the saturation humidity at 135°F. is $Y'_s = 0.131$, and the per cent humidity at $D$ is therefore $(0.030/0.131)100 = 22.9\%$.

*b.* The molal absolute humidity $= Y = Y'(M_B/M_A) = 0.030(28.97/18.02) = 0.0482$ mole water/mole dry air.

*c.* The partial pressure of water vapor in the sample, by Eq. (7.12), is

$$p_A = YP/(1 + Y) = 0.0482(1)/1.0482 = 0.0460 \text{ atm.}$$

*d.* The vapor pressure of water at 135°F. is 0.1727 atm. $= P_A$ (steam tables). The relative humidity $= p_A(100)/P_A = 0.0460(100)/0.1727 = 26.6\%$.

*e.* Dew point. From point $D$ proceed at constant humidity to the saturation curve at point $E$, at which the dew-point temperature is 89°F.

*f.* Humid volume. At 135°F., the specific volume of dry air is 15.00 cu. ft./lb. dry air. The humid volume of saturated air is 18.15 cu. ft./lb. dry air. Interpolating for 22.9% humidity,

$$v_H = 15.00 + (18.15 - 15.00)(0.229) = 15.72 \text{ cu. ft. wet air/lb. dry air}$$

*g.* Humid heat, Eq. (7.16)

$$C_s = C_B + Y'C_A = 0.24 + 0.45(0.030) = 0.254 \text{ B.t.u. for wet air/(lb. dry air)(°F.)}$$

*h.* Enthalpy. At 135°F., the enthalpy of dry air is 24.7 B.t.u./lb. dry air; that for saturated air is 171 B.t.u./lb. dry air. Interpolating for 22.9% humidity,

$$H' = 24.7 + (171 - 24.7)0.229 = 58.2 \text{ B.t.u. for wet air/lb. dry air}$$

Alternatively, Eq. (7.19),

$$H' = C_S(t - t_0) + Y'\lambda_0 = 0.254(135 - 32) + 0.030(1,075.2) = 58.4 \text{ B.t.u./lb. dry air}$$

Alternatively, line $DF$ is drawn parallel to the adjacent adiabatic saturation curves. At $F$, the enthalpy is nearly the same as at $D$, or 58.8 B.t.u./lb. dry air.

**Illustration 8.** One hundred cubic feet of the moist air of Illustration 7 is heated to 200°F. How many B.t.u. are required?

*Solution.* After heating, the mixture will be at point $G$ (Fig. 7.7). The mass of dry air $= w_B = 100/v_H = 100/15.72 = 6.35$ lb.

Eq. (7.17): $\qquad Q = w_B C_S \, \Delta t = 6.35(0.254)(200 - 135) = 105 \text{ B.t.u.}$

Alternatively, the enthalpy of the mixture at $G$, computed by the methods of Illustration 7, is 74.9 B.t.u./lb. dry air.

$$Q = w_B(H'_G - H'_D) = 6.35(74.9 - 58.4) = 105 \text{ B.t.u.}$$

**Adiabatic-saturation Curves.** Consider the operation indicated schematically in Fig. 7.8. Here the entering gas is contacted with liquid,

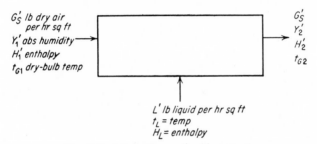

$G'_S$ lb dry air per hr sq ft
$Y'_1$ abs humidity
$H'_1$ enthalpy
$t_{G1}$ dry-bulb temp

$G'_S$
$Y'_2$
$H'_2$
$t_{G2}$

$L'$ lb liquid per hr sq ft
$t_L$ = temp
$H_L$ = enthalpy

FIG. 7.8. Adiabatic gas-liquid contact.

for example, in a spray, and as a result of diffusion and heat transfer between gas and liquid the gas leaves at conditions of humidity and temperature different from those at the entrance. The operation is adiabatic inasmuch as no heat is gained or lost to the surroundings. A mass balance for substance $A$,

$$L' = G'_S(Y'_2 - Y'_1) \tag{7.20}$$

An enthalpy balance,

$$G'_S H'_1 + L'H_L = G'_S H'_2 \tag{7.21}$$
$$\therefore H'_1 + (Y'_2 - Y'_1)H_L = H'_2 \tag{7.22}$$

This may be expanded by the definition of $H'$ given in Eq. (7.19),

$$C_{S1}(t_{G1} - t_0) + Y'_1\lambda_0 + (Y'_2 - Y'_1)C_{AL}(t_L - t_0) = C_{S2}(t_{G2} - t_0) + Y'_2\lambda_0 \tag{7.23}$$

In the special case where the leaving gas-vapor mixture is saturated, and therefore at conditions $t_{as}$, $Y'_{as}$, $H'_{as}$, and the liquid enters at $t_{as}$, the gas is humidified by evaporation of liquid and cooled. Equation (7.23) becomes, on expansion of the humid-heat terms,

$$C_B(t_{G1} - t_0) + Y_1'C_A(t_{G1} - t_0) + Y_1'\lambda_0 + (Y_{as}' - Y_1')C_{AL}(t_{as} - t_0)$$
$$= C_B(t_{as} - t_0) + Y_{as}'C_A(t_{as} - t_0) + Y_{as}'\lambda_0 \quad (7.24)$$

By subtracting $Y_1'C_A t_{as}$ from both sides and simplifying, this becomes

$$(C_B + Y_1'C_A)(t_{G1} - t_{as}) = C_{S1}(t_{G1} - t_{as})$$
$$= (Y_{as}' - Y_1')[C_A(t_{as} - t_0)$$
$$+ \lambda_0 - C_{AL}(t_{as} - t_0)] \quad (7.25)$$

Reference to Fig. 7.4 shows the quantity in brackets to be equal to $\lambda_{as}$. Consequently,

$$C_{S1}(t_{G1} - t_{as}) = (Y_{as}' - Y_1')\lambda_{as} \quad (7.26)$$

or
$$t_{G1} - t_{as} = (Y_{as}' - Y_1') \frac{\lambda_{as}}{C_{S1}} \qquad \text{✳} \quad (7.27)$$

This is the equation of a curve on the psychrometric chart, the "adiabatic-saturation curve"† which passes through the points $(Y_{as}',t_{as})$ on the 100 per cent saturation curve and $(Y_1',t_{G1})$. Since the humid heat $C_{S1}$ contains the term $Y_1'$, the curve is not straight but instead slightly concave upward. For any vapor-gas mixture there is an *adiabatic-saturation temperature* $t_{as}$ such that, if contacted with liquid at $t_{as}$, the gas will become humidified and cooled. If sufficient contact time is available, the gas will become saturated at $(Y_{as}',t_{as})$ but otherwise will leave unsaturated at $(Y_2',t_{G2})$, a point on the adiabatic-saturation curve for the initial mixture. Eventually, as Eq. (7.26) indicates, the sensible heat given up by the gas in cooling equals the latent heat required to evaporate the added vapor.

The psychrometric chart (Fig. 7.6) for air-water contains a family of adiabatic-saturation curves, as previously noted. Each point on the curve represents a mixture whose adiabatic-saturation temperature is at the intersection of the curve with the 100 per cent humidity curve.

**Illustration 9.** Air at 190°F., $Y' = 0.030$ lb. water/lb. dry air, 1 atm., is contacted with water at the adiabatic-saturation temperature and is thereby humidified and cooled to 90% saturation. What are the final temperature and humidity of the air?

*Solution.* The point representing the original air is located on the psychrometric chart (Fig. 7.6). The adiabatic-saturation curve through the point reaches the 100% saturation curve at 105°F., the adiabatic-saturation temperature. This is the water temperature. On this curve, 90% saturation occurs at 108°F., $Y' = 0.0504$ lb. water/lb. air, the exit-air conditions.

**Wet-bulb Temperature.** The wet-bulb temperature is the equilibrium temperature reached by a small amount of liquid evaporating into a large amount of unsaturated vapor-gas mixture. Under properly controlled

† The adiabatic-saturation curve is nearly one of constant enthalpy per pound of dry gas. As Eq. (7.22) indicates, $H_{as}'$ differs from $H_1'$ by the enthalpy of the evaporated liquid at its entering temperature $t_{as}$ but this difference is usually unimportant.

conditions it can be used to measure the humidity of the mixture. For this purpose a thermometer whose bulb has been covered with a wick kept wet with the liquid is immersed in a rapidly moving stream of the gas mixture. The temperature indicated by this thermometer will ultimately reach a value lower than the dry-bulb temperature of the gas if the latter is unsaturated, and from a knowledge of this the humidity is computed.

Consider a drop of liquid immersed in a rapidly moving stream of unsaturated vapor-gas mixture. If the liquid is initially at a temperature higher than the gas dew point, the vapor pressure of the liquid will be higher at the drop surface than the partial pressure of vapor in the gas and the liquid will evaporate and diffuse into the gas. The latent heat required for the evaporation will at first be supplied at the expense of the sensible heat of the liquid drop, which will then cool down. As soon as the liquid temperature is reduced below the dry-bulb temperature of the gas, heat will flow from the gas to the liquid, at an increasing rate as the temperature difference becomes larger. Eventually the rate of heat transfer from the gas to the liquid will equal the rate of heat requirement for the evaporation, and the temperature of

Vapor-gas mixture $\begin{cases} t_G = dry\text{-}bulb\ temp \\ p_A = part.\ pres.\ of\ vapor \\ Y' = obs\ humidity \end{cases}$

Effective gas film

Liquid drop $t_w$

$t_G$

Temperature $t_w$ — Sensible heat

$p_{Aw}$

Partial pressure — Vapor latent heat

$p_A$

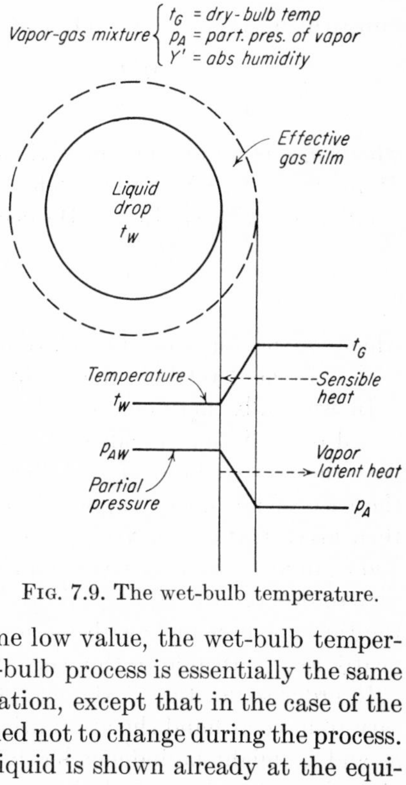

FIG. 7.9. The wet-bulb temperature.

the liquid will remain constant at some low value, the wet-bulb temperature $t_w$. The mechanism of the wet-bulb process is essentially the same as that governing the adiabatic saturation, except that in the case of the former the humidity of the gas is assumed not to change during the process.

Refer to Fig. 7.9, where a drop of liquid is shown already at the equilibrium conditions and the mass of gas is so large as it passes the drop that its humidity is not measurably affected by the evaporation. Let the surface of the drop be $S$ and the mass rate of evaporation $W$. Ignoring the sensible heat required to superheat the evaporated matter from $t_w$ to $t_G$, the heat required for evaporation is

$$q = \lambda_w W \qquad (7.28)$$

Applying Eq. (3.4) to the mass transfer,

$$W = M_A S k_G (p_{Aw} - p_A) \qquad (7.29)$$

The rate of heat transfer $q$ will be the sum of that resulting from conduction, convection, and radiation. That transferred by conduction and convection is characterized by a heat-transfer gas-film coefficient $h_G$ operating through a temperature difference $t_G - t_w$. That by radiation may involve radiation from the warm gas and from the walls of a surrounding container or duct. Assuming that for small temperature differences this may also be characterized by a film coefficient $h_R$ operating through the same temperature gradient,

$$q = (h_G + h_R)S(t_G - t_w) \qquad (7.30)$$

Substituting Eqs. (7.29) and (7.30) in Eq. (7.28),

$$t_G - t_w = \frac{\lambda_w M_A k_G}{h_G + h_R}(p_{AW} - p_A) = \frac{\lambda_w M_B p_{BM} k_G}{h_G + h_R}(Y'_w - Y') \qquad (7.31)$$

where $p_{BM}$ is an average partial pressure of the gas. Since (Table 3.1) $M_B p_{BM} k_G = k_Y$, and under such conditions that $h_R$ will be negligible in comparison with $h_G$, Eq. (7.31) becomes

$$t_G - t_w = \frac{\lambda_w k_Y}{h_G}(Y'_w - Y') \qquad ✳ \qquad (7.32)$$

which is the form of the relationship commonly used. The quantity $t_G - t_w$ is the "wet-bulb depression."

In wet-bulb thermometry, the radiation coefficient $h_R$ may be minimized by radiation shields and by maintaining a high velocity of the gas past the wetted bulb of the thermometer (at least 15 to 20 ft./sec. in the case of air–water vapor mixtures at ordinary temperatures), which then gives rise to relatively large values of $h_G$. The relative size of $h_G$ and $h_R$ in any case may be estimated by standard methods.[10] It is necessary to observe the additional precaution of feeding the wick surrounding the thermometer bulb with an adequate supply of liquid preadjusted as nearly as practicable to the wet-bulb temperature.

In order to use Eq. (7.31) or (7.32) for determination of $Y'$, it is necessary to have at hand the appropriate value of the ratio $h_G/k_Y$. Values of $h_G$ and $k_Y$ might be independently estimated for the particular shape of wetted surface by correlations such as those of Fig. 3.11. Alternatively, experimental values of the ratio for special circumstances may be employed. For the case of *flow of gas past a wetted cylinder such as a wet-bulb thermometer*, a limited number of investigations have been made for a variety of vapors in air. The best of these data show that so long as turbulent flow prevails there is no effect of Reynolds number on the ratio; the effective film resistances to both heat and mass transfer are equally affected by change in Reynolds number. Bedingfield and Drew[1] have made a critical study of the reported data and have contributed additional values of the ratio for cases where the "wet-bulb thermometer" was a cast cylinder of a volatile solid which sublimed into the gas stream. For air as the noncondensable gas, they conclude that

$$\frac{h_G}{k_Y} = 0.294 \left(\frac{\mu}{\rho D_{AB}}\right)^{0.56} \tag{7.33}$$

and, for other gases,

$$\frac{h_G}{k_Y} = C_S \left(\frac{k}{C_{S\rho}D_{AB}}\right)^{0.56} = C_S \left(\frac{Sc}{Pr}\right)^{0.56} \tag{7.34}$$

The last equation results from a consideration of the heat transfer–mass transfer correlation of curve 3 (Fig. 3.11). Figure 7.10 compares Eq.

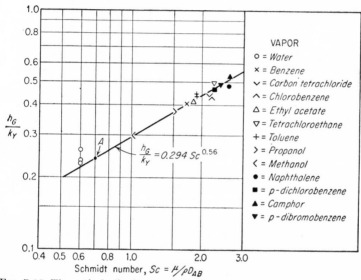

FIG. 7.10. The ratio $h_G/k_Y$ for wet-bulb thermometry in air-vapor systems.

(7.33) with some of the better data culled from the literature, each different plotted symbol representing a different vapor. For pure air, for which $Sc = Pr = 0.70$, $h_G/k_Y$ should equal $C = 0.24$, and the line has been forced through this point at $A$ on the figure.[1]

A thorough study[7] of Dropkin's[3] carefully measured data on wet-bulb thermometers with the air–water vapor system led to the value of $h_G/k_Y$ for air-water = 0.236, which is recommended for this system. Other reported values range up to 0.27. It will be noted that Eq. (7.32) is identical with Eq. (7.27) for the adiabatic-saturation temperature, with, however, the replacement of $C_{S1}$ by $h_G/k_Y$. In the case of the air-water system, at moderate humidities $C_{S1}$ is not greatly different from 0.236, and for most practical purposes the adiabatic-saturation curves of Fig.

7.6 may be used instead of Eq. (7.32). For most other systems, however, the wet-bulb temperature of an unsaturated mixture will be higher than the corresponding adiabatic-saturation temperature.

**Illustration 10.** For an air–water vapor mixture of dry-bulb temperature 150°F., a wet-bulb temperature of 90°F. was determined under such conditions that the radiation coefficient may be considered negligible. The total pressure was 1 atm. Compute the humidity of the air.

*Solution.* At $t_w = 90°F.$, $\lambda_w = 1042.2$ B.t.u./lb., and $Y'_w = 0.031$ lb. $H_2O$/lb. dry air (Fig. 7.6); $h_G/k_Y = 0.236$, $t_G = 150°F.$

Eq. (7.32):
$$150 - 90 = \frac{1,042.4}{0.236} (0.031 - Y')$$
$$Y' = 0.0174 \text{ lb. water/lb. air}$$

Alternatively as an approximation, the adiabatic-saturation curve for $t_{as} = 90°F.$ on Fig. 7.6 is followed down to a dry-bulb temperature 150°F., where $Y'$ is read as 0.0170.

**Illustration 11.** Estimate the wet-bulb and adiabatic-saturation temperatures for a toluene-air mixture of 140°F. dry-bulb temperature, $Y' = 0.050$ lb. vapor/lb. air, 1 atm.

*Solution.* a. Wet-bulb temperature. $t_G = 140°F.$ (60°C.), $Y' = 0.050$ lb. toluene/lb. air. From Table 2.1 $D_{AB} = 0.092$ sq. cm./sec. at 59.0°C., 1 atm., or 0.092 (3.87) = 0.356 sq. ft./hr. At 140°F., $\rho$ for air = 0.0663 lb./cu. ft., and $\mu = 0.0195$ centipoise, or 0.0472 lb./(ft.)(hr.).

Sc *should* be calculated for mean conditions between those of the gas-vapor mixture and the wet-bulb saturation conditions, but for dilute gas mixtures the values of $\rho$ and $\mu$ for air are satisfactory.

$$\text{Sc} = \frac{\mu}{\rho D_{AB}} = \frac{0.0472}{0.0663(0.356)} = 2.00$$

Eq. (7.33):

$$h_G/k_Y = 0.294(2.00)^{0.56} = 0.431 \text{ B.t.u./(lb.)(°F.)(obsvd. value = 0.44)}$$

Eq. (7.32):
$$140 - t_w = \frac{\lambda_w}{0.431} (Y'_w - 0.050)$$

Solution for $t_w$ is by trial and error. Try $t_w = 90°F.$ $\lambda_w = 183$ B.t.u./lb. The vapor pressure of toluene at 90°F. = 41.3 mm. Hg.

$$\therefore Y'_w = \frac{41.3}{760 - 41.3} \frac{92.1}{29} = 0.1827 \text{ lb. vapor/lb. air}$$

and the equation gives $t_w = 83.8°F.$ instead of the 90°F. assumed. On repeated trials, $t_w$ is computed to be 88°F.

b. Adiabatic-saturation temperature. $t_1 = 140°F.$, $Y'_1 = 0.050.$ $C$ for toluene vapor = 0.30 B.t.u./(lb.)(°F.). $C_{S1} = 0.24 + 0.05(0.30) = 0.255$ B.t.u./(lb. air)(°F.).

Eq. (7.27):
$$140 - t_{as} = (Y'_{as} - 0.05) \frac{\lambda_{as}}{0.255}$$

In the same fashion as the wet-bulb temperature, $t_{as}$ is calculated by trial and found to be 79°F.

**Illustration 12.** Estimate the ratio $h_G/k_Y$ for the case of a spherical drop of toluene falling rapidly through the toluene-air mixture of Illustration 11.

*Solution.* Refer to Fig. 3.11, curve 4, for spheres. Above an abscissa value of 1,000, this curve is nearly a straight line on the logarithmic coordinates whose equation may be estimated as

$$\frac{k_c d_p}{D_{AB}} (10^{-3}) = 0.00058[\mathrm{Re}''(\mathrm{Sc})^{2/3}]^{0.52} \qquad \text{for mass transfer}$$

$$\frac{h_G d_p}{k} (10^{-3}) = 0.00058[\mathrm{Re}''(\mathrm{Pr})^{2/3}]^{0.52} \qquad \text{for heat transfer}$$

Dividing one equation by the other,

$$\frac{h_G}{k_c} = \frac{k}{D_{AB}} \left(\frac{\mathrm{Pr}}{\mathrm{Sc}}\right)^{0.347}$$

From Table 3.1, $k_c = k_Y(RT/p_{BM}M_B) = k_Y/\rho$.

$$\therefore \frac{h_G}{k_Y} = \frac{k}{\rho D_{AB}} \left(\frac{\mathrm{Pr}}{\mathrm{Sc}}\right)^{0.347}$$

Since $k/\rho D_{AB} = (\mathrm{Sc}/\mathrm{Pr})C_S$,

$$\frac{h}{k_Y} = C_S \left(\frac{\mathrm{Sc}}{\mathrm{Pr}}\right)^{0.653}$$

For this dilute vapor-gas mixture, the properties of air may be used to compute Pr. At 140°F., $C = 0.24$, $k = 0.0167$ B.t.u. (ft.)/(hr.)(°F.)(sq. ft.), $\mu = 0.0472$ lb./(ft.)(hr.).

$$\mathrm{Pr} = \frac{C\mu}{k} = \frac{0.24(0.0472)}{0.0167} = 0.68$$

$C_S = 0.255$, and $\mathrm{Sc} = 2.00$ (Illustration 11).

$$\therefore \frac{h_G}{k_Y} = 0.255 \left(\frac{2.00}{0.68}\right)^{0.653} = 0.515 \text{ B.t.u./(lb.)(°F.)}$$

It was one of the purposes of this illustration to emphasize that the $h_G/k_Y$ may be a function of the shape of the wetted surface, and the values obtained with conventional wet-bulb thermometers do not necessarily apply to all situations.

**The Psychrometric Ratio.** It has been shown that for the system air–water vapor the psychrometric ratio $h_G/k_Y C_S$ is approximately unity. This is the so-called "Lewis relation" (after W. K. Lewis). The conditions under which the Lewis relation is generally true can be established as follows (after Eckert[4]):

Consider the heat- and mass-transfer processes of Figs. 3.5 and 3.6. When both processes occur simultaneously, each has an influence on the other, since, for example, a vapor diffusing through a gas in which there is a temperature gradient carries heat with it in addition to that transferred by convection and conduction (see, for example, Colburn and Drew[2] and Bedingfield and Drew[1]). Ignoring these effects in dilute mixtures, Eqs. (3.10) and (3.17) give, for the turbulent core,

$$\frac{C_S M_{av} P N_A}{q} = \frac{\Delta p_A}{\Delta t} \tag{7.35}$$

For the turbulent region, a turbulent-heat-transfer coefficient $h_{turb}$ and a turbulent-mass-transfer coefficient $k_{G,turb}$ can be defined as

$$h_{turb} = \frac{q}{\Delta t} \qquad k_{G,turb} = \frac{N_A}{\Delta p_A} \tag{7.36}$$

$$\frac{M_{av} P N_A}{\Delta p_A} = M_{av} P k_{G,turb} \doteq M_B p_{BM} k_{G,turb} = k_{Y,turb} \tag{7.37}$$

Equation (7.35) then reduces to

$$\frac{h_{t\,turb}}{h_{Y,turb}} = C_S \tag{7.38}$$

In the turbulent core, therefore, the psychrometric ratio equals unity for any vapor-gas mixture.

For heat and mass transfer in a laminar film, Eqs. (2.21) and (2.42) similarly give

$$\frac{p_{Ai} - p_{AF}}{t_i - t_F} = \frac{kRTp_{BM}N_A}{qD_{AB}P} \tag{7.39}$$

Comparison of Eqs. (7.35) and (7.39) shows the mechanisms of the transfer to be the same for laminar and turbulent regions only provided

$$C_S M_{av}P = \frac{kRTp_{BM}}{D_{AB}P} \doteq \frac{kRT}{D_{AB}} \tag{7.40}$$

But $PM_{av}/RT = \rho$, and since $\alpha$ = thermal diffusivity = $k/C_S\rho$, the criterion of Eq. (7.40) becomes

$$\frac{\alpha}{D_{AB}} = \frac{\mathrm{Pr}}{\mathrm{Sc}} = 1$$

For heat and mass transfer through *both* laminar and turbulent regions, therefore, $h_G/k_Y = C_S$ only if Pr = Sc. For this reason, for example, the line of Fig. 7.10 was forced through point $A$ for air, for which Pr substantially equals Sc.

## GAS-LIQUID CONTACT OPERATIONS

Direct contact of a vapor-gas mixture with a liquid may have any of several purposes such as cooling the liquid and humidifying or dehumidifying the gas. The direction of vapor diffusion, i.e., whether humidification or dehumidification of the gas results, depends upon the sign of the difference in humidity existing in the bulk of the gas and at the liquid surface. Since the liquid is a pure substance, no concentration gradient exists within it and the mass-transfer resistance therefore always lies entirely within the gas. Since evaporation or condensation of vapor simultaneously involves a latent heat of vaporization or condensation, there will always be a transfer of latent heat in the direction of mass transfer. The temperature differences existing within the system additionally control the direction of any sensible heat transfer which may occur, and since the temperature gradients may reside within the liquid, within the gas, or within both, the sensible-heat-transfer resistance may include effects in either or both phases. The effects of latent and sensible heat transfer may be simultaneously considered in terms of the enthalpy changes which occur.

**Over-all Mass and Enthalpy Balances.** Consider any process whatsoever involving direct contact with gas and liquid, as in Fig. 7.11. The liquid and gas streams flow through an apparatus of unit cross section, and the system is supplied with heat amounting to $Q$ B.t.u./(hr.)(sq. ft.). A mass balance for substance $A$ is

$$L_2' + G_s' Y_1' = L_1' + G_s' Y_2' \qquad (7.41)$$

or
$$L_2' - L_1' = G_s'(Y_2' - Y_1') \qquad (7.42)$$

An enthalpy balance is

$$L_2' H_{L2} + G' H_1' + Q = L_1' H_{L1} + G' H_2' \qquad (7.43)$$

For adiabatic operation, $Q = 0$. Although countercurrent operation is shown in the figure, the equations are readily modified to take care of parallel flow or other changes in the flow sheet.

**Adiabatic Gas-Liquid Contact.** For the special case of adiabatic contact, where $Q = 0$, consider the detailed changes in conditions experienced by the fluids as they flow through the apparatus, as shown in Fig. 7.12. For purposes of establishing the relationships existing in the system, the figure has been set up generally for a water cooler (see below). The curves, however, are drawn more or less schematically, and necessary modification for other processes will be considered later. In Fig. 7.12a, the terminal conditions of the streams are shown, as well as the changes which may occur

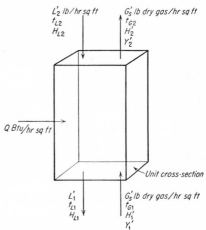

FIG. 7.11. Continuous countercurrent liquid-gas contact.

across a differential length of the apparatus, $dZ$. Heat and mass transfer between the phases occur across a total interfacial surface $S$ sq. ft./sq. ft. apparatus cross section. This may be defined in terms of the interfacial surface per active cubic foot of apparatus, $a$, as in Eq. (7.45).

The major consideration in operations of this sort is the transfer of energy by virtue of an enthalpy difference between the phases, as shown in Fig. 7.12b. Equations (7.46) to (7.48) are enthalpy balances for the differential length of apparatus, and Eq. (7.49) follows from the definition of enthalpy of the vapor-gas mixture [Eq. (7.19)]. The change in enthalpy of the gas is made up of two parts, a change in sensible heat and a change in latent heat, as shown in Eq. (7.50). The individual parts may be effective in the same direction, i.e., the sign of the change in sensible and latent heats may be the same, or they may be opposite. Irrespective of the individual parts, the net change in enthalpy of the gas as it flows through the apparatus will be an increase if the value of

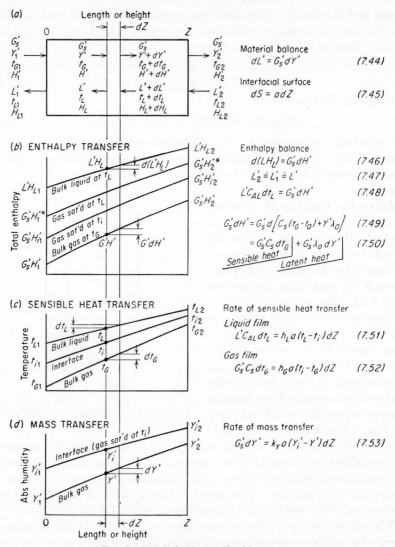

FIG. 7.12. Adiabatic gas-liquid contact.

$H'_i$ is greater than $H'$ at any value of $Z$, a decrease if less. The interfacial value of $H'_i$, in accordance with the two-film theory (Chap. 5), is the saturated-gas enthalpy corresponding to the temperature $t_i$, in equilibrium with the liquid at the interface. The sensible-heat portion of the change is a result of a temperature difference as shown in Fig. 7.12c, the latent heat portion as a result of mass transfer as shown in Fig. 7.12d.

1. *Water Cooling.* If a hot liquid is contacted with a cooler gas, the liquid will be cooled owing to a loss in sensible heat as well as by evapo-

ration of a portion of the liquid. The gas, in turn, will be warmed and humidified. In this manner, water which has become heated by circulation through condensers or other heat-exchange equipment may be cooled for reuse by contact with air. Since the enthalpy difference is the significant driving force, an analysis is made in terms of this quantity. From Eq. (7.48),

$$L'C_{AL} \int_{t_{L1}}^{t_{L2}} dt_L = G'_S \int_{H_1'}^{H'} dH' \qquad (7.54)$$

$$L'C_{AL}(t_{L2} - t_{L1}) = G'_S(H'_2 - H'_1) \qquad (7.55)$$

This enthalpy balance may be represented graphically by plotting the gas enthalpy $H'$ against liquid enthalpy, or more simply against liquid

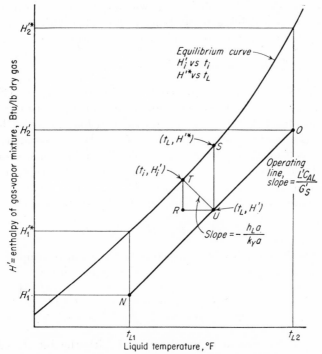

Fig. 7.13. Operating diagram for a water cooler.

temperature $t_L$ to which the latter is proportional if $C_{AL}$ may be considered constant, as in Fig. 7.13. The line $ON$ on this chart represents Eq. (7.55) and passes through the points representing the terminal conditions for the two fluids. In so far as $L'_2 - L'_1$ is small in comparison with $L'$, the line is straight and of slope $L'C_{AL}/G'_S$. The equilibrium curve on the chart is plotted for conditions of the gas at the gas-liquid interface, i.e., the enthalpy of saturated gas at each temperature.

The two terms of Eq. (7.50) may be described in terms of Eqs. (7.52) and (7.53),

$$G_S' \, dH' = h_G a(t_i - t_G) \, dZ + \lambda_0 k_Y a(Y_i' - Y') \, dZ \tag{7.56}$$

If $h_G/k_Y C_S = r$, this becomes

$$G_S' \, dH' = k_Y a[(C_S r t_i + \lambda_0 Y_i') - (C_S r t_G + \lambda_0 Y')] \, dZ \tag{7.57}$$

*For the special case where $r = 1$*,[11] which, under limited conditions, can describe the important system air-water, Eq. (7.57) becomes

$$G_S' \, dH' = k_Y a(H_i' - H') \, dZ \tag{7.58}$$

where the mass-transfer coefficient $k_Y$, which is defined in terms of humidity difference as a driving force, is also applicable with gas enthalpies. Combining Eqs. (7.48), (7.51), and (7.58) then provides

$$G_S' \, dH' = k_Y a(H_i' - H') \, dZ = h_L a(t_L - t_i) \, dZ \tag{7.59}$$

At a position in the apparatus corresponding to point $U$ (Fig. 7.13) point $T$ represents the interfacial conditions and the distance $TR$ the enthalpy driving force $H_i' - H'$ within the gas phase. As we have seen in Chap. 5, provided the equilibrium curve is nearly straight over the range of conditions encountered, an over-all driving force representing the enthalpy differences in both phases but expressed in terms of $H'$ may be used, such as the vertical distance $SU$ (Fig. 7.13). This will require a corresponding over-all coefficient, and Eq. (7.59) becomes

$$G_S' \, dH' = K_Y a(H'^* - H') \, dZ \tag{7.60}$$

where $H'^*$ is the enthalpy of a gas saturated at $t_L$, or in equilibrium with the bulk of the liquid. Assuming $K_Y a$ to remain constant,

$$\int_{H_1'}^{H_2'} \frac{dH'}{H'^* - H'} = \frac{K_Y a}{G_S'} \int_0^Z dZ = \frac{K_Y a Z}{G_S'} \tag{7.61}$$

The over-all coefficient $K_Y$ is combined with the interfacial-surface term $a$ to give a combined coefficient $K_Y a$, since the surface is not always separately determinable. The height or length $Z$ of the equipment may then be computed by graphical integration of the left-hand side of Eq. (7.61) by plotting $1/(H'^* - H')$ as ordinate against $H'$ as abscissa and determining the area under the resulting curve between the appropriate limits. Alternatively,

$$\int_{H_1'}^{H_2'} \frac{dH'}{H'^* - H'} = \frac{H_2' - H_1'}{(H'^* - H')_{\text{av}}} = N_{toG} \tag{7.62}$$

The middle part of this equation is the number of times the average enthalpy-difference driving force will divide into the change in gas enthalpy. This is a measure of the difficulty of enthalpy transfer and is called the *over-all number of transfer units*, $N_{toG}$. Consequently,

$$Z = H_{toG}N_{toG} \tag{7.63}$$

where $H_{toG}$ is the over-all height of a transfer unit. Therefore

$$H_{toG} = \frac{G'_s}{K_Y a} \tag{7.64}$$

and either $H_{toG}$ or $K_Y a$, which are each characteristic of the nature of the contacting equipment and the operating conditions, may be used for design. $H_{toG}$ is sometimes preferred since it is less dependent upon rate of flow than $K_Y a$.

The use of over-all coefficients or transfer units in the manner described is justified only if (a) the equilibrium curve is straight over the range of conditions encountered, which is not strictly so, or (b) if the resistance to sensible heat transfer within the liquid is zero ($h_L a = \infty$). The few data available respecting the latter condition are inconclusive owing to the fact that most of them were obtained under conditions such that the psychrometric ratio $r$ did not equal unity. There is further indication that perhaps the interfacial surface for diffusion in packed towers, which is the gas-liquid interface, is not necessarily the same as the surface for heat transfer, since particularly at low liquid rates heat may be transferred across the dry surface of unirrigated packing. Nevertheless, the use of over-all coefficients and transfer units seems to be satisfactory in practice.

Just as with concentrations (Chap. 5), an operating line on the enthalpy coordinates of Fig. 7.13 which anywhere touches the equilibrium curve results in a zero driving force and consequently an infinite interfacial surface, or infinite height $Z$, to accomplish a given temperature change in the liquid. This condition would then represent the limiting ratio of $L'/G'_s$ permissible. It is also clear that point $N$, for example, will be below the equilibrium curve so long as the entering-air enthalpy $H'_1$ is less than the saturation enthalpy $H_1'^*$ for air at $t_{L1}$. Since the enthalpy $H'$ is for most practical purposes only a function of the adiabatic-saturation temperature (or, for air-water, the wet-bulb temperature), the entering-air wet-bulb temperature must be below $t_{L1}$ *but its dry-bulb temperature need not be*. For this reason, it is perfectly possible to cool water to a value of $t_{L1}$ less than the entering-air dry-bulb temperature $t_{G1}$. It is also possible to operate a cooler with entering air saturated, so long as its temperature is less than $t_{L1}$. The difference between the exit-liquid temperature and the entering-air wet-bulb temperature, $t_{L1} - t_{W1}$, called the "wet-bulb temperature approach," is then a measure of the driving force available for diffusion at the lower end of the equipment.

In the design of cooling towers, this is ordinarily specified to be from 5 to 10°F. The use of over-all mass-transfer coefficients does not distinguish between convective and evaporative cooling of the liquid and consequently will not permit computation of the humidity or dry-bulb temperature of the air leaving the equipment. The air will ordinarily be very nearly saturated, and for purposes of estimating the evaporation to be expected it may be so assumed.

For systems other than air-water, for which $h_G/k_Y$ does not approximate $C_S$, it is necessary to calculate the height by numerical integration of Eq. (7.56), for which Sherwood and Reed[19] provide an example. It has also been suggested[12] that a modified enthalpy $C_S r t + \lambda_0 Y'$ be used, whereupon Eqs. (7.58) to (7.64) become useful for such cases as well.

**Illustration 13.** A plant requires 2,000 lb./min. of cooling water to flow through its distillation-equipment condensers, thereby removing 55,000 B.t.u./min. from the

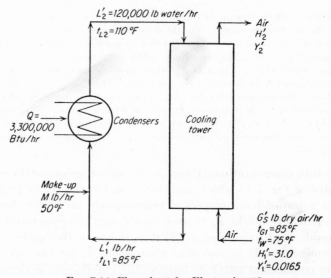

FIG. 7.14. Flow sheet for Illustration 13.

condensers. The water will leave the condensers at 110°F. It is planned to cool it for reuse by contact with air in an induced-draft cooling tower. Make-up water will come from a well at 50°F. The design conditions chosen are entering air at 85°F. dry-bulb, 75°F. wet-bulb temperature; water cooled to within 10°F. of the inlet-air wet-bulb temperature, i.e., to 85°F.; an air/water ratio of 1.5 times the minimum. For the packing to be used, $K_Y a$ is expected to be 200 lb./(hr.) (cu. ft.) ($\Delta Y'$), provided the liquid rate is at least 2,000 lb./(hr.)(sq. ft.) and the gas rate 1,500 lb./(hr.)(sq. ft.). Compute the required cross section and packed height of the cooling tower, and estimate the make-up water required.

*Solution.* Refer to Fig. 7.14, which represents the flow sheet of the operation. The entering-air humidity and enthalpy are taken from Fig. 7.6. The operating diagram (Fig. 7.15) contains the saturated air–enthalpy curve, and on this plot is point $N$ representing the conditions at the bottom of the tower ($t_{L1} = 85°$F., $H_1' = 31.0$). The operating line will pass through $N$ and end at $t_{L2} = 110°$F. For the minimum value of $G_S'$, the operating line will have the least slope which causes it to

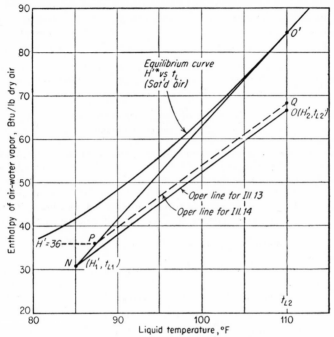

FIG. 7.15. Solution to Illustrations 13 and 14.

touch the equilibrium curve and will consequently pass through point $O'$, where $H_2' = 84.7$ B.t.u./lb. dry air. The slope of line $O'N$ is therefore

$$\frac{L'C_{AL}}{G_{S,\text{min}}'} = \frac{120,000(1)}{G_{S,\text{min}}'} = \frac{84.7 - 31.0}{110 - 85}$$

and $G_{S,\text{min}}' = 55,900$ lb. dry air/hr. For a gas rate of 1.5 times the minimum, $G_S' = 1.5(55,900) = 83,800$ lb. dry air/hr. Therefore

$$\frac{H_2' - 31.0}{110 - 85} = \frac{120,000(1)}{83,800}$$

and $H_2' = 66.8$ B.t.u./lb. dry air, plotted at point $O$. The operating line is therefore line $ON$. For a liquid rate of at least 2,000 lb./(hr.)(sq. ft.), the tower cross section would be $120,000/2,000 = 60$ sq. ft. For a gas rate of at least 1,500 lb./(hr.)(sq. ft.), the cross section will be $83,800/1,500 = 56$ sq. ft. The latter will therefore be used, since the liquid rate will then exceed the minimum to ensure $K_Ya = 200$.

Basis: 1 sq ft. cross section. $G_S' = 1,500$ lb. dry gas/hr. The driving force $H'^* - H'$ is computed at frequent intervals of $t_L$ from Fig. 7.15 as listed below:

| $t_L$, °F. | $H'^*$(equilibrium curve) | $H'$ (operating line) | $1/(H'^* - H')$ |
|:---:|:---:|:---:|:---:|
| 85 | 41.9 | 31.0 | 0.0917 |
| 90 | 48.2 | 38.3 | 0.1011 |
| 95 | 55.7 | 45.3 | 0.0980 |
| 100 | 64.0 | 52.5 | 0.0885 |
| 105 | 74.2 | 59.5 | 0.0680 |
| 110 | 84.7 | 66.8 | 0.0558 |

The data of the last two columns are plotted against each other, $H'$ as abscissa, and the area under the curve is 3.18. From Eq. (7.61),

$$3.18 = K_Y a Z / G'_S = 200Z/1,500$$
$$Z = 23.8 \text{ ft. of packed height}$$

(NOTE: For this case, $N_{tOG} = 3.18$, and $H_{tOG} = G'_S/K_Y a = 1,500/200 = 7.5$ ft.)

The make-up water requirement, $M$ lb./hr., can only be estimated. Refer to Fig. 7.14. If the exit air is assumed to be saturated, its humidity $Y'_2$ must be that for saturated air at $H'_S = H'_2 = 66.8$, or $Y'_2 = 0.0453$. Since $G'_S$ was calculated on the assumption that $L'_2 = L'_1$ (a straight operating line), thus not allowing for evaporation, it is best to eliminate $G'_S$ in estimating $M$. An enthalpy balance for the entire plant,

$$3,300,000 + M(1)(50 - 32) + G'_S(31.0) = G'_S H'_2$$

A water balance,

$$M = G'_S(Y'_2 - 0.0165)$$

Eliminating $G'_S$,

$$M = \frac{3,300,000}{\dfrac{H'_2 - 31.0}{Y'_2 - 0.0165} - 18} = \frac{3,300,000}{\dfrac{66.8 - 31.0}{0.0453 - 0.0165} - 18} = 2,690 \text{ lb./hr.}$$

**Illustration 14.** In the cooler of Illustration 13, to what temperature would the water be cooled if, after the tower was built and operated at the design $L'/G'_S$ ratio, the entering air should enter at dry-bulb temperature $t_{G1} = 85°F$. and wet-bulb temperature $t_{w1} = 80°F$.?

*Solution.* For the new conditions, $t_{L2} = 110°F$., and $H'_1 = 36.0$ B.t.u./lb. dry air, and the slope of the operating line is the same as that for Illustration 13. Refer to Fig. 7.15. The new operating line will be parallel to line $ON$ and end at $H'_1 = 36.0$ and at $t_{L2} = 110°F$. Since the coefficient $K_Y a$ is unchanged, the line is located by trial and error so that the area under a curve of $1/(H'^* - H')$ against $H'$ remains at 3.18, the value found previously. The line $PQ$ (Fig. 7.15) is found to satisfy these conditions, and $t_{L1}$ is read at point $P$ as 87.4°F., the new outlet-water temperature.

2. *Dehumidification.* If a warm vapor-gas mixture is contacted with cold liquid so that the humidity of the gas mixture is greater than that at the liquid-gas interface, vapor will diffuse toward the liquid and the gas will be dehumidified. In addition, sensible heat may be transferred as a result of temperature differences existing within the system. Fundamentally the operation is the same as that considered for water coolers, except for the direction of enthalpy and vapor transfer, and the previous

equations apply with only obvious modification. For the case where the psychrometric ratio equals unity, the enthalpy diagram shows the operating line to lie above the equilibrium curve, as in Fig. 7.16, and its slope is $L'C_{AL}/G'_S$. The driving force is $H' - H'^*$, and Eqs. (7.61) and (7.62) may be used with this driving force. The indications are that the coefficients $K_Ya$ are the same for a given set of operating conditions irrespective of direction of diffusion, and those applicable to water coolers are likewise applicable here.

*Tray towers.* Liquid cooling and gas dehumidification may be carried out in stagewise fashion in bubble-cap tray towers as well as in packed towers, although it is not generally the custom to do so. The determination of the number of ideal trays, following the principles of Chap. 5, is done on the gas enthalpy–liquid temperature operating diagram.

3. *Adiabatic Humidification-Cooling.* This is the special case of gas-liquid contact where the liquid enters the equipment at the adiabatic-saturation temperature of the entering gas. In any contact system when the liquid leaving is continually recirculated to recontact fresh gas flowing through the apparatus, the temperature of the entire liquid will fall to and remain at

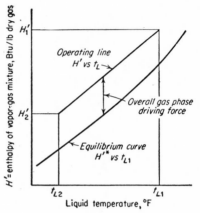

FIG. 7.16. Operating diagram for dehumidification.

the adiabatic-saturation temperature. The gas will be cooled and humidified, following along the path of the adiabatic-saturation curve on the psychrometric chart which passes through the entering-gas conditions. Depending upon the degree of contact, the gas will approach more or less closely equilibrium with the liquid, or its adiabatic-saturation conditions. This supposes that the make-up liquid enters at the adiabatic-saturation temperature also, but for most purposes the quantity of evaporation is so small relative to the total liquid circulation that minor deviations from the adiabatic-saturation temperature for the make-up may be ignored.

As has been shown previously, the enthalpy of the gas is practically a function only of its adiabatic-saturation temperature, which remains constant throughout the operation. The enthalpy of the liquid at constant temperature is also constant, so that an operating "line" on a plot such as Fig. 7.13 would be merely a single point on the equilibrium curve. This diagram cannot therefore be used for design purposes. The temperature and humidity changes, which lie entirely within the gas phase, can be used, however, and these are shown schematically in Fig. 7.17. If

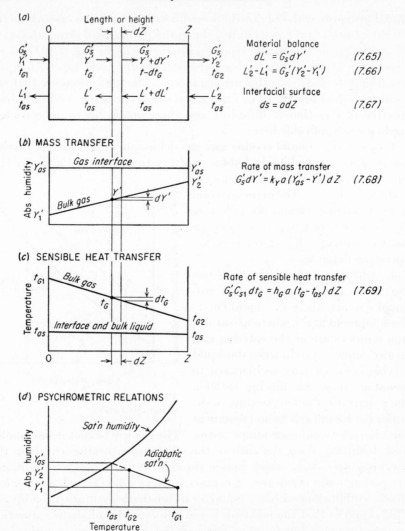

FIG. 7.17. Adiabatic humidification and cooling.

mass transfer is used as the basis for design, Eq. (7.68) may be integrated as follows,

$$\int_{Y_1'}^{Y_2'} \frac{dY'}{Y_{as}' - Y'} = \frac{k_Y a}{G_s'} \int_0^Z dZ \qquad (7.70)$$

and since $Y_{as}'$ is constant,

$$\ln \frac{Y_{as}' - Y_1'}{Y_{as}' - Y_2'} = \frac{k_Y a Z}{G_s'} \qquad (7.71)$$

Equation (7.71) may be used directly for determining $Z$, or it may be rearranged by solving for $G_s'$ and multiplying each side by $Y_2' - Y_1'$ or its equivalent,

$$G'_s(Y'_2 - Y'_1) = \frac{k_Y a Z[(Y'_{as} - Y'_1) - (Y'_{as} - Y'_2)]}{\ln [(Y'_{as} - Y'_1)/(Y'_{as} - Y'_2)]} = k_Y a Z (\Delta Y')_{av} \quad (7.72)$$

where $(\Delta Y')_{av}$ is the logarithmic average of the humidity-difference driving forces at the ends of the equipment. Alternatively,

$$N_{tG} = \frac{Y'_2 - Y'_1}{(\Delta Y')_{av}} = \ln \frac{Y'_{as} - Y'_1}{Y'_{as} - Y'_2} \quad (7.73)$$

and

$$H_{tG} = \frac{G'_s}{k_Y a} = \frac{Z}{N_{tG}} \quad (7.74)$$

where $N_{tG}$ is the number of gas-phase transfer units and $H_{tG}$ the corresponding height of a transfer unit.†

In contacting operations of this sort, where one phase approaches equilibrium with the other under conditions such that the characteristics of the latter do not change, the maximum change in the first phase corresponds to the operation of one theoretical stage (see Chap. 5). Since the humidity in adiabatic equilibrium with the liquid is $Y'_{as}$, the Murphree gas-phase stage efficiency is then

$$\mathbf{E}_G = \frac{Y'_2 - Y'_1}{Y'_{as} - Y'_1} = 1 - \frac{Y'_{as} - Y'_2}{Y'_{as} - Y'_1} = 1 - e^{-k_Y a Z/G_s'} = 1 - e^{-N_{tG}} \quad (7.75)$$

If heat transfer is used as the basis for design, similar treatment of Eq. (7.69) leads to

$$G'_s C_{s1}(t_{G1} - t_{G2}) = \frac{h_G a Z[(t_{G1} - t_{as}) - (t_{G2} - t_{as})]}{\ln [(t_{G1} - t_{as})/(t_{G2} - t_{as})]} = h_G a Z (\Delta t)_{av} \quad (7.76)$$

where $h_G a$ is the volumetric-heat-transfer coefficient of sensible-heat transfer between the bulk of the gas and the liquid surface.

**Illustration 15.** A horizontal spray chamber (Fig. 7.21) with recirculated water is to be used for the adiabatic humidification and cooling of air. The active part of the chamber is 5 ft. long and has a cross section of 20 sq. ft. With the nozzle arrangement provided, and when operated with the water-circulation rate recommended by the nozzle manufacturer, the coefficient of heat transfer is expected to be $h_G a = 85$ B.t.u./(hr.)(cu. ft.)(°F.). An amount 7,500 cu. ft./min. of air at 150°F., $Y' = 0.0170$ lb. water/lb. dry air, is to be blown through the spray.

    *a.* What exit temperature and humidity can be expected for the air?

    *b.* What make-up water will be needed?

    *c.* Express the performance in terms of $k_Y a$, $N_{tG}$, $H_{tG}$, and stage efficiency.

    *d.* If a duplicate spray chamber, operated in the same manner, were to be added in series with the first, what exit conditions would be expected for the air?

† To be entirely consistent with the definition of Chap. 8, Eq. (7.74) should read $H_{tG} = G'_s/k_Y a(1 - y_A)$. The value of $1 - y_A$ in the present application is, however, ordinarily very close to unity.

*Solution.* *a.* From the psychrometric chart (Fig. 7.6), the initial air has a percentage humidity of 8.0%. The dry specific volume of air at 150°F. = 15.38, and the saturated volume = 20.60 cu. ft./lb. dry air. The humid volume of the entering air is therefore

$$v_H = 15.38 + 0.08(20.60 - 15.38) = 15.80 \text{ cu. ft. humid air/lb. dry air}$$

$$G_S' = \frac{7,500(60)}{15.80(20)} = 1,422 \text{ lb. dry air/(hr.)(sq. ft.)}$$

The initial humid heat = $C_{S1} = 0.24 + 0.45Y' = 0.24 + 0.45(0.017) = 0.248$ B.t.u./-(lb. dry air)(°F.). $t_{G1} = 150$°F., and the air lies on the adiabatic-saturation line for $t_{as} = 90$°F. $Z = 5$ ft.

Eq. (7.76):

$$1,422(0.248)(150 - t_{G2}) = \frac{85(5)[(150 - 90) - (t_{G2} - 90)]}{\ln \dfrac{150 - 90}{t_{G2} - 90}}$$

$$= \frac{85(5)(150 - t_{G2})}{\ln \dfrac{60}{t_{G2} - 90}}$$

$$t_{G2} = 108°F.$$

On the 90°F. adiabatic-saturation curve, the humidity at this temperature is $Y_2' = 0.0268$ lb. water/lb. dry air.

*b.* The make-up water,

$$G_S'(20)(Y_2' - Y_1') = 1,422(20)(0.0268 - 0.0170) = 278 \text{ lb./hr.}$$

*c.* $Y_{as}'$ (at 90°F.) = 0.0312 lb. water/lb. dry air.

Eq. (7.73):

$$N_{tG} = \ln \frac{Y_{as}' - Y_1'}{Y_{as}' - Y_2'} = \ln \frac{0.0312 - 0.0170}{0.0312 - 0.0268} = 1.15 \text{ transfer units}$$

Eq. (7.71):

$$k_y a = \frac{G_S'}{Z} \ln \frac{Y_{as}' - Y_1'}{Y_{as}' - Y_2'} = \frac{1,422}{5}(1.15) = 327 \text{ lb. water evapd./(hr.)(cu. ft.)}(\Delta Y')$$

Eq. (7.74): $\qquad H_{tG} = Z/N_{tG} = 5/1.15 = 4.35$ ft.

Eq. (7.75): $\qquad \mathbf{E}_G = 1 - e^{-N_{tG}} = 1 - 1/e^{1.15} = 0.684$, or 68.4%

*d.* $Z = 10$ ft. At the same air rate and spray density, the coefficients are unchanged.

Eq. (7.76):

$$1,422(0.248)(150 - t_{G2}) = \frac{85(10)(150 - t_{G2})}{\ln \dfrac{60}{t_{G2} - 90}}$$

$$t_{G2} = 95.4°F.$$

$Y_2'$, read from the adiabatic-saturation curve as before, is 0.0298 lb. water/lb. dry air.

## EQUIPMENT

Any of the gas-liquid contact devices described in Chap. 6 are applicable to the problems of water cooling, humidification, or dehumidification, and conventional packed towers and tray towers are very effective in this service. Air and water are low-cost materials, however, and when large volumes must be handled, as in many water-cooling operations, for example, equipment of low initial cost and low operating cost is essential. For this reason large-scale installations are more frequently of the type described below.

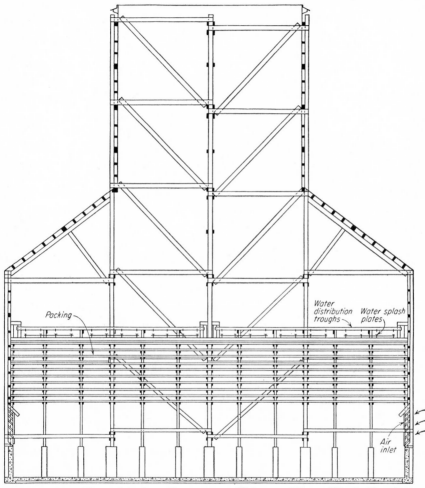

Fig. 7.18. Natural-draft cooling tower. (*Courtesy of Foster Wheeler Corp.*)

**Cooling Towers.** These are largely constructed of redwood, a material which is very durable when in continuous contact with water. The internal packing is usually in the form of horizontal wooden slats, most frequently of rectangular cross section, arranged either in staggered formation or with alternate tiers set at right angles. The free void space is very large, usually greater than 90 per cent, in order that the pressure drop experienced by the gas be as low as possible. The air-water interfacial surface consequently includes not only that of the liquid films which wet the slats but also the surface of droplets which fall as a rain from each tier of slats to the next.

*Natural-circulation* towers are of two types, atmospheric and natural-draft. In the case of the atmospheric tower, air circulation is dependent solely on the prevailing winds, which produce essentially a crossflow of the air and water. The towers are generally long and narrow in their horizontal cross section, in order to ensure adequate penetration of the air into the central portions. Louvers on the sides of the tower help reduce the losses of water entrained in the gas stream. Natural-draft towers, as in Fig. 7.18, ensure more positive air movement even in calm weather by depending upon the displacement of the warm air inside the tower by the relatively cooler air outside, in the manner of a chimney. Large cross sections are required so as to keep the air velocity and consequently the air-pressure drop low. Both these tower types must be relatively tall in order to operate at a small wet-bulb temperature approach and consequently may have a high first cost. The cost of pumping water to the top may then also be high, but there is of course no requirement for fans or power cost for blowing air. Natural-circulation equipment is used in such areas as the southwestern United States and in the Middle East, where the humidity of the air is usually very low, and in parts of Europe where the air temperatures are generally low, but the emphasis in this country in recent years has been almost entirely on mechanical-draft equipment.

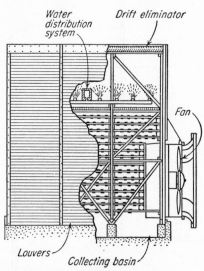

Fig. 7.19. Forced-draft cooling tower. (*Courtesy of The Marley Co., Inc.*)

*Mechanical-draft* towers may be of the forced-draft type, where the air is blown into the tower by a fan at the bottom, as in Fig. 7.19, or of the induced-draft type, where the air is drawn through by a fan at the top, as in Fig. 7.20. The forced-draft tower is particularly subject to recirculation of the hot, humid discharged air into the fan intake, owing to the low velocity of discharge from the top, and this will of course reduce the effectiveness of the tower materially. On the other hand, the induced-draft tower discharges the air at high velocity and furthermore can more

readily be provided with uniform air distribution into the packing.    For
these reasons it has been more popular in this country in recent years,
despite the fact that the fan power will be somewhat larger since the fan
operates on air of lower density.    Water may be distributed over the
packing by a system of troughs, which deliver it in a series of streams to
the packing, or by a series of spray nozzles, which spray the water upward,

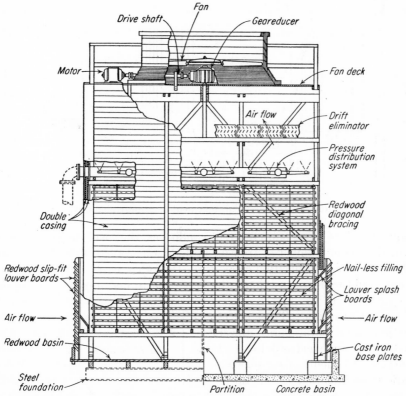

FIG. 7.20. Induced-draft cooling tower.    (*Courtesy of The Marley Co., Inc.*)

allowing it to fall back upon the packing.    Liquid rates are ordinarily in
the range of 1 to 5 gal./(min.)(sq. ft.) ($L' = 500$ to $2,500$) and superficial
air velocities of the order 4 to 7 ft./sec. ($G'_s = 1,200$ to $2,100$), whereupon the pressure drop for the air is ordinarily less than 2 in. of water.
Entrainment, or "drift," eliminators at the top can maintain losses of
water from this cause to less than 0.3 per cent of the circulated water.
An additional loss of water may be incurred as "blowdown," water which
is deliberately wasted in order to keep the percentage of dissolved solids
(hardness) at a permissible value.    Make-up water must then account
for evaporation, entrainment losses, and blowdown.

*Spray towers* are forced- or induced-draft towers without internal packing, depending entirely on the water sprays at the top to provide interfacial surface. They are useful where low pressure drop for the gas is absolutely essential. Owing to internal recirculation of the gas and con-

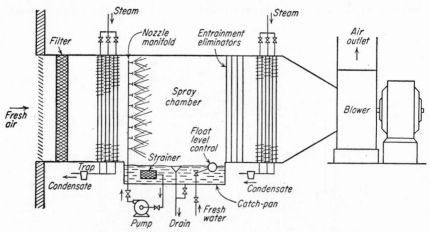

FIG. 7.21. Schematic arrangement of a spray chamber.

sequent lack of true countercurrent conditions, they will not successfully provide a large number of transfer units or theoretical stages. In cases of adiabatic humidification-cooling, on the other hand, where the constant liquid temperature limits the operation to one stage in any event, they are useful.

**Spray Chambers.** These are essentially horizontal spray towers and may be arranged as in Fig. 7.21. They are frequently used for adiabatic humidification-cooling operations. With large liquid drops, gas rates up to roughly 600 to 900 lb./(hr.)(sq. ft.) are possible, but in any case entrainment eliminators are necessary.

Heat-transfer surfaces at the inlet and outlet provide for preheating and after heating of the air, so that processes of the type shown in Fig.

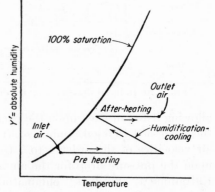

FIG. 7.22. A simple conditioning process.

7.22 may be carried out. If large humidity changes by this method are required, preheating of the air to unusually high temperatures is necessary, however. As an alternative, the spray water may be heated above the adiabatic-saturation temperature to which it will tend to come by direct injection of steam or by heating coils. Dehumidification may be practiced by cooling the water prior to spraying or by refrigerating coils directly in the spray chamber. Operations of this sort cannot be followed with assurance on the enthalpy-temperature diagrams described earlier owing to the departure from strictly countercurrent-flow conditions which prevail. When an adequate spray density is maintained, it may be assumed that three banks of sprays in series will bring the gas to substantial equilibrium with the incoming spray liquid.

For comfort air conditioning, many compact devices are provided with a variety of these facilities, and automatic controls are available.

**Spray Ponds.** These are sometimes used for water cooling where close approach to the air wet-bulb temperature is not required. Spray ponds are essentially fountains, where the water is sprayed upward into the air and allowed to fall back into a collection basin. They are subject to high windage losses of water.

## MASS-TRANSFER RATES

Despite the relative simplicity of these systems in that concentration gradients reside entirely in the gas phase, there are surprisingly few data available for general design purposes. This is a result of the considerable difficulty attending the gathering of reliable data. For systems other than air-water, where enthalpy driving forces cannot be conveniently used, it is necessary to measure inlet and outlet humidities of the gas as it passes through the contacting equipment. Very short contact time in efficient packed towers will nearly saturate the gas, making the measurement of correct driving forces very difficult and the data correspondingly less accurate.

As a consequence very short packed heights must be used, which in turn lead to sizable "end effects." This refers to the mass transfer brought about by contact of gas and liquid at the ends of the towers, i.e., at introduction of sprays, at packing supports, by liquid dripping from the lower end of the packed section, etc. For proper evaluation of the packing itself, correction must be made for these. This usually involves operation at several packing heights followed by extrapolation of the data to zero packed height, but the procedure is subject to considerable error. New equipment designed with uncorrected data will therefore be conservatively designed if shorter than the experimental equipment but underdesigned if taller. Alternatively, equipment designed with corrected data will include a factor of safety represented by the end effects which will be large for short equipment but small for tall equipment. The use of uncorrected data in design probably accounts in part for the

TABLE 7.2. MASS-TRANSFER RATES FOR CONTACT OF A PURE LIQUID WITH A GAS

| Item | Equipment | Process and notes | Range of flow rates | Equation | Reference |
|---|---|---|---|---|---|
| 1 | 8-in.-diam. tower, 1-in. Raschig rings | Liquid cooling with air and water, methanol, benzene, ethyl butyrate. $k_Ga$ corrected for end effects and independent of $L'$ for $L' = 1,600-5,000$ | $L' = 1,600$ $G'_S = 150-500$ | $k_Ga = 0.486D^{0.15}G'^{0.72}_S$ | Surosky and Dodge[21] |
| 2 | 10-in.-diam. tower; 12.5-in. depth of 15, 25, and 35-mm. Raschig rings | Humidification-cooling, liquid cooling, and dehumidification with air-water | $L' = 200-4,160$ $G'_S = 137-586$ | $k_Ya = 0.45G'_S L^{0.2}$ | Yoshida and Tanaka[24] |
| 3 | 21.5-in.-square tower, 1½-in. Berl saddles | Humidification-cooling with air-water. Corrected for end effects | $L' = 120-6,800$ $G'_S = 100-700$ | $k_Ya = 1.25G'^{0.39}_S L^{0.48}$ | Hensel and Treybal[8] |
| 4 | 4-in.-diam. tower, ½-in. spheres | Humidification-cooling with air-water. Corrected for end effects | $d_pG'/\mu = 304-927$ $L' = 85-1,895$ | $H_{tG} = \dfrac{13.4}{L'^{0.5}}\left(\dfrac{d_pG'}{\mu}\right)^{0.1}$ | Weisman and Bonilla[22] |
| 5 | 6-ft.-square tower, 11-ft. 3-in. packed height. Wood slats, ⅜ × 2 in., spaced parallel, 15 in. between tiers | Liquid cooling with air-water | $L' = 350-3,000$ $G'_S = 664-1,680$ | $K_Ya = 0.197L'^{0.4}G'^{0.5}$ | Lichtenstein[9] |

TABLE 7.2. MASS-TRANSFER RATES FOR CONTACT OF A PURE LIQUID WITH A GAS (*Continued*)

| Item | Equipment | Process and notes | Range of flow rates | Equation | Reference |
|---|---|---|---|---|---|
| 6 | 41⅝ × 23⅞-in. tower, packed height = 41⅜ in. Wood slats, ¼ × 2 × 23.5 in., bottom edge serrated, on ⅝-in. horiz. centers, 3⅝- to 2⅝-in. vert. centers. 18 spray nozzles | Liquid cooling with air-water | $L' = 880–1,500$ $G'_S = 700–1,500$ | $K_Y a = 0.00029L'G'_S - 0.114G'_S - 0.133L' + 311$ | Simpson and Sherwood[20] |
| 7 | 6⅜-in.-square tower × 6 ft. Carbon slats, 6 × 1 × ⅛ in., bottom edge serrated, on ¾-in. horiz. centers, 1¼-in. vert. centers. Alternate tiers at right angles. $a = 23.6$ sq. ft./cu. ft. | Liquid cooling with air-water | $G'_S = 1,000–3,000$ $L' = 930–2,100$ $L' = 2,100–2,810$ | $K_G a = \left(\dfrac{0.0222L'}{1,000} + 0.0526\right)G'^{0.8}_S$ $K_G a = 0.0992G'^{0.8}_S$ | Norman[13] |
| 8 | Spray tower, 31.5 in. diam. × 52 in. high. 6 solid-cone spray nozzles | Liquid cooling and dehumidification with air-water | $L' = 300–800$ $G'_S = 200–750$ | $N_{tOG} = \dfrac{0.0526L'}{G'^{0.58}_S}$ | Pigford and Pyle[16] |
| 9 | Perforated plate (sieve tray). 83 ⅛-in. holes on ⅜-in. triangular centers | Humidification-cooling with air-water | $G'_S = 670–1,920$ | Liquid depth, in.    $N_{tG}$<br>0.5    ca. 1.5<br>1    2<br>2    2.5 | West, Gilbert, and Shimizu[23] |

frequently made observation that tall towers are less effective per unit height than short towers.

The presence of important heat-transfer resistance in the liquid phase in such operations as liquid cooling and dehumidification has not been adequately established. In wetted-wall towers it is apparently quite unimportant, and in packed towers it appears to be relatively minor if present at all. In so far as this is true, $k_Y a = K_Y a$. In adiabatic humidification-cooling the liquid resistance is of course completely absent. In any given situation an experimental program to establish its importance will first involve operation as an adiabatic humidifier-cooler at constant liquid temperature to establish values of $k_Y a$, followed by operation for liquid cooling or dehumidification to give values of $K_Y a$.

**Wetted-wall Towers.** When the gas is in turbulent flow, mass-transfor coefficients are given by Eq. (3.43) for this simple case.

**Packed Towers.** Table 7.2 contains a summary of a few of the data available. It is included principally for purposes of discussion and the solution of problems here, and for design purposes the original references should be consulted for further details. The empirical equations included in the table are strictly limited to the conditions covered by the respective experiments and should not be extrapolated to other conditions without study of the original references. Additional data are summarized and reviewed in detail elsewhere.[15,18]

The discussion of Chap. 3 on mass-transfer rates for the simpler shapes permits only a limited indication of the effect of operating variables on the coefficients for packed towers. Rate of gas flow, gas-phase Schmidt number, and type of packing can be expected to influence the gas-film coefficient. The interfacial area $a$ is not identical with the packing surface and will vary with liquid-irrigation rate; for this reason as well as possible effects of liquid rate on gas-phase turbulence the liquid rate becomes an important variable.

Surosky and Dodge[21] (item 1, Table 7.2) found $L'$ to be significant up to a value of 1,600 lb./(hr.)(sq. ft.) but of no effect on $k_G a$ at higher values, for 1-in. Raschig rings. At this rate presumably the packing becomes completely wetted. At $L' = 1,600$, the Schmidt number (or diffusivity, since only $D$ of this group was varied) entered only as $D^{0.15}$. The coefficients are therefore nearly independent of type of vapor diffusing, in contrast with the strong effect found for wetted-wall towers [see Eq. (3.43)]. Presumably this is due to the relative insignificance of the laminar gas film and the predominance of the turbulent core with such packings. This is confirmed by Sherwood and Holloway,[17] who report an effect of $D^{0.17}$. Other data are conflicting, and it has become the general practice to include the Schmidt number effect as $Sc^{0.5}$ ($k_Y a$ proportional to $1/Sc^{0.5}$, $H_{tG}$ proportional to $Sc^{0.5}$) in unknown cases. The data of Yoshida and Tanaka[24] (item 2, Table 7.2) proved conclusively that direction of diffusion, i.e., whether the operation is liquid cooling or dehumidification, has no influence on the coefficients.

**Sprays.** Horizontal and vertical spray chambers are apparently subject to very large end effects, and it is well established that short sprays are much more effective per unit length than long. The performance can be expected to be influenced by spray-nozzle design, liquid rate and

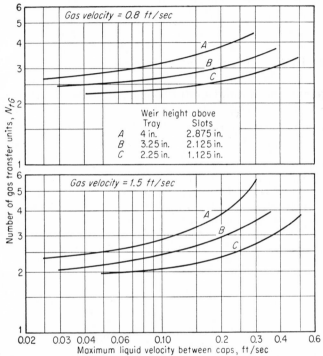

FIG. 7.23. Gas-film transfer units for a bubble-cap tray, humidification of air with water[5] (Sc = 0.60). Gas velocity based on tray area devoted to caps.

pressure behind the nozzle, gas rate, and the number of nozzles per unit cross section of spray chamber. A few data are summarized in item 8 (Table 7.2).

**Stagewise Equipment.** Bubble-cap trays are effective in humidification but are not frequently used owing to the relatively high pressure drop for the gas and high initial cost. Relatively few data on tray performance in this service are available. The most complete are those of Gerster *et al.*,[5] part of which are summarized in Fig. 7.23. These were taken on a 13-in.-diameter tray arranged for simple crossflow of liquid, in the humidification of air with water (Sc = 0.60). It has been shown[5] that these data can predict performance of larger trays, and for different designs, provided adequate information on foaming is available. The number of gas-transfer units, which is related to the tray efficiency through Eq. (7.75), is relatively independent of gas velocity above values of 1.5 ft./sec. and at lower values varies roughly linearly with gas velocity. The height of froth on the plate, and hence the time of gas-liquid contact, has been shown to be the other principal factor, but since this cannot be generally estimated, the figure has been prepared in terms of horizontal liquid velocity between caps and liquid depth. On this basis, the slot submergence is probably more significant than weir height. For systems other than air-water, the value of $N_{tG}$ can be expected to vary inversely as $Sc^{0.5}$.

Item 9 (Table 7.2) lists a few data for sieve plates in this type of service.

**Atmospheric and Natural-draft Cooling Towers, Spray Ponds.** These devices, which depend greatly on wind velocity for their performance, are largely designed on an empirical basis with the help of performance data gathered from existing equipment (see, for example, Perry[15]).

**Illustration 16.** In the construction of a pilot plant for the development of a process involving vapor-phase catalytic oxidation of toluene, it is desired to produce continuously a mixture of toluene and air containing 5 mole % toluene, at 1 atm., 90°F., with 250 lb. air/hr. One of the suggested designs calls for adiabatic humidification-cooling of the air with toluene in a tower packed with 1.5-in. Berl saddles. Estimate the size of the packed section required.

*Solution.* Mol. wt. air = 29, mol. wt. toluene = 92.1. At 5 mole % toluene, the humidity is $Y_2' = (\frac{5}{95})(92.1/29) = 0.1675$ lb. toluene/lb. air; $t_{G2} = 90°F.$; $C_B = 0.24$, $C_A = 0.30$ B.t.u./(lb.)(°F.); $C_{S2} = 0.24 + 0.30(0.1675) = 0.29$ B.t.u./(lb.)(°F.).

Eq. (7.27):
$$t_{G2} - t_{as} = (Y_{as}' - Y_2') \frac{\lambda_{as}}{C_{S2}}$$

$$90 - t_{as} = (Y_{as}' - 0.1675) \frac{\lambda_{as}}{0.29}$$

By trial as in Illustration 11, $t_{as}$ and $Y_{as}'$ are calculated to be 88.2°F. and 0.1700 lb. toluene/lb. air, respectively. $\lambda_{as} = 183.5$ B.t.u./lb.

$$Y_1' \text{ for pure air} = 0$$

Eq. (7.27):
$$t_{G1} - 88.2 = (0.1700 - 0) \frac{183.5}{0.24}$$

Therefore, $t_{G1} = 218°F.$, which is the temperature to which the entering air must be preheated. The recirculated toluene will come to $t_{as} = 88.2°F.$

For 1.5-in. Berl saddles, the smallest acceptable tower diameter is 1.5(8) = 12 in., for which 12-in. schedule 30 steel pipe may be used (I.D. = 12.09 in., inside cross-sectional area = 0.7972 sq. ft.). $G_S' = 250/0.7972 = 314$ lb. dry gas/(hr.)(sq. ft.).

At the bottom of the packed section (or gas inlet), the total gas flow is $G_S'(1 + Y_1') = 314(1 + 0) = 314$ lb./(hr.)(sq. ft.).

Eq. (7.15): $\quad v_{H1} = 0.730 \frac{1}{29} \frac{218 + 460}{1} = 17.08$ cu. ft./lb. dry gas

The superficial linear velocity of the gas is $314(17.08)/3,600 = 1.49$ ft./sec. Gas-inlet conditions control flooding, and from Fig. 6.26 the flooding liquid rate is calculated to be 23,000 lb. liquid toluene/(hr.)(sq. ft.). The mass-transfer data of Table 7.2 (item 3) are limited to $L' = 6,800$ lb./(hr.)(sq. ft.) (total liquid flow = 5,410 lb./hr.), and if this rate is used, the conditions will be well below flooding. From Table 7.2, for air-water on 1.5-in. saddles,

$$k_Y a = 1.25 G_S'^{0.39} L'^{0.48} = 1.25(314)^{0.39}(6,800)^{0.48}$$
$$= 811 \text{ lb./(hr.)(cu. ft.)}(\Delta Y')$$

Sc for air-water = 0.60, for air-toluene = 2.00 (see Illustration 11).

$$k_Y a \text{ for air-toluene} = 811 \left(\frac{0.6}{2.00}\right)^{0.5} = 444 \text{ lb./(hr.)(cu. ft.)}(\Delta Y')$$

Eq. (7.71):
$$\ln \frac{0.1700 - 0}{0.1700 - 0.1675} = \frac{444Z}{314}$$
$$Z = 3.0 \text{ ft. of packed height}$$

The total height of 12-in. pipe will additionally include 6 in. for a liquid distributor, 6 in. of packing above the liquid distributor for removal of entrained toluene from the exit gas, and 12 in. below the packing support for collection of liquid and providing for a gas inlet, making a total tower height of 5 ft.

**Illustration 17.** How many bubble-cap trays of the type sketched in Fig. 7.24 would be required for the humidification of Illustration 16, assuming the same gas- and liquid-flow rates?

*Solution.* The area between weir plates (bubbling area) is 1.23 sq. ft. For 250 lb. air/hr. at $v_{H1} = 17.08$ cu. ft./lb., the gas velocity based on the bubble-cap area is

$$\frac{250(17.08)}{3,600(1.23)} = 0.963 \text{ ft./sec.}$$

For 5,410 lb./hr. of toluene, with a density at 88.2°F. of 53.5 lb./cu. ft., the liquid rate is 0.0282 cu. ft./sec. For a weir length = $10/12 = 0.833$ ft., the height of liquid over the weir, by Eq. (6.4), is

$$5.38(0.995)(1.15)(0.0282/0.833)^{2/3}$$
$$= 0.645 \text{ in.}$$

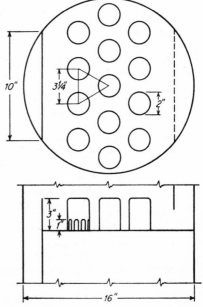

FIG. 7.24. Bubble-cap tray for Illustration 17.

The total liquid depth is then $(3 + 0.645)/12 = 0.303$ ft. The minimum free width for liquid flow (center row of caps) is $16 - 5(2) = 6$ in., or 0.5 ft., and the maximum liquid velocity is $0.0282/0.5(0.303) = 0.186$ ft./sec. The weir height above the slots is 2 in.

From Fig. 7.23, at a gas velocity of 0.8 ft./sec., $N_{tG} = 2.9$, and, at a gas velocity of 1.5 ft./sec., $N_{tG} = 2.8$. For 0.963 ft./sec., take $N_{tG} = 2.8$. This is for the air-water system and must be corrected for Schmidt number,

$$N_{tG} = 2.8 \left( \frac{0.6}{2.00} \right)^{0.5} = 1.53 \text{ transfer units for toluene-air}$$

This corresponds to the tray efficiency $= \mathbf{E}_G = 1 - e^{-1.53} = 0.784$, or 78.4%.
The number of transfer units required is, by Eq. (7.73),

$$N_{tG} = \ln \frac{Y'_{as} - Y'_1}{Y'_{as} - Y'_2} = \ln \frac{0.1700 - 0}{0.1700 - 0.1675} = 4.25$$

Therefore $4.25/1.53 = 2.8$, or 3 trays are required.

Methods of dehumidification other than those discussed in this chapter include adsorption, such as those methods using activated silica gel or alumina as adsorbents, and washing the gas with liquids containing dissolved substances which appreciably lower the partial pressure of water, such as lithium chloride or the glycols.

## NOTATION FOR CHAPTER 7

$a$ = interfacial surface per unit volume of equipment, sq. ft./cu. ft.

$C$ = heat capacity (for a gas or vapor unless otherwise indicated) at constant pressure, B.t.u./(lb.)(°F.)

$C_L$ = heat capacity for a liquid at constant pressure, B.t.u./(lb.)(°F.)

$C_S$ = humid heat, B.t.u. (for vapor-gas mixture)/(lb. dry gas)(°F.)

$d$ = differential operator

$d_p$ = diameter of a sphere, ft.

$D$ = diffusivity, sq. ft./hr.

$e$ = 2.7183

$\mathbf{E}_G$ = Murphree gas-phase stage efficiency, as a fraction

$G'_S$ = rate of flow of gas, lb. dry gas/(hr.)(sq. ft. cross section)

$h_G$ = gas-film coefficient for heat transfer by convection and conduction, B.t.u./(hr.)(sq. ft.)(°F.)

$h_R$ = film coefficient for heat transfer by radiation, B.t.u./(hr.)(sq. ft.)(°F.)

$h_{turb}$ = coefficient for heat transfer for a turbulent core, B.t.u./(hr.)(sq. ft.)(°F.)

$H$ = enthalpy, B.t.u./lb.

$H'$ = enthalpy of a vapor-gas mixture, B.t.u./lb. dry gas

$H'^*$ = enthalpy of a saturated vapor-gas mixture, in equilibrium with the bulk of the liquid, B.t.u./lb. dry gas

$H'_{as}$ = enthalpy of a saturated vapor-gas mixture at $t_{as}$, B.t.u./lb. dry gas

$H_{tG}$ = height of a gas-phase transfer unit, ft.

$H_{tOG}$ = over-all height of transfer unit, ft.

$k$ = thermal conductivity, B.t.u. (ft.)/(hr.)(sq. ft.)(°F.)

$k_c$ = mass-transfer film coefficient, lb. moles $A$ transferred/(hr.)(sq. ft.)(lb. moles/cu. ft.)

$k_G$ = mass-transfer film coefficient, lb. moles $A$ transferred/(hr.)(sq. ft.)(atm.)

$k_{G,turb}$ = mass-transfer coefficient for turbulent core, lb. moles/(hr.)(sq. ft.)(atm.)

$k_Y$ = mass-transfer film coefficient, lb. $A$ transferred/(hr.)(sq. ft.)($\Delta Y'$)

$K_G$ = over-all mass-transfer coefficient, lb. moles $A$ transferred/(hr.)(sq. ft.)(atm.)

$K_Y$ = over-all mass-transfer coefficient, lb. $A$ transferred/(hr.)(sq. ft.)($\Delta Y'$)

$L'$ = rate of flow of liquid, lb./(hr.)(sq. ft. cross section)

ln = natural logarithm

log = common logarithm

$M$ = molecular weight, lb./lb. mole

$n$ = number of lb. moles

$N$ = rate of mass transfer, lb. moles/(hr.)(sq. ft.)

$N_{tG}$ = number of gas-phase transfer units

$N_{tOG}$ = over-all number of transfer units

$P$ = vapor pressure of a pure substance, total pressure, atm.

Pr = Prandtl number = $C\mu/k$

$(Pv)$ = product of pressure and specific volume, B.t.u./lb.

$p$ = partial pressure, atm.

$p_{BM}$ = average partial pressure of component $B$, atm.

$q$ = rate of heat transfer, B.t.u./hr.

$Q$ = heat absorbed, B.t.u. /(hr.)(sq. ft.)

$r$ = psychrometric ratio = $h_G/k_Y C_S$

$R$ = universal gas constant, 0.729 cu. ft.(atm.)/(lb. mole)(°R.)

Re″ = Reynolds number for a sphere

$S$ = interfacial surface, sq. ft./sq. ft. cross section

Sc = Schmidt number = $\mu/\rho D$

$t$ = temperature, °F.

$t_{as}$ = adiabatic-saturation temperature, °F.

$t_{DP}$ = dew-point temperature, °F.

$t_G$ = gas temperature, °F.

$t_L$ = liquid temperature, °F.

$t_{nbp}$ = normal boiling point, °F.

$t_0$ = temperature of a reference state for computing relative enthalpy, °F.

$t_w$ = wet-bulb temperature, °F.

$T$ = absolute temperature, °R.

$U$ = internal energy, B.t.u./lb.

$v_G$ = molal specific volume of vapor, cu. ft./lb. mole

$v_H$ = humid volume, cu. ft. vapor-gas mixture/lb. dry gas

$v_L$ = molal specific volume of liquid, cu. ft./lb. mole

$w$ = mass of a substance, lb.

$W$ = rate of evaporation, lb./hr.

$y$ = concentration in gas, mole fraction

$Y$ = molal absolute humidity, lb. moles vapor/lb. mole dry gas

$Y'$ = absolute humidity, lb. vapor/lb. dry gas

$Y'_{as}$ = saturated absolute humidity at adiabatic-saturation temperature, lb. vapor/lb. dry gas

$Y'_w$ = saturated absolute humidity at wet-bulb temperature, lb. vapor/lb. dry gas

$Z$ = length or height of active part of equipment, ft.

$\alpha$ = thermal diffusivity, sq. ft./hr.

$\Delta$ = difference

$(\Delta t)_{av}$ = logarithmic mean $\Delta t$, °F.

$(\Delta Y')_{av}$ = logarithmic mean $\Delta Y'$, lb. vapor/lb. dry gas

$\lambda$ = latent heat of vaporization, B.t.u./lb.

$\lambda'$ = molal latent heat of vaporization, cu. ft. (atm.)/lb. mole

$\lambda_{as}$ = latent heat of vaporization at $t_{as}$, B.t.u./lb.

$\lambda_0$ = latent heat of vaporization at $t_0$, B.t.u./lb.
$\lambda_w$ = latent heat of vaporization at $t_w$, B.t.u./lb
$\mu$ = viscosity, lb./(ft.)(hr.)
$\rho$ = density, lb./cu. ft.

Subscripts:

    1, 2 = positions 1, 2
    $as$ = adiabatic saturation
    av = average
    $A$ = substance $A$, the vapor
    $B$ = substance $B$, the gas
    $F$ = at the limit of the laminar film
    $G$ = pertaining to the gas
    $i$ = interface
    $L$ = pertaining to the liquid
  min = minimum
    0 = at the reference temperature
    $r$ = reference substance
    $s$ = saturated
    $w$ = at the wet-bulb temperature

## REFERENCES

1. Bedingfield, C. H., and T. B. Drew: *Ind. Eng. Chem.*, **42**, 1164 (1950).
2. Colburn, A. P., and T. B. Drew: *Trans. Am. Inst. Chem. Engrs.*, **33**, 197 (1937).
3. Dropkin, D.: *Cornell Univ. Eng. Expt. Sta. Bull.* **23** (1936); **26** (1939).
4. Eckert, E. R. G.: "Introduction to the Transfer of Heat and Mass," McGraw-Hill Book Company, Inc., New York, 1950.
5. Gerster, J. A., *et al.*: *Chem. Eng. Progr.*, **45**, 716 (1949); **47**, 523, 621 (1951).
6. Grosvenor, W. M.: *Trans. Am. Inst. Chem. Engrs.*, **1**, 184 (1908).
7. Hensel, S. L.: Doctor of engineering science thesis, New York University, 1950.
8. ———— and R. E. Treybal: *Chem. Eng. Progr.*, **48**, 362 (1952).
9. Lichtenstein, J.: *Trans. ASME*, **65**, 779 (1943).
10. McAdams, W. H.: "Heat Transmission," 2d ed., McGraw-Hill Book Company, Inc., New York, 1942.
11. Mickley, H. S.: *Chem. Eng. Progr.*, **45**, 739 (1949).
12. Mizushina, T., and T. Kotoo: *Chem. Eng. (Japan)*, **13**, 75 (1949).
13. Norman, W. S.: *Trans. Inst. Chem. Engrs. (London)*, **29**, 226 (1951).
14. Othmer, D. F., *et al.*: *Ind. Eng. Chem.*, **32**, 841 (1940); **34**, 952 (1942); and many other articles.
15. Perry, J. H., ed.: "Chemical Engineers' Handbook," 3d ed., McGraw-Hill Book Company, Inc., New York, 1950.
16. Pigford, R. L., and C. Pyle: *Ind. Eng. Chem.*, **43**, 1649 (1951).
17. Sherwood, T. K., and F. A. L. Holloway: *Trans. Am. Inst. Chem. Engrs.*, **36**, 21 (1940).
18. ———— and R. L. Pigford: "Absorption and Extraction," 2d ed., McGraw-Hill Book Company, Inc., New York, 1952.
19. ———— and C. E. Reed: "Applied Mathematics in Chemical Engineering," McGraw-Hill Book Company, Inc., New York, 1939.
20. Simpson, W. M., and T. K. Sherwood: *Refrig. Eng.*, **52**, 535 (1946).
21. Surosky, A. E., and B. F. Dodge: *Ind. Eng. Chem.*, **42**, 1112 (1950).

22. Weisman, J., and C. F. Bonilla: *Ind. Eng. Chem.*, **42**, 1099 (1950).
23. West, F. B., W. D. Gilbert, and T. Shimizu: *Ind. Eng. Chem.*, **44**, 2470 (1952).
24. Yoshida, F., and T. Tanaka: *Ind. Eng. Chem.*, **43**, 1467 (1951).

## PROBLEMS

**1.** Prepare a logarithmic reference substance plot of the vapor pressure of acetone over a temperature range 10°C. to its critical temperature, 235°C., with water as reference substance. With the help of the plot, determine (*a*) the vapor pressure of acetone at 65°C., (*b*) the temperature at which acetone has a vapor pressure of 500 mm. Hg, and (*c*) the latent heat of vaporization of acetone at 40°C. (accepted value = 230.5 B.t.u./lb.).

**2.** *a*. Compute the heat required to convert 5 lb. acetone from a condition of saturated liquid at 10°C. to superheated vapor at 500 mm. Hg abs. and 100°C. The heat capacity of acetone as a liquid is 0.52, as a vapor 0.35 B.t.u./(lb.)(°F.).

*b*. Calculate the enthalpy of the acetone in the superheated condition of part *a* relative to liquid acetone at the same temperature, B.t.u./lb.

**3.** Prepare a plot of enthalpy vs. temperature for the substance water, using the steam tables as a source of data. Cover the temperature range 32 to 1000°F., show the curves for saturated vapor and saturated liquid, and include lines of constant pressure for 1, 5, 14.7, 50, 100, 500, 1,000, 2,000, 3,206, and 3,500 lb./sq. in. abs.

**4.** A mixture of nitrogen and acetone vapor at 800 mm. Hg total pressure, 80°F., has a percentage saturation of 80%. Calculate (*a*) the absolute molal humidity, (*b*) the absolute humidity, lb. acetone/lb. nitrogen, (*c*) the partial pressure of acetone, (*d*) the relative humidity, (*e*) the volume % acetone, (*f*) grains acetone/cu. ft. mixture, and (*g*) the dew point.

**5.** In a plant for the recovery of acetone which has been used as a solvent, the acetone is evaporated into a stream of nitrogen gas. A mixture of acetone vapor and nitrogen is flowing through a duct, 12 by 12 in. cross section. The pressure and temperature at one point in the duct are 800 mm. Hg, 100°F., and at this point the average velocity is 10 ft./sec. A wet-bulb thermometer (wick wet with acetone) indicates a wet-bulb temperature at this point of 80°F. Calculate lb. acetone/hr. carried by the duct.

**6.** Repeat Prob. 5, but assume that the carrier gas is an inert mixture containing 21% carbon dioxide, 79% nitrogen, with all other quantities the same as in Prob. 5.

**7.** Prepare a psychrometric chart of the mixture acetone-nitrogen at a pressure of 800 mm. Hg over the ranges 0 to 140°F., $Y' = 0$ to 3 lb. vapor/lb. dry gas. Include the following curves, all plotted against temperature: (*a*) 100, 75, 50, and 25 percentage humidity; (*b*) dry and saturated humid volumes; (*c*) enthalpy of dry and saturated mixtures expressed as B.t.u./lb. dry gas, referred to liquid acetone and nitrogen gas at 0°F.; (*d*) wet-bulb curve for $t_w = 80$°F.; (*e*) adiabatic-saturation curves for $t_{as} = 80$ and 100°F.

**8.** A drier requires 3,000 cu. ft./min. of air at 150°F., 20% humidity. This is to be prepared from air at 80°F. dry-bulb, 65°F. wet-bulb temperature by direct injection of steam into the air stream followed by passage of the air over steam-heated finned tubes. The available steam is saturated at 5 lb./sq. in. gauge. Compute lb. of steam/hr. required (*a*) for direct injection and (*b*) for the heat exchanger.

**9.** Air in an amount 1,000 cu. ft./min. at 150°F., 20% humidity (condition 1), is passed over a refrigerated coil and thereby brought to 60°F., 90% humidity (condition 2), with the condensed moisture withdrawn at 55°F. The air is then reheated by means of a steam coil to 150°F. (condition 3).

*a.* Tabulate the absolute humidity, wet-bulb temperature, dew point, enthalpy, and volume in cu. ft./min. for the moist air at each of the three conditions.

*b.* Compute the moisture removed, lb./min.

*c.* Compute the heat removed by the refrigerated coil, expressed as tons of refrigeration (1 ton of refrigeration = 200 B.t.u./min. removed).

*d.* Compute the heat added by the steam coil, B.t.u./min.

**10.** It is desired to produce 21,000 cu. ft./hr. air at 140°F., 0.030 lb. water/lb. dry air, from fresh air at 80°F. dry-bulb, 70°F. wet-bulb temperature. A spray tower of design identical with that of item 8 (Table 7.2) will be used, with a recirculated water spray operated at a rate of 700 lb. water/(hr.)(sq. ft.). Two schemes are being considered.

*a.* The air will be preheated, adiabatically humidified and cooled, and reheated. For this operation, $N_{tG}$ will be the same as $N_{tOG}$. Steam at 5 lb./sq. in. gauge, saturated, will be used in the heaters. Calculate (1) the value of $N_{tG}$; (2) the temperature of the spray; (3) the temperature to which the air must be preheated; (4) the make-up water required; (5) lb. steam/hr. required to operate the heaters.

*b.* The recirculated spray water will be heated before spraying by mixing with steam, and the air will be sprayed without preheating. The air leaving the tower may be presumed saturated at the desired final humidity and will then be heated to 140°F. Calculate (1) the entering and leaving temperatures for the water; (2) the steam required for heating the water and that required in the after heater.

**11.** It is desired to dehumidify 2,500 cu. ft. air/min., available at 100°F. dry-bulb, 85°F. wet-bulb temperature, to a wet-bulb temperature of 60°F. in a countercurrent tower using water chilled to 50°F. Packing of the design of item 6 (Table 7.2) will be used. To keep entrainment at a minimum, $G$ will be 900 lb. air/(hr.)(sq. ft.), and a liquid rate of 1.5 times the minimum will be used. (*a*) Specify the cross section and height of the packed portion of the tower. (*b*) What will be the temperature of the outlet water?

**12.** A recently installed induced-draft cooling tower was guaranteed by the manufacturer to cool 2,000 gal./min. of water at 110°F. to 85°F. when the available air has a wet-bulb temperature of 75°F. A test on the tower, when operated at full fan capacity, provided the following data:

Inlet water, 2,000 gal./min., 115.0°F.
Outlet water, 78.0°F.
Inlet air, 75°F. dry-bulb, 60°F. wet-bulb temperature
Outlet air, 99.8°F., saturated

*a.* What is the fan capacity, cu. ft./min.?

*b.* Can the tower be expected to meet the guarantee conditions?

**13.** Raschig-ring packing is to be compared with a simple wetted-wall tower for a particular humidification problem.

*a.* Calculate the height of a 1-in. I.D. wetted-wall tower required to bring dry air at 140°F. to 90% saturation with water by adiabatic humidification-cooling. The air rate is to be 3,000 lb./(hr.)(sq. ft.), and the thickness of the film of liquid should be neglected. Use gas properties at the average conditions in the gas film.

*b.* Calculate the dimensions of a packed tower for the same humidification, using 1-in. Raschig rings. Owing to limitations of the available data, $L'/G'_s$ will be set at 3, and a gas rate equal to 50% of the flooding rate will be used rather than the rate in (*a*).

*c.* Calculate the pressure drop, lb./sq. ft., for the gas in both cases.

*d.* Compare the two devices by calculating $N_{tG}/\Delta P$ for each. What other factors should be considered in comparing the two?

# CHAPTER 8

# GAS ABSORPTION

Gas absorption is an operation in which a gas mixture is contacted with a liquid for the purposes of preferentially dissolving one or more components of the gas and to provide a solution of these in the liquid. For example, the gas from by-product coke ovens is washed with water to remove ammonia and again with an oil to remove benzene and toluene vapors. Objectionable hydrogen sulfide is removed from such a gas or from naturally occurring hydrocarbon gases by washing with various alkaline solutions in which it is absorbed. Valuable solvent vapors carried by a gas stream may be recovered for reuse by washing the gas with an appropriate solvent for the vapors. Such operations require mass transfer of a substance from the gas stream to the liquid. When mass transfer occurs in the opposite direction, i.e., from the liquid to the gas, the operation is called desorption, or stripping. For example, the benzene and toluene are removed from the absorption oil mentioned above by contacting the liquid solution with steam, whereupon the vapors enter the gas stream and are carried away, and the absorption oil may be used again. The principles of both absorption and desorption are basically the same, and we may study both operations at the same time.

## EQUILIBRIUM SOLUBILITY OF GASES IN LIQUIDS

The rate at which a gaseous constituent of a mixture will dissolve in an absorbent liquid depends upon the departure from equilibrium which is maintained, and therefore it is necessary to consider the equilibrium characteristics of gas-liquid systems. A very brief discussion of such matters was presented in Chap. 5, but some elaboration will be required here.

**Two-component Systems.** Suppose quantities of a pure gas and a pure, relatively nonvolatile liquid in which the gas readily dissolves are both put in the cylinder fitted with a piston described in Chap. 7 (Fig. 7.2). Let the weights on the piston be adjusted so as always to maintain a specific pressure, and let the entire apparatus be maintained at constant temperature. Molecules of the gas will enter the liquid to form

a solution which will eventually become uniform in composition throughout the entire liquid mass. The gas molecules also tend to leave the
solution and reenter the gas phase, at a rate which increases as the concentration of gas in the solution increases, until eventually the gas pressure exerted by the solution exactly balances the pressure maintained on
the piston. At this time the solution concentration no longer changes,
and a dynamic equilibrium between the gas and liquid phases has been

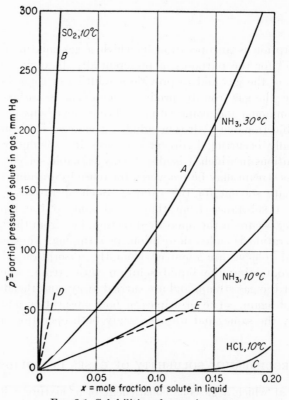

FIG. 8.1. Solubilities of gases in water.

established. The concentration of gas in the solution is then said to be
the solubility of the gas in the liquid at the prevailing pressure and temperature. If now the pressure on the piston is increased, additional gas
will dissolve until a new equilibrium is reached, this time at a higher
concentration in the liquid phase. In this manner, concentrations or
solubilities and corresponding pressures of the gas may be obtained, and
these data may be shown graphically in the manner of curve A (Fig. 8.1),
which shows a portion of the equilibrium solubility of ammonia in water
at 30°C.

Different gases and liquids give separate solubility curves, which must
ordinarily be determined experimentally for each system. If the equi-

librium pressure of a gas at a given liquid concentration is high, as in the case of curve $B$ (Fig. 8.1), the gas is said to be relatively insoluble in the liquid, while if it is low, as for curve $C$, the solubility is said to be high. But these are relative matters only, for it is possible to produce any ultimate gas concentration in the liquid if sufficient pressure is applied, so long as the liquefied form of the gas is completely soluble in the liquid.

The solubility of any gas is influenced by the temperature, in a manner which is described by van't Hoff's law of mobile equilibrium: If the temperature of a system at equilibrium is raised, that change will occur which will absorb heat. Usually, but not always, the solution of a gas results in an evolution of heat, and it follows that in most cases the solubility of a gas decreases with increasing temperature. As an example, curve $A$ (Fig. 8.1) for ammonia in water at 30°C. lies above the corresponding curve for 10°C. At the boiling point of the solvent, provided its vapor pressure is less than that of the gas or vapor solute, the gas solubility will be zero.

**Multicomponent Systems.** If a mixture of gases is brought into contact with a liquid, under certain conditions the equilibrium solubilities of each gas will be independent of the others, provided, however, that the equilibrium is described in terms of the *partial pressures* in the gas mixture. If all but one of the components of the gas are substantially insoluble, their concentrations in the liquid will be so small that they cannot influence the solubility of the relatively soluble component and the generalization applies. For example, curve $A$ (Fig. 8.1) will also describe the solubility of ammonia in water when the ammonia is diluted with air, since air is so insoluble in water, provided that the ordinate of the plot be considered as the partial pressure of ammonia in the gas mixture. This is most fortunate, since the amount of experimental work in gathering useful solubility data is thereby considerably reduced. If several components of the mixture are appreciably soluble, the generalization will be applicable only provided that the solute gases are indifferent to the nature of the liquid, which will be the case only for ideal solutions. For example, a mixture of propane and butane gases will dissolve in a nonvolatile paraffin oil independently since the solutions that result are substantially ideal. On the other hand, the solubility of ammonia in water can be expected to be influenced by the presence of methylamine, since the resulting solutions of these gases are not ideal. The solubility of a gas will also be influenced by the presence of a nonvolatile solute in the liquid, such as a salt in water solution, when such solutions are nonideal.

**Ideal Liquid Solutions.** When the liquid phase may be considered ideal, we may compute the equilibrium partial pressure of a gas from the solution without resort to experimental determination.

There are four significant characteristics of ideal solutions, all inter-related:

1. The average intermolecular forces of attraction and repulsion in the solution are unchanged on mixing the constituents.

2. The volume of the solution varies linearly with composition.

3. There is neither absorption nor evolution of heat on mixing of the constituents. In the case of gases dissolving in liquids, however, this criterion should not include the latent heat of condensation of the gas to the liquid state.

4. The total vapor pressure of the solution varies linearly with composition expressed as mole fractions.

In reality there are no ideal solutions, and actual mixtures only approach ideality as a limit. Ideality would require that the molecules of the constituents be similar in size, structure, and chemical nature, and the nearest approach to such a condition is perhaps exemplified by solutions of optical isomers of organic compounds. Practically, however, many solutions are so nearly ideal that for engineering purposes they may be so considered. Adjacent or nearly adjacent numbers of a homologous series of organic compounds particularly fall in this category. So, for example, solutions of benzene in toluene, ethyl and propyl alcohols, or the paraffin hydrocarbon gases in paraffin oils may ordinarily be considered as ideal solutions.

When the gas mixture in equilibrium with an ideal liquid solution also follows the ideal-gas law, the partial pressure $p^*$ of a solute gas $A$ equals the product of its vapor pressure $P$ at the same temperature and its mole fraction in the solution $x$. This is *Raoult's law*.

$$p^* = Px \tag{8.1}$$

The nature of the solvent liquid does not enter into consideration except in so far as it establishes the ideality of the solution, and it follows that the solubility of a particular gas in ideal solution in any solvent is always the same.

**Illustration 1.** A gas mixture, after long contact with a hydrocarbon oil and establishment of equilibrium, had the following composition at 2 atm. total pressure, 75°F.: methane 60%, ethane 20%, propane 8%, $n$-butane 6%, $n$-pentane 6%. Calculate the composition of the equilibrium solution.

*Solution.* The equilibrium partial pressure $p^*$ of each constituent in the gas is its volume fraction multiplied by the total pressure. These and the vapor pressures $P$ of the constituents at 75°F. are tabulated below. The prevailing temperature is above the critical value for methane, and at this low total pressure its solubility may be considered negligible. For each constituent its mole fraction in the liquid is calculated by Eq. (8.1), $x = p^*/P$, and the last column of the table lists these as the answers to the problem. The remaining liquid, $1 - 0.264 = 0.736$ mole fraction, is the solvent oil.

| Component | $p^*$, equilibrium partial pressure, atm. | $P$, vapor pressure at 75°F., atm. | Mole fraction in the liquid, $x = \dfrac{p^*}{P}$ |
|---|---|---|---|
| Methane............... | $1.20 = 0.6(2.0)$ | | |
| Ethane................ | 0.40 | 41.5 | 0.0097 |
| Propane............... | 0.16 | 8.84 | 0.018 |
| n-Butane.............. | 0.12 | 2.33 | 0.052 |
| n-Pentane............. | 0.12 | 0.65 | 0.184 |
| Total................. | .............. | ..... | 0.264 |

For total pressures in excess of those for which the ideal-gas law applies, Raoult's law may frequently be used with fugacities substituted for the pressure terms.[15]

**Nonideal Liquid Solutions.** For liquid solutions which are not ideal, Eq. (8.1) will give highly incorrect results. Line $D$ (Fig. 8.1), for example, is the calculated partial pressure of ammonia in equilibrium with water solutions at 10°C., assuming Raoult's law to be applicable, and it clearly does not represent the data. On the other hand, the straight line $E$ is seen to represent the 10°C. ammonia-water data very well up to mole fractions of 0.06 in the liquid. The equation of such a line is

$$p^* = m'x \qquad (8.2)$$

where $m'$ is a constant. This is *Henry's law*, and it is seen to be applicable with different values of $m'$ for each of the gases in the figure over at least a modest liquid-concentration range. Failure to follow Henry's law over wide concentration ranges may be the result of chemical interaction with the liquid or electrolytic dissociation, as is the case with ammonia-water, or nonideality in the gas phase. The less soluble gases, such as nitrogen or oxygen in water, can be expected to follow the law up to equilibrium partial pressures of 1 atm., and gases of the vapor type (which are below their critical temperature) will generally follow the law up to pressures of approximately 50 per cent of the saturation value at the prevailing temperature provided no chemical action occurs in the liquid. In any case $m'$ must be established experimentally. Expressed in terms of mole fractions in the gas, Henry's law becomes[†]

$$y^* = mx \qquad (8.3)$$

where $m = m'/P_t$.

The advantages of straight-line plotting for interpolation and extrap-

[†] For conditions under which Henry's law is inapplicable, Eq. (8.3) may be used in empirical fashion to describe experimental data, but the value of $m$ (or $K = y^*/x$, which is sometimes used) will then be expected to vary with temperature, pressure, and concentration and must be listed as a function of these variables.

olating experimental data are, of course, very great, and an empirical method of wide utility is an extension of the "reference-substance" vapor-pressure plot described in Chap. 7.[12]  As an example of this, Fig. 8.2 shows the data for ammonia-water solutions, covering a wide range of concentrations and temperatures.  The coordinates are logarithmic.  The abscissa is marked with the vapor pressure of a convenient reference substance, in this case water, and the ordinate is the equilibrium partial

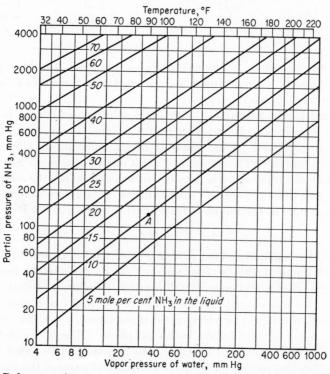

FIG. 8.2. Reference-substance plot for gas solubility.  The system ammonia-water, water as reference.

pressure of the solute gas.  Points are plotted where the corresponding temperatures for the vapor pressure of the reference substance and the partial pressure of solute are identical.  For example, at 90°F. the vapor pressure of water is 36 mm. Hg, and the partial pressure of ammonia for a 10 mole per cent solution is 130 mm. Hg, and these pressures locate point $A$ on the figure.  The lines for constant liquid composition are straight with few exceptions.  A temperature scale may later be substituted for the reference vapor-pressure scale, using the steam tables in the case of water as reference substance.

**Choice of Solvent for Absorption.**  If the principal purpose of the absorption operation is to produce a specific solution, as in the manufacture of hydrochloric acid, for example, the solvent is specified by the nature of the product. If the principal purpose is to remove some constituent from the gas, some choice is frequently possible. Water is, of course, the cheapest and most plentiful solvent, but the following properties are important considerations.

1. *Gas Solubility.* The gas solubility should be high, thus increasing the rate of absorption and decreasing the quantity of solvent required. Generally solvents of a chemical nature similar to that of the solute to be absorbed will provide good solubility. Thus hydrocarbon oils, and not water, are used to remove benzene from coke-oven gas. For cases where the solutions formed are ideal, the solubility of the gas is the same in terms of mole fractions for all solvents. But it is greater in terms of weight fractions for solvents of low molecular weight, and smaller weights of such solvents, as measured in pounds, need to be used. Chemical reaction of solvent with the solute will frequently result

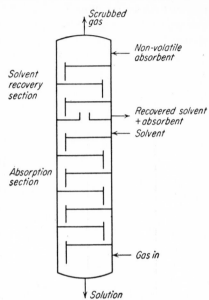

FIG. 8.3. Bubble-tray absorber with volatile-solvent recovery section.

in very high gas solubility, but if the solvent is to be recovered for reuse, the reaction must be reversible. For example, hydrogen sulfide may be removed from gas mixtures using ethanolamine solutions since the sulfide is readily absorbed at low temperatures and easily stripped at high temperatures. Caustic soda absorbs hydrogen sulfide excellently but will not release it in a stripping operation.

2. *Volatility.* The solvent should have a low vapor pressure since the gas leaving an absorption operation is ordinarily saturated with the solvent and much may thereby be lost. If necessary, a second, less volatile liquid may be used to recover the evaporated portion of the first, as in Fig. 8.3. This is sometimes done, for example, in the case of hydrocarbon absorbers, where a relatively volatile solvent oil is used in the principal portion of the absorber because of the superior solubility characteristics and the volatilized solvent is recovered from the gas by a nonvolatile oil. Similarly, hydrogen sulfide may be absorbed by a water solution of sodium phenolate, but the desulfurized gas is further washed with water to recover the evaporated phenol.

3. *Corrosiveness.* The materials of construction required for the equipment should not be unusual or expensive.

4. *Cost.*   The solvent should be inexpensive so that losses are not costly, and should be readily available.

5. *Viscosity.*   Low viscosity is preferred for reasons of rapid absorption rates, improved flooding characteristics in absorption towers, low pressure drops on pumping, and good heat-transfer characteristics.

6. *Miscellaneous.*   The solvent if possible should be nontoxic, nonflammable, and chemically stable and should have a low freezing point.

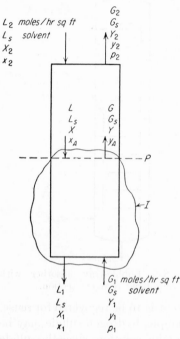

FIG. 8.4.   Flow quantities for an absorber or stripper.

## MATERIAL BALANCES

The basic expressions for material balances and their graphical interpretation were presented for any mass-transfer operation in Chap. 5.   Here they are adapted to the problems of gas absorption and stripping.

**Countercurrent Flow.**   Figure 8.4 shows a countercurrent tower which may be either a packed or spray tower, filled with bubble-cap trays, or of any internal construction to bring about liquid-gas contact.   The gas stream at any point in the tower consists of $G$ total moles/(hr.)(sq. ft. tower cross section), made up of diffusing solute $A$ of mole fraction $y$, partial pressure $p$, or mole ratio $Y$, and nondiffusing, essentially insoluble gas $G_s$ moles/(hr.)(sq. ft.).   The relationship among these are

$$Y = \frac{y}{1 - y} = \frac{p}{P_t - p} \qquad (8.4)$$

$$G_s = G(1 - y) = \frac{G}{1 + Y} \qquad (8.5)$$

Similarly the liquid stream consists of $L$ total moles/(hr.)(sq. ft.), containing $x$ mole fraction soluble gas, or mole ratio $X$, and essentially nonvolatile solvent $L_s$ moles/(hr.)(sq. ft.).

$$X = \frac{x}{1 - x} \qquad (8.6)$$

$$L_s = L(1 - x) = \frac{L}{1 + X} \qquad (8.7)$$

Since the solvent gas and solvent liquid are essentially unchanged in quantity as they pass through the tower, it is convenient to express the material balance in terms of these. A solute balance about the lower part of the tower (envelope I) is

$$G_S(Y_1 - Y) = L_S(X_1 - X) \qquad (8.8)$$

This is the equation of a straight line (the operating line) on $X$, $Y$ coordinates, of slope $L_S/G_S$, which passes through $(X_1, Y_1)$. Substitution of $X_2$ and $Y_2$ for $X$ and $Y$ shows the line to pass through $(X_2, Y_2)$, as on Fig. 8.5a for an absorber. This line indicates the relation between the liquid and gas concentration at any level in the tower, as at point $P$.

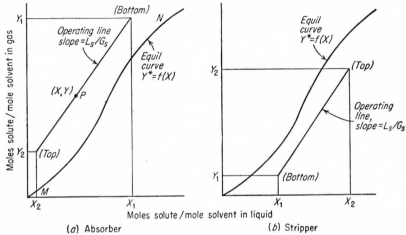

FIG. 8.5. Operating lines for absorber and stripper.

(a) Absorber          (b) Stripper

The equilibrium-solubility data for the solute gas in the solvent liquid may also be plotted in terms of these concentration units on the same diagram, as curve $MN$, for example. Each point on this curve represents the gas concentration in equilibrium with the corresponding liquid at its local concentration and temperature. For an absorber (mass transfer from gas to liquid) the operating line always lies above the equilibrium-solubility curve, while for a stripper (mass transfer from liquid to gas) the line is always below, as in Fig. 8.5b.

The operating line is straight only when plotted in terms of the mole-ratio units. In terms of mole fractions or partial pressures the line is curved, as in Fig. 8.6 for an absorber. The equation of the line is then

$$G_S \left( \frac{y_1}{1 - y_1} - \frac{y}{1 - y} \right) = G_S \left( \frac{p_1}{P_t - p_1} - \frac{p}{P_t - p} \right)$$
$$= L_S \left( \frac{x_1}{1 - x_1} - \frac{x}{1 - x} \right) \qquad (8.9)$$

and its slope at any point is $L/G$. The total pressure $P_t$ at any point may ordinarily be considered constant throughout the tower for this purpose.

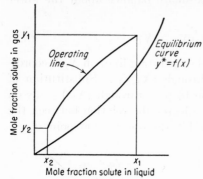

FIG. 8.6. Operating line in mole fractions.

**Minimum Liquid/Gas Ratio for Absorbers.** In the design of absorbers, the quantity of gas to be treated $G$ or $G_s$, the terminal concentrations $Y_1$ and $Y_2$, and the composition of the entering liquid $X_2$ are ordinarily fixed by process requirements, but the quantity of liquid to be used is subject to choice. Refer to Fig. 8.7$a$. The operating line must pass through point $D$ and must end at the ordinate $Y_1$. If such a quantity of liquid is used to give operating line $DE$, the exit liquid will have the composition $X_1$. If less liquid is used, the exit-liquid composition will clearly be greater, as at point $F$, but since the driving forces for diffusion are less, the absorption is more difficult. The time of contact between gas and liquid must then be

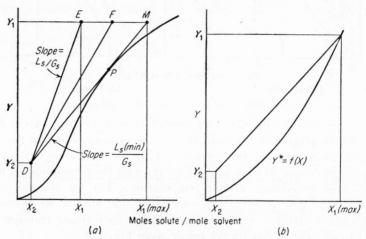

FIG. 8.7. Minimum liquid/gas ratio.

greater, and the absorber must be correspondingly taller. The minimum liquid which may be used corresponds to the operating line $DM$, which has the greatest slope for any line touching the equilibrium curve and is tangent to the curve at $P$. At $P$ the diffusional driving force is zero, the required time of contact for the concentration change desired is infinite, and an infinitely tall tower results. This then represents the limiting liquid/gas ratio.

The equilibrium curve is frequently concave upward, as in Fig. 8.7b, and the minimum liquid/gas ratio then corresponds to an exit-liquid concentration in equilibrium with the entering gas.

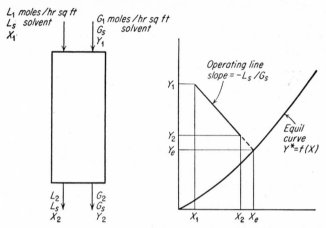

FIG. 8.8. Cocurrent absorber.

These principles also apply to strippers, where an operating line which anywhere touches the equilibrium curve represents a maximum ratio of liquid to gas and a minimum exit-liquid concentration.

**Cocurrent Flow.** When gas and liquid flow cocurrently as in Fig. 8.8, the operating line has a negative slope $-L_S/G_S$. There is no limit on this ratio, but an infinitely tall tower would produce an exit liquid and gas in equilibrium, as at $(X_e, Y_e)$. Cocurrent flow is not used frequently, except in the case where an exceptionally tall tower is built in two sections, as in Fig. 8.9, with the second section operated in cocurrent flow to save on the large-diameter gas pipe connecting the two.

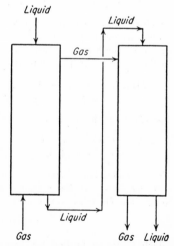

FIG. 8.9. Countercurrent-cocurrent arrangement for very tall towers.

**Illustration 2.** A coal gas is to be freed of its light oil by scrubbing with wash oil as an absorbent and the light oil recovered by stripping the resulting solution with steam. The circumstances are:

*a. Absorber.* Gas in, 30,000 cu. ft./hr. at 800 mm. Hg, 75°F., containing 2.0% by volume of light oil. The light oil will be assumed to be entirely benzene, and a 95% removal is required. The wash oil enters the absorber at 75°F., containing 0.005 mole fraction benzene, and has an average molecular weight of 260. An oil

circulation rate of 1.5 times the minimum is to be used.    Wash oil–benzene solutions
are ideal.

 b. *Stripper.* The solution from the absorber is heated to 250°F. and enters the
stripper at 1 atm. pressure.   Stripping steam is at atmospheric pressure, superheated
to 250°F.   The debenzolized oil, 0.005 mole fraction benzene, is cooled to 75°F.
and returned to the absorber.   A steam rate of 1.5 times the minimum is to be used.

 Compute the oil-circulation rate and the steam rate required.

 *Solution. a. Absorber.*   Basis: 1 hr.   Define $L$, $L_S$, $G$, $G_S$ in terms of moles/hr.

$$G_1 = 30,000 \, \frac{492}{460 + 75} \, \frac{800}{760} \, \frac{1}{359} = 80.8 \text{ moles gas in/hr.}$$

$y_1 = 0.02$, $Y_1 = 0.02/(1 - 0.02) = 0.0204$ mole benzene/mole dry gas
$G_S = 80.8(1 - 0.02) = 79.1$ moles dry gas/hr.

For 95% removal of benzene,

$Y_2 = 0.05(0.0204) = 0.00102$ mole benzene/mole dry gas
$x_2 = 0.005$, $X_2 = 0.005/(1 - 0.005) = 0.00502$ mole benzene/mole oil

At 75°F., the vapor pressure of benzene

$$P = 90 \text{ mm. Hg} = {}^{90}\!/_{760} = 0.1184 \text{ atm.}$$

Eq. (8.1) for ideal solutions:          $p^* = 0.1184x$

$y^* = p^*/P_t$      $P_t = {}^{800}\!/_{760} = 1.053$ atm.      $Y^* = y^*/(1 - y^*)$      $X = x/(1 - x)$

Substitution in Eq. (8.1) yields

$$Y^*/(1 + Y^*) = 0.1250X/(1 + X)$$

which is the equilibrium curve for the absorber, and it is plotted in Fig. 8.10.   Operating lines originate at point $D$ in this figure.   For the minimum oil rate, line $DE$ is
drawn as the line of maximum slope which touches the equilibrium curve (tangent
to the curve).   At $Y_1 = 0.0204$, $X_1 = 0.176$ mole benzene/mole wash oil (point $E$).

 Min. $L_S = G_S(Y_1 - Y_2)/(X_1 - X_2)$
          $= 79.1(0.0204 - 0.00102)/(0.176 - 0.00502) = 8.95$ moles oil/hr.

For 1.5 times the minimum, $L_S = 1.5(8.95) = 13.43$ moles oil/hr.

 $X_1 = G_S(Y_1 - Y_2)/L_S + X_2 = 79.1(0.0204 - 0.00102)/13.43 + 0.00502$
          $= 0.1192$ mole benzene/mole oil

The operating line is $DF$.

 b. *Stripper.*   At 250°F. the vapor pressure of benzene is 2,400 mm. Hg, or 3.16
atm.   The equilibrium curve for the stripper is therefore

$$Y^*/(1 + Y^*) = 3.16X/(1 + X)$$

which is drawn in Fig. 8.11.   For the stripper, $X_2 = 0.1192$, $X_1 = 0.00502$ mole
benzene/mole oil.   $Y_1 = 0$ moles benzene/mole steam.   For the minimum steam
rate, line $MN$ is drawn tangent to the equilibrium curve, and at $N$ the value of
$Y_2 = 0.45$ mole benzene/mole steam.

 Min. $G_S = L_S(X_2 - X_1)/(Y_2 - Y_1)$
          $= 13.43(0.1192 - 0.00502)/(0.45 - 0) = 3.41$ moles steam/hr.

For 1.5 times the minimum, the steam rate is $1.5(3.41) = 5.11$ moles steam/hr.,
corresponding to line $MP$.

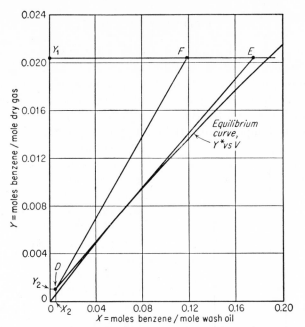

FIG. 8.10. Solution to Illustration 2, absorption.

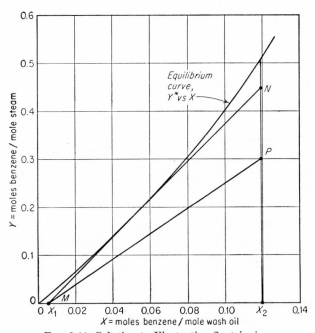

FIG. 8.11. Solution to Illustration 2, stripping.

## ENTHALPY BALANCES

Many absorbers and strippers deal with dilute gas mixtures and liquids, and it is frequently satisfactory in these cases to assume that the operation is isothermal.   But actually absorption operations are usually exothermic, and when large quantities of solute gas are absorbed to form concentrated solutions, the temperature effects cannot be ignored.   If by absorption the temperature of the liquid is raised to a considerable extent,

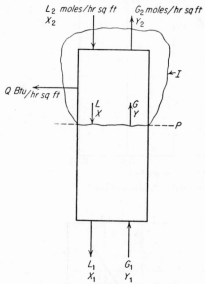

the equilibrium solubility of the solute will be appreciably reduced and the capacity of the absorber decreased.  If the heat evolved is excessive, cooling coils may be installed in the absorber or the liquid may be removed at intervals, cooled, and returned to the absorber.

Consider the absorber of Fig. 8.12.   If $Q$ B.t.u./(hr.)(sq. ft. tower cross section) is removed from the upper section of the absorber by any means whatsoever, an enthalpy balance about the upper section (envelope I) is

$$H_{L2}L_2 + H_G G$$
$$= H_{G2}G_2 + H_L L + Q \quad (8.10)$$

FIG. 8.12. Enthalpy balance.

where $H$ represents in each case the *molal* enthalpy of the stream at its particular temperature and concentration.   It is convenient to refer all enthalpies to the condition of pure liquid solvent, pure solvent gas, and pure solute at some base temperature $t_0$, with each substance assigned zero enthalpy for its normal state of aggregation at $t_0$ and 1 atm. pressure.   Thus the molal enthalpy of the solution at composition $X$ and temperature $t_L$ is

$$H_L = C_L(t_L - t_0)M_{av} + \Delta H_S \quad (8.11)$$

where the first term on the right represents the sensible heat and the second the molal enthalpy of mixing, or the integral heat of solution at the prevailing concentration and at the base temperature $t_0$, per mole of solution.   If heat is evolved on mixing, $\Delta H_S$ will be a negative quantity. If the absorbed solute is a liquid at $t_0$, 1 atm., as in the case of many vapors, $\Delta H_S$ will normally include the enthalpy of mixing the liquid solute with the liquid solvent, in which case the enthalpy of the gas stream $H_G$ must include the latent heat of vaporization of the solute vapor (see Chap. 7). For ideal solutions $\Delta H_S$ is zero, and the heat evolution is due to the latent heat of condensation of the absorbed solute only. Some adjustment of the units of Eqs. (8.10) and (8.11) may be convenient depending upon the form of the heat of solution data.

Equation (8.10) may be used to compute the heat to be removed $Q$ in order to maintain isothermal operation, or in the case of adiabatic operation ($Q = 0$) the temperature of the solution $L$. In this case it is necessary to know the temperature of the gas stream $G$ as it enters the section at $P$ (Fig. 8.12). This in turn requires simultaneous consideration of the rate of solute absorption, possible vaporization of the solvent, the rates of heat transfer between liquid and gas, together with enthalpy balances,[15] which is beyond the scope of the present discussion. For many purposes, however, it is satisfactory to assume that the sensible-heat change of the gas stream is unimportant and that the entire evolution of heat gas goes to raising the liquid temperature.

**Illustration 3.** Moist air is to be dried from humidity 0.013 lb. water/lb. dry air to 0.001 lb. water/lb. dry air by a countercurrent scrubbing with aqueous sodium hydroxide containing 50% NaOH, liquid and gas both entering at 68°F. Assuming adiabatic operation and neglecting the sensible-heat change for the gas, compute the equilibrium curve for this absorber.

*Solution.* The properties of aqueous sodium hydroxide are, at 68°F., as follows:

| $X \dfrac{\text{moles } H_2O}{\text{mole NaOH}}$ | Integral ht. of soln.,† B.t.u./lb. mole NaOH | $C_L$ = sp. ht., B.t.u./(lb. soln.)(°F.) |
|---|---|---|
| 0 | 0 | |
| 2 | −8,270 | 0.782 |
| 3 | −12,600 | 0.787 |
| 4 | −15,300 | 0.795 |
| 5 | −17,800 | 0.800 |

† Referred to solid NaOH and liquid $H_2O$.

In this problem the "solvent" in the liquid phase is NaOH, and the solute is water. Since the heat of solution is referred to liquid water, the enthalpy of the gas streams must include the latent heat of water.

$$Y_1 = 0.013(29/18) = 0.0209 \text{ mole water/mole air}$$
$$Y_2 = 0.001(29/18) = 0.00161 \text{ mole water/mole air}$$
$$X_2 = (50/50)(40/18) = 2.22 \text{ moles water/mole NaOH}$$

Basis: $L_S = 1$ lb. mole NaOH, $t_0 = 68°F$.

Rewrite Eq. (8.10), letting $Q = 0$ for adiabatic operation. The enthalpy balance is then

$$H_L L - H_{L2} L_2 = H_G G - H_{G2} G_2 = G_S(H'_G - H'_{G2})$$

where $H'_G$ is the enthalpy of the gas expressed as B.t.u./lb. mole dry air. Since the gas is assumed to be at the base temperature, 68°F., its enthalpy includes only the

heat of vaporization of water at 68°F., which is 19,000 B.t.u./lb. mole water. $H'_G =$
19,000$Y$.

$$G_S(H'_G - H'_{G2}) = G_S(19,000)(Y - Y_2)$$

A material balance, $G_S(Y - Y_2) = L_S(X - X_2) = X - X_2$.

$$\therefore G_S(H'_G - H'_{G2}) = 19,000(X - 2.22)$$

The heat-of-solution data may be converted to units of B.t.u./lb. mole solution by
multiplying the tabulated values by $1/(1 + X)$ moles NaOH/mole solution.

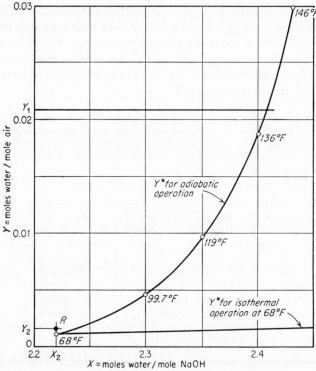

FIG. 8.13. Solution to Illustration 3.

For solution $L_2$ the sensible heat is zero. The heat of solution is $\Delta H_S = -9,600/-$
$(1 + 2.22) = -2,980$ B.t.u./mole soln. $= H_{L2}$.

$$L_2 = L_S(1 + X_2) = 1(1 + 2.22) = 3.22 \text{ moles}$$

Let $X = 2.3$ moles water/mole NaOH. $L = L_S(1 + X) = 1(1 + 2.3) = 3.3$
moles soln.

$$\Delta H_S = -10,100/(1 + 2.3) = -3,060 \text{ B.t.u./mole soln.}$$
$$M_{av} = \frac{2.3(18) + 1(40)}{3.3} = 24.7 \qquad C_L = 0.784 \text{ B.t.u./(lb. soln.)(°F.)}$$
$$H_L = 0.784(t_L - 68)24.7 - 3,060$$

The heat balance becomes

$$[0.784(t_L - 68)24.7 - 3,060]3.3 - 3.22(-2,980) = 19,000(2.3 - 2.22)$$
$$t_L = 99.7°F.$$

The equilibrium partial pressure of water from such a solution ($X = 2.3, t_L = 99.7°F.$) is 3.50 mm. Hg. This must be obtained by cross plotting and interpolation of vapor-pressure data for NaOH solutions as found, for example, in the "Chemical Engineers' Handbook." The reference-substance plot is most convenient for this.

$$Y^* = 3.50/(760 - 3.50) = 0.00463 \text{ mole } H_2O/\text{mole air}$$

In similar fashion values for other concentrations were computed, and plotted in Fig. 8.13. The equilibrium curve for isothermal operation at 68°F. is included. The operating line passes from point $R$ to the ordinate at $Y_1$, and the influence that adiabatic operation will have on the required liquid/gas ratio is evident.

## COUNTERCURRENT MULTISTAGE OPERATION

Tray towers and similar devices bring about stepwise contact of the liquid and gas and are therefore countercurrent multistage cascades. On each tray of a bubble-cap tower, for example, the gas and liquid are brought into intimate contact and separated, somewhat in the manner of Fig. 5.14, and the tray thus constitutes a stage. Few of the tray devices described in Chap. 6 actually provide the parallel flow on each tray as shown in Fig. 5.14. Nevertheless it is convenient to use the latter as an arbitrary standard for design and for measurement of performance of actual trays regardless of their method of operation. For this purpose a *theoretical*, or *ideal*, tray is defined as one where the average composition of all the gas leaving the tray is in equilibrium with the average composition of all the liquid leaving the tray.

The number of trays required to bring about a given change in composition of the liquid or the gas, for either absorbers or strippers, may then be determined graphically in the manner of Fig. 5.15. This is illustrated for an absorber in Fig. 8.14, where the liquid and gas compositions corresponding to each tray are marked on the operating diagram. Ideal tray $a$, for example, brings about a change in liquid composition from $X_2$ to $X_a$ and of gas composition from $Y_b$ to $Y_a$ (or $Y_2$). The step marked $a$ on the operating diagram therefore represents this ideal tray. The nearer the operating line to the equilibrium curve, the more steps will be required, and should the two curves touch at any points corresponding to a minimum $L_S/G_S$ ratio, the number of steps and trays would be infinite. The steps may equally well be constructed on diagrams plotted in terms of any concentration units, such as mole fractions or partial pressures. The construction for strippers is the same, with the exception, of course, that the operating line lies below the equilibrium curve.

**Dilute Gas Mixtures.** For cases where both operating line and equilibrium curve may be considered straight, the number of theoretical trays may be determined without recourse to graphical methods. This will frequently be the case for relatively dilute gas and liquid mixtures. Henry's law [Eq. (8.3)] often applies to dilute solutions, for example. If the quantity of gas absorbed is small, the total flow of liquid entering

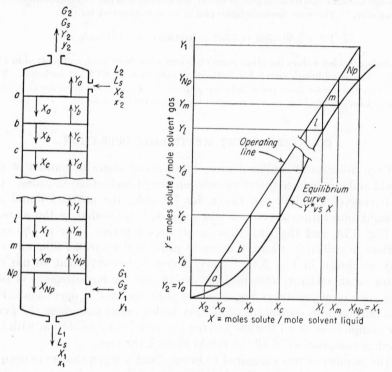

FIG. 8.14. Tray absorber.

and leaving the absorber remains substantially constant, $L_1 = L_2 \doteq L$ total moles/(hr.)(sq. ft.), and similarly the total flow of gas is substantially constant at $G$ total moles/(hr.)(sq. ft.). An operating line plotted in terms of mole fractions will then be substantially straight.

A material balance about tray $a$ of the absorber of Fig. 8.14 is then

$$G(y_b - y_a) = L(x_a - x_2) \tag{8.12}$$

where $x$ and $y$ are mole fractions of solute. Since Henry's law applies and the gas and liquid leaving the theoretical tray are in equilibrium,

$$x_a = \frac{y_a}{m} \tag{8.13}$$

$$\therefore G(y_b - y_a) = L\left(\frac{y_a}{m} - x_2\right) \tag{8.14}$$

Let

$$\frac{L}{mG} = A \tag{8.15}$$

Solving for $y_a$,

$$y_a = \frac{y_b + Amx_2}{1 + A} = \frac{(A - 1)y_b + A(A - 1)mx_2}{A^2 - 1} \tag{8.16}$$

Similarly for tray $b$,

$$y_b = \frac{y_c + Ay_a}{1 + A} \tag{8.17}$$

and substituting Eq. (8.16) in (8.17) and resolving,

$$y_b = \frac{(1 + A)y_c + A^2 mx_2}{A^2 + A + 1} = \frac{(A^2 - 1)y_c + A^2(A - 1)mx_2}{A^3 - 1} \tag{8.18}$$

If this is continued for additional trays, the form of the corresponding equations obtained soon becomes evident. For an absorber of $N_p$ trays, as in Fig. 8.14,

$$y_{Np} = \frac{(A^{Np} - 1)y_1 + A^{Np}(A - 1)mx_2}{A^{Np+1} - 1} \tag{8.19}$$

where $N_p$ is the number of theoretical trays.

A material balance for the entire $N_p$ trays is

$$L(x_{Np} - x_2) = G(y_1 - y_2) \tag{8.20}$$

or

$$A(y_{Np} - mx_2) = y_1 - y_2 \tag{8.21}$$

Eliminating $y_{Np}$ between Eqs. (8.19) and (8.21) and rearranging,

$$\frac{y_1 - y_2}{y_1 - mx_2} = \frac{A^{Np+1} - A}{A^{Np+1} - 1} \tag{8.22}$$

This is known as the Kremser-Brown-Souders equation.[8,16]

The quantity $mx_2$ represents a gas composition in equilibrium with the entering liquid. For cases where the entering liquid contains no solute, $x_2 = 0$, and the left-hand side of Eq. (8.22) represents the fractional absorption of solute from the gas. In this form the equation is most suitable for computing the fractional absorption for a fixed number of theoretical trays. For computing $N_p$, the equation may be rearranged,[5]

$$N_p = \frac{\log\left[\frac{y_1 - mx_2}{y_2 - mx_2}\left(1 - \frac{1}{A}\right) + \frac{1}{A}\right]}{\log A} \tag{8.23}$$

A corresponding derivation for strippers leads to

$$\frac{x_2 - x_1}{x_2 - y_1/m} = \frac{(1/A)^{Np+1} - (1/A)}{(1/A)^{Np+1} - 1} \tag{8.24}$$

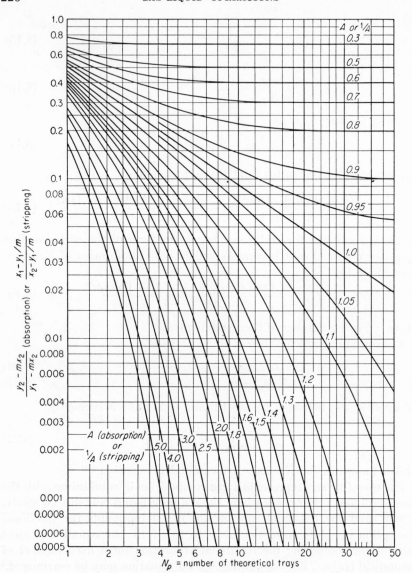

Fig. 8.15. Number of theoretical trays for absorbers or strippers, with constant absorption or stripping factor. (*After Hachmuth and Vance.*[7])

Figure 8.15 presents a graphical solution of the equations convenient for rapid calculation.†

† Equations (8.22) to (8.24) and Fig. 8.15 may also be used with concentration units other than mole fractions, where the use of such units provides straight-line equilibrium and operating lines, but the Henry's law constant must be defined consistently. For use with mole-ratio units, for example, $m$ must be defined as $Y^*/X$.

The success of the equations or Fig. 8.15 hinges on the constancy of $A$ from one end of the tower to the other. Small variations in $A$, owing either to changing $L/G$ ratio as the result of absorption or to changes in gas solubility with concentration or temperature, may be roughly allowed for by use of the geometric average of the values at top and bottom.[7] For large variations, either more elaborate corrections[15] for $A$ or graphical computation of trays must be used.

**The Absorption Factor $A$.** The absorption factor $A = L/mG$ is the ratio of the slope of the operating line to that of the equilibrium curve. For values of $A$ less than unity, corresponding to convergence of the operating line and equilibrium curve for the lower end of the absorber, Fig. 8.15 indicates clearly that the fractional absorption of solute is definitely limited, even for infinite theoretical trays. On the other hand, for values of $A$ greater than unity, any degree of absorption is possible if sufficient trays are provided. For a fixed degree of absorption from a fixed amount of gas, as $A$ increases beyond unity, the absorbed solute is dissolved in more and more liquid and becomes therefore less valuable. At the same time, the number of trays decreases so that the equipment cost decreases. From these opposing cost tendencies it follows that, in all such cases, there will be a value of $A$, or of $L/G$ ratio, for which the most economical absorption results. This should be obtained generally by computing the total costs for several values of $A$ and observing the minimum. As a rule of thumb for purposes of rapid estimates, it has been frequently found[4] that the most economical $A$ will be in the range from 1.25 to 2.0.

**Illustration 4.** Determine the number of theoretical trays required for the absorber and stripper of Illustration 2.

*Solution.* *a. Absorber.* The operating diagram established, in Illustration 2 was replotted in Fig. 8.16 and the theoretical trays stepped off. Between 7 and 8 (approximately 7.6) theoretical trays are required.

Alternatively, the number of theoretical trays may be computed.

$$y_1 = 0.02 \qquad y_2 = 0.00102/(1 + 0.00102) = 0.00102$$
$$x_2 = 0.005 \qquad m = y^*/x = 0.125$$
$$L_1 = L_S(1 + X_1) = 13.43(1 + 0.1192) = 15.0 \text{ moles/hr.}$$
$$A_1 = L_1/mG_1 = 15.0/(0.125)(80.8) = 1.485$$
$$L_2 = L_S(1 + X_2) = 13.43(1 + 0.005) = 13.5 \text{ moles/hr.}$$
$$G_2 = G_S(1 + Y_2) = 79.1(1 + 0.00102) = 79.1 \text{ moles/hr.}$$
$$A_2 = L_2/mG_2 = 13.5/(0.125)(79.1) = 1.368$$
$$\text{Av. } A = [1.485(1.368)]^{0.5} = 1.425$$
$$\frac{y_2 - mx_2}{y_1 - mx_2} = \frac{0.00102 - 0.125(0.005)}{0.02 - 0.125(0.005)} = 0.0204$$

From Fig. 8.15 or Eq. (8.23), $N_p = 7.7$ theoretical trays.

*b. Stripper.* The trays were determined graphically in the same manner as for the absorber and found to be 6.7. Figure 8.15 for this case gives 6.0 trays, owing to the relative nonconstancy of the stripping factors: $1/A_1 = 1.197$, $1/A_2 = 1.561$. The graphical method should be used.

**Over-all Tray Efficiency.** The number of real trays required in a tower will be different from the number of theoretical trays, depending upon how closely the flow pattern approximates the parallel flow assumed in the definition of the theoretical tray and upon the excellence of the liquid-vapor contact achieved.

The simplest measure of the approach to the standard is the over-all tray efficiency **E**, which is the ratio of the number of theoretical trays

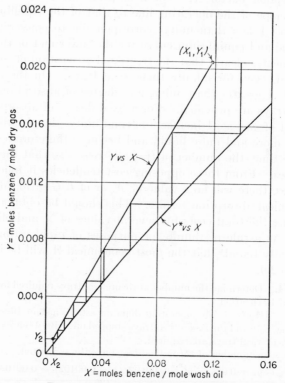

FIG. 8.16. Illustration 4, the absorber.

to the number of real trays required to bring about a given change in composition. By observation of the performance of towers containing a particular type of tray the over-all efficiency can be obtained, and this can be used in future designs with this type of tray. Such an accumulation of data is shown in Fig. 8.17, where the over-all efficiencies for a number of bubble-cap tray absorbers of commercial and laboratory size are correlated as a function of the fluid properties.[11] Bubble-cap tray efficiencies for absorbers are generally low, owing to the relatively low temperature of operation and consequent high liquid viscosity, which increases the resistance to mass transfer within the liquid phase. The curve shows the efficiency to decrease as liquid viscosity increases.  As explained in Chap. 5, the greater part of the resistance to diffusion will be within the liquid for cases of low gas solubility, and the curve of the figure reflects this (low solubility corresponds to large values of $m$).

The success of an empirical correlation of this sort depends upon the fact that the bubble-cap trays represented all were built following the general principles of design outlined in Chap. 6 for this type of device, so that the vigor of the gas-liquid contact, the liquid and gas velocities, and all other mechanical features which might be expected to influence

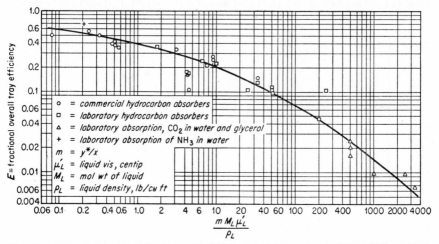

FIG. 8.17. Over-all tray efficiencies of bubble-cap tray absorber.  (*After O'Connell.*[11])

the tray efficiency were controlled within reasonably close limits.  The correlation should be used only as a rough indication of efficiency for bubble-tray towers designed in the conventional manner.

**Illustration 5.**   Estimate the number of real trays of conventional design required for the absorber of Illustrations 2 and 4.  The viscosity of the liquid at 75°F. is 5 centipoises, and its density 0.84 gm./cu. cm.
*Solution*

$$\frac{mM_L\mu_L'}{\rho_L} = \frac{0.125(260)(5)}{0.84(62.4)} = 3.1$$

From Fig. 8.17, $E = 0.3$.   The number of real trays is therefore

$$\frac{N_p}{0.3} = \frac{7.6}{0.3} = 25.3 \text{ or } 26$$

**Point, or Local, Efficiencies.**   Consider the bubble-cap tray of Fig. 8.18, where the bubbling action has been shown in greatly simplified fashion.   The approach to equilibrium experienced by individual bubbles of gas leaving a bubble-cap slot with the liquid at that position, as at $P$ in the figure, is the point, or local, efficiency. Point efficiencies may be conveniently studied under circumstances such that there is no change in the composition of the liquid on the tray, as in the humidification of air with pure water. In this manner, for example, the data of Fig. 7.23 were obtained, representing the contributions to the diffusional resistance by the gas phase. By studying absorption and desorption of very insoluble gases such as oxygen in water, for example, it is similarly possible to obtain the contributions of the liquid phase.[6] These studies show the point efficiency to be related closely to such quantities as the time of contact between liquid and gas and the interfacial surface between

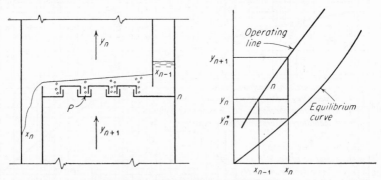

FIG. 8.18. Murphree tray efficiency.

the phases, in turn related to the height and density of froth on the plate. These cannot as yet be readily estimated for new designs.

**Murphree Tray Efficiency.** If the tray of Fig. 8.18 represents the $n$th tray of an absorber, counting from the top down, let $y_{n+1}$ be the average composition of all the gas rising to the tray and $y_n$ the average composition of all the gas leaving. If the tray were a theoretical tray, the gas leaving would be in equilibrium with the liquid leaving, of composition $x_n$, or $y_n^*$. The Murphree gas efficiency $\mathbf{E}_G$ of the tray [Eq. (5.30)] is then the approach to this equilibrium actually realized by all the gas,

$$\mathbf{E}_G = \frac{y_{n+1} - y_n}{y_{n+1} - y_n^*} \tag{8.25}$$

Since the liquid in flowing across the tray suffers many contacts with the gas and consequently changes its composition from $x_{n-1}$ to $x_n$, it follows that the gas leaving various parts of the tray will vary in composition from place to place even if the point efficiency is constant at all positions on the tray. The point efficiency is always a fraction less than unity. If all the liquid were thoroughly contacted with all the gas, the Murphree tray efficiency and the point efficiency would be the same. With a very wide tray, where in effect the liquid is subjected to a multiplicity of contacts with gas, and with little mixing in the liquid itself, it is sometimes possible to obtain Murphree tray efficiencies greater than unity. The relationship between the tray and point efficiencies clearly depends upon the degree of mixing within the liquid and within the vapor before the latter approaches the tray. Esti-mates have been made of these effects for the simple cases represented by the assumptions of complete mixing or complete absence of mixing of the vapor with no liquid mixing,[9] but none of these assumptions in reality applies to a tray column. For ab-sorbers, where the point efficiency and Murphree efficiency are ordinarily low, the effect in any case is small.

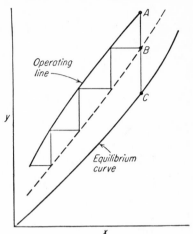

Considering that in absorption and stripping the diffusional resistance resides partly in both liquid and gas, Eq. (7.75) can be modified to contain an over-all mass-transfer coefficient. Assuming that the contributions of

Fig. 8.19. Use of Murphree tray efficiencies.

the various point efficiencies on the tray can in some fashion be integrated, the expression becomes

$$\mathbf{E}_G = 1 - e^{-PK_{Ga}Z/G} = 1 - e^{-K} \tag{8.26}$$

Walter and Sherwood[17] studied the values of $K$ for a large variety of bubble-tray absorbers and concluded that

$$K = \frac{h}{\left(2.5 + \dfrac{0.37mM_L}{\rho_L}\right)\mu_L'^{0.68}b^{0.33}} \tag{8.27}$$

where $h$ = vert. distance from center of slots to top of weir, in.
$\quad m$ = slope of equilibrium curve = $dy^*/dx$ or $y^*/x$ if constant
$\quad M_L$ = mol. wt. of liquid
$\quad \rho_L$ = density of liquid, lb./cu. ft.
$\quad \mu_L'$ = viscosity of liquid, centipoises
$\quad b$ = width of slot, in.

In this empirical equation the two terms within the parentheses repre-sent, respectively, the relative resistances of gas and liquid phases. The slot width accounts for bubble size and together with $h$, therefore, the interfacial area, while the term involving $\mu_L'$ accounts for the major effect of liquid viscosity on the low diffusion rates within liquids. The definition of $m$ as $dy^*/dx$ permits estimates of the variation in tray efficiency for gas solubilities which do not follow Henry's law.

The number of real trays may be computed as in Fig. 8.19. The broken line is drawn between equilibrium curve and operating line at a fractional vertical distance from the operating line equal to the prevailing Murphree gas efficiency.[2] Thus the value of $\mathbf{E}_G$ for the bottom tray is the ratio of the lines $AB/AC$. When operating line and equilibrium curve are both straight, as for dilute mixtures, and where $\mathbf{E}_G$ is constant for all trays,[9]

$$E = \frac{\log\left[1 + \mathbf{E}_G\left(\frac{1}{A} - 1\right)\right]}{\log(1/A)} \qquad (8.28)$$

**Illustration 6.** A process for making small amounts of hydrogen by cracking ammonia is being considered, and it is desired to remove residual uncracked ammonia from the resulting gas. The gas will consist of $H_2$ and $N_2$ in the molar ratio of $3:1$, containing $3\%$ $NH_3$ by volume, at 2 atm., 80°F.

There is available a bubble-tray absorber, 30 in. in diameter, containing 14 cross-flow trays of conventional design at 18 in. tray spacing. The downflow weir on each tray is 21 in. long and extends 2.25 in. above the tray. The bubble-cap slots are $\frac{1}{4}$ in. wide by 1 in., and the vertical distance from the top of the slots to the top of the weir is 0.75 in. The total slot area is 0.5 sq. ft. per tray. Estimate the capacity of this absorber for removing ammonia from the gas by scrubbing with water. Assume operation will be isothermal at 80°F.

*Solution.* The static submergence of the slots is 0.75 in. Assume a liquid seal of 1.5 in. (Table 6.1), which permits a weir head of $1.5 - 0.75 = 0.75$ in. Weir length/-tower diam. $= {}^{21}\!/_{30} = 0.7$; weir head/tower diam. $= 0.75/30 = 0.025$ in./ft. From Fig. 6.12, $(W/W_{eff})^{2/3} = 1.01$. After a trial calculation, $k_W$ from Fig. 6.13 is 0.975. Eq. (6.4):   $0.75 = 5.38(0.975)(1.01)(q/W)^{2/3}$
$$q/W = 0.0532 \text{ cu. ft.}/(\text{sec.})(\text{ft.})$$
$$q = 0.0532(2\frac{1}{12}) = 0.0931 \text{ cu. ft. } H_2O/\text{sec., or } 5.8 \text{ lb./sec.,}$$
$$\text{or } 0.322 \text{ lb. mole/sec.}$$

While this is not the maximum liquid flow that could be handled, it represents an amount which will probably cause no difficulty with pressure drop, flooding, or entrainment.
$$\rho_L = 62.3 \text{ lb./cu. ft.}$$

Av. mol. wt. gas $= 0.03(17.03) + 0.97(0.25)(28.02) + 0.97(75)(2.02) = 8.78 \text{ lb./mole}$

$$\rho_G = \frac{8.78}{359} \frac{2}{1} \frac{492}{460 + 80} = 0.0446 \text{ lb./cu. ft.}$$
From Fig. 6.4, $K = 0.13$.

Eq. (6.1):   $V = 0.13\left(\frac{62.3 - 0.0446}{0.0446}\right)^{0.5} = 4.84 \text{ ft./sec. superficial velocity}$

Cross-sectional area of tower $= (\pi/4)(30)^2/144 = 4.90$ sq. ft.   Gas rate $= 4.84(4.90) = 23.8$ cu. ft. gas/sec. at 2 atm., 80°F., corresponding to $23.8(0.0446)/8.78 = 0.121$ lb. mole gas/sec. This represents a probable safe gas velocity, which, together with the liquid rate calculated, should be checked for pressure drop by the methods of Chap. 6. In any case, slot velocities should probably not exceed $12/\rho_G^{0.5} = 12/(0.0446)^{0.5} = 56.8$ ft./sec., corresponding to $56.8(0.5) = 28.4$ cu. ft. gas/sec. or 0.145 lb. mole gas/sec.

For dilute solutions, ammonia-water follows Henry's law, and at 80°F. the Henry's law constant is $m' = 1.414$ atm. $NH_3$/mole fraction. $m = y^*/x = m'/P_t = 1.414/2 = 0.707$.

$M_L = 18$, substantially; $\rho_L = 62.3$ lb./cu. ft., $\mu_L' = 0.86$ centipoise, $b = 0.25$ in., $h = 0.75 + 0.5 = 1.25$ in.

Eq. (8.27):
$$K = \frac{1.25}{\left[2.50 + \dfrac{0.37(0.707)(18)}{62.3}\right](0.86)^{0.68}(0.25)^{0.33}} = 0.847$$

Eq. (8.26):
$$E_G = 1 - \frac{1}{e^K} = 1 - \frac{1}{e^{0.847}} = 0.575$$

If the maximum flow rates previously calculated are used, $A = L/mG = 0.322/0.707(0.145) = 3.14$.

Eq. (8.28):
$$E = \frac{\log\,[1 + E_G(1/A - 1)]}{\log\,(1/A)} = \frac{\log\,[1 + 0.575(1/3.14 - 1)]}{\log\,(1/3.14)} = 0.435$$

$$N_p = 14(0.435) = 6.1 \text{ theoretical trays}$$

Fig. 8.15:
$$\frac{y_2 - mx_2}{y_1 - mx_2} = \frac{y_2}{0.03} = 0.0006$$

$y_2 = 0.000018$ mole fraction $NH_3$, or 0.0018% $NH_3$ by volume in the effluent

If less gas is used for the same amount of water, correspondingly more ammonia will be removed. For example, for 0.1 mole gas/sec., $A = 4.55$, $E = 0.394$, $N_p = 5.5$ theoretical trays, and $y_2$ [by Eq. (8.22)] = 0.000006, or 0.0006% $NH_3$ by volume in the effluent.

NOTE: If the absorption factors had varied sufficiently so that Fig. 8.15 and Eq. (8.22) were not applicable, the operating line would be located by trial to fit the number of real trays and the tray efficiency, in the manner of Fig. 8.19.

## CONTINUOUS-CONTACT EQUIPMENT

Countercurrent packed and spray towers operate in a different manner from plate towers in that the fluids are in contact continuously in their path through the tower, rather than intermittently. Thus, in a packed tower the liquid and gas compositions change continuously with height of packing. Every point on an operating line therefore represents conditions found somewhere in the tower, whereas for tray towers only the isolated points on the operating line corresponding to trays have real significance.

**Height Equivalent to a Theoretical Plate.** A simple method for designing packed towers, which was introduced many years ago, ignores the differences between stagewise and continuous contact. In this method the number of theoretical trays or plates required for a given change in concentration is computed by the methods of the previous section. This is then multiplied by a quantity, the height equivalent to a theoretical plate (H.E.T.P.), to give the required height of packing to do the same job. The H.E.T.P. must be an experimentally determined quantity characteristic for each packing. Unfortunately it is found that H.E.T.P. varies, not only with the type and size of packing, but also very strongly with flow rates of each fluid, and for every system with concentration as well, so that an enormous number of experimental data would have to be accumulated to permit utilization of the method. The difficulty lies in the failure to account for the fundamentally different action of the plate and packed towers, and the method has now largely been abandoned.

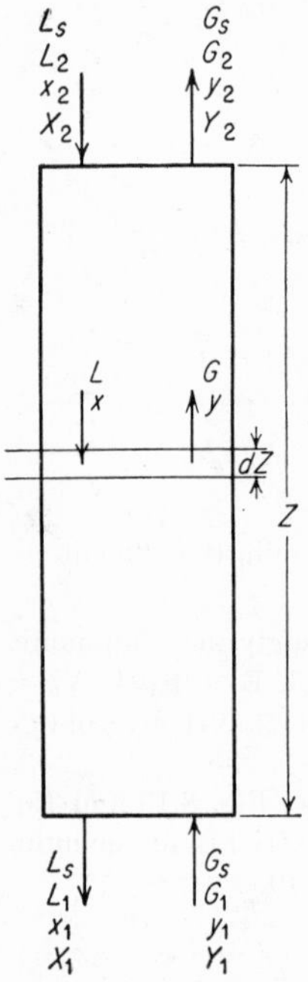

**The Transfer Unit. Principal Diffusional Resistance in the Gas.** Consider a packed or spray tower of unit cross-sectional area, as in Fig. 8.20. The total interfacial surface between gas and liquid, as a result of dispersion of the liquid in a thin film over the packing, is $S$ sq. ft./sq. ft. tower cross section. This is conveniently described as the product of $a$ sq. ft. interfacial surface/cu. ft. packed volume by the volume of the packing, $Z$ cu. ft./sq. ft. The quantity $a$ should not be confused with the surface of the dry packing, $a_p$, used in Chap. 6; it will depend not only upon the type of packing used but also upon the liquid and gas rates of flow which prevail. In the differential height $dZ$ of the packing, the interfacial surface is

$$dS = a \, dZ \qquad (8.29)$$

FIG. 8.20. Packed tower.

The quantity of solute in the gas passing the differential section of the tower under consideration is $Gy$ moles/(hr.)(sq. ft.), and the rate of mass transfer to the liquid is therefore $d(Gy)$. This can be related to the mass-transfer coefficient and the concentration driving force prevailing at this section of the tower. If the equilibrium-solubility curve can be considered straight over the concentration range considered, so that an over-all mass-transfer coefficient can be used (see Chap. 5),

$$d(Gy) = K_y(y - y^*) \, dS = K_y a(y - y^*) \, dZ \qquad (8.30)$$

Since $a$ is not ordinarily known, it is always combined with the coefficient to give a composite coefficient $K_y a$.

Both $G$ and $y$ vary from one end of the tower to the other, but $G_s$, the solvent gas which is essentially insoluble, does not. Therefore

$$d(Gy) = G_s \, d \, \frac{y}{1-y} = G_s \frac{dy}{(1-y)^2} = \frac{G \, dy}{1-y} \qquad (8.31)$$

The mass-transfer coefficient for diffusion of one component (the solute) through a second nondiffusing gas (the solvent) includes, it will be recalled, a term involving the average concentration of the nondiffusing gas over the path of the diffusion, $(1-y)_M$ [Eq. (3.4)]. If the concentration of solute varies considerably from one end of the tower to the other, the quantity $K_y a(1-y)_M$ will be much more constant than $K_y a$ alone. Equation (8.30) then becomes

$$\frac{G \, dy}{1-y} = \frac{[K_y a(1-y)_M](y-y^*) \, dZ}{(1-y)_M} \qquad (8.32)$$

or

$$\frac{(1-y)_M}{(1-y)} \frac{dy}{y-y^*} = \frac{K_y a(1-y)_M \, dZ}{G} \qquad (8.33)$$

Equation (8.33) may be integrated to obtain $Z$ in terms of $K_y a$, but it is more convenient to proceed as follows: For many situations the first term on the left-hand side of Eq. (8.33) is very nearly unity, whereupon it is easy to recognize the remainder of the left-hand side of the equation as the number of times the driving force must divide into the change in gas concentration. This is a measure of the difficulty of the mass-transfer operation and in integrated form is called the *number of transfer units* $N_{tOG}$. It can be related[3] to the height of packing required by the *height per transfer unit* $H_{tOG}$.

$$N_{tOG} = \int_{y_2}^{y_1} \frac{(1-y)_M \, dy}{(1-y)(y-y^*)} \qquad (8.34)$$

$$Z = N_{tOG} H_{tOG} \qquad (8.35)$$

where

$$H_{tOG} = \frac{G}{K_y a(1-y)_M} = \frac{G}{K_G a P_t(1-y)_M} \qquad (8.36)$$

The height per transfer unit $H_{tOG}$ is an experimental quantity which is more convenient to use than $K_y a$ or other mass transfer coefficients. The coefficients can be expected to vary strongly with gas-flow rate [compare the expression for a wetted-wall tower, Eq. (3.39), for example], and the ratio $G/K_y a$ can be expected therefore to be much less dependent upon rate of flow. Furthermore, $H_{tOG}$ has but a single dimension of length, expressed as feet in engineering work, and much of the confusion owing to different units can thereby be avoided. The subscripts $OG$ are used on the terms $N_{tOG}$ and $H_{tOG}$ to indicate that they are based on *over-all* driving forces $y - y^*$ within the gas phase (see Chap. 5, Fig. 5.4). The term $y - y^*$ is therefore the vertical distance between operating line and equilibrium curve at any liquid concentration on an operating diagram plotted in terms of mole fractions.

The quantity $(1 - y)_M$ is the average of the concentrations of non-diffusing gas at either end of the diffusing path, $1 - y$ in the main body of the gas and $1 - y^*$ at the liquid-gas interface [Eqs. (2.20), (2.21)],

$$(1 - y)_M = \frac{(1 - y^*) - (1 - y)}{\ln \dfrac{(1 - y^*)}{1 - y}} \doteq \frac{(1 - y^*) + (1 - y)}{2} \quad (8.37)$$

For all ordinary purposes the arithmetic average rather than the logarithmic average is entirely satisfactory, and substitution of this in Eq. (8.34) results in[5]

$$N_{tOG} = \int_{y_2}^{y_1} \frac{dy}{y - y^*} + \frac{1}{2} \ln \frac{1 - y_2}{1 - y_1} \quad (8.38)$$

or, in terms of mole ratios,

$$N_{tOG} = \int_{Y_2}^{Y_1} \frac{dY}{Y - Y^*} - \frac{1}{2} \ln \frac{1 + Y_1}{1 + Y_2} \quad (8.39)$$

The first terms of the right-hand sides of Eqs. (8.38) and (8.39) must ordinarily be evaluated by graphical integration.

**Illustration 7.** The absorber of Illustration 2 is to be a packed tower. Determine the number of transfer units $N_{tOG}$ required for the liquid rate of 1.5 times the minimum.

*Solution.* The operating line and equilibrium curve may be plotted either in terms of mole fractions for use with Eq. (8.38) or in terms of mole ratios for use with Eq. (8.39). Figure 8.10 is already plotted in terms of the latter, and it will be used. The integral of Eq. (8.39) is determined graphically by plotting $1/(Y - Y^*)$ as ordinate against $Y$ as abscissa. For each value of $X$, values of $Y$ are read from the operating line $DF$ and $Y^*$ from the equilibrium curve (alternatively these may be computed from the equations of these curves). The curve to be integrated graphically

| $X$ | $Y$ | $Y^*$ | $1/(Y - Y^*)$ |
|---|---|---|---|
| $X_2 = 0.00502$ | 0.00102 | 0.00062 | 2,500 |
| 0.02 | 0.00356 | 0.00245 | 901 |
| 0.04 | 0.00695 | 0.00483 | 462 |
| 0.06 | 0.01035 | 0.00712 | 310 |
| 0.08 | 0.01374 | 0.00935 | 228 |
| 0.10 | 0.01714 | 0.01150 | 177.5 |
| $X_1 = 0.1192$ | 0.0204 | 0.01350 | 145.0 |

is plotted in Fig. 8.21. The shaded area under the curve between the limits of $Y_1$ and $Y_2$ is 8.63.

Eq. (8.39):         $N_{tOG} = 8.63 - \dfrac{1}{2} \ln \dfrac{1 + 0.0204}{1 + 0.00102} = 8.62$   *Ans.*

**Principal Diffusional Resistance in the Liquid.** When the principal resistance to diffusion resides within the liquid, as in the case of absorption or desorption of very insoluble gases, it is more logical to measure the driving force for diffusion in terms of concentration in the liquid (compare Chap. 5). A development similar to that described above for this case leads to

$$N_{toL} = \int_{x_2}^{x_1} \frac{(1-x)_M \, dx}{(1-x)(x^*-x)} = \frac{Z}{H_{toL}} \tag{8.40}$$

where $H_{toL} = \dfrac{L}{K_x a(1-x)_M} = \dfrac{L}{K_L ac(1-x)_M} = \dfrac{LM_L}{K_L a\rho_L(1-x)_M}$ (8.41)

and $(1-x)_M = \dfrac{(1-x)-(1-x^*)}{\ln\dfrac{1-x}{1-x^*}} \doteq \dfrac{(1-x)+(1-x^*)}{2}$ (8.42)

Substitution of the second definition of Eq. (8.42) into Eq. (8.40) then leads to

$$N_{toL} = \int_{x_2}^{x_1} \frac{dx}{x^*-x} + \frac{1}{2}\ln\frac{1-x_2}{1-x_1} \tag{8.43}$$

and $$N_{toL} = \int_{X_2}^{X_1} \frac{dX}{X^*-X} - \frac{1}{2}\ln\frac{1+X_1}{1+X_2}\Big| \tag{8.44}$$

The operating line and equilibrium curve are plotted as usual, and the latter is considered to be a curve of $y$ vs. $x^*$ (or $Y$ vs. $X^*$). The *horizontal* distance between operating line and equilibrium curve, at any value of $y$, is then $x^* - x$, and the integral of Eq. (8.43), for example, is then evaluated graphically by determining the area under a curve of $1/(x^* - x)$ as ordinate against $x$ as abscissa.

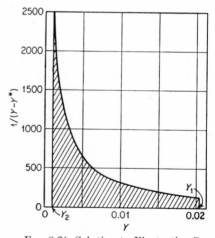

FIG. 8.21. Solution to Illustration 7.

When neither gas- nor liquid-phase resistances to mass transfer can be said to dominate, or "control," it is still satisfactory to use over-all concentration differences, over-all transfer units, and over-all mass-transfer coefficients, provided (a) that the equilibrium curve remains reasonably straight and (b) that the ratio of the mass-transfer coefficients for each phase remains constant. Either over-all gas- or liquid-concentration differences are applicable. A discussion of this is presented in detail in Chap. 5, to which reference should now be made. Situations not covered by these categories are outside the province of this book but are treated in detail elsewhere.[15]

**Dilute Solutions.** The computation of the number of transfer units for dilute mixtures can be greatly simplified. When the gas mixture is dilute, for example, the second term of the definition of $N_{tOG}$ [Eq. (8.38)] becomes entirely negligible and may be discarded,

$$N_{tOG} = \int_{y_2}^{y_1} \frac{dy}{y - y^*} \tag{8.45}$$

If the equilibrium curve in terms of mole fractions is linear over the range of compositions $x_1$ to $x_2$, then

$$y^* = mx + r \tag{8.46}$$

If the solutions are dilute, the operating line may be considered as a straight line as well,

$$y = \frac{L}{G}(x - x_2) + y_2 \tag{8.47}$$

so that the driving force $y - y^*$ is then linear in $x$,

$$y - y^* = qx + s \tag{8.48}$$

where $q$, $r$, and $s$ are constants. Therefore Eq. (8.45) becomes

$$N_{tOG} = \frac{L}{G}\int_{x_2}^{x_1} \frac{dx}{qx + s} = \frac{L}{Gq} \ln \frac{(y - y^*)_1}{(y - y^*)_2} = \frac{y_1 - y_2}{\dfrac{(y - y^*)_1 - (y - y^*)_2}{\ln \dfrac{(y - y^*)_1}{(y - y^*)_2}}} \tag{8.49}$$

$$N_{tOG} = \frac{y_1 - y_2}{(y - y^*)_M} \tag{8.50}$$

where $(y - y^*)_M$ is the logarithmic average of the concentration differences at the ends of the tower. This equation is sometimes used in the familiar rate form obtained by substituting the definition of $N_{tOG}$,

$$G(y_1 - y_2) = K_G aZP_t (y - y^*)_M \tag{8.51}$$

**Dilute Solutions, Henry's Law.** If Henry's law applies [$r$ of Eq. (8.46) = 0], by elimination of $x$ between Eqs. (8.46) and (8.47) and substitution of $y^*$ in Eq. (8.45) there results for absorbers[5]

$$N_{tOG} = \frac{\ln\left[\left(\dfrac{y_1 - mx_2}{y_2 - mx_2}\right)\left(1 - \dfrac{1}{A}\right) + \dfrac{1}{A}\right]}{1 - (1/A)} \tag{8.52}$$

where $A = L/mG$, as before. For strippers, the corresponding expression in terms of $N_{tOL}$ is similar,

$$N_{tOL} = \frac{\ln\left[\left(\dfrac{x_2 - y_1/m}{x_1 - y_1/m}\right)(1 - A) + A\right]}{1 - A} \tag{8.53}$$

These are shown in convenient graphical form in Fig. 8.22.

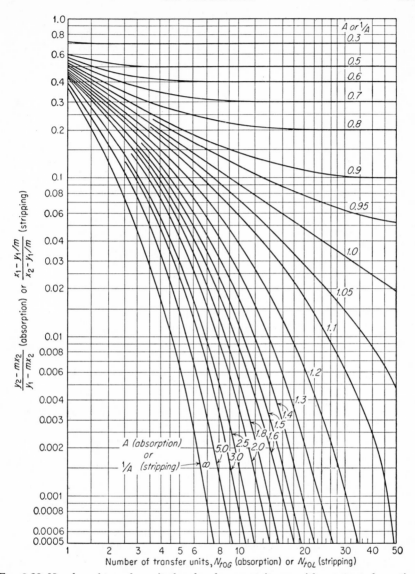

FIG. 8.22. Number of transfer units for absorbers or strippers with constant absorption or stripping factor.

**Graphical Construction for Transfer Units.**[1] Equation (8.50) demonstrates that one over-all gas transfer unit results when the change in gas composition equals the average over-all driving force causing the change. Consider now the operating diagram of Fig. 8.23, where line $KB$ has been drawn so as to be everywhere vertically halfway between the operating line and equilibrium curve. The step $CFD$ which corresponds to one transfer unit has been constructed by drawing the horizontal line $CEF$ so that lines $CE = EF$ and continuing vertically to $D$. $y_G - y_H$ may be considered as the average driving force for the change in gas composition $y_D - y_F$ corresponding to this step. Since $GE = EH$, and if the operating line may be considered straight $DF = 2(GE) = GH$, the step $CFD$ corresponds to one transfer unit. In similar fashion the other transfer units were stepped off ($JK = KL$, etc.). For computing $N_{toL}$, the line $KB$ would be drawn horizontally halfway between equilibrium curve and operating line and would bisect the vertical portions of the steps.

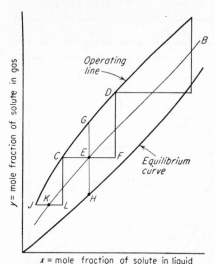

$x$ = mole fraction of solute in liquid

FIG. 8.23. Graphical determination of transfer units.

**Illustration 8.** Repeat the computation of Illustration **7**, using the simplified procedures for dilute mixtures.

*Solution.* a. Use Eq. (8.50).

$y_1 = 0.02 \qquad x_1 = X_1/(1 + X_1) = 0.1192/1.1192 = 0.1065$

$y_1^* = mx_1 = 0.125(0.1065) = 0.01331 \qquad (y - y^*)_1 = 0.02 - 0.01331 = 0.00669$

$y_2 = Y_2/(1 + Y_2) = 0.00102/1.00102 = 0.00102$

$y_2^* = mx_2 = 0.125(0.005) = 0.000625 \quad (y - y^*)_2 = 0.00102 - 0.000625 = 0.000395$

$(y - y^*)_M = (0.00669 - 0.000395)/\ln (0.00669/0.000395) = 0.00222$

$N_{toG} = (0.02 - 0.00102)/0.00222 = 8.55$

b. Eq. (8.52) or Fig. 8.22: The average $A$ (Illustration 4) is 1.425.

$$\frac{y_2 - mx_2}{y_1 - mx_2} = \frac{0.00102 - 0.125(0.005)}{0.02 - 0.125(0.005)} = 0.0204$$

From either Eq. (8.52) or Fig. 8.22, $N_{toG} = 8.8$.

c. The graphical construction for transfer units is shown on Fig. 8.24. The mole-ratio coordinates are satisfactory for dilute mixtures, and the operating line and equilibrium curves were redrawn from Fig. 8.10. The line $BD$ was drawn everywhere midway vertically between the operating line and equilibrium curve and the transfer-unit steps constructed by making the horizontal-line segments such as $AB$ and $BC$ equal. The number of transfer units required is $8\frac{2}{3}$.

**Heights of Transfer Units.** Experimental data in the form of mass-transfer coefficients or heights of transfer units are necessary to complete the computation of the height of packing required in a packed tower. These are frequently obtained from relatively small pilot-plant-scale absorbers filled with the packing to be used in the large-scale equipment. Adequate precautions must be taken to ensure sufficiently large tower diameters so that the packing density is the same as for the large tower, and adequate liquid distribution is necessary (see Chap. 6). The precautions respecting "end effects" described in Chap. 7 should also be observed. The pilot-plant equipment is then operated under the same conditions of flow rates, concentrations, and temperatures which are expected to prevail in the large plant. By measuring the concentration changes which occur, the $H_t$'s may be computed for the prevailing conditions and later may be used in design.

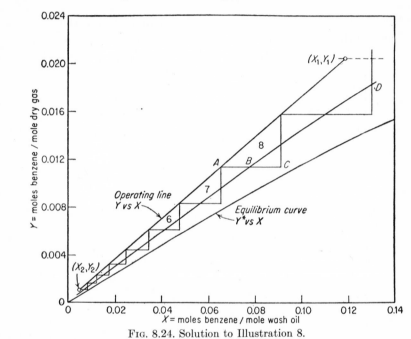

FIG. 8.24. Solution to Illustration 8.

The resistance to mass transfer in absorption and desorption is divided between that residing in the gas and that in the liquid, as shown by Eq. (5.22). Adapting this equation to our present needs,

$$\frac{1}{K_y a} = \frac{1}{k_y a} + \frac{m}{k_x a} \tag{8.54}$$

This may also be written as

$$\frac{G}{K_y a (1-y)_M} = \frac{G}{k_y a (1-y)_M} + \frac{mG}{L} \frac{L}{k_x a (1-x)_M} \frac{(1-x)_M}{(1-y)_M} \tag{8.55}$$

The term on the left is $H_{toG}$, and, by analogy with Eqs. (8.36) and (8.41), the terms on the right can be used to define the contributions to the overall height of a transfer unit made by the individual phase resistances,

$$H_{toG} = H_{tG} + \frac{mG}{L} (H_{tL}) \frac{(1-x)_M}{(1-y)_M} \tag{8.56}$$

For all except very concentrated solutions, the ratio of concentrations of nondiffusing substances will be nearly unity, and consequently

$$H_{toG} = H_{tG} + \frac{mG}{L}\,(H_{tL}) = H_{tG} + \frac{H_{tL}}{A} \qquad (8.57)$$

Similarly, through Eq. (5.23),

$$H_{toL} = H_{tL} + \frac{L}{mG}\,(H_{tG}) = H_{tL} + A H_{tG} \qquad (8.58)$$

There have now been accumulated sufficient data for the common packings so that reasonable estimates of $H_{tG}$ and $H_{tL}$ may be made for

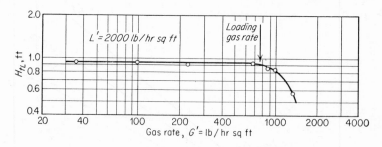

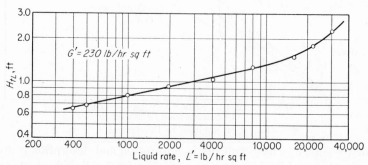

FIG. 8.25. Desorption of oxygen from water, 23 to 25°C., with 1.5-in. Raschig rings. (*Data of Sherwood and Holloway.*[14] *With permission of the American Institute of Chemical Engineers.*)

at least the simple situations. These may be used to compute over-all $H_t$'s through Eqs. (8.57) and (8.58), although for large installations it is desirable nevertheless to conduct pilot-plant studies.

**Liquid Phase** $H_{tL}$. By choosing experimental conditions such that the second term of the right-hand side of Eq. (8.58) is negligible, measurements of $H_{toL}$ may be considered as those of $H_{tL}$. This is the case for the absorption or desorption of very insoluble gases such as oxygen or hydrogen in water ($m$ very large). Typical measurements of this sort are shown in Fig. 8.25. The resistance to mass transfer in the liquid, of which $H_{tL}$ is a direct measure, is independent of gas rate until "loading" occurs (see Chap. 6), whereupon the resistance falls owing possibly to the increased interfacial surface resulting from increased turbulence in the tower at loading. The increase in $H_{tL}$ with increased liquid rate is orderly until loading occurs, as indicated in the figure. Since the rate of diffusion in liquids is so strongly influenced by liquid viscosity, the values of $H_{tL}$ decrease rapidly with increased temperature. All these characteristics can be described for the common packing by the empirical expression[14]

$$H_{tL} = \phi \left(\frac{L'}{\mu_L}\right)^\eta \text{Sc}_L^{0.5} \tag{8.59}$$

which applies for gas and liquid rates up to loading. $\text{Sc}_L$ is the dimensionless Schmidt number $\mu_L/\rho_L D_L$, which accounts for the variation in

TABLE 8.1. LIQUID-FILM HEIGHT OF TRANSFER UNIT†

$$H_{tL} = \phi \left(\frac{L'}{\mu_L}\right)^\eta \text{Sc}_L^{0.5}$$

where $H_{tL}$ = ft., $L'$ = lb./(hr.)(sq. ft.), $\mu_L$ = lb./(ft.)(hr.), $\text{Sc}_L$ = dimensionless

| Packing | $\phi$ | $\eta$ | Range of $L'$ |
|---|---|---|---|
| Raschig rings: | | | |
| ⅜ in. | 0.00182 | 0.46 | 400–15,000 |
| ½ in. | 0.00357 | 0.35 | 400–15,000 |
| 1 in. | 0.0100 | 0.22 | 400–15,000 |
| 1.5 in. | 0.0111 | 0.22 | 400–15,000 |
| 2 in. | 0.0125 | 0.22 | 400–15,000 |
| Berl saddles: | | | |
| ½ in. | 0.00666 | 0.28 | 400–15,000 |
| 1 in. | 0.00588 | 0.28 | 400–15,000 |
| 1.5 in. | 0.00625 | 0.28 | 400–15,000 |
| 3-in. partition rings (stacked staggered) | 0.0625 | 0.09 | 3,000–14,000 |
| Spiral rings (stacked staggered): | | | |
| 3-in. single spiral | 0.00909 | 0.28 | 400–15,000 |
| 3-in. triple spiral | 0.0116 | 0.28 | 3,000–14,000 |
| Drip-point grids (continuous flue): | | | |
| No. 6146 | 0.0154 | 0.23 | 3,500–30,000 |
| No. 6295 | 0.00725 | 0.31 | 2,500–22,000 |

† From the data of Sherwood and Holloway[14] and of Molstad, McKinney, and Abbey.[10]

$H_{tL}$ from one system to another. Values for the empirical constants are listed in Table 8.1.

**Gas Phase** $H_{tG}$. It should be possible to measure $H_{tG}$ by eliminating the liquid-film resistance, whereupon measurements of $H_{tOG}$ become those of $H_{tG}$. This will be the case either for humidification of a gas with a pure liquid (see Chap. 7), by absorption of a very soluble gas, or for the case where a rapid chemical reaction occurs between the absorbed solute and the liquid which substantially reduces the value of $m$ to zero. Actually the most complete and consistent data for $H_{tOG}$ have been taken for the absorption of ammonia from air into water, where the liquid-film resistance is still not negligible despite the fact that ammonia is very soluble in water. These may, however, be converted to values of $H_{tG}$ through Eq. (8.57) with the help of the data on $H_{tL}$. Figure 8.26 shows such calculated data for $\frac{1}{2}$-in. Raschig rings. Flow rate of each phase influences $H_{tG}$, and at gas rates greater than those corresponding to loading the values fall rapidly, as in the case of $H_{tL}$. The effect of temperature on $H_{tG}$ is, however, negligibly small. The extensive data of Fellinger have been published in graphical form[13,15] and many of these can be described by the empirical equation

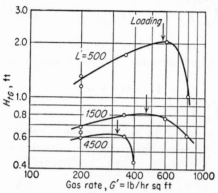

FIG. 8.26. Gas phase $H_{tG}$ for absorption of ammonia from air into water with 0.5-in. Raschig rings. [Data of Fellinger, as reprinted in the "Chemical Engineers' Handbook"[13] (with permission).]

$$H_{tG} = \frac{\alpha G'^{\beta}}{L'^{\gamma}} Sc_G^{0.5} \qquad (8.60)$$

The inclusion of the Schmidt number $Sc_G = \mu_G/\rho_G D_G$ in the fashion shown is somewhat arbitrary, as described in Chap. 7, but seems to be at present the best method for extending the ammonia-air data to other systems. Values of the empirical constants of Eq. (8.60) are listed in Table 8.2; for liquid and gas rates outside the indicated ranges, the original data should be consulted.

**Illustration 9.** Calculate the value of $H_{tOG}$ for the absorber of Illustrations 2, 7, and 8, assuming that a 1.5-ft.-diameter tower packed with 1.5-in. Berl saddles is to be used. The absorbent oil, mol. wt. 260, has a viscosity of 5 centipoises and a density of 0.84 gm./cu. cm. at 75°F. The benzene-free gas may be considered to be a single substance, mol. wt. 11, viscosity 0.01 centipoise.

*Solution.* The cross-sectional area of the absorber is $(1.5)^2\pi/4 = 1.77$ sq. ft. The solvent oil rate is 13.43 moles/hr. (Illustration 2), and it contains 0.1192 mole benzene/mole oil as it leaves the absorber. At the bottom of the tower,

$$L' = \frac{13.43(260) + 0.1192(13.43)(78)}{1.77} = 2,040 \text{ lb./(hr.)(sq. ft.)}$$

Similarly at the top $L' = 1,970$. Av. $L' = 2,005$ lb./(hr.)(sq. ft.).

The gas rate entering is 80.8 moles/hr., with 2% benzene. At the bottom of the tower,

$$G' = \frac{80.8(0.98)(11) + 80.8(0.02)(78)}{1.77} = 563 \text{ lb./(hr.)(sq. ft.)}$$

Similarly at the top $G' = 493$.    Av. $G' = 528$ lb./(hr.)(sq. ft.).

$$\rho_G = \frac{528(1.77)}{30,000} = 0.031 \text{ lb./cu. ft.}$$

The diffusivity of benzene through the gas is estimated to be 0.33 sq. ft./hr., and $\text{Sc}_G = 0.01(2.42)/0.031(0.33) = 2.37$. From Table 8.2, for 1.5-in Berl saddles, $\alpha = 5.05$, $\beta = 0.32$, $\gamma = 0.45$.

TABLE 8.2. GAS-FILM HEIGHT OF TRANSFER UNIT[†]

$$H_{tG} = \frac{\alpha G'^{\beta}}{L'^{\gamma}} \text{Sc}_G^{0.5}$$

where $H_{tG}$ = ft., $G'$ = lb./(hr.)(sq. ft.), $L'$ = lb./(hr.)(sq. ft.), $\text{Sc}_G$ = dimensionless

| Packing | $\alpha$ | $\beta$ | $\gamma$ | Range of | |
|---|---|---|---|---|---|
| | | | | $G'$ | $L'$ |
| Raschig rings: | | | | | |
| ⅜ in. | 2.32 | 0.45 | 0.47 | 200–500 | 500–1,500 |
| 1 in. | 7.00 | 0.39 | 0.58 | 200–800 | 400–500 |
| | 6.41 | 0.32 | 0.51 | 200–600 | 500–4,500 |
| 1½ in. | 17.3 | 0.38 | 0.66 | 200–700 | 500–1,500 |
| | 2.58 | 0.38 | 0.40 | 200–700 | 1,500–4,500 |
| 2 in. | 3.82 | 0.41 | 0.45 | 200–800 | 500–4,500 |
| Berl saddles: | | | | | |
| ½ in. | 32.4 | 0.30 | 0.74 | 200–700 | 500–1,500 |
| | 0.811 | 0.30 | 0.24 | 200–700 | 1,500–4,500 |
| 1 in. | 1.97 | 0.36 | 0.40 | 200–800 | 400–4,500 |
| 1½ in. | 5.05 | 0.32 | 0.45 | 200–1,000 | 400–4,500 |
| 3-in. partition rings (stacked staggered) | 650 | 0.58 | 1.06 | 150–900 | 3,000–10,000 |
| Spiral rings (stacked staggered): | | | | | |
| 3-in. single spiral | 2.38 | 0.35 | 0.29 | 130–700 | 3,000–10,000 |
| 3-in. triple spiral | 15.6 | 0.38 | 0.60 | 200–1,000 | 500–3,000 |
| Drip-point grids (continuous flue): | | | | | |
| No. 6146 | 3.91 | 0.37 | 0.39 | 130–1,000 | 3,000–6,500 |
| No. 6295 | 4.65 | 0.17 | 0.27 | 100–1,000 | 2,000–11,500 |

† From the data of Fellinger[13,15] and of Molstad, McKinney, and Abbey.[10]

Eq. (8.60):          $H_{tG} = 5.05(528)^{0.32}(2.37)^{0.5}/2,005^{0.45} = 1.88$ ft.

$D_L$ is estimated to be $1.92(10^{-6})$ sq. cm./sec. (Fig. 2.4, $\phi = 0.9$).   $\text{Sc}_L = 5/100(0.84)$ $(1.92)(10^{-6}) = 31,000$.   From Table 8.1, $\phi = 0.00625$, $\eta = 0.28$.

Eq. (8.59):          $H_{tL} = 0.00625 \left[ \dfrac{2,005}{5(2.42)} \right]^{0.28} 31,000^{0.5} = 4.60$ ft.

The average absorption factor $A = 1.425$ (Illustration 4).

Eq. (8.57):               $H_{tOG} = 1.88 + 4.60/1.425 = 5.11$ ft.

The height of packing required, since $N_{tOG} = 8.62$, is $8.62(5.11) = 44.0$ ft.   This considerable packed height is principally the result of the large liquid-phase resistance caused by the high viscosity of the oil, despite the high solubility of the benzene.

**Illustration 10.** In a plant for manufacturing ethyl alcohol by molasses fermentation, the carbon dioxide, $CO_2$, evolved during fermentation, which contains ethanol vapor, is presently discarded without attempt to recover the ethanol. The $CO_2$ issues from the fermenters at 1 atm., av. temp. 80°F., and may be assumed to be in equilibrium at this temperature with an alcohol-water solution containing 6.5 wt. % ethanol. The gas volume is 15,000 cu. ft./hr. The fermentation liquor (beer) is presently distilled to recover the ethanol, which has a value of $0.06 per pound in the dilute solution (before distillation).

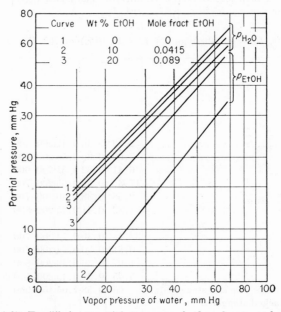

FIG. 8.27. Equilibrium partial pressures of ethanol-water solutions.

It is proposed to recover the ethanol in the $CO_2$ by washing the gas with water at 80°F. and to use the resultant dilute ethanol solution in making up the fresh fermentation liquor. The plant operates 350 days per year. Duct work presently used to lead the gas away from the fermenters will be adapted to the new absorber. Design the absorber.

*Solution.* Partial pressures of ethanol and water of aqueous ethanol solutions are shown, in the manner of Othmer and White,[12] in Fig. 8.27. The ethanol pressure from pure water is, of course, zero. The data are from "International Critical Tables," vol. III, p. 290. Interpolating for 6.5 wt. % ethanol at 80°F. (vapor pressure pure $H_2O$ = 26.3 mm. Hg), $p_{EtOH}$ = 7.5 mm. Hg, $p_{H_2O}$ = 25.5 mm. Hg. For the gas entering the absorber, therefore, $y_1$ = 7.5/760 = 0.00986 mole fraction ethanol.

*Gas in*

$15{,}000(492/540)(1/359)$ = 38.1 moles/hr.

Ethanol in = 38.1(0.00986) = 0.376 mole/hr. = 17.3 lb./hr.

Water vapor in = 38.1(25.5/760) = 1.28 moles/hr. = 23.1 lb./hr.

$CO_2$ in = 38.1 − 0.376 − 1.28 = 36.4 moles/hr. = 1,600 lb./hr.

Total wt. = 1,640 lb./hr.

Value of ethanol presently lost = 17.3(350)(24)(0.06) = $8,740 per year

*Gas out.* Assume temporarily that all ethanol is removed, that the pressure is 1 atm., and that the gas leaving is saturated with water. The $CO_2$ absorption will be negligible.

$CO_2$ out = 36.4 moles/hr. = 1,600 lb./hr.
Water vapor out = 36.4(26.3)/(760 − 26.3) = 1.305 moles/hr.
Total gas out = 36.4 + 1.305 = 37.7 moles/hr.
Av. gas rate = (38.1 + 37.7)/2 = 37.9 moles/hr.

*Enthalpy, or heat, balance.* "International Critical Tables," vol. V, pp. 159–160, lists heats of solution of ethanol in water. For 80°F., expressed in engineering units, some of these are as follows:

| $x$ of ethanol | 0.05 | 0.10 | 0.15 | 0.20 | 0.25 |
|---|---|---|---|---|---|
| Ht. of soln. at 80°F., B.t.u./mole ethanol | −3350 | −2750 | −2020 | −1463 | −1075 |

The heats of solution are referred to liquid water and liquid ethanol at 80°F. Use a base temperature $t_0 = 80$°F. Rewrite Eq. (8.10) for adiabatic operation ($Q = 0$),

$$H_L L - H_{L2} L_2 = H_G H - H_{G2} G_2 = G_S(H_G' - H_{G2}')$$

where $H_G'$ is molal enthalpy gas/mole dry gas, $CO_2$. The water content of the gas will be essentially constant throughout the absorber, and, neglecting any sensible-heat change of the gas (gas temperature constant at 80°F.), the enthalpy of the gas is only the latent heat of vaporization of the ethanol content, **17,920 B.t.u./mole** ethanol at 80°F. $Y$ = moles ethanol/mole $CO_2$.

$$G_S(H_G' - H_{G2}') = G_S(17,920)(Y - Y_2)$$

Ethanol balance: $G_S(Y - Y_2) = L_S(X - X_2) = L_S X$

Since the entering liquid is pure water at 80°F., $H_{L2} = 0$. The heat balance then becomes

$$H_L \frac{L}{L_S} = 17,920X$$

Let $X = 0.01$ mole ethanol/mole water.

$$\therefore L/L_S = 1.01 \qquad x_{EtOH} = 0.01/1.01 = 0.00989$$

From the preceding table, by extrapolation, the heat of solution is −3830 B.t.u./mole ethanol. This is converted to B.t.u./mole solution by multiplying by moles ethanol/mole solution or $X/(1 + X)$.

$\Delta H_S = -3,850(0.01)/(1 + 0.01) = -38.2$ B.t.u./mole solution
$M_{av} = [0.01(46.05) + 1(18.02)]/1.01 = 18.31$ lb./mole
$C_L = 1.0$ B.t.u./(lb.)(°F.)

Eq. (8.11): $H_L = 1.0(t_L - 80)18.31 - 38.2$
$\therefore [1.0(t_L - 80)18.31 - 38.2]1.01 = 17,920(0.01)$
$t_L = 91.9$°F.

From Fig. 8.27 at this temperature and concentration, the partial pressure of ethanol = 5.0 mm. Hg. $y_{EtOH}^* = 5.0/760 = 0.00658$. In similar fashion,

| $x_{EtOH}$ | 0 | 0.00497 | 0.00989 | 0.01475 |
|---|---|---|---|---|
| $t_L$, °F. | 80 | 86 | 91.9 | 97.4 |
| $y_{EtOH}^*$ | 0 | 0.00302 | 0.00658 | 0.01316 |

This provides the equilibrium curve of Fig. 8.28.

*Diameter of absorber.* Use 1-in. stoneware Raschig-ring packing. The average slope of the equilibrium curve $= m = 0.73$. For an economical liquid rate, take $A = L/mG = 1.6$. Therefore $L/G = 1.6(0.73) = 1.17$ moles water/mole gas. Therefore use $1.17(37.9) = 44.5$ moles water/hr. $= 804$ lb./hr.

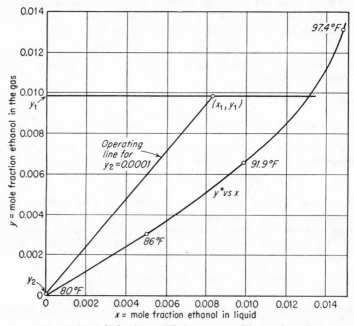

FIG. 8.28. Adiabatic equilibrium curve, Illustration 10.

At the bottom of the tower, assuming all ethanol is absorbed, the liquid rate is $804 + 17.3 = 821$ lb./hr.

$$\rho_G = 1,640/15,000 = 0.1093 \text{ lb./cu. ft.}$$
$$\rho_L = 62.0 \text{ lb./cu. ft.}$$

From Fig. 6.26 (with the symbols used on this figure),

$$\frac{L'}{G'}\left(\frac{\rho_G}{\rho_L}\right)^{0.5} = \frac{821}{1,640}\left(\frac{0.1093}{62.0}\right)^{0.5} = 0.021$$

At flooding, the ordinate of Fig. 6.26 $= 0.2$, and at loading 0.072. For 1-in. rings, $a_p/\epsilon^3 = 164$ (Table 6.2). $\mu_L = 0.95$ centipoise. At flooding,

$$G' = \left[\frac{0.2 g_c' \rho_G \rho_L}{(a_p/\epsilon^3)\mu_L^{0.2}}\right]^{0.5} = \left[\frac{0.2(4.17)(10^8)(0.1093)(62.0)}{164(0.95)^{0.2}}\right]^{0.5}$$
$$= 1,865 \text{ lb./(hr.)(sq. ft.)}$$

Similarly at loading, $G' = 1,120$ lb./(hr.)(sq. ft.). To allow for future expansion of the process, use $G' = 800$ lb./(hr.)(sq. ft.). Therefore $L' = 800 (821)/1,640 = 400$ lb./(hr.)(sq. ft.). Cross section of tower $= 1,640/800 = 2.05$ sq. ft.

$$\text{Tower diam.} = [4(2.05)/\pi]^{0.5} = 1.62 \text{ ft.} = 19.5 \text{ in.}$$

Use 20-in. standard pipe.

*Tower height.* Assume $y_2 = 0.0001$ mole fraction ethanol. For such dilute solutions, the operating line equation may be written in terms of mole fractions,

$$G(y_1 - y_2) = L(x_1 - x_2)$$
$$37.9(0.00986 - 0.0001) = 44.7(x_1 - 0)$$
$$x_1 = 0.00828 \text{ mole fraction}$$

The operating line is drawn on Fig. 8.28.

The great majority of the transfer units are located at the dilute end of the tower, and the slope of the equilibrium curve at the dilute end is 0.607 (up to $x = 0.007$). Therefore use the dilute-end absorption factor,

$$A = L_2/mG_2 = 44.5/(0.607)(37.7) = 1.94$$
$$\frac{y_2 - mx_2}{y_1 - mx_2} = \frac{y_2}{y_1} = \frac{0.0001}{0.00986} = 0.01014$$

Fig. 8.22: $\qquad\qquad N_{tOG} = 8.0$ transfer units

$H_{tL}$. The average liquid temperature $= 85°F. = 29.4°C$. "International Critical Tables," vol. V, p. 970, gives the diffusivity of ethanol in water at $x = 0.004$ and $10°C. = D_L = 0.8(10^{-5})$ sq. cm./sec. The viscosity of water at $10°C. = 1.308$ centipoises, at $29.4°C. = 0.80$ centipoise.

Refer to Chap. 2. $T/D_L\mu = \text{const.}$

$$\therefore D_L \text{ at } 29.4°C. = \frac{29.4 + 273}{10 + 273} \frac{1.308}{0.80} (0.8)(10^{-5}) = 1.4(10^{-5}) \text{ sq. cm./sec.}$$
$$\text{Sc}_L = \mu_L/\rho_L D_L = 0.008/0.994(1.4)(10^{-5}) = 575$$

Table 8.1: $\qquad\qquad \phi = 0.010, \eta = 0.22$

Eq. (8.59): $\qquad H_{tL} = 0.010 \left[ \frac{400}{0.8(2.42)} \right]^{0.22} (575)^{0.5} = 0.775 \text{ ft.}$

$H_{tG}$. To determine the gas diffusivity, use Eq. (2.23). The normal boiling point of ethanol is $351.4°K.$, and its critical volume is $167.5$ cu. cm./gm. mole.

Eq. (2.25): $\qquad\qquad \epsilon/k = 1.39(351.4) = 488°K.$
Eq. (2.26): $\qquad\qquad r = 0.833(167.5)^{0.33} = 4.59 \text{ A}$

For $CO_2$, $\epsilon/k = 190$, $r = 3.996$ A (Table 2.2).

$$\therefore \epsilon/k = [488(190)]^{0.5} = 304°K.$$
$$kT/\epsilon = (273 + 29.4)/304 = 0.995$$

Fig. 2.3: $\qquad\qquad f(kT/\epsilon) = 0.72$
$$r = (4.59 + 3.996)/2 = 4.29 \text{ A}$$

Eq. (2.23):

$$D_{\text{EtOH-CO}_2} = \frac{0.0009292(273 + 29.4)^{1.5} \left( \frac{1}{46.05} + \frac{1}{44} \right)^{0.5}}{1(4.29)^2(0.72)} = D_G$$

$D_G = 0.0785$ sq. cm./sec. or $3.87(0.0785) = 0.304$ sq. ft./hr.

$\mu$ for $CO_2 = 0.015$ centipoise at $85°F.$

$$\text{Sc}_G = \mu_G/\rho_G D_G = 0.015(2.42)/0.1093(0.304) = 1.092$$

Table 8.2: $\qquad \alpha = 7.00 \qquad \beta = 0.39 \qquad \gamma = 0.58$
Eq. (8.60): $\qquad H_{tG} = 7.00(800)^{0.39}(1.092)^{0.5}/400^{0.58} = 3.06 \text{ ft.}$

*Packed height*

Eq. (8.57): $\qquad H_{tOG} = 3.06 + 0.775/1.94 = 3.46 \text{ ft.}$
Eq. (8.35): $\qquad Z = 8.0(3.46) = 28.5 \text{ ft. of packing}$

The shell of the tower will be 32.5 ft. tall, allowing 2 ft. below the packing for gas entrance and liquid accumulation and 2 ft. above the packing for liquid distribution and mist eliminator.

[*Estimation of* $CO_2$ *absorption.* The liquid leaving will be saturated with $CO_2$. Assuming the solubility to be the same as that in water, the Henry's law coefficient is $m' = 1,860$ atm./mole fraction ("Chemical Engineers' Handbook"). Since $p_{CO_2} = 0.955$ atm. in the entering gas, $x_{CO_2} = 0.955/1,860 = 0.000514$ and the $CO_2$ absorption is approximately $44.9(0.000514) = 0.023$ mole/hr., or 1 lb./hr.]

*Pressure drop and power cost*

Table 6.3:             $m = 32.1, \quad n = 0.00434$
Eq. (6.28):           $\Delta P/Z = 32.1(10^{-8})10^{0.00434(400)/62}800^2/0.1093$
                              $= 2.0$ lb./(sq. ft.)(ft.)

With an over-all efficiency of blower and motor $= 50\%$, the power required is

$$2.0(28.5)(15,000)/3,600(550)(0.50) = 0.865 \text{ hp.}$$

The power for pumping the liquid is required for the 32.5-ft. elevation of the tower (pipe friction is negligible). For a motor-pump efficiency of $15\%$, the power required is

$$32.5(800)/3,600(550)(0.15) = 0.088 \text{ hp.}$$

The total power is $0.865 + 0.088 = 0.953$ hp. At 1.5 cents per kilowatthour, the annual power cost is

$$0.953(0.7457)(350)(24)(0.015) = \$89.6 \text{ per year}$$

*Cost.* The packing cost is $15/cu. ft., or $2.05(28.5)(15) = \$875$. Twenty-inch schedule 40 pipe weighs 123 lb./ft., and, at $0.15 per pound, the shell costs $123(32.5)(0.15) = \$600$. Taking the cost of pump and motor at $100 and of the blower with motor at $400, and allowing a factor of $100\%$ for piping, foundations, and installation, the equipment cost is

$$(875 + 600 + 100 + 400)2 = \$3,950$$

With an amortization rate of $35\%$ and maintenance cost of $5\%$, the annual cost of equipment and operation is

$$3,950(0.35 + 0.05) + 89.6 = \$1,670 \text{ per year}$$

The value of the alcohol lost in the scrubbed gas is

$$0.0001(37.7)(46.05)(0.06)(350)(24) = \$87.6 \text{ per year}$$

The total annual cost is $1,670 + 87.6 = \$1,758$ per year.

For larger concentrations of ethanol in the exit gas, the number of transfer units, and consequently the cost of equipment and operation, is less, but the loss of ethanol is greater, while for smaller concentrations the reverse is true. This is shown in Fig. 8.29, where the costs are plotted as a function of $y_2$. The minimum annual cost, $1,540 per year, occurs at $y_2 = 0.0003$, for which a 24-ft. packed height is required. For such a tower, the annual savings over present practice is $8,740 - 1,540 = \$7,200$ per year.

Additional economic balances may be struck for this design: (1) depending upon the cost of recovery of the alcohol from the beer, there is an optimum absorption factor which was here taken somewhat arbitrarily; (2) larger packings cost less per cubic foot and offer less gas-pressure drop per foot, but their $H_{tOG}$ is greater, and there is therefore an optimum packing size, assumed in this illustration; (3) for each packing there is an optimum tower diameter, since the rates of flow and hence pressure drop and $H_{tOG}$ change with tower diameter.

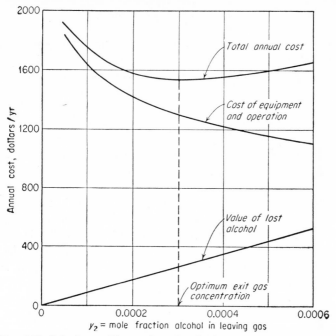

FIG. 8.29. Solution to Illustration 10. Optimum gas concentration.

## MULTICOMPONENT SYSTEMS

The previous discussion has assumed that only one component of the gas stream has an appreciable solubility in the absorbent liquid. When the gas contains more than one soluble component, or where the solvent gas itself has an appreciable solubility, some modifications are necessary. The almost complete lack of solubility data for multicomponent systems, except where ideal solutions are formed in the liquid phase and the solubilities of the various components are therefore mutually independent, unfortunately makes estimates of even the ordinary cases almost impossible. However, some of the more important industrial applications fall in the ideal-solution category, for example, the absorption of hydrocarbons from gas mixtures in nonvolatile hydrocarbon oils as in the manufacture of natural gasoline. This discussion is limited to dilute ideal mixtures only, but a few very important principles can be established which are applicable to all situations.

**Dilute Ideal Solutions.** When both the gas and liquid phases may be considered ideal, the simple form of Raoult's law [Eq. (8.1)] describes the solubility. This may be written for each component as

$$y^* = \frac{p^*}{P_t} = \frac{Px}{P_t} = mx \tag{8.61}$$

where $m = P/P_t$ is a constant for each substance at a constant temperature and total pressure. When the pressures are sufficiently high so that the gas may not be considered ideal, fugacities rather than pressures may be used to compute $m$. When in addition the liquid phase is nonideal, $m$ is an empirical relation between gas and liquid compositions which varies with composition, but such situations will not be considered here.

Since particularly in the case of hydrocarbon mixtures all components of the gas may have an appreciable solubility, there may be no gaseous substance which passes through the absorber in constant quantity. It is convenient, therefore, to base compositions of the gas in the various parts of the absorber on the amount of gas entering (rich, or "wet," gas), $Y'$ moles component/mole rich gas entering.[15] Similarly it is convenient to express liquid compositions in terms of the entering liquid (the "lean" oil in hydrocarbon work), $X'$ moles component/mole liquid entering. Therefore for any component $A$,

$$y_A = \frac{Y'_A}{Y'_A + Y'_B + Y'_C + \cdots} = \frac{Y'_A}{\Sigma Y'} \tag{8.62}$$

and

$$x_A = \frac{X'_A}{1 + X'_A + X'_B + X'_C + \cdots} = \frac{X'_A}{1 + \Sigma X'} \tag{8.63}$$

Equation (8.61) then becomes, for each component,

$$\frac{Y'^*}{\Sigma Y'} = m \frac{X'}{1 + \Sigma X'} \tag{8.64}$$

If only a small portion of the entering gas is absorbed in a relatively large amount of liquid, then approximately for each component

$$Y'^* = mX' \tag{8.65}$$

which is a straight line on $X'$, $Y'$ coordinates, one for each component.

A material balance for the lower part of the absorber, up to a point where the gas and liquid compositions are $Y'$ and $X'$, respectively, provides an operating line equation for each component,

$$G_1(Y'_1 - Y') = L_2(X'_1 - X') \tag{8.66}$$

This is a straight line on $X'$, $Y'$ coordinates owing to the constancy of $G_1$ and $L_2$. The equilibrium curves and operating lines may be plotted for each substance on the same diagram. The following illustration demonstrates the methods which may be used:

**Illustration 11.** A gas which analyzes 86% $CH_4$, 8% $C_2H_6$, 4% $C_3H_8$, 2% $n$-$C_4H_{10}$ is to be scrubbed at 75°F. with a completely stripped nonvolatile hydrocarbon oil. The total pressure is 2 atm., and a lean oil/rich gas ratio = 3.5 moles/mole is to be used. A 60% removal of $C_3H_8$ is required. Determine the number of theoretical trays and the composition of the gas leaving the absorber. The solutions are ideal.

*Solution.* Basis: 1 mole rich gas entering. The values of $m$ are computed from vapor pressures of the pure substances according to Raoult's law [Eq. (8.61)]. The solubility of the methane is too small to be considered.

| Component | Vapor pressure at 75°F., $P$ atm. | $m = \dfrac{P}{P_t} = \dfrac{P}{2}$ | $y_1 = Y_1'$ moles/mole gas in |
|---|---|---|---|
| $CH_4$ .......... | ..... | ..... | 0.86 |
| $C_2H_6$ ......... | 41.5 | 20.8 | 0.08 |
| $C_3H_8$ ......... | 8.84 | 4.42 | 0.04 |
| $n$-$C_4H_{10}$ ...... | 2.33 | 1.67 | 0.02 |

The equilibrium curves corresponding to Eq. (8.65) are plotted, with slopes $m$, in Fig. 8.30.

Consider the absorption of $C_3H_8$. For 60% removal, $Y_2'$ for $C_3H_8$ is 0.40(0.04) = 0.016 mole in gas out/mole gas in, and 0.024 mole $C_3H_8$ is absorbed. Since the lean oil contains no $C_3H_8$, $X_2' = 0$. $X_1' = 0.024/3.5 = 0.00685$ mole $C_3H_8$ in leaving oil/mole lean oil entering. The operating line $AB$ on the figure may now be drawn and the number of theoretical trays determined graphically as 2.2. The number of real trays in the tower is now fixed.

Consider next the $C_4H_{10}$. $Y_1' = 0.04$, $X_2' = 0$. The value of $L_2/G_1$ is the same for all components, and therefore the operating line for $C_4H_{10}$ must be parallel to $AB$. Although Eq. (8.27) indicates that the tray efficiency will be different for each substance, we will here assume that the number of theoretical trays is the same for all. The operating line $DC$ for $C_4H_{10}$ is then located by trial and error, parallel to $AB$, ending on the $Y'$ axis since $X_2' = 0$, and ending at an ordinate $Y' = 0.02$ so that 2.2 theoretical trays can be drawn between operating line and equilibrium curve. This produces at $D$ a value of $Y_2' = 0.0024$, and the $C_4H_{10}$ absorbed is 0.02 − 0.0024 = 0.0176 mole, or 88% of that entering.

Similarly for ethane, the line $EF$ is located by trial parallel to $AB$, ending at $Y' = 0.08$ and at $X_2' = 0$ so as to fit 2.2 theoretical trays. At $E$, $Y_2' = 0.0666$, and the $C_2H_6$ absorbed is 0.08 − 0.0666 = 0.0134 mole, or 16.8% of that entering.

The gas leaving then consists of 0.86 mole $CH_4$, 0.0666 mole $C_2H_6$, 0.016 mole $C_3H_8$, and 0.0024 mole $C_4H_{10}$. The total absorption is 0.0550 mole. With sufficient additional information to estimate the tray efficiencies for each constituent, allowance could easily be made for the different rates of absorption of each component in the gas.

Alternatively, since the solutions are dilute, the Kremser equation, Eqs. (8.22) and (8.23), or Fig. 8.15 can be used with the mole-ratio units directly. Thus, for $C_3H_8$, $A = 3.5/4.42 = 0.79$, and, from Fig. 8.15 at $Y_2'/Y_1' = 0.40$, 2.2 theoretical trays are obtained. For $C_4H_{10}$, at $N_p = 2.2$ trays and $A = 3.5/1.67 = 2.1$, $Y_2'/Y_1' = 0.12$, or 88% absorption. For $C_2H_6$, $A = 3.5/20.8 = 0.168$, corresponding to 16.8% absorption.

Had a packed tower been considered for the above example, the procedure would require the computation of the number of transfer units for $C_3H_8$ by Eq. (8.50) with substitution of $Y'$ for $y$, and location of the operating lines for the other components so that the logarithmic average driving forces for each component are the same. Alternatively, Eq. (8.52) and Fig. 8.22 could be used. It is also possible to account for

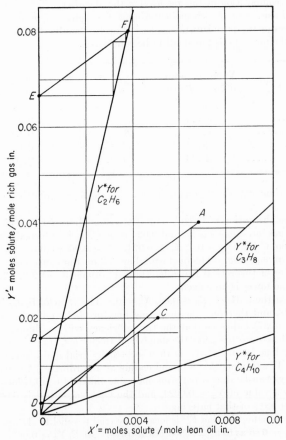

Fig. 8.30. Solution to Illustration 11.

the difference in $H_{tOG}$ and the consequent difference in $N_{tOG}$ for each component for a fixed packing height.

The simplified procedures outlined above are satisfactory so long as the total absorption is small and the liquid dilute in absorbed components. A possible upper limit on the total absorption or increase in liquid flow is 10 per cent before appreciable error is incurred. With greater percentage absorption, Eq. (8.65) is no longer a satisfactory approximation for Eq. (8.64), and the equilibrium curves are no longer straight. A trial-and-error procedure is then required to locate them. The same is true for cases of appreciable temperature rise. These matters are discussed in detail elsewhere.[15]

Despite these limitations, however, several important principles may be established from the preceding illustration which are applicable to all multicomponent absorbers:

1. There is one component ($C_3H_8$ in the illustration) whose operating-line and equilibrium curve are most nearly parallel, or with an absorption factor most nearly equal to unity. This is the "key" component.

2. Substances less soluble than the key component ($C_2H_6$ in the illustration) will be absorbed to a lesser extent than the key, and the exit liquid will be substantially in equilibrium with the concentration of these substances in the entering gas (as at point $F$ in the figure).

3. Substances more soluble than the key component ($C_4H_{10}$ in the illustration) will be absorbed to a greater extent than the key, and if they are substantially more soluble, the exit gas will be substantially in equilibrium with the concentration of these in the entering liquid (as at point $D$ in the figure).

4. The principal variables for the design of a multicomponent absorber are (a) the number of trays (or depth of packing), (b) $L/G$ ratio, and (c) fractional absorption of one component.

The total absorption, unspecified as to components, may be substituted for item c. Any two of these, but *not all three*, may be arbitrarily fixed for a given design. Having specified two, the third is automatically fixed, as is the extent of absorption for all substances not specified under (c).

**Use of Reflux. Reboiled Absorbers.** Refer again to the preceding illustration. Considering only the three substances absorbed, the wet gas contained these roughly in the proportions $C_2H_6:C_3H_8:C_4H_{10} = 57:29:14$. The rich oil leaving the absorber contained the same substances in the approximate ratio 24:44:32. Despite its low solubility, the proportion of absorbed gas which is ethane is high, owing to the relatively high proportion of this substance in the original wet gas. If it is desired to reduce the relative proportions of ethane in the rich oil, the oil just as it leaves the tower must be in contact with a gas relatively leaner in ethane and richer in propane and butane. Such a gas can be obtained by heating a part of the rich oil, which will then evolve a gas of the required low ethane content. This evolved gas may then be returned to an extension of the absorber below the inlet of the wet gas, where in rising past the oil it will strip out the ethane (and also any methane which may have been absorbed as well). The ethane not absorbed will now, of course, leave with the lean gas. The heat exchanger where a portion of the rich oil is heated is called a *reboiler*, and the arrangement of Fig. 8.31 may be used.

A stream returned to a cascade of stages, as represented by the trays in the absorber, for the purposes of obtaining an enrichment beyond that obtained by countercurrent contact with the feed to the cascade, is called *reflux*. This principle is used extensively in distillation, liquid extraction, and adsorption, but it is applicable to any countercurrent enrichment operation.

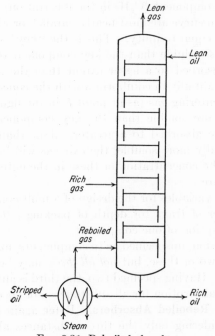

Fig. 8.31. Reboiled absorber.

## NOTATION FOR CHAPTER 8

$a$ = interfacial surface, sq. ft./cu. ft. active volume

$A$ = absorption factor = $L/mG$, dimensionless

$b$ = bubble-cap slot width, in.

$c$ = concentration, lb. moles/cu. ft.

$C_L$ = specific heat of the liquid, B.t.u./(lb.)(°F.)

$d$ = differential operator

$D$ = diffusivity, sq. ft./hr.

$e$ = 2.7183

$E$ = over-all tray efficiency, fractional, dimensionless

$E_G$ = Murphree gas-tray efficiency, fractional, dimensionless

$G$ = total gas rate, lb. moles/(hr.)(sq. ft.)

$G'$ = total gas rate, lb./(hr.)(sq. ft.)

$G_S$ = rate of solvent gas, lb. moles/(hr.)(sq. ft.)

$h$ = vertical distance, center of bubble-cap slot to top of weir, in.

$H_G$ = enthalpy of the gas, B.t.u./lb. mole gas

$H'_G$ = enthalpy of the gas, B.t.u./lb. mole solvent gas

$H_L$ = enthalpy of the liquid, B.t.u./lb. mole

$H_{tG}$ = gas-film height of a transfer unit, ft.

$H_{tL}$ = liquid-film height of a transfer unit, ft.

$H_{tOG}$ = over-all height of a transfer unit, gas, ft.

$H_{tOL}$ = over-all height of a transfer unit, liquid, ft.

$\Delta H_S$ = integral heat of solution, B.t.u./lb. mole solution

H.E.T.P. = height of packing equivalent to a theoretical plate, ft.

$k_x a$ = liquid-film mass-transfer coefficient, lb. moles/(hr.)(cu. ft.)(mole fraction)

$k_y a$ = gas-film mass-transfer coefficient, lb. moles/(hr.)(cu. ft.)(mole fraction)

$K$ = defined by Eqs. (8.26) and (8.27)

$K_G a$ = over-all gas mass-transfer coefficient, lb. moles/(hr.)(cu. ft.)(atm.)

$K_L a$ = over-all liquid mass-transfer coefficient, lb. moles/(hr.)(cu. ft.)(lb. mole/cu. ft.)

$K_x a$ = over-all liquid mass-transfer coefficient, lb. moles/(hr.)(cu. ft.)(mole fraction)

$K_y a$ = over-all gas mass-transfer coefficient, lb. moles/(hr.)(cu. ft.)(mole fraction)

ln = natural logarithm

log = common logarithm

$L$ = total liquid rate, lb. moles/(hr.)(sq. ft.)

$L'$ = total liquid rate, lb./(hr.)(sq. ft.)

$L_S$ = rate of solvent liquid, lb. moles/(hr.)(sq. ft.)

$m$ = slope of the equilibrium-solubility curve, mole fraction in gas/mole fraction in liquid = $dy^*/dx$. If constant, $m = y^*/x = y/x^*$

$m'$ = Henry's law constant, atm./mole fraction

$M$ = molecular weight, lb./lb. mole

$N_p$ = number of theoretical stages or trays, dimensionless

$N_{tOG}$ = over-all number of transfer units, gas, dimensionless

$N_{tOL}$ = over-all number of transfer units, liquid, dimensionless

$p$ = partial pressure of a gas in a mixture, atm.

$p^*$ = partial pressure in equilibrium with a liquid, atm.

$P$ = vapor pressure of a pure liquid, atm.

$P_t$ = total pressure, atm.

$q$ = a constant

$Q$ = heat evolved, B.t.u./(hr.)(sq. ft.)

$r$ = a constant

$s$ = a constant

$S$ = interfacial surface, sq. ft./sq. ft. tower cross section

Sc = Schmidt number, $\mu/\rho D$, dimensionless

$t_L$ = liquid temperature, °F.

$t_0$ = base temperature for enthalpy balance, °F.

$x$ = concentration solute in liquid, mole fraction

$x^*$ = concentration solute in the liquid in equilibrium with the gas, mole fraction

$X$ = concentration solute in liquid, lb. moles solute/lb. mole solvent

$X^*$ = concentration solute in liquid in equilibrium with the gas, moles solute/mole solvent

$X'$ = concentration solute in the liquid, lb. moles solute/lb. mole liquid in

$y$ = concentration solute in the gas, mole fraction

$y^*$ = concentration solute in the gas in equilibrium with the liquid; mole fraction

$Y$ = concentration solute in the gas, lb. moles solute/lb. mole solvent gas

$Y^*$ = concentration solute in the gas in equilibrium with the liquid, lb. moles solute/lb. mole solvent gas

$Y'$ = concentration solute in the gas, lb. moles solute/lb. mole gas in

$Z$ = height of packing, ft

$\alpha$ = a constant

$\beta$ = a constant

$\gamma$ = a constant

$\eta$ = a constant

$\mu$ = viscosity, lb./(ft.)(hr.)

$\mu'$ = viscosity, centipoises

$\pi$ = 3.1416

$\rho$ = density, lb./cu. ft.

$\Sigma$ = summation

$\phi$ = a constant

Subscripts:

av = average

$A$ = substance $A$, the solute

$G$ = gas

$L$ = liquid

$M$ = logarithmic average

1 = bottom of tower

2 = top of tower

## REFERENCES

1. Baker, T. C.: *Ind. Eng. Chem.*, **27**, 977 (1935).
2. Baker, T., and J. S. Stockhardt: *Ind. Eng. Chem.*, **22**, 376 (1930).
3. Chilton, T. H., and A. P. Colburn: *Ind. Eng. Chem.*, **27**, 255 (1935).
4. Colburn, A. P.: *Trans. Am. Inst. Chem. Engrs.*, **35**, 211 (1939).
5. ———: *Ind. Eng. Chem.*, **33**, 111 (1941).
6. Gerster, J. A., *et al.: Chem. Eng. Progr.*, **45**, 716 (1949); **47**, 523, 621 (1951).
7. Hachmuth, K. H.: *Chem. Eng. Progr.*, **48**, 523, 570, 617 (1952).
8. Kremser, A.: *Natl. Petroleum News*, **22**(21), 42 (1930).
9. Lewis, W. K., Jr.: *Ind. Eng. Chem.*, **28**, 399 (1936).
10. Molstad, M. C., J. F. McKinney, and R. G. Abbey: *Trans. Am. Inst. Chem. Engrs.*, **39**, 605 (1943).
11. O'Connell, H. E.: *Trans. Am. Inst. Chem. Engrs.*, **42**, 741 (1946).
12. Othmer, D. F., and R. E. White: *Ind. Eng. Chem.*, **34**, 952 (1942).
13. Perry, J. H., ed., "Chemical Engineers' Handbook," 3d ed., pp. 688–690, McGraw-Hill Book Company, Inc., New York, 1950.
14. Sherwood, T. K., and F. A. L. Holloway: *Trans. Am. Inst. Chem. Engrs.*, **36**, 39 (1940).
15. ——— and R. L. Pigford: "Absorption and Extraction," 2d ed., McGraw-Hill Book Company, Inc., New York, 1952.
16. Souders, M., and G. G. Brown: *Ind. Eng. Chem.*, **24**, 519 (1932).
17. Walter, J. F., and T. K. Sherwood: *Ind. Eng. Chem.*, **33**, 493 (1941).

## PROBLEMS

**1.** A scheme for removal of hydrogen sulfide from a gas by scrubbing with water at 75°F. is being considered. The gas contains 2% $H_2S$ and is to be scrubbed to a concentration of 0.1% $H_2S$. The water is $H_2S$-free. Henry's law describes the solubility, and $m' = 545$ atm./mole fraction.

*a.* For a countercurrent absorber, calculate the liquid/ratio, moles water/mole gas for 1.2 times the minimum, and the composition of the exit liquid, (1) if the pressure is 1 atm., and (2) if the pressure is 10 atm.

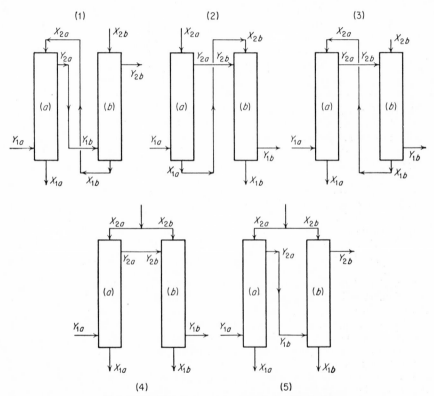

FIG. 8.32. Absorber arrangements for Prob. 1.

*b.* The absorber for (*a*) would have to be excessively tall, and the various schemes in Fig. 8.32 are being considered as means of using two shorter absorbers. Make freehand sketches of operating diagrams, one for each scheme, showing the relation between operating lines for the two absorbers and the equilibrium curve. Mark the concentrations of Fig. 8.32 on each diagram, but do not compute the concentrations.

**2.** The equilibrium partial pressures of carbon dioxide over aqueous solutions of monoethanolamine (30 wt. %) [Mason and Dodge, *Trans. Am. Inst. Chem. Engrs.*, **32**, 27(1936)] are as follows:

| Moles CO$_2$ | Partial pressure CO$_2$, mm. Hg | | |
|---|---|---|---|
| Mole solution | 77°F. | 122°F. | 167°F. |
| 0.050 | .... | .... | 65 |
| 0.052 | .... | 7.5 | 93.5 |
| 0.054 | .... | 13.6 | 142.6 |
| 0.056 | .... | 25.0 | 245 |
| 0.058 | 5.6 | 47.1 | 600 |
| 0.060 | 12.8 | 96.0 | |
| 0.062 | 29.0 | 259 | |
| 0.064 | 56.0 | | |
| 0.066 | 98.7 | | |
| 0.068 | 155 | | |
| 0.070 | 232 | | |

A plant for manufacturing dry ice will burn coke in air to produce a flue gas, which when cleaned and cooled will contain 15% CO$_2$, 5% O$_2$, 79% N$_2$. The gas will be blown into a bubble-tray scrubber at 1.2 atm., 77°F., to be scrubbed with 30% ethanolamine solution entering at 77°F. The scrubbing liquid, which is recycled from a stripper, will contain 0.058 mole CO$_2$/mole solution. The gas leaving the scrubber is to contain 2% CO$_2$. Assume isothermal operation.

*a.* Determine the minimum liquid/gas ratio, moles/mole.

*b.* Determine the number of pounds of solution to enter the absorber per cubic foot of entering gas, for an $L/G$ ratio of 1.2 times the minimum.

*c.* Determine the number of theoretical trays for the conditions of (*b*).

*d.* The viscosity of the solution is 6.0 centipoises; sp. gr. = 1.012. Estimate the average $m$, and the over-all tray efficiency to be expected. How many real trays are required?

**3.** *a.* Repeat the computations of parts *a* to *c* of Prob. 2, but assume adiabatic operation. The heat of solution of CO$_2$ in the solution is 720 B.t.u. evolved/lb. CO$_2$ absorbed, referred to gaseous CO$_2$ and liquid solution. The specific heat of the solution is 0.82 B.t.u./(lb. solution)(°F.), at all CO$_2$ concentrations.

*b.* Suppose the absorber planned for isothermal operation ($L/G$ and theoretical trays of Prob. 2) were operated adiabatically. What concentration of CO$_2$ in the exit gas could be expected?

**4.** Carbon disulfide, CS$_2$, used as a solvent in a chemical plant is evaporated from the product in a drier into an inert gas (essentially nitrogen, N$_2$) in order to avoid an explosion hazard. The vapor-nitrogen mixture is to be scrubbed with an absorbent hydrocarbon oil which will be subsequently steam-stripped to recover the CS$_2$. The CS$_2$-N$_2$ mixture has a partial pressure of CS$_2$ equal to 50 mm. Hg, at 75°F. and is to be blown into the absorber at essentially atmospheric pressure at the rate of 50,000 cu. ft./hr. The vapor content of the gas is to be reduced to 0.5%. The absorption oil has an average molecular weight 180, viscosity 2 centipoises, and specific gravity 0.81 at 75°F. The oil enters the absorber essentially stripped of all CS$_2$, and solutions of oil and CS$_2$ are ideal. The vapor pressure of CS$_2$ at 75°F. = 346 mm. Hg. Assume isothermal operation.

*a.* Determine the minimum liquid/gas ratio.

b. For a liquid/gas ratio of twice the minimum, determine the pounds of oil per hour to enter the absorber.

c. Determine the number of theoretical trays required, both graphically and analytically.

d. For a conventional bubble-tray design, slot width 0.25 in., and vertical distance from center of slots to the top of the weir 1.5 in., compute the Murphree gas-tray efficiency. Determine the number of real trays graphically as in Fig. 8.19.

e. Compute the over-all tray efficiency [Eq. (8.28)], and determine the number of real trays.

f. Determine the number of real trays with the help of Fig. 8.17.

5. Solve Prob. 4, assuming adiabatic operation. The specific heat of the oil is 0.475 and of carbon disulfide 0.368 B.t.u./(lb.)(°F.). The viscosity of the oil is 2.0 centipoises at 75°F. and 1.7 centipoises at 85°F.

6. a. Derive Eq. (8.39).

b. With the help of Eqs. (8.23) and (8.52), derive the relation between $N_p$ and $N_{tOG}$. Show that, for an operating line parallel to the equilibrium curve, $N_p = N_{tOG}$.

7. Design a tower packed with 2-in. Raschig rings for the carbon disulfide scrubber of Prob. 4. Use a liquid/gas ratio of twice the minimum and 50% of the flooding velocity.

a. Compute the number of transfer units by Eq. (8.39).

b. Repeat, using the graphical procedure as in Fig. 8.23.

c. Repeat, using Eq. (8.50).

d. Repeat, using Eq. (8.52) and Fig. 8.22.

e. Determine the diameter of the tower.

f. Determine the value of $H_{tG}$, $H_{tL}$, and $H_{tOG}$.

g. What is the value of $K_Ga$?

h. Determine the packed height.

i. Estimate the pressure drop for the gas and the power required for the blower.

j. Make a sketch of the final design, showing liquid distribution, packing support, and gas inlet.

8. It is desired to reduce the ammonia content of 6,000 cu. ft./hr. (80°F., 1 atm.) of an ammonia-air mixture from 5.0 to 0.04% by volume by water scrubbing. There is available a 1-ft.-diameter tower packed to a depth of 12 ft. with 1-in. Berl saddles. Is the tower satisfactory, and if so, what water rate should be used? At 80°F., ammonia-water solutions follow Henry's law up to 5.0 mole % ammonia in the liquid, and $m = 1.414$.

9. A new process is being considered which involves the crystallization of a product from methanol and drying of the wet crystals by evaporation of the methanol into air. The resulting air-methanol mixture, estimated as 15,000 cu. ft./hr. at 80°F., 1 atm., will contain 5% methanol, which is to be recovered by countercurrent scrubbing in a packed tower with water at 80°F. The methanol content of the gas is to be reduced to 0.1%, whereupon the gas will be recirculated to the driers. For purposes of distilling the methanol-water solution, it is agreed that the concentration in the liquid leaving the absorber is to be 0.04 mole fraction methanol. The absorber is to be designed for 60% of the loading gas velocity to allow for future expansion.

The tower shell is to be schedule 40 steel pipe, valued at $0.15 per pound. Allow $500 for blower and motor, which will operate at 50% over-all efficiency, and $100 for a pump and motor, at 15% efficiency. Stoneware Raschig rings cost $15 per cubic foot for the 1-in., $12 per cubic foot for the 1.5-in., and $10 per cubic foot for the 2-in. size. Allow 100% of equipment cost for installation and connecting piping, and use a 20% amortization rate. Power costs 1.2 cents per kilowatthour, and operation for 350 days per year, 24 hr. per day, is anticipated.

Design the tower for the packing size which results in the least annual cost.

The following data were interpolated from the listings in "International Critical Tables," vol. III, p. 290; vol. V, p. 159:

| Mole fraction methanol in water soln. | Equilibrium partial pressure of methanol, mm. Hg | | Heat of soln. in water, 80°F., B.t.u./lb. mole methanol |
|---|---|---|---|
| | 39.9°C | 59.4°C | |
| 0 | 0 | 0 | |
| 5 | 25.0 | 50 | −2715 |
| 10 | 46.0 | 102 | −2370 |
| 15 | 66.5 | 151 | −2030 |

The heat of solution is referred to liquid water and liquid methanol at 80°F. The partial-pressure data may be extended by the methods of Fig. 8.2.

**10.** A gas containing 88% methane, 4% ethane, 5% propane, and 3% n-butane is to be scrubbed at 100°F., 5 atm. abs. pressure, in a tower containing the equivalent of eight theoretical trays. It is desired to remove 80% of the propane. The lean oil will contain 0.5 mole % butane but none of the other gaseous constituents. What quantity of lean oil, moles/mole wet gas, should be used, and what will be the composition of the rich oil and scrubbed gas? At these conditions, the Henry's law constants,[15] $m = y^*/x$, are methane 38; ethane 7.0; propane 2.3; n-butane 0.75.

# CHAPTER 9

# DISTILLATION

Distillation is a method of separating the components of a solution which depends upon the distribution of the substances between a gas and a liquid phase, applied to cases where all components are present in both phases. Instead of introducing a new substance into the mixture in order to provide the second phase, as is done in gas absorption or desorption, the new phase is created from the original solution by vaporization or condensation.

In order to make clear the distinction among distillation and the other operations, let us cite a few specific examples. In the separation of a solution of common salt and water, the water may be completely vaporized from the solution without removal of salt since the latter is for all practical purposes quite nonvolatile at the prevailing conditions. This is the operation of evaporation. Distillation, on the other hand, is concerned with the separation of solutions where all the components are appreciably volatile. In this category, consider the separation of the components of a liquid solution of ammonia and water. By contacting the ammonia-water solution with air which is essentially insoluble in the liquid, the ammonia may be stripped or desorbed by processes which were discussed in Chap. 8, but the ammonia is then mixed with water vapor and air and is not obtained in pure form. On the other hand, by application of heat, we may partially vaporize the solution and thereby create a gas phase consisting of nothing but water and ammonia. And since the gas will be richer in ammonia than the residual liquid, a certain amount of separation will have resulted. By appropriate manipulation of the phases, or by repeated vaporizations and condensations, it is then ordinarily possible to make as complete a separation as may be desired, recovering both components of the mixture in as pure a state as we wish.

The advantages of such a separation method are clear. In distillation the new phase differs from the original by its heat content, but heat is readily added or removed without difficulty, although of course the cost of doing this must inevitably be considered. Absorption or desorption operations, on the other hand, which depend upon the introduction of a foreign substance, provide us with a new solution which in turn may have to be separated by one of the diffusional operations unless it happens that the new solution is useful directly.

There are in turn certain limitations to distillation as a separation process. In absorption or similar operations, where it has been agreed to introduce a foreign substance to provide a new phase for distribution purposes, we may ordinarily choose from a great variety of solvents in order to provide the greatest possible separation effect. For example, since water is ineffectual in absorbing hydrocarbon gases from a gas mixture, we choose instead a hydrocarbon oil which provides a high solubility. But in distillation there is no such choice. The gas which may be created from a liquid by application of heat inevitably consists only of the components comprising the liquid. Since the gas is therefore chemically very similar to the liquid, the change in composition resulting from the distribution of the components between the two phases is ordinarily not very great. Indeed, in some cases the change in composition is so small that the process becomes impractical; it may even happen that there is no change in composition whatsoever.

Nevertheless the direct separation which is ordinarily possible by distillation, into pure products requiring no further processing, has made this perhaps the most important of all the mass-transfer operations.

## VAPOR-LIQUID EQUILIBRIA

The successful application of distillation methods depends greatly upon an understanding of the equilibria which exist between the vapor and liquid phases of the mixtures encountered. A brief review of these is therefore essential. The emphasis here will be on binary mixtures.

**Pressure-Temperature-Concentration Phase Diagram.** Let us first consider binary mixtures which we shall term "ordinary," by which is meant that the liquid components dissolve in all proportions to form homogeneous solutions which are not necessarily ideal and that no complications of maximum or minimum boiling points occur. We shall consider component $A$ of the binary mixture $A$-$B$ as the more volatile, i.e., the vapor pressure of pure $A$ at any temperature is higher than the vapor pressure of pure $B$. The vapor-liquid equilibrium for each pure substance of the mixture is of course its vapor pressure–temperature relationship, as indicated in Fig. 7.1. For binary mixtures an additional variable, concentration, must likewise be considered. Mole fractions are the most convenient concentration terms to use, and throughout this discussion $x$ will be the mole fraction of the more volatile substance $A$ in the liquid and $y^*$ the corresponding equilibrium mole fraction of $A$ in the vapor.

Complete graphical representation of the equilibria requires a three-dimensional diagram, as in Fig. 9.1. The curve marked $P_A$ is the vapor-pressure curve of $A$, lying entirely in the nearest composition plane at $x = 1.0$. The curve extends from its critical point $C_A$ to its triple point $T_A$, but the complications of the solid phase which do not enter into distillation operations will not be considered. Similarly curve $P_B$ is the vapor pressure of pure $B$, in the far plane at $x = 0$. The liquid and vapor regions at compositions between $x = 0$ and 1.0 are separated by a double surface which extends smoothly from $P_A$ to $P_B$. The shape of this double surface is most readily studied by considering sections at constant

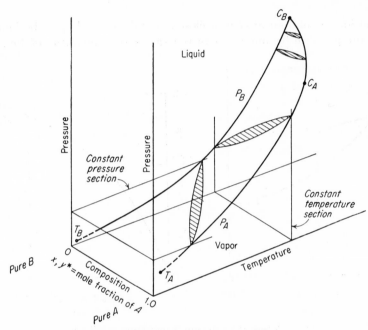

FIG. 9.1. Binary liquid-vapor equilibria.

pressure and constant temperature, examples of which are shown in the figure.

**Constant-pressure Equilibria.** Consider first a typical section at constant pressure (Fig. 9.2a). The intersection of the double surface of Fig. 9.1 with the constant-pressure plane produces a looped curve without maxima or minima extending from the boiling point of pure $B$ to that of pure $A$ at the pressure in question. The upper curve provides the temperature-vapor composition ($t$-$y^*$) relationship, the lower that of the temperature-liquid composition ($t$-$x$). Liquid and vapor mixtures at equilibrium are at the same temperature and pressure throughout, so that horizontal *tie lines* such as line $DF$ join equilibrium mixtures at $D$ and $F$. There are an infinite number of such tie lines for this diagram. A mixture on the lower curve, as at point $D$, is a saturated liquid; a mixture on the upper curve, as at $F$, is a saturated vapor. A mixture at $E$ is a two-phase mixture, consisting of a liquid phase of composition at $D$ and a vapor phase of composition at $F$, in such proportions that the average composition of the entire mixture is represented by $E$. The relative amounts of the equilibrium phases are related to the segments of the tie line,

$$\frac{\text{Moles of } D}{\text{Moles of } F} = \frac{\text{line } EF}{\text{line } DE} \tag{9.1}$$

Consider a solution at $G$ in a closed container which may be kept at constant pressure by moving a piston (as in the apparatus of Fig. 7.2,

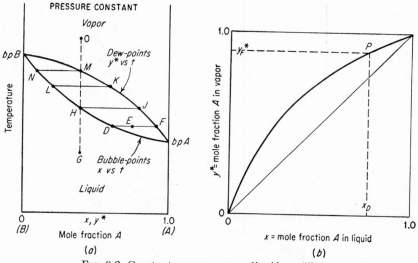

FIG. 9.2. Constant-pressure vapor-liquid equilibria.

for example). The solution is entirely liquid. If it is heated, the first bubble of vapor forms at $H$ and has the composition at $J$, richer in the more volatile substance, and hence the lower curve is called the bubble-point temperature curve. As more of the mixture is vaporized, more of the vapor forms at the expense of the liquid, giving rise, for example, to liquid $L$ and its equilibrium vapor $K$, although the composition of the entire mass is still the original as at $G$. The last drop of liquid vaporizes at $M$ and has the composition at $N$. Superheating the mixture follows the path $MO$. The mixture has vaporized over a temperature range from $H$ to $M$, unlike the single vaporization temperature of a pure substance. If the mixture at $O$ is cooled, all the phenomena reappear in reverse order. Condensation, for example, starts at $M$, whence the upper curve is termed the dew-point curve, and continues to $H$.

If a solution such as that at $H$ is boiled in an open vessel, on the other hand, with the vapors escaping into the atmosphere, since the vapor is richer in the more volatile substance the liquid residue must therefore become leaner.  The temperature and composition of the saturated residual liquid therefore move along the lower curve toward $N$ as the distillation proceeds.

The vapor-liquid equilibrium compositions may be shown also on a distribution diagram ($x$ vs. $y^*$) as in Fig. 9.2$b$.  Point $P$ on the diagram represents the tie line $DF$, for example.  Since the vapor is richer in the more volatile substance, the curve lies above the 45° diagonal line, which has been drawn in for comparison.

**Relative Volatility.**  The greater the distance between the equilibrium curve and the diagonal of Fig. 9.2$b$, the greater the difference in liquid and vapor compositions and the more readily is the separation by distillation made.  One numerical measure of this is called the *separation factor*, or, particularly in the case of distillation, the *relative volatility* $\alpha$.  This is the ratio of the concentration ratio of $A$ and $B$ in one phase to that in the other and is a measure of the separability,

$$\alpha = \frac{y^*/(1 - y^*)}{x/(1 - x)} = \frac{y^*(1 - x)}{x(1 - y^*)} \tag{9.2}$$

The value of $\alpha$ will ordinarily change as $x$ varies from 0 to 1.0.  If $y^* = x$ (except at $x = 0$ or 1), $\alpha = 1.0$ and no separation is possible.  The larger the value of $\alpha$ above unity, the greater the degree of separability.

**Increased Pressures.**  At higher pressures the sections at constant pressure will of course intersect the double surface of Fig. 9.1 at increased temperatures.  The intersections may be projected onto a single plane, as in Fig. 9.3$a$.  It should be noted that, not only do the looped curves occur at higher temperatures, but also they usually become narrower.  This is readily seen from the corresponding distribution curves of Fig. 9.3$b$.  The relative volatilities, and hence the separability, therefore usually become less at higher pressures.  As the critical pressure of one component is exceeded, there is no longer a distinction between vapor and liquid for that component and for mixtures the looped curves are therefore shorter, as at pressures above $P_{t3}$, the critical for $A$ in the figure.  Distillation separations can be made only in the region where a looped curve exists.

For particular systems, the critical pressure of the less volatile substance may be reached before that of the more volatile, and it is also possible that the double surface of Fig. 9.1 will extend at intermediate compositions to a small extent beyond the critical pressures of either substance.

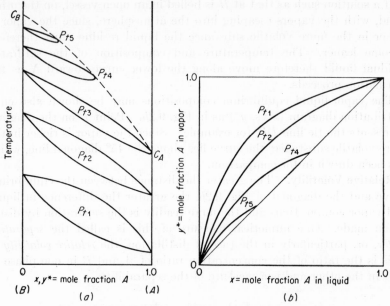

FIG. 9.3. Vapor-liquid equilibria at increased pressure.

**Constant-temperature Equilibria.** A typical constant-temperature section of the three-dimensional phase diagram is shown in Fig. 9.4.

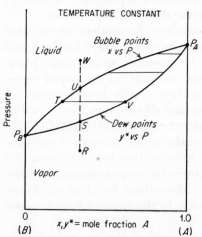

FIG. 9.4. Constant-temperature vapor-liquid equilibria.

The intersection of the constant-temperature plane with the double surface of Fig. 9.1 provides the two curves which extend without maxima or minima from the vapor pressure of pure $B$ to that of pure $A$. As before, there are an infinite number of horizontal tie lines, such as $TV$, which join an equilibrium vapor as at $V$ to its corresponding liquid at $T$. A solution in a closed container at $W$ is entirely a liquid, and if the pressure is reduced at constant temperature, the first bubble of vapor forms at $U$, complete vaporization occurs at $S$, and further reduction in pressure results in a superheated vapor as at $R$.

**Ideal Solutions. Raoult's Law.** Before studying the characteristics of mixtures which deviate markedly from those just described, let us consider the equilibria for the limiting case of mixtures whose vapors and liquids are ideal. The nature of ideal solutions and the types of mixtures which approach ideality were discussed in Chap. 8.

For an ideal solution, the equilibrium partial pressure $p^*$ of a constituent at a fixed temperature equals the product of its vapor pressure $P$ when pure at this temperature and its mole fraction in the liquid. This is Raoult's law.

$$p_A^* = P_A x \qquad p_B^* = P_B(1 - x) \tag{9.3}$$

If the vapor phase is also ideal,

$$P_t = p_A^* + p_B^* = P_A x + P_B(1 - x) \tag{9.4}$$

and the total as well as the partial pressures are linear in $x$ at a fixed temperature. These relationships are shown graphically in Fig. 9.5. The equilibrium vapor composition may then be computed at this temperature. For example, the value of $y^*$ at point $D$ on the figure equals the ratio of the distances $FG$ to $EG$,

$$y^* = \frac{p_A^*}{P_t} = \frac{P_A x}{P_t} \tag{9.5}$$

$$1 - y^* = \frac{p_B^*}{P_t} = \frac{P_B(1 - x)}{P_t} \tag{9.6}$$

The relative volatility $\alpha$ is, by substitution in Eq. (9.2),

$$\alpha = \frac{P_A}{P_B} \tag{9.7}$$

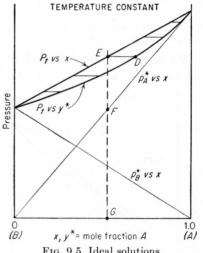

Fig. 9.5. Ideal solutions.

For ideal solutions, it is possible then to compute the entire vapor-liquid equilibria from the vapor pressures of the pure substances. For all other mixtures, however, it is necessary to obtain the data experimentally.

**Illustration 1.** Compute the vapor-liquid equilibria at constant pressure of 1 atm. for mixtures of n-heptane with n-octane, which may be expected to form ideal solutions.

*Solution.* The boiling points at 1 atm. of the substances are n-heptane $(A)$, 98.4°C.; n-octane $(B)$, 125.6°C. Computations are therefore made between these temperatures. For example, at 110°C., $P_A = 1050$ mm. Hg, $P_B = 484$ mm. Hg, $P_t = 760$ mm. Hg.

Eq. (9.4): $\quad x = \dfrac{P_t - P_B}{P_A - P_B} = \dfrac{760 - 484}{1,050 - 484} = 0.487$ mole fraction heptane in liquid

Eq. (9.5): $\quad y^* = \dfrac{P_A x}{P_t} = \dfrac{1,050(0.487)}{760} = 0.674$ mole fraction heptane in vapor

Eq. (9.7): $\quad\quad\quad \alpha = P_A/P_B = 1,050/484 = 2.17$

In similar fashion, the data of the following table may be computed:

| $t$, °C. | $P_A$, mm. Hg | $P_B$, mm. Hg | $x$ | $y^*$ | $\alpha$ |
|---|---|---|---|---|---|
| 98.4 | 760 | 333 | 1.0 | 1.0 | 2.28 |
| 105 | 940 | 417 | 0.655 | 0.810 | 2.25 |
| 110 | 1,050 | 484 | 0.487 | 0.674 | 2.17 |
| 115 | 1,200 | 561 | 0.312 | 0.492 | 2.14 |
| 120 | 1,350 | 650 | 0.1571 | 0.279 | 2.08 |
| 125.6 | 1,540 | 760 | 0 | 0 | 2.02 |

Curves of the type of Fig. 9.2 may now be plotted. Note that although the vapor pressures of the pure substances vary considerably with temperature, $\alpha$ for ideal solutions does not. In this case, an average of the computed $\alpha$'s is 2.16, and substituting this in Eq. (9.2), rearranged,

$$y^* = \frac{\alpha x}{1 + x(\alpha - 1)} = \frac{2.16x}{1 + 1.16x}$$

provides an expression which for many purposes is a satisfactory empirical relation between $y^*$ and $x$ for this system at 1 atm.

**Positive Deviations from Ideality.** A mixture whose total pressure is greater than that computed for ideality [Eq. (9.4)] is said to show positive deviations from Raoult's law. Most mixtures fall into this category. In these cases the partial pressures of each component are larger than the ideal, as shown in Fig. 9.6.† It should be noted that as the concentration for each component approaches unity mole fraction, the partial pressures for that substance approach ideality tangentially. Raoult's law, in other words, is nearly applicable to the substance present in very large concentrations. This is the case for all substances except where association within the vapor or electrolytic dissociation within the liquid occurs.

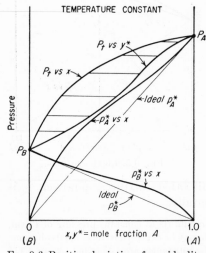

FIG. 9.6. Positive deviations from ideality.

The distribution diagram ($x$ vs. $y^*$) for systems of this type appears much the same as that of Fig. 9.2b.

† The ratio of the actual equilibrium partial pressure of a component $p^*$ to the ideal value $Px$ is the activity coefficient referred to the pure substance: $\gamma = p^*/Px$. Since $\gamma$ is greater than unity in these cases and log $\gamma$ is therefore positive, the deviations are termed *positive* deviations from ideality.

*Minimum-boiling Mixtures. Azeo-*
*tropes.* When the positive deviations from ideality are sufficiently
large and the vapor pressures of the
two components are not too far
apart, the total-pressure curves at
constant temperature may rise
through a maximum at some concentration, as in Fig. 9.7a. Such a mixture is said to form an azeotrope, or
constant-boiling mixture. The significance of this is more readily seen
by study of the constant-pressure
section (Fig. 9.7b or c). The liquid-
and vapor-composition curves are
tangent at point $L$, the point of azeotropism at this pressure, which represents the minimum boiling temperature for this system. For all
mixtures of composition less than $L$,
such as those at $C$, the equilibrium
vapor ($E$) is richer in the more volatile
component than the liquid ($D$). For
all mixtures richer than $L$, however,
such as at $F$, the equilibrium vapor
($G$) is less rich in the more volatile
substance than the liquid ($H$). A
mixture of composition $L$ gives rise to
a vapor of composition identical with
the liquid, and it consequently boils
at constant temperature and without
change in composition. If solutions
either at $D$ or $H$ are boiled in an open
vessel with continual escape of the
vapors, the temperature and composition of the residual liquids in
each case move along the lower curve

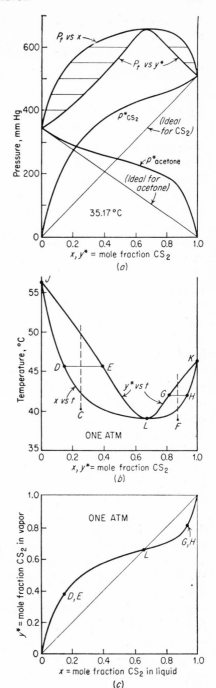

Fig. 9.7. Minimum-boiling azeotropism in
the system carbon disulfide–acetone (a) at
constant temperature, (b) and (c) at constant pressure.

away from point $L$ (toward $K$ for a liquid at $H$, and toward $J$ for one at $D$).

Solutions such as these cannot be completely separated by ordinary distillation methods at this pressure, since at the azeotropic composition $y^* = x$ and $\alpha = 1.0$.† The azeotropic composition as well as its boiling point changes with pressure. In some cases, changing the pressure may eliminate azeotropism from the system.

Azeotropic mixtures of this sort are very common, and over 3,000 have been recorded.[13] One of the most important is the ethanol-water azeotrope which at 1 atm. occurs at 89.4 mole per cent ethanol and 78.2°C. Azeotropism disappears in this system at pressures below 70 mm. Hg.

*Partial Liquid Miscibility.* Some substances exhibit such large positive deviations from ideality that they do not dissolve completely in the liquid state, as in the case of isobutanol-water (Fig. 9.8). The curve through points $C$ and $E$ represent the solubility limits of the constituents at relatively low temperatures. Mixtures of composition and temperature represented by points within the central area, such as point $D$, form two liquid phases at equilibrium at $C$ and $E$, and line $CE$ is a liquid tie line. Mixtures in the regions on either side of the solubility limits such as at $F$ are homogeneous liquids. The solubility ordinarily increases with increased temperature, and the central area consequently decreases in width. If the pressure were sufficiently high so that vaporization did not occur, the liquid-solubility curves would continue along the broken extensions as shown. At the prevailing pressure, however, vaporization occurs before this can happen, giving rise to the branched vapor-liquid equilibrium curves. For homogeneous liquids such as that at $F$, the vapor-liquid equilibrium phenomena are normal, and such a mixture boils initially at $H$ to give the first bubble of vapor of composition $J$. The same is true of any solution richer than $M$, except that here the vapor is leaner in the more volatile component. Any two-phase liquid mixture within the composition range from $K$ to $M$ will boil at the temperature of the line $KM$, and all these give rise to the same vapor of composition $L$. A liquid mixture of average composition $L$, which produces a vapor of the same composition, is sometimes called a *heteroazeotrope.* The corresponding distribution diagram with the tie line $HJ$, solubility limits at the boiling point $K$ and $M$, and the azeotropic point $L$, is shown in Fig. 9.8*b*.

In relatively few instances the azeotropic composition lies outside the limits of insolubility. One such case is the system methyl ethyl ketone–water.

† For compositions to the right of $L$ (Fig. 9.7) $\alpha$ as usually computed is less than unity, and the reciprocal of $\alpha$ is then ordinarily used.

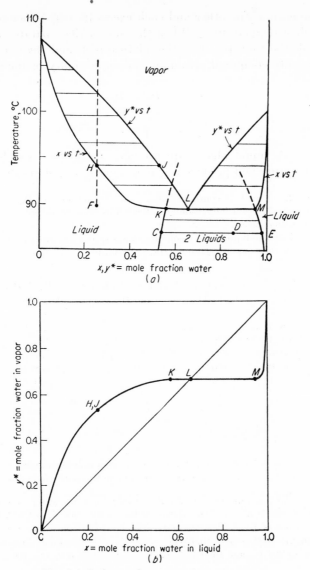

Fig. 9.8. Isobutanol-water at 1 atm. pressure.

*Insoluble Liquids. Steam Distillation.* The mutual solubility of some liquids is so small that they may be considered substantially insoluble: points $K$ and $M$ (Fig. 9.8) are then for all practical purposes on the vertical axes of these diagrams. This is the case for a mixture such as a hydrocarbon and water, for example. If the liquids are completely insoluble, the vapor pressure of either component cannot be influenced by the presence of the other and each exerts its true vapor pressure at the prevailing temperature. When the sum of the separate vapor pressures equals the total pressure, the mixture boils and the vapor composition is readily computed, assuming the applicability of the simple gas law,

$$P_A + P_B = P_t \qquad (9.8)$$

$$y^* = \frac{P_A}{P_t} \qquad (9.9)$$

So long as two liquid phases are present, the mixture will boil at the same temperature and produce a vapor of constant composition.

**Illustration 2.**  A mixture containing 50 gm. water and 50 gm. ethylaniline, which may be assumed to be essentially insoluble, is boiled at atmospheric pressure. Describe the phenomena that occur.

*Solution.*  Since the liquids are insoluble, each exerts its own vapor pressure, and when the sum of these equals 760 mm. Hg, the mixture boils.

| $t$, °C | $P_A$ (water), mm. Hg | $P_B$ (ethylaniline), mm. Hg | $P_t = P_A + P_B$, mm. Hg |
|---|---|---|---|
| 38.5 | 51.1 | 1 | 52.1 |
| 64.4 | 199.7 | 5 | 205 |
| 80.6 | 363.9 | 10 | 374 |
| 96.0 | 657.6 | 20 | 678 |
| 99.15 | 737.2 | 22.8 | 760 |
| 113.2 | 1,225 | 40 | 1,265 |
| 204 | . . . . . . . | 760 | |

The mixture boils at 99.15°C.

$$y^* = P_A/P_t = 737.2/760 = 0.97 \text{ mole fraction water}$$
$$1 - y^* = P_B/P_t = 22.8/760 = 0.03 \text{ mole fraction ethylaniline}$$

The original mixture contained 50/18.02 = 2.78 gm. moles water and 50/121.1 = 0.412 gm. mole ethylaniline. The mixture will continue to boil at 99.15°C., with an equilibrium vapor of the indicated composition, until all the water has evaporated together with 2.78(0.03/0.97) = 0.086 gm. mole of the ethylaniline. The temperature will then rise to 204°C., and the equilibrium vapor will be pure ethylaniline.

Note that, by this method of distillation with steam, so long as liquid water is present the high-boiling organic liquid can be made to vaporize at a temperature much lower than its normal boiling point without the necessity of a vacuum-pump equipment operating at 22.8 mm. Hg. If boiled at 204°C., this compound will undergo considerable decomposition. However, the heat requirements of the steam-distillation process are great since such a large amount of water must be evaporated simultaneously. Alternatives would be (*a*) to operate at a different total pressure in the presence of liquid water where the ratio of the vapor pressures of the substances may be more favorable and (*b*) to bubble superheated steam (or other insoluble gas) through the mixture in the absence of liquid water and to vaporize the ethylaniline by allowing it to saturate the steam.

**Negative Deviations from Ideality.** When the total pressure of a system at equilibrium is less than the ideal value, the system is said to deviate negatively from Raoult's law. Such a situation is shown in Fig.

9.9 at constant temperature. Note that in this case as with positive deviations, where neither vapor association nor liquid dissociation occurs, the partial pressures of the constituents of the solution approach ideality as their concentrations approach 100 per cent. The constant-pressure diagram for such a case has the same general appearance as the diagrams shown in Fig. 9.2.

**Maximum-boiling Mixtures. Azeotropes.** When the difference in vapor pressures of the components is not too great and in addition the negative deviations are large, the curve for total pressure

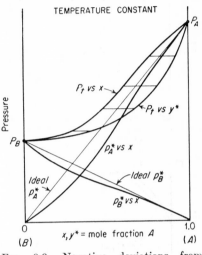

FIG. 9.9. Negative deviations from ideality.

against composition may pass through a minimum, as in Fig. 9.10*a*. This condition gives rise to a maximum in the boiling temperatures, as at point *L* (Fig. 9.10*b*), and a condition of azeotropism. The equilibrium vapor is leaner in the more volatile substance for liquids whose *x* is less than the azeotropic composition and greater if *x* is larger. Solutions on either side of the azeotrope, if boiled in an open vessel with escape of the vapor, will ultimately leave a residual liquid of the azeotropic composition in the vessel.

Maximum-boiling azeotropes are less common than the minimum type. One which is very well known is that of hydrochloric acid–water (11.1 mole % HCl, 110°C., at 1 atm.), which may be prepared simply by boiling a solution of any strength of the acid in an open vessel. This is one method of standardizing hydrochloric acid.

**Multicomponent Systems.** Nonideal systems of three components may be treated graphically, using triangular coordinates to express the compositions in the manner of Chap. 10, but for more than three components graphical treatment becomes very complicated if not impossible. Actually our knowledge of nonideal systems of this type is extremely

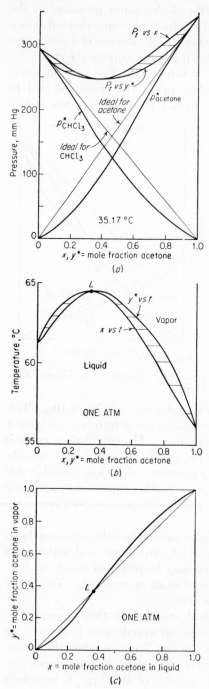

(a)

(b)

(c)

limited, and very few data have been accumulated. It is generally unsafe to predict detailed behavior of a multicomponent system from considerations of the pure components alone, or even from a knowledge of the simple binary systems that may be formed from the components. For example, three-component systems sometimes form ternary azeotropes, whose equilibrium vapor and liquid phases have identical composition. But the fact that one, two, or three binary azeotropes are known among the components does not make the formation of a ternary azeotrope certain, and a ternary azeotrope need not necessarily coincide with the composition of minimum or maximum boiling temperature for the system at constant pressure.

*Ideal Systems.* Many of the multicomponent systems of industrial importance may be considered nearly ideal in the liquid phase for all practical purposes. This is particularly true for hydrocarbon mixtures of the same homologous series, such as those of the paraffin series, or the lower-boiling aromatic hydrocarbons.† In such cases Raoult's law may be applied. If the components

† Hydrocarbons of different molecular structure, however, frequently form such nonideal solutions that azeotropism occurs, as, for example, in the binary systems hexane–methyl cyclopentane, hexane-benzene, and benzene-cyclohexane.

Fig. 9.10. Maximum-boiling azeotropism in the system acetone-chloroform (*a*) at constant temperature, (*b* and *c*) at constant pressure.

are $A$, $B$, $C$, etc., then, at a fixed temperature,

$$p_A^* = P_A x_A \qquad p_B^* = P_B x_B \qquad p_C^* = P_C x_C \qquad p_J^* = P_J x_J \quad (9.10)$$

and, for an ideal vapor,

$$P_t = p_A^* + p_B^* + p_C^* + \cdots = \Sigma p^* \qquad (9.11)$$

Since $y_A^* = p_A^*/P_t$, etc., then, for any component $J$,

$$y_J^* = \frac{p_J^*}{\Sigma p^*} = \frac{P_J x_J}{\Sigma P x} \qquad (9.12)$$

The relative volatility of two substances forming an ideal solution is the ratio of their vapor pressures [Eq. (9.7)], so that the relative volatility of substance $J$ with respect to substance $C$, for example, is

$$\alpha_{JC} = \frac{P_J}{P_C} \qquad (9.13)$$

Dividing numerator and denominator of Eq. (9.12) by $P_C$, we obtain, since $\alpha_{CC} = 1$,

$$y_J^* = \frac{\alpha_{JC} x_J}{\alpha_{AC} x_A + \alpha_{BC} x_B + x_C + \alpha_{DC} x_D + \cdots} = \frac{\alpha_{JC} x_J}{\Sigma \alpha x} \qquad (9.14)$$

This form of the equation is sometimes more convenient for computing compositions than Eq. (9.12) since, as has been demonstrated, the relative volatilities change much more slowly with temperature than do vapor pressures.

**Illustration 3.** A liquid contains 50 mole % benzene, 25 mole % toluene, and 25 mole % o-xylene. At 1 atm. pressure, compute its bubble point and the composition of the equilibrium vapor. The solution may be considered ideal.

*Solution.* For a first estimate the temperature of initial boiling (bubble point) will be assumed to be 90°C. This will be the bubble point provided the sum of the partial pressures equals the prevailing total pressure, 760 mm. Hg. The following table shows the sum to be only 652.5 mm. Hg, and subsequent trials show 95°C. to be the correct temperature. The vapor composition is then calculated with the final partial pressures.

| Substance | $x$ | Temp. = 90°C. | | Temp. = 95°C. | | $y^*$ |
|---|---|---|---|---|---|---|
| | | Vapor pressure $P$, mm. Hg | $p^* = Px$, mm. Hg | Vapor pressure $P$, mm. Hg | $p^* = Px$, mm. Hg | |
| Benzene... | 0.50 | 1,030 | 515 = 0.5(1,030) | 1,200 | 600 | 0.789 = $\frac{600}{760}$ |
| Toluene... | 0.25 | 410 | 102.5 | 475 | 118.5 | 0.156 |
| o-Xylene.. | 0.25 | 140 | 35.0 | 166 | 41.5 | 0.0545 |
| | | | $\Sigma p^* = 652.5$ | | $\Sigma p^* = 760$ | $\Sigma y^* = 1.0$ |

Had it been desired to obtain the vapor composition only, the first estimate of the temperature would for many purposes have been satisfactory. As an alternative calculation, relative volatilities may be based on toluene (taken arbitrarily; any of the three substances would have served equally well) and $y^*$ calculated by means of Eq. (9.14) as follows:

| Substance | $x$ | $P,$ 90°C. mm. Hg | $\alpha$ | $\alpha x$ | $y^*$ |
|---|---|---|---|---|---|
| Benzene.. | 0.50 | 1,030 | 2.51 = 1,030/410 | 1.255 = 2.51(0.5) | 0.789 = 1.255/1.5905 |
| Toluene... | 0.25 | 410 | 1.0 | 0.250 | 0.157 |
| o-Xylene.. | 0.25 | 140 | 0.342 | 0.0855 | 0.0537 |
| | | | | $\Sigma\alpha x = 1.5905$ | $\Sigma y^* = 1.0$ |

Note that the $y^*$'s are practically the same as those computed at the correct temperature, 95°C.

For purposes of computing liquid compositions in equilibrium with a given vapor and the dew point, the Raoult's law equations may be written for any component $J$ as

$$x_J = \frac{p_J^*}{P_J} = \frac{P_t y_J^*}{P_J} = \frac{y_J^*/\alpha_{JC}}{\Sigma(y^*/\alpha)} \qquad (9.15)$$

and

$$\Sigma x = 1.0 \qquad (9.16)$$

For cases where the ideal-gas law is inapplicable, fugacities may be used instead of vapor pressures and total pressures, and the ideal-solution law becomes at constant temperature†

$$y_J^* = m_J x_J \qquad (9.17)$$

where $m$ for a particular component changes with temperature and pressure, but not with composition.[8] In this case,

$$\alpha_{JC} = \frac{m_J}{m_C} \qquad (9.18)$$

and the expressions for computing bubble points and dew points containing $\alpha$ may still be used. If in addition the liquid is nonideal, Eq. (9.17) may be used as an empirical relationship with $m$ varying with temperature, pressure, and composition.

It must be emphasized that for all ordinary purposes the vapor-liquid equilibria should be experimentally determined. Very few systems can be considered sufficiently close to ideality to permit computation of the data from vapor pressures. The techniques for experimental determi-

† $K$ rather than $m$ is frequently used to denote the proportionality between $y^*$ and $x$.

nation have been reasonably well established, and a critical review of these has been given by Robinson and Gilliland.[19]   Methods of extending scanty data, which depend upon thermodynamic treatment, are most useful and are discussed very thoroughly by Dodge.[8]

## MATERIAL AND ENTHALPY BALANCES

Almost all distillation operations, no matter how complex, may ultimately be reduced to an over-all flow sheet of the sort shown in Fig. 9.11. Here the box represents the entire apparatus used, inside of which there may be many recirculating streams, but for the process as a whole these are of no concern.   Our relationships will be written for two-component $(A, B)$ systems, with all mole-fraction compositions referred to the more

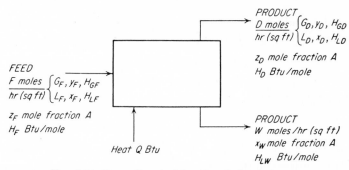

FIG. 9.11. Over-all material and enthalpy balances.

volatile substance $(A)$, $x$ for the liquid, $y$ for the vapor, or $z$ for the average composition of a mixture of liquid and vapor.

The feed to the system, $F$ lb. moles/(hr.)(sq. ft. apparatus cross section),† of average composition $z_F$ mole fraction of more volatile component, may be entirely a liquid, entirely a gas, or a mixture of $G_F$ lb. moles/(hr.)(sq. ft.) of gas of composition $y_F$ with $L_F$ lb. moles/(hr.)(sq. ft.) of liquid of composition $x_F$.   This is to be separated into two product streams.   One of these, $D$ moles/(hr.)(sq. ft.), will be richer in the more volatile substance and may also be entirely a gas, entirely a liquid, or a mixture.   The other, $W$ lb. moles/(hr.)(sq. ft.), richer in the less volatile component, may be gas, liquid, or a mixture, but since in almost all cases it will be liquid, it is so shown in the figure.   An over-all material balance, including both components, is

$$F = D + W \tag{9.19}$$

† Quantities will be consistently defined on the basis of 1 sq. ft. of apparatus cross section, but for purposes of complete material and enthalpy balances total quantities (as, for example, $F$ moles/hr. for continuous operation, or $F$ moles for batch operation) are equally satisfactory.

and, for substance $A$,

$$Fz_F = Dz_D + Wx_W \tag{9.20}$$

This may be expanded to

$$G_F y_F + L_F x_F = G_D y_D + L_D x_D + W x_W \tag{9.21}$$

The enthalpies $H$ of the various streams will be consistently defined as molal enthalpies, B.t.u./lb. mole solution, referred to the pure components in the liquid state at some base temperature $t_0$. The *net* heat added, $Q$ B.t.u./(hr.)(sq. ft.), may actually be the resultant of several heat streams, of which some represent heat removal. An over-all enthalpy balance for the entire operation is

$$FH_F + Q = DH_D + WH_W \tag{9.22}$$

If the feed $F$ and product $D$ are mixtures of liquids and vapors, each of their enthalpies may be defined in terms of their individual parts,

$$FH_F = G_F H_{GF} + L_F H_{LF} \tag{9.23}$$

where $H_{GF}$ is the molal enthalpy of the gaseous portion of the feed $H_{LF}$ that of the liquid portion. Similarly,

$$DH_D = G_D H_{GD} + L_D H_{LD} \tag{9.24}$$

Any of the liquid enthalpies will include both sensible heat and the heat of mixing the components,

$$H_L = C_L(t_L - t_0)M_{av} + \Delta H_S \tag{9.25}$$

where $C_L$ is the heat capacity of the solution, B.t.u./(lb. solution)(°F.), and $\Delta H_S$ is the integral heat of solution at $t_0$ and the prevailing concentration referred to the pure liquid components. Heat-of-solution data vary in form, and some adjustment of the units of tabulated data may be necessary. If heat is evolved on mixing, $\Delta H_S$ will be negative and for ideal solutions it is zero. For ideal solutions the heat capacity is the weighted average of those of the pure components.

Gaseous enthalpies may be calculated in several fashions. According to one method, if the pure liquids are heated separately as liquids from the base temperature to the temperature of the gas $t_G$, each vaporized at this temperature, and the vapors are then mixed,

$$H_G = y[C_{LA}M_A(t_G - t_0) + \lambda_{AG}M_A] + (1 - y)[C_{LB}M_B(t_G - t_0) + \lambda_{BG}M_B] \tag{9.26}$$

since the enthalpy of mixing the vapors is negligible at ordinary pressures. $\lambda_{AG}$ and $\lambda_{BG}$ are the latent heats of vaporization, B.t.u./lb., of the pure substances at temperature $t_G$, and $C_{LA}$ and $C_{LB}$ the separate average liquid heat capacities, B.t.u./(lb.)(°F.), over the temperature range $t_0$ to $t_G$.

For a few systems, complete enthalpy-concentration data have been computed, and the data are available in tabular or graphical form.

## SINGLE-STAGE OPERATION—FLASH VAPORIZATION

Flash vaporization, or equilibrium distillation as it is sometimes called, is a single-stage operation wherein a liquid mixture is partially vaporized, the vapor allowed to come to equilibrium with the residual liquid, and the resulting vapor and liquid phases are separated and removed from the apparatus. It may be carried out batchwise or in continuous fashion.

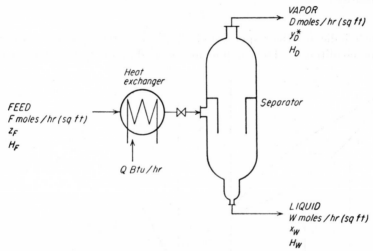

FIG. 9.12. Continuous flash vaporization.

A typical flow sheet is shown schematically in Fig. 9.12 for continuous operation. Here the liquid feed is heated in a conventional tubular heat exchanger or by passing it through the heated tubes of a fuel-fired furnace. The pressure is then reduced, vapor forms at the expense of the liquid adiabatically, and the mixture is introduced into a vapor-liquid separating vessel. The separator shown is of the cyclone type, where the feed is introduced tangentially into a covered annular space. The liquid portion of the mixture is thrown by centrifugal force to the outer wall and leaves at the bottom, while the vapor rises through the central chimney and leaves at the top. The vapor may then pass to a condenser, not shown in the figure. Particularly for flash vaporization of a volatile substance from a relatively nonvolatile one, operation in the separator may be carried out under reduced pressure, but not so low that ordinary cooling water will not condense the vapor product.

The product richer in the more volatile substance, $D$ moles/(hr.)(sq. ft.), is in this case entirely a vapor. Since the composition of the vapor $y_D^*$ is at least theoretically in equilibrium with the residual liquid of composition $x_W$, a series of material balances and the equilibrium relationship are sufficient to determine the material quantities.

$$F = D + W \tag{9.27}$$

For substance $A$,

$$F z_F = D y_D^* + W x_W \tag{9.28}$$

Eliminating $F$,

$$\frac{W}{D} = \frac{y_D^* - z_F}{z_F - x_W} \tag{9.29}$$

In addition,

$$y_D^* = f(x_W) \tag{9.30}$$

where $f$ indicates the vapor-liquid equilibrium relationship at the prevailing conditions. The compositions $y_D^*$ and $x_W$ are at the opposite ends

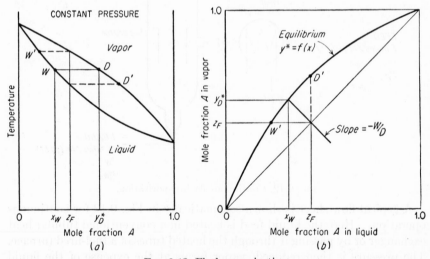

Fig. 9.13. Flash vaporization.

of a tie line (Fig. 9.13a). Alternatively on $x$, $y$ coordinates (Fig. 9.13b), Eq. (9.29) is a straight line of slope $-W/D$, the operating line, passing through the point $(y = z_F, x = z_F)$ on the 45° diagonal, and intersecting the equilibrium curve at $(y = y_D^*, x = x_W)$. Note that the richest vapor, but infinitesimal in amount, is that corresponding to $D'$ at the bubble point of the mixture; and the leanest liquid, but also infinitesimal in amount, is that corresponding to $W'$ at the dew point. The composition of actual products will vary between these limits, depending upon the relative amounts of $W$ and $D$. Since the separation obtained in ordinary cases is poor ($x_W$ and $z_F$ do not differ greatly), such an operation is generally used only on mixtures of large relative volatility or in conjunction with other distillation operations.

The enthalpy balance, which gives the heat requirement of the operation, is

$$FH_F + Q = DH_D + WH_W \qquad (9.31)$$

This does not, of course, include heat removed in any condenser for the vapor product.

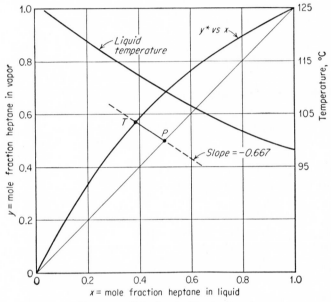

Fig. 9.14. Solution to Illustration 4.

All the equations apply equally well to the case of equilibrium condensation, where a vapor feed is partially condensed to yield the two products. The heat $Q$ will then be a negative quantity.

**Illustration 4.** A liquid mixture containing 50 mole % $n$-heptane ($A$), 50 mole % $n$-octane ($B$), at 80°F., is to be continuously flash-vaporized at 1 atm. pressure to vaporize 60 mole % of the feed. What will be the composition of the vapor and liquid, the temperature in the separator, and the heat requirement?

*Solution.* Basis: $F = 100$ moles feed, $z_F = 0.50$. $D = 60$ moles, $W = 40$ moles, $-W/D = -^{40}\!/_{60} = -0.667$.

The equilibrium data were determined in Illustration 1 and are plotted in Fig. 9.14. The point representing the feed composition is plotted at $P$, and the operating line is drawn with a slope $-0.667$ to intersect the equilibrium curve at $T$, where $y_D^* = 0.575$ mole fraction heptane and $x_W = 0.387$ mole fraction heptane. The temperature at $T$ is 113°C. (235.4°F. $= t_L = t_G$).

The heat capacity of heptane in the range 80 to 235.4°F. is $C_{LA} = 0.507$, that of octane $C_{LB} = 0.505$ B.t.u./(lb.)(°F.), $M_A = 100.2$, $M_B = 114.2$. The heat capacities are additive since the mixture is ideal,

$$C_L M_{av} = C_{LA} M_A x + C_{LB} M_B (1 - x)$$

For the liquid product,

$$C_L M_{av} = 0.507(100.2)(0.387) + 0.505(114.2)(1 - 0.387) = 55.0 \text{ B.t.u./(lb. mole)(°F.)}$$

The latent heats of vaporization at 235.4°F. are $\lambda_A = 133$ B.t.u./lb. and $\lambda_B = 134$ B.t.u./lb. The heat of solution is zero since the solutions are ideal. Take the base temperature $t_0 = 80°F$. $H_F = 0$.

Eq. (9.25): $H_W = 55.0(235.4 - 80) = 8,550$ B.t.u./lb. mole
Eq. (9.26): $H_D = 0.575[0.507(100.2)(235.4 - 80) + 133(100.2)]$
$$+ (1 - 0.575)[0.505(114.2)(235.4 - 80) + 134(114.2)]$$
$$= 22,500 \text{ B.t.u./lb. mole}$$
Eq. (9.31): $100(0) + Q = 60(22,500) + 40(8,550)$
$$Q = 1,692,000 \text{ B.t.u./100 lb. moles feed}$$

**Multicomponent Systems. Ideal Solutions.** For mixtures which form ideal liquid solutions containing components $A$, $B$, $C$, etc., the equilibrium relation for any component $J$ may be written as

$$y_{JD}^* = m_J x_{JW} \tag{9.32}$$

Equation (9.29) also applies for each of the components, and when combined with Eq. (9.32) for any component $J$,

$$\frac{W}{D} = \frac{m_J x_{JW} - z_{JF}}{z_{JF} - x_{JW}} = \frac{y_{JD}^* - z_{JF}}{z_{JF} - y_{JD}^*/m_J} \tag{9.33}$$

This provides the following, useful for equilibrium vaporization,

$$y_{JD}^* = \frac{z_{JF}\left(\dfrac{W}{D} + 1\right)}{1 + W/Dm_J} \tag{9.34}$$

$$\Sigma y_D^* = 1.0 \tag{9.35}$$

and for condensation,

$$x_{JW} = \frac{z_{JF}\left(\dfrac{W}{D} + 1\right)}{m_J + W/D} \tag{9.36}$$

$$\Sigma x_W = 1.0 \tag{9.37}$$

Thus Eq. (9.34) may be used for each of the components with appropriate values of $m$ and $z_F$, and the sum of the $y_D^*$'s so calculated must equal unity if the correct conditions of $W/D$, temperature, and pressure have been chosen. A similar interpretation is used for Eqs. (9.36) and (9.37). These expressions reduce in the limit to the dew-point and bubble-point equations [Eqs. (9.15) and (9.14)], respectively.

**Illustration 5.** A liquid containing 50 mole % benzene ($A$), 25 mole % toluene ($B$), and 25 mole % o-xylene ($C$) is flash-vaporized at 1 atm. pressure and 100°C.

Compute the amounts of liquid and vapor products and their compositions. The solutions follow Raoult's law.

*Solution.* For Raoult's law, $y^* = Px/P_t = mx$, so that for each component $m = P/P_t$. $P_t = 760$ mm. Hg. In the following table, column (2) lists the vapor pressures $P$ at 100°C. for each substance and column (3) the corresponding value of $m$. The feed composition is listed in column (4). A value of $W/D$ is arbitrarily chosen as 3.0 and Eq. (9.34) used to compute $y_D^*$'s in column (5). Since the sum of the $y_D^*$'s is not unity, a new value of $W/D$ is chosen until finally [column (6)] $W/D = 2.08$ is seen to be correct.

Basis: $F = 100$ moles.

$$100 = W + D \qquad W/D = 2.08$$
$$\therefore D = 32.5 \text{ moles}$$
$$W = 67.5 \text{ moles}$$

The composition of the residual liquid may be found by material balance or by equilibrium relation, as in column (7).

| (1) | (2) | (3) | (4) | (5) | (6) | (7) |
|---|---|---|---|---|---|---|
| Sub-stance | $P =$ vapor pres-sure, mm. Hg | $m = \dfrac{P}{760}$ | $z_F$ | $\dfrac{W}{D} = 3.0$ $\dfrac{z_F(W/D + 1)}{1 + W/Dm} = y_D^*$ | $\dfrac{W}{D} = 2.08$ $y_D^*$ | $x_W = \dfrac{Fz_F - Dy_D^*}{W}$ $= \dfrac{y_D^*}{m}$ |
| A | 1,370 | 1.803 | 0.50 | $\dfrac{0.5(3 + 1)}{1 + 3/1.803} = 0.750$ | 0.715 | 0.397 |
| B | 550 | 0.724 | 0.25 | 0.1940 | 0.1983 | 0.274 |
| C | 200 | 0.263 | 0.25 | 0.0805 | 0.0865 | 0.329 |
| | | | | $\Sigma = 1.0245$ | 0.9998 | 1.000 |

Successive flash vaporizations may be made on the residual liquids in a series of single stage operations, whereupon the separation will be better than that obtained if the same amount of vapor were formed in a single operation. As the amount of vapor formed in each stage becomes smaller and the total number of vaporizations larger, the operation approaches differential distillation in the limit.

## DIFFERENTIAL OR SIMPLE DISTILLATION

If during an infinite number of successive flash vaporizations of a liquid only an infinitesimal portion of the liquid were flashed each time, the net result would be equivalent to a differential or simple distillation.

In practice this can only be approximated. A batch of liquid is charged to a kettle or still fitted with some sort of heating device such as a steam jacket, as in Fig. 9.15. The charge is boiled slowly, and the vapors are withdrawn as rapidly as they form to a condenser, where they are lique-fied, and the condensate (distillate) is collected in the receiver. The apparatus is essentially a large-scale replica of the ordinary laboratory distillation flash and condenser. The first portion of the distillate will be the richest in the more volatile substance, and as distillation proceeds, the vaporized product becomes leaner. The distillate may therefore be collected in several separate batches, called "cuts," to give a series of distilled products of various purities. Thus, for example, if a ternary mixture contained a small amount of a very volatile substance $A$, a

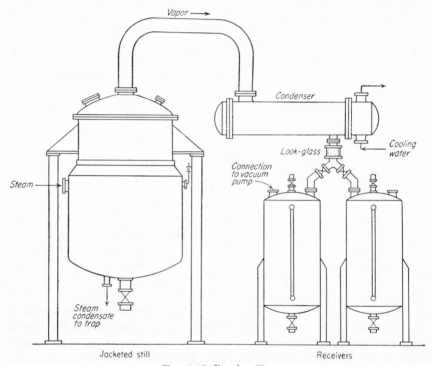

Fig. 9.15. Batch still.

majority of substance $B$ of intermediate volatility, and a small amount of $C$ of low volatility, the first cut, which would be small, would contain the majority of $A$. A large second cut would contain the majority of $B$ reasonably pure but nevertheless contaminated with $A$ and $C$, and the residue left in the kettle would be largely $C$. While all three cuts would contain all three substances, nevertheless some separation would have been obtained.

For such an operation to approach even approximately the theoretical characteristics of a differential distillation, it would have to proceed infinitely slowly so that the vapor issuing from the liquid would at all times be in equilibrium with the liquid. All entrainment would have to be eliminated, and there could be no cooling and condensation of the vapor prior to its entering the condenser. Despite the fact that these conditions are substantially impossible to attain, it is nevertheless useful to study the limiting results which a differential distillation could produce as a standard for comparison.

**Binary Mixtures.** The vapor issuing from a true differential distillation is at any time in equilibrium with the liquid from which it rises, but changes continuously in composition. The mathematical approach must therefore be differential. Assume that at any time during the course of the distillation there are $L$ moles of liquid in the still of composition $x$ mole fraction $A$ and that an amount $dL$ moles is vaporized of mole fraction $y^*$ in equilibrium with the liquid. The residual liquid, $L - dL$ moles, will have the composition $x - dx$, and a material balance for $A$ is

$$Lx = y^* \, dL + (L - dL)(x - dx) \tag{9.38}$$

Ignoring the second-order differential, this becomes

$$\frac{dL}{L} = \frac{dx}{y^* - x} \tag{9.39}$$

which can be integrated as follows,

$$\int_W^F \frac{dL}{L} = \ln \frac{F}{W} = \int_{x_W}^{x_F} \frac{dx}{y^* - x} \tag{9.40}$$

where $F$ is the moles of charge of composition $x_F$ and $W$ the moles of residual liquid of composition $x_W$. This is known as the Rayleigh equation, after Lord Rayleigh, who first derived it. It may be used to determine $F$, $W$, $x_F$, or $x_W$ when three of these are known. Integration of the right-hand side of Eq. (9.40), unless an algebraic equilibrium relationship between $y^*$ and $x$ is available, is done graphically by plotting $1/(y^* - x)$ as ordinate against $x$ as abscissa and determining the area under the curve between the indicated limits. The data for this are taken from the vapor-liquid equilibrium relationship. The *composited* distillate composition $y_{D,\text{av}}$ can be determined by a simple material balance,

$$F x_F = D y_{D,\text{av}} + W x_W \tag{9.41}$$

**Differential Condensation.** This is a similar operation where a vapor feed is slowly condensed under equilibrium conditions and the condensate withdrawn as rapidly as it forms. As in the case of distillation, the results can be approximated only in practice. A derivation similar to that above leads to

$$\ln \frac{F}{D} = \int_{y_F}^{y_D} \frac{dy}{y - x^*} \tag{9.42}$$

where $F$ is the moles of feed vapor of composition $y_F$ and $D$ the vaporous residue of composition $y_D$.

**Constant Relative Volatility.** If Eq. (9.2) can describe the equilibrium relation at constant pressure by use of some average relative volatility $\alpha$ over the concentration range involved, this may be substituted in Eq. (9.40) to yield

$$\ln \frac{F}{W} = \frac{1}{\alpha - 1} \ln \frac{x_F(1 - x_W)}{x_W(1 - x_F)} + \ln \frac{1 - x_W}{1 - x_F} \qquad (9.43)$$

and graphical integration can be avoided. This may be rearranged to another useful form,

$$\log \frac{Fx_F}{Wx_W} = \alpha \log \frac{F(1 - x_F)}{W(1 - x_W)} \qquad (9.44)$$

which relates the number of moles of $A$ remaining in the residue, $Wx_W$, to that of $B$ remaining, $W(1 - x_W)$. These expressions are most likely to be valid for ideal mixtures, for which $\alpha$ is most nearly constant.

**Illustration 6.** Suppose the liquid of Illustration 4 [50 mole % $n$-heptane ($A$), 50 mole % $n$-octane ($B$)] were subjected to a differential distillation at atmospheric pressure, with 60 mole % of the liquid distilled. Compute the composition of the composited distillate and the residue.

*Solution.* Basis: $F = 100$ moles. $x_F = 0.50$, $D = 60$ moles, $W = 40$ moles.

Eq. (9.40):
$$\ln \frac{100}{40} = 0.916 = \int_{x_W}^{0.50} \frac{dx}{y^* - x}$$

The equilibrium data are given in Illustrations 1 and 4. From these, the following are calculated:

| $x$ | 0.50 | 0.46 | 0.42 | 0.38 | 0.34 | 0.32 |
|---|---|---|---|---|---|---|
| $y^*$ | 0.689 | 0.648 | 0.608 | 0.567 | 0.523 | 0.497 |
| $1/(y^* - x)$ | 5.29 | 5.32 | 5.32 | 5.35 | 5.50 | 5.65 |

$x$ as abscissa is plotted against $1/(y^* - x)$ as ordinate, and the area under the curve obtained beginning at $x_F = 0.50$. When the area equals 0.916, integration is stopped and this occurs at $x_W = 0.33$ mole fraction heptane in the residue. The composited distillate composition is obtained through Eq. (9.41),

$$100(0.50) = 60y_{D,\text{av}} + 40(0.33)$$
$$y_{D,\text{av}} = 0.614 \text{ mole fraction heptane}$$

Note that, for the same percentage vaporization, the separation in this case is better than that obtained by flash vaporization, i.e., each product is purer in its majority component.

Alternatively, since for this system the average $\alpha = 2.16$ at 1 atm. (Illustration 1),

Eq. (9.44):
$$\log \frac{100(0.5)}{40x_W} = 2.16 \log \frac{100(1 - 0.5)}{40(1 - x_W)}$$

from which by trial and error $x_W = 0.33$.

**Multicomponent Systems. Ideal Solutions.** For multicomponent systems forming ideal liquid solutions, Eq. (9.44) can be written for any two components. Ordinarily one component is chosen on which to base the relative volatilities, whereupon Eq. (9.44) is written once for each of the others. For example, for substance $J$, with relative volatility based on substance $B$,

$$\log \frac{Fx_{JF}}{Wx_{JW}} = \alpha_{JB} \log \frac{Fx_{BF}}{Wx_{BW}} \tag{9.45}$$

and

$$\Sigma x_W = 1.0 \tag{9.46}$$

where $x_{JF}$ is the mole fraction of $J$ in the feed, $x_{JW}$ that in the residue.

**Illustration 7.** A liquid containing 50 mole % benzene ($A$), 25 mole % toluene ($B$), and 25 mole % o-xylene ($C$) is differentially distilled at 1 atm., with vaporization of 32.5 mole % of the charge. Raoult's law applies. Compute the distillate and residue compositions. Note that this is the same degree of vaporization as in Illustration 5.

*Solution.* The average temperature will be somewhat higher than the bubble point of the feed (see Illustration 3) but is unknown. It will be taken as 100°C. Corrections can later be made by computing the bubble point of the residue and repeating the work, but $\alpha$'s vary little with moderate changes in temperature. The vapor pressures at 100°C. are tabulated and $\alpha$'s calculated relative to toluene, as follows:

| Substance | $P$ = vapor pressure, 100°C., mm. Hg | $\alpha$ | $x_F$ |
|---|---|---|---|
| $A$ | 1,370 | $1{,}370/550 = 2.49$ | 0.50 |
| $B$ | 550 | 1.0 | 0.25 |
| $C$ | 200 | 0.364 | 0.25 |

Basis: $F = 100$ moles, $D = 32.5$ moles, $W = 67.5$ moles.

Eq. (9.45): For $A$, $\log \dfrac{100(0.50)}{67.5x_{AW}} = 2.49 \log \dfrac{100(0.25)}{67.5x_{BW}}$

For $C$, $\log \dfrac{100(0.25)}{67.5x_{CW}} = 0.364 \log \dfrac{100(0.25)}{67.5x_{BW}}$

Eq. (9.46): $x_{AW} + x_{BW} + x_{CW} = 1.0$

Solving simultaneously by assuming values of $x_{BW}$, computing $x_{AW}$ and $x_{CW}$, and checking their sum until it equals unity, there is obtained $x_{AW} = 0.385$, $x_{BW} = 0.285$, $x_{CW} = 0.335$. The sum is 1.005, which is taken as satisfactory.

The composited distillate composition is computed by material balances.

For $A$, $100(0.50) = 32.5y_{AD,av} + 67.5(0.385)$ $\qquad y_{AD,av} = 0.742$

Similarly, $\qquad y_{BD,av} = 0.178 \quad$ and $\quad y_{CD,av} = 0.075$

Note the improved separation over that obtained by flash vaporization (Illustration 5).

## CONTINUOUS RECTIFICATION—BINARY SYSTEMS

Continuous rectification or fractionation is a multistage countercurrent distillation operation. For a binary solution, with certain exceptions it

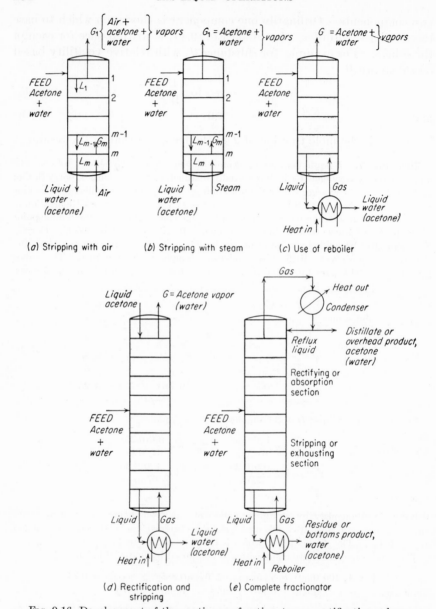

FIG. 9.16. Development of the continuous fractionator or rectification column.

is ordinarily possible by this method to separate the solution into its components, recovering each in any state of purity that is desired.

**The Fractionation Process.** In order to understand how such an operation may be carried out, consider first the simple process of stripping, of which a discussion has been given in Chap. 8. In Fig. 9.16a there is shown a multistage stripper for separating acetone from its water solution by countercurrent contact with air. The tower may be of any convenient design, containing any of the internal fillings described in Chap. 6 such as random packing, or the trays which are shown. Suppose the acetone-water feed solution contains equal amounts of both substances. By countercurrent contact with the air, we have seen how the less volatile water can be largely but not entirely stripped of the more volatile acetone. Dilute acetone-water solution $L_{m-1}$ from the $(m-1)$st tray meets acetone-free air on the $m$th tray, and as a result of the diffusional interaction on the tray the gas leaving the tray contains acetone, while the water leaving the bottom of the tower contains very little. Since air is insoluble in water, little dissolves in the liquid $L_m$. If the trays are equivalent to theoretical trays, the gas $G_m$ is in equilibrium with the liquid $L_m$. Owing to the evaporation which occurs on the tray, the liquid tends to be cooled, giving up its sensible heat to provide the latent heat for evaporation. Similar action occurs on all the other trays, and the gas leaving the top theoretical tray, $G_1$, is in equilibrium with liquid $L_1$ and is therefore rich in acetone vapor. Although it is true that acetone is more volatile than water, the vapor pressures are actually of the same order of magnitude, and therefore the gas $G_1$ also contains an appreciable amount of water vapor as well. By this operation, then, the water leaving has been made substantially acetone-free, but no pure acetone has been obtained.

Next consider the case where air as the stripping medium is replaced by another gas, in particular saturated steam as in Fig. 9.16b. The dilute acetone solution $L_{m-1}$ now is contacted on tray $m$ with acetone-free steam. As before, acetone will evaporate into the gas stream, but a very important additional interaction also occurs. The liquid flowing down the tower may be considered to be a solution of water in acetone, and therefore a water-concentration difference exists between the steam and the liquid. Since the steam is highly soluble, appreciable quantities of it diffuse into the liquid. The latent heat liberated by this condensed material is considerable, and the liquid on each tray is therefore brought to its boiling point. On tray $m$, therefore, the liquid $L_{m-1}$ at its boiling temperature (or bubble point) is contacted with the steam at its saturation temperature (or dew point), and the heat required for evaporation of the acetone is provided not by cooling of the liquid but rather by the latent heat liberated by condensation of the water. The entire operation occurs at the boiling temperatures. As in the case of air stripping, a nearly pure water solution may issue from the bottom of the tower, but at the top the gas is a mixture of acetone vapor and steam.

The steam used in Fig. 9.16b could be obtained from any independent source such as a coal-fired boiler, but it is also possible to obtain it nearly pure by boiling the liquid issuing from the bottom of the tower, as in Fig. 9.16c. The heat exchanger used for this purpose is called a *reboiler*, and the stripping column is seen to be similar to the lower part of the reboiled absorber of Fig. 8.31. This method of obtaining a stripping vapor is almost always used in those cases where the liquid from the bottom of the tower is not an aqueous solution, as, for example, if we wished to separate a solution of acetone and benzene. The liquid issuing from the bottom of the tower would then be nearly pure benzene, and this would be partly vaporized to provide the stripping vapor. The gas issuing from the top of the tower would then contain only acetone and benzene.

In order to provide a purer acetone than the process of Fig. 9.16c, the gas from the top tray of the stripper may be countercurrently washed, as in an absorber, with a liquid in which the water vapor will dissolve. To prevent the resulting acetone vapor from being contaminated with vapors of a foreign absorbent, liquid acetone itself can be used as in Fig. 9.16d, and the absorption, or *rectifying*, column, as it is called, can be built directly on top of the stripper, as shown. The temperatures throughout are still maintained at the boiling point by the mechanism previously described. Any independent source of acetone as an absorbent liquid will serve. But the only practical source in most cases would be the product vapor itself, which is therefore condensed to provide both the absorbent and the product, as in Fig. 9.16e.

The entire separation device, known as a *fractionator*, is shown in Fig. 9.16e. It operates continuously and ordinarily under steady-state conditions, continuously separating the feed mixture into its components. The more volatile substance, or lower-boiling product, is withdrawn from the top (*distillate*, or *overhead*), but part of this must be returned to the top of the column as liquid *reflux* in order to scrub and condense out the less volatile substance in the rectifying section of the column. The less volatile substance (*residue*, or *bottoms*) is withdrawn from the bottom, but part of it must be returned as a vapor to the stripping section of the tower to strip and boil out the more volatile substance. This returned vapor serves a purpose somewhat similar to that of the liquid reflux used in the upper part of the tower, but the term reflux is usually reserved for the returned liquid at the top.

The purities obtained for the products, from the previous study of absorption and stripping, clearly depend upon the liquid/gas ratios used and the number of theoretical stages provided in the two sections of the column, and the interrelation of these must now be established. The cross-sectional area of the column, however, is governed entirely by the quantities of materials to be handled, in accordance with the principals of Chap. 6.

**Material and Enthalpy Balances.**   The over-all material and enthalpy balances [Eqs. (9.19) to (9.26)] are all equally applicable to the continuous fractionator.   It will be useful in addition to establish the particular quantities necessary to compute the heat loads of the condenser and reboiler, and the rates of flow of the various streams.

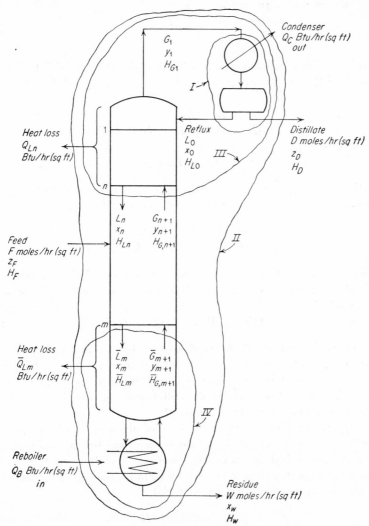

Fig. 9.17. Material and enthalpy balances of a fractionator.

Figure 9.17 shows schematically the complete fractionator for the general case.   The trays are numbered from the top down, and the subscripts generally indicate the tray from which each stream originates: for example, $L_n$ is moles liquid/(hr.)(sq. ft.) falling from the $n$th tray.

A bar over the quantity indicates that it applies to the section of the column below the point of introduction of the feed. The distillate product may be liquid, vapor, or a mixture, in accordance with the relationships established earlier. The reflux, however, must be liquid. The molar ratio of reflux to withdrawn distillate is the *reflux ratio*, sometimes called the *external* reflux ratio,

$$R = \frac{L_0}{D} \tag{9.47}$$

which is specified in accordance with principles to be established later.

Consider the condenser, envelope I (Fig. 9.17). A total material balance is

$$G_1 = D + L_0 \tag{9.48}$$

or
$$G_1 = D + RD = D(R + 1) \tag{9.49}$$

For substance $A$,

$$G_1 y_1 = D z_D + L_0 x_0 \tag{9.50}$$

Equations (9.48) to (9.50) establish the concentrations and quantities at the top of the tower. An enthalpy balance, envelope I,

$$G_1 H_{G1} = Q_c + L_0 H_{L0} + D H_D \tag{9.51}$$

$$Q_c = D[(R + 1)H_{G1} - R H_{L0} - H_D] \tag{9.52}$$

provides the heat load of the condenser. The reboiler heat is then obtained by a complete enthalpy balance about the entire apparatus, envelope II,

$$Q_B = D H_D + W H_W + Q_c + Q_L - F H_F \tag{9.53}$$

where $Q_L$ is the sum of all the heat losses. Heat economy is frequently obtained by heat exchange between the residue product, which issues from the column at its boiling point, and the feed for purposes of preheating the feed. Equation (9.53) still applies provided that any such exchanger is included inside envelope II.

**The Operating Lines.** As in the case of absorbers and strippers, the operating-line equations are obtained by material balances covering the ends of the tower and any horizontal section. For the enriching section, consider envelope III (Fig. 9.17), which includes the top of the apparatus through the $n$th tray. For total material,

$$G_{n+1} = L_n + D \tag{9.54}$$

and, for component $A$;

$$G_{n+1} y_{n+1} = L_n x_n + D z_D \tag{9.55}$$

from which

$$\frac{L_n}{G_{n+1}} = \frac{y_{n+1} - z_D}{x_n - z_D} \tag{9.56}$$

The ratio $L_n/G_{n+1}$ is sometimes called the *internal* reflux ratio at the $n$th tray. The equation is that of a curve on $x$, $y$ coordinates which passes through the points $(x_n, y_{n+1})$ and $(x = z_D, y = z_D)$. Owing to the simultaneous transfer of large heat quantities when diffusion occurs in the fractionator, the enthalpy balance is also important,

$$G_{n+1}H_{G,n+1} = L_n H_{Ln} + Q_c + Q_{Ln} + DH_D \qquad (9.57)$$

where $Q_{Ln}$ is the heat loss which occurs above tray $n$. Letting

$$Q_0 = \frac{Q_c}{D} + \frac{Q_{Ln}}{D} + H_D \qquad (9.58)$$

where $Q_0$ is the net upward flow of heat past tray $n$, per unit of distillate, Eq. (9.57) becomes

$$G_{n+1}H_{G,n+1} = L_n H_{Ln} + DQ_0 \qquad (9.59)$$

or

$$\frac{L_n}{G_{n+1}} = \frac{Q_0 - H_{G,n+1}}{Q_0 - H_{Ln}} \qquad (9.60)$$

and the internal reflux ratio is seen to be related to the condenser heat load. From Eqs. (9.56) and (9.60), we obtain

$$y_{n+1} = \frac{Q_0 - H_{G,n+1}}{Q_0 - H_{Ln}} x_n + z_D \left( 1 - \frac{Q_0 - H_{G,n+1}}{Q_0 - H_{Ln}} \right) \qquad (9.61)$$

Equation (9.61) is a completely general expression for the operating line applicable to all parts of the column above the point of introducing the feed. Since it is based on nothing but material and enthalpy balances, it must be universally applicable.

The operating line for the exhausting section is similarly obtained by considering envelope IV (Fig. 9.17),

$$\bar{L}_m = W + \bar{G}_{m+1} \qquad (9.62)$$
$$\bar{L}_m x_m = W x_W + \bar{G}_{m+1} y_{m+1} \qquad (9.63)$$
$$\frac{\bar{L}_m}{\bar{G}_{m+1}} = \frac{y_{m+1} - x_W}{x_m - x_W} \qquad (9.64)$$

which is the equation of a curve on $x$, $y$ coordinates through the points $(x_m, y_{m+1})$ and $(x = x_W, y = x_W)$. An enthalpy balance is

$$Q_B + \bar{L}_m \bar{H}_{Lm} = W H_W + \bar{G}_{m+1} \bar{H}_{G,m+1} + \bar{Q}_{Lm} \qquad (9.65)$$

where $\bar{Q}_{Lm}$ is the heat loss below tray $m$. Letting

$$\bar{Q}_0 = \frac{\bar{Q}_{Lm}}{W} - \frac{Q_B}{W} + H_W \qquad (9.66)$$

where $\bar{Q}_0$ is the net heat flow downward (a negative quantity) past tray

$m$, per unit of $W$, there results

$$\bar{G}_{m+1}\bar{H}_{G,m+1} = \bar{L}_m\bar{H}_{Lm} - W\bar{Q}_0 \tag{9.67}$$

or

$$\frac{\bar{L}_m}{\bar{G}_{m+1}} = \frac{\bar{H}_{G,m+1} - \bar{Q}_0}{\bar{H}_{Lm} - \bar{Q}_0} \tag{9.68}$$

Equations (9.64) and (9.68) provide the general expression for the exhausting-section operating line,

$$y_{m+1} = \frac{\bar{H}_{G,m+1} - \bar{Q}_0}{\bar{H}_{Lm} - \bar{Q}_0} x_m - x_W \left(\frac{\bar{H}_{G,m+1} - \bar{Q}_0}{\bar{H}_{Lm} - \bar{Q}_0} - 1\right) \tag{9.69}$$

**Equimolal Overflow and Vaporization.** While Eqs. (9.61) and (9.69) are perfectly general expressions for the operating lines of the two sections of the fractionator, they are unnecessarily cumbersome for most purposes. Furthermore, the detailed enthalpy data which they require are not usually available. If, however, it can be shown that for most practical purposes the ratio $L_n/G_{n+1}$ is a constant, the operating line for the enriching section becomes straight on $x$, $y$ coordinates, thereby simplifying the work of using it immensely. From Eq. (9.60),

$$\frac{L_n}{G_{n+1}} = 1 - \frac{H_{G,n+1} - H_{Ln}}{Q_0 - H_{Ln}} \tag{9.70}$$

The heat losses $Q_{Ln}$ included in $Q_0$ can be and ordinarily are made completely negligible by adequate thermal insulation of the tower. Further, the enthalpy of the liquid $H_{Ln}$ is very small in comparison with $Q_0$ since the condenser heat load must include the latent heat of condensation of the reflux liquid. If then $H_{G,n+1} - H_{Ln}$ is substantially constant, $L_n/G_{n+1}$ will be constant also.[19]

From Eq. (9.26),

$$H_{G,n+1} = [y_{n+1}C_{LA}M_A + (1 - y_{n+1})C_{LB}M_B](t_{n+1} - t_0) + y_{n+1}\lambda_A M_A + (1 - y_{n+1})\lambda_B M_B \tag{9.71}$$

where $t_{n+1}$ is the temperature of the vapor from tray $n + 1$ and the $\lambda$'s are the latent heats of vaporization at this temperature. If the deviation from ideality of liquid solutions of $A$ and $B$ is not very great, then the first term in brackets of this equation is

$$y_{n+1}C_{LA}M_A + (1 - y_{n+1})C_{LB}M_B \doteq C_L M_{av} \tag{9.72}$$

From Eq. (9.25),

$$H_{Ln} = C_L M_{av}(t_n - t_0) + \Delta H_S \tag{9.73}$$

and

$$H_{G,n+1} - H_{Ln} = C_L M_{av}(t_{n+1} - t_n) + y_{n+1}\lambda_A M_A + (1 - y_{n+1})\lambda_B M_B - \Delta H_S \tag{9.74}$$

For all but unusual cases, the only important items in Eq. (9.74) are those containing latent heats. The temperature change between adjacent trays is small, so that the sensible heat term is insignificant. The heat of solution can be measured in terms of hundreds of B.t.u./lb. mole of solution except in unusual cases. On the other hand, the molal latent heats at ordinary pressures are usually of the order of 10,000 B.t.u./lb. mole or more. Therefore for practically all purposes,

$$H_{G,n+1} - H_{Ln} = (\lambda M)_{av} \tag{9.75}$$

where the last term is a weighted average of the molal latent heats of $A$ and $B$.  For many pairs of substances, the molal latent heats are themselves nearly identical, so that averaging is unnecessary.  In any case, it is possible to assign a fictitious molecular weight to one of the components so that the molal latent heats are then forced to be the same (if this is done, the entire computation must be made with the fictitious molecular weight, including operating lines and equilibrium data).  This is, however, rarely necessary.

It is concluded, therefore, that for all but exceptional cases the ratio of $L/G$ for the entire upper section of the tower is constant.  The same reasoning can be applied to the exhausting section, applicable from the bottom of the tower to the point of introducing the feed, but the ratio $\bar{L}/\bar{G}$, while constant, will be different from $L/G$.

Consider next the section between two trays $n$ and $r$, between which neither addition nor withdrawal of any material from the tower occurs.  A material balance provides

$$L_{r-1} + G_{n+1} = L_n + G_r \qquad (9.76)$$

Since $L_{r+1}/G_r = L_n/G_{n+1}$, it follows that $L_n = L_{r-1}$ and $G_{n+1} = G_r$, which is called the "principle of equimolal overflow and vaporization."  Note that the rate of the liquid flow from each tray per unit time in a given section of the tower is constant on a molal basis, but since the average molecular weight changes from tray to tray, the weight rates of flow are different.  The general assumptions involved in these simplifications are called the "usual simplifying assumptions."

## MULTISTAGE (TRAY) TOWERS

Of the many methods used to compute the number of trays required in a fractionator of the multistage type, that of McCabe and Thiele[15] is by far the easiest and most rapid to use, and at the same time it provides a convenient graphical picture of the concentrations and temperatures, if desired, throughout the apparatus.  It is the basis of what follows.†

**Theoretical Stage or Tray.**  A theoretical stage or tray is defined for present purposes as one which gives rise to an effluent vapor in equilibrium with the liquid leaving the tray or stage.  Computations according to the methods outlined below are made for theoretical trays, but the real number of trays built into a tower requires consideration of the tray or stage efficiency.

**Enriching Section.  Total Condenser, Reflux at the Bubble Point.** Consider a section of the fractionator entirely above the point of introduction of feed, shown schematically in Fig. 9.18a.  The condenser removes all the latent heat from the overhead vapor but does not cool

---

† For an excellent exposition of the graphical methods based on charts of enthalpy of liquid and vapor plotted against the corresponding concentrations, the Savarit-Ponchon method, reference should be made to the treatise by Dodge.[8]  More general application of these methods, some of which are applied to other unit operations in later parts of this book, is provided by the comprehensive series of articles by Randall and Longtin [*Ind. Eng. Chem.*, **30**, 1063, 1188, 1311 (1938); **31**, 908, 1295 (1938); **32**, 125 (1940)].

the resulting liquid further. The reflux and distillate product are therefore liquids at the bubble point, and $y_1 = x_D = x_0$. Since the liquid, $L$ moles/(hr.)(sq. ft.), falling from each tray and the vapor, $G$ moles/-(hr.)(sq. ft.), rising from each tray are each constant if the usual simplifying assumptions pertain, subscripts are not needed to identify the source of these streams. The compositions, however, change. The trays shown are theoretical trays, so that the composition $y_n$ of the vapor

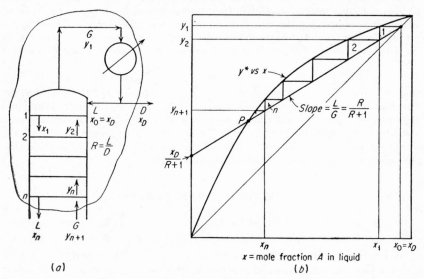

FIG. 9.18. Enriching section.

from the $n$th tray is in equilibrium with the liquid of composition $x_n$ leaving the same tray. The point $(x_n, y_n)$, on $x$, $y$ coordinates, therefore falls on the equilibrium curve.

A total material balance for the envelope in the figure is

$$G = L + D = D(R + 1) \tag{9.77}$$

For component $A$,

$$Gy_{n+1} = Lx_n + Dx_D \tag{9.78}$$

from which the enriching-section operating line is

$$y_{n+1} = \frac{L}{G} x_n + \frac{D}{G} x_D \tag{9.79}$$

$$y_{n+1} = \frac{R}{R + 1} x_n + \frac{x_D}{R + 1} \tag{9.80}$$

This is the equation of a straight line on $x$, $y$ coordinates (Fig. 9.18$b$) of slope $L/G = R/(R + 1)$, and with a $y$ intercept of $x_D/(R + 1)$.

Setting $x_n = x_D$ shows $y_{n+1} = x_D$, so that the line passes through the point $y = x = x_D$ on the 45° diagonal. This point and the $y$ intercept permit easy construction of the line. The concentration of liquids and vapors for each tray is shown in accordance with the principles of Chap. 5, and the usual "staircase" construction between operating line and equilibrium curve is seen to provide the theoretical tray-concentration variation. The construction obviously cannot be carried farther than point $P$.

In plotting the equilibrium curve of the figure, it is generally assumed that the pressure is constant throughout the tower. If necessary, the

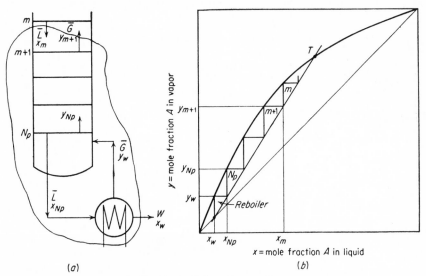

FIG. 9.19. Exhausting section.

variation in pressure from tray to tray may be allowed for after determining the number of real trays but this will require a trial-and-error procedure. It is ordinarily unnecessary except for operation under very low pressures.

**Exhausting Section. Reboiled Vapor in Equilibrium with Residue.**
Consider next a section of the fractionator below the point of introducing the feed, shown schematically in Fig. 9.19a. The trays are again theoretical trays. The rates of flow $\bar{L}$ and $\bar{G}$ are each constant from tray to tray, but not necessarily equal to the values for the enriching section. A total material balance,

$$\bar{L} = \bar{G} + W \tag{9.81}$$

and, for component $A$,

$$\bar{L}x_m = \bar{G}y_{m+1} + Wx_W \tag{9.82}$$

These provide the equation of the exhausting-section operating line,

$$y_{m+1} = \frac{\bar{L}}{\bar{G}} x_m - \frac{W}{\bar{G}} x_W \tag{9.83}$$

$$y_{m+1} = \frac{\bar{L}}{\bar{L} - W} x_m - \frac{W}{\bar{L} - W} x_W \tag{9.84}$$

This is a straight line of slope $\bar{L}/\bar{G} = \bar{L}/(\bar{L} - W)$, and since when $x_m = x_W$, $y_{m+1} = x_W$, it passes through $x = y = x_W$ on the 45° diagonal (Fig. 9.19$b$). If the reboiled vapor $y_W$ is in equilibrium with the residue $x_W$, the first step of the staircase construction represents the reboiler. The steps can be carried no farther than point $T$.

It should be noted that the graphical determination of trays as shown does not necessarily require *straight* operating lines. The lines may be computed and plotted as curves through Eqs. (9.61) and (9.69) and the steps representing theoretical trays constructed in the usual fashion. For all but unusual cases, the number of trays required for a given concentration change by either method will be very nearly the same, i.e., the curvature of the operating lines is ordinarily negligible (refer to Illustration 9).

**Introduction of Feed.** It is convenient before proceeding further to establish how the introduction of the feed influences the change in slope

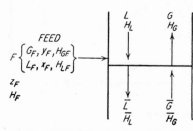

FIG. 9.20. Introduction of feed.

of the operating lines as we pass from the enriching to the exhausting sections of the fractionator.

Consider the section of the column at the tray where the feed is introduced (Fig. 9.20). The quantities of the liquid and vapor streams change abruptly at this tray, since the feed may consist of liquid, vapor, or a mixture of both. If, for example, the feed is a saturated liquid, $\bar{L}$ will exceed $L$ by the amount of the added feed liquid. To establish the general relationship, an over-all material balance about this section is

$$F + L + \bar{G} = G + \bar{L} \tag{9.85}$$

and an enthalpy balance,

$$FH_F + LH_L + \bar{G}\bar{H}_G = GH_G + \bar{L}\bar{H}_L \tag{9.86}$$

The vapors and liquids inside the tower are all saturated, and the molal enthalpies of all saturated vapors at this section are essentially identical since the temperature and composition changes over one tray are small. The same is true of the molal enthalpies of the saturated liquids, so that $H_G = \bar{H}_G$, and $H_L = \bar{H}_L$. Equation (9.86) then becomes

$$(\bar{L} - L)H_L = (\bar{G} - G)H_G + FH_F \tag{9.87}$$

Combining this with Eq. (9.85),

$$\frac{\bar{L} - L}{F} = \frac{H_G - H_F}{H_G - H_L} = q \tag{9.88}$$

The quantity $q$ is thus seen to be the heat required to convert 1 mole of feed from its condition $H_F$ to a saturated vapor, divided by the molal latent heat $H_G - H_L$. The feed may be introduced under any of a variety

TABLE 9.1. THERMAL CONDITIONS FOR THE FEED

| Feed condition | $G_F$, moles (hr.)(sq. ft.) | $L_F$, moles (hr.)(sq. ft.) | $H_{GF}$, B.t.u. mole | $H_{LF}$, B.t.u. mole | $H_F$, B.t.u. mole | $q = \dfrac{H_G - H_F}{H_G - H_L}$ | $\dfrac{q}{q-1}$ |
|---|---|---|---|---|---|---|---|
| Liquid below bubble point...... | 0 | $F$ | ... | $H_F$ | $H_F < H_L$ | 1.0 | >1.0 |
| Saturated liquid...... | 0 | $F$ | ... | $H_F$ | $H_L$ | 1.0 | $\infty$ |
| Mixture of liquid and vapor† | $G_F$ $F = G_F + L_F$ | ... $L_F$ | ... $H_G$ | ... $H_L$ | $H_G > H_F$ $> H_L$ | $\dfrac{L_F}{F}$ $1.0 > q > 0$ | $\dfrac{L_F}{L_F - F}$ |
| Saturated vapor...... | $F$ | 0 | $H_F$ | ... | $H_G$ | 0 | 0 |
| Superheated vapor...... | $F$ | 0 | $H_F$ | ... | $H_F > H_G$ | <0 | $1.0 > \dfrac{q}{q-1} > 0$ |

† In this case the intersection of the $q$ line with the equilibrium curve gives the compositions of the equilibrium liquid and vapor which comprise the feed. The $q$ line is the flash-vaporization operating line for the feed.

of thermal conditions ranging from a liquid well below its boiling point to a superheated vapor, for each of which the value of $q$ will be different. Typical circumstances are listed in Table 9.1, with the corresponding range of values of $q$. Combining Eqs. (9.85) and (9.88),

$$\bar{G} - G = F(q - 1) \tag{9.89}$$

which provides a convenient method for determining $\bar{G}$.

The point of intersection of the two operating lines will help locate the exhausting-section operating line. This may be established as follows: Rewriting Eqs. (9.79) and (9.83) without the tray subscripts,

$$yG = Lx + Dx_D \tag{9.90}$$
$$y\bar{G} = \bar{L}x - Wx_W \tag{9.91}$$

Subtracting,

$$(\bar{G} - G)y = (\bar{L} - L)x - (Wx_W + Dx_D) \tag{9.92}$$

Further, by an over-all material balance,

$$Fz_F = Dx_D + Wx_W \tag{9.20}$$

Substituting this and Eqs. (9.88) and (9.89) in (9.92),

$$y = \frac{q}{q-1}\, x - \frac{z_F}{q-1} \qquad (9.93)$$

This, the locus of intersection of operating lines (the $q$ line), is a straight line of slope $q/(q-1)$, and since $y = z_F$ when $x = z_F$, it passes through the point $x = y = z_F$ on the 45° diagonal. The range of the values of the slope $q/(q-1)$ is listed in Table 9.1, and the graphical interpretation for typical cases is shown in Fig. 9.21. Here the operating-line intersection is shown for a particular case of feed as a mixture of liquid and

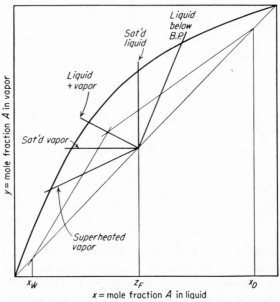

FIG. 9.21. Location of $q$ line for typical feed conditions.

vapor. It is clear that, for a given feed condition, fixing the reflux ratio at the top of the column automatically establishes the liquid/vapor ratio in the exhausting section and the reboiler heat load as well.

**Location of the Feed Tray.** The $q$ line is useful in simplifying the graphical location of the exhausting line, but the point of intersection of the two operating lines does not necessarily establish the demarcation between the enriching and exhausting sections of the tower. Rather it is the introduction of feed which governs the change from one operating line to the other and establishes the demarcation, and at least in the design of a new column some latitude in the introduction of the feed is available.

Consider the separation shown partially in Fig. 9.22, for example. For a given feed, $z_F$ and the $q$ line are fixed. For particular overhead and residue products, $x_D$ and $x_W$ are fixed. If the reflux ratio is specified, the location of the enriching line $DG$ is fixed and the exhausting line $KC$ must pass through the $q$ line at $E$. If the feed is introduced upon the seventh tray from the top (Fig. 9.22$a$), line $DG$ is used for trays 1 through 6 and, beginning with the seventh tray, the line $KC$ must be used. If, on the other hand, the feed is introduced upon the fourth from the top

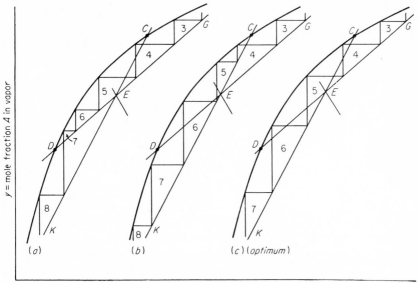

Fig. 9.22. Location of feed tray.

(Fig. 9.22$b$), line $KC$ is used for all trays below the fourth. Clearly a transition from one operating line to the other must be made somewhere between points $C$ and $D$, but anywhere within these limits will serve.† The least total number of trays will result if the steps on the diagram are kept as large as possible, or if the transition is made at the first opportunity after passing the operating-line intersection, as shown in Fig. 9.22$c$. In the design of a new column, this is the practice to be followed.

In the adaptation of an existing column to a new separation, the point of introducing the feed is limited to the location of existing nozzles in the column wall. The slope of the operating lines (or reflux ratio) and the product compositions to be realized must then be determined by trial and error, in order to obtain numbers of theoretical trays in the two sec-

† The diagrams as shown in Fig. 9.22 are all applicable to their respective cases so long as the molal enthalpies of all saturated vapors are identical, and those of saturated liquids are also identical, despite the discrepancy in composition of the feed and that of the liquid on the feed tray.

tions of the column consistent with the number of real trays in each section and the expected tray efficiency.

**Total Reflux, or Infinite Reflux Ratio.** As the reflux ratio $R = L/D$ is increased, the ratio $L/G$ increases, until ultimately, when $R = \infty$, $L/G = 1$ and the operating lines of both sections of the column coincide with the 45° diagonal as in Fig. 9.23. In practice this can be realized by

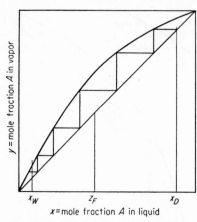

returning all the overhead product back to the column as reflux (total reflux) and reboiling all the residue product, whereupon the forward flow of fresh feed must be reduced to zero. Alternatively such a condition may be interpreted as requiring infinite reboiler heat and condenser cooling capacity for a given rate of feed.

As the operating lines move farther away from the equilibrium curve with increased reflux ratio, the number of theoretical trays required to produce a given separation becomes less, until at total reflux the number of trays is the minimum $N_m$.

Fig. 9.23. Total reflux and minimum stages.

**Constant Relative Volatility.** A useful analytical expression for the minimum number of theoretical stages can be obtained for cases where the relative volatility is reasonably constant.[9,22] Applying Eq. (9.2) to the residue product,

$$\frac{y_W}{1 - y_W} = \alpha_W \frac{x_W}{1 - x_W} \tag{9.94}$$

where $\alpha_W$ is the relative volatility at the reboiler. At total reflux the operating line coincides with the 45° diagonal so that $y_W = x_{Nm}$. Therefore

$$\frac{x_{Nm}}{1 - x_{Nm}} = \alpha_W \frac{x_W}{1 - x_W} \tag{9.95}$$

Similarly for the last tray of the column, where $\alpha_{Nm}$ pertains,

$$\frac{y_{Nm}}{1 - y_{Nm}} = \alpha_{Nm} \frac{x_{Nm}}{1 - x_{Nm}} = \alpha_{Nm}\alpha_W \frac{x_W}{1 - x_W} \tag{9.96}$$

This procedure may be continued up the column until ultimately

$$\frac{y_1}{1 - y_1} = \frac{x_D}{1 - x_D} = \alpha_1\alpha_2 \cdots \alpha_{Nm}\alpha_W \frac{x_W}{1 - x_W} \tag{9.97}$$

If some average relative volatility $\alpha_{av}$ can be used,

$$\frac{x_D}{1 - x_D} = \alpha_{av}{}^{N_m+1} \frac{x_W}{1 - x_W} \tag{9.98}$$

or

$$N_m + 1 = \frac{\log \dfrac{x_D}{1 - x_D} \dfrac{1 - x_W}{x_W}}{\log \alpha_{av}} \tag{9.99}$$

which is known as Fenske's equation. The total minimum number of theoretical stages to produce products $x_D$ and $x_W$ is $N_m + 1$, which then includes the reboiler. For small variations in $\alpha$, $\alpha_{\mathrm{av}}$ may be taken as the geometric average of the values for the overhead and bottom products, $\sqrt{\alpha_1 \alpha_W}$. The expression may be used only with nearly ideal mixtures, for which $\alpha$ is nearly constant.

**Minimum Reflux Ratio.** The minimum reflux ratio $R_m$ is the maximum ratio which will require an infinite number of trays for the separation desired, and it corresponds to the minimum reboiler heat and

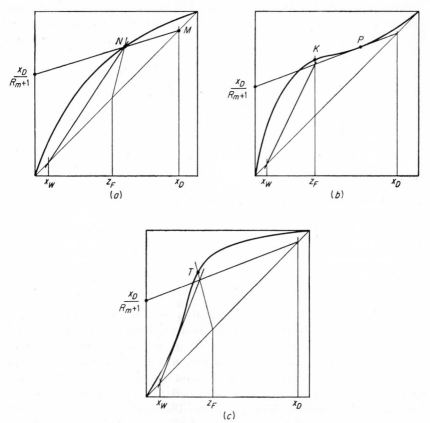

Fig. 9.24. Minimum reflux ratio and infinite stages.

condenser cooling capacity for the separation. Refer to Fig. 9.24a. As the reflux ratio is decreased, the slope of the enriching operating line becomes less and the number of trays required increases. Operating line $MN$, which passes through the point of intersection of the $q$ line and the equilibrium curve, corresponds to the minimum reflux ratio, and an infinite number of trays would be required to reach point $N$ from either end of the tower. In some cases, as in Fig. 9.24b, the minimum-reflux operating line will be tangent to the equilibrium curve in the enriching section as at point $P$, while a line through $K$ would clearly represent too small a reflux ratio. Owing to the interdependence of the liquid/vapor ratios in the two sections of the column, a tangent operating line in the exhausting section may also set the minimum reflux ratio, as in Fig. 9.24c. It is recommended that the appropriate operating lines be established graphically as in the figure and that the value of $R_m$ be calculated from the corresponding $y$ intercept $x_D/(R_m + 1)$ of the enriching line.

**Optimum Reflux Ratio.** Any reflux ratio between the minimum and infinity will provide the desired separation, with the corresponding number of theoretical trays required varying from infinity to the minimum

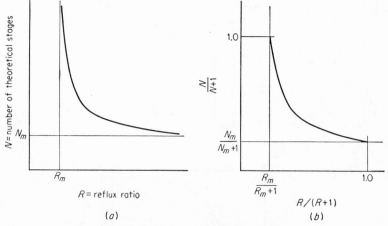

FIG. 9.25. Reflux ratio–stage relation.

number, as in Fig. 9.25a. Determination of the number of trays at several values of $R$, together with the limiting values of $N_m$ and $R_m$, will usually permit plotting the entire curve with sufficient accuracy for most purposes. The coordinate system of Fig. 9.25b[10] will permit locating the ends of the curve readily by avoiding the awkward asymptotes. There have been several attempts at generalizing the curves of Fig. 9.25,[3,10,11] but the resulting charts yield only approximate results.

The reflux ratio which should be used for a new design should be the optimum, or the most economical, reflux ratio, for which the costs will be the least. Refer to Fig. 9.26. At the minimum reflux ratio the column requires an infinite number of trays, and consequently the fixed cost is infinite, but the operating costs (heat for the reboiler, condenser cooling water, power for reflux pump) are least. As $R$ increases, the number of trays rapidly decreases but the column diameter increases owing to the larger quantities of recycled liquid and vapor per unit quantity of feed. The condenser, reflux pump, and reboiler must also be larger. The fixed costs therefore fall through a minimum and rise to infinity again at total reflux. The heat and cooling requirements increase almost directly with reflux ratio, as shown. The total cost, which is the sum of operating and fixed costs, must therefore pass through a minimum at the optimum reflux ratio. This will frequently but not always occur at a reflux ratio near the minimum value ($1.2R_m$ to $1.5R_m$).

**Illustration 8.** Five thousand pounds per hour of a methanol ($A$)–water ($B$) solution containing 50 wt. % methanol at 80°F. is to be continuously rectified at 1 atm. pressure to provide a distillate containing 95% methanol and a residue containing 1.0% methanol (by weight). The feed is to be preheated by heat exchange with the residue, which will leave the system at 100°F. The distillate is to be totally condensed to a liquid and the reflux returned at the bubble point. The withdrawn distillate will be separately cooled before storage. A reflux ratio of 1.5 times the minimum will be used. Determine (a) quantity of the products; (b) $q$ for the feed; (c) minimum reflux

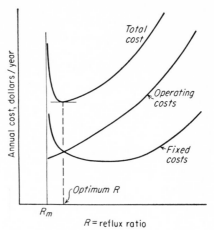

FIG. 9.26. Most economical (optimum) reflux ratio.

ratio; (d) minimum number of theoretical trays; (e) condenser and reboiler heat loads for specified reflux ratio; (f) number of theoretical trays for specified reflux ratio, and liquid and vapor quantities inside the tower. (g) Repeat (e) and (f) for various reflux ratios.

*Solution.* a. Mol. wt. methanol = 32.04, mol. wt. water = 18.02. Basis: 1 hr. Define quantities in terms of moles/hr.

$$F = 5,000(0.50)/32.04 + 5,000(0.50)/18.02 = 78.0 + 138.8 = 216.8 \text{ moles/hr.}$$
$$z_F = 78/216.8 = 0.360 \text{ mole fraction methanol}$$
$$M_{av} \text{ for feed} = 5,000/216.8 = 23.1 \text{ lb./mole}$$
$$x_D = \frac{95/32.04}{95/32.04 + 5/18.02} = \frac{2.94}{3.217} = 0.915 \text{ mole fraction methanol}$$
$$M_{av} \text{ for distillate} = 100/3.217 = 31.1 \text{ lb./mole}$$
$$x_W = \frac{1/32.04}{1/32.04 + 99/18.02} = \frac{0.0312}{5.53} = 0.00565 \text{ mole fraction methanol}$$
$$M_{av} \text{ for residue} = 100/5.53 = 18.08 \text{ lb./mole}$$

Eq. (9.19):                $216.8 = D + W$
Eq. (9.20):                $216.8(0.360) = D(0.915) + W(0.00565)$

Solving simultaneously,

$$D = 84.4 \text{ moles/hr., or } 84.4(31.1) = 2,620 \text{ lb./hr.}$$
$$W = 132.4 \text{ moles/hr., or } 132.4(18.08) = 2,380 \text{ lb./hr.}$$

b. Refer to Fig. 9.27, which shows the vapor-liquid equilibria at 1 atm. pressure ("Chemical Engineers' Handbook," 3d ed., p. 574). The temperature of the residue as it leaves the reboiler is 210°F. Sp. ht. of residue = 0.998, of feed = 0.920 ("Chemical Engineers' Handbook," 3d ed., p. 235). Enthalpy balance for feed preheat exchanger,

$$5{,}000(0.92)(t_F - 80) = 2{,}380(0.998)(210 - 100)$$
$$t_F = 136°F., \text{ temp. at which feed enters tower}$$

From Fig. 9.27, bubble point of feed = 169°F., dew point = 193°F. (Note: Had $t_F$ as computed above been higher than the bubble point, the above enthalpy balance

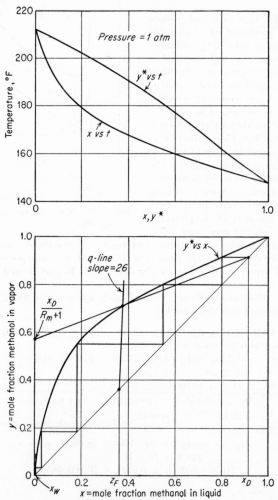

Fig. 9.27. Solution to Illustration 8. Minimum reflux ratio and minimum trays.

would be discarded and made in accordance with flash-vaporization methods [Eqs. (9.27) to (9.31)].

For all enthalpy calculations, take $t_0 = 80°F$. For the feed solution, $\Delta H_S = -400$ B.t.u./lb. mole solution ("International Critical Tables," vol. V, p. 159).

Enthalpy of feed as it enters the tower [Eq. (9.25)],

$$H_F = 0.92(136 - 80)(23.1) - 400 = 792 \text{ B.t.u./lb. mole}$$

Enthalpy of feed as a saturated liquid [Eq. (9.25)],

$$H_L = 0.92(169 - 80)(23.1) - 400 = 1,490 \text{ B.t.u./lb. mole}$$

At 193°F., latent heats of vaporization are $\lambda_A = 450$ B.t.u./lb. for methanol, $\lambda_B = 982$ B.t.u./lb. for water. Sp. ht. liquid methanol $= 0.65$; liquid water $= 1.0$ ("Chemical Engineers' Handbook," pp. 216, 228, 773).

Enthalpy of feed as a saturated vapor [Eq. (9.26)],

$$H_G = 0.36[0.65(32.04)(193 - 80) + 450(32.04)] \\ + (1 - 0.36)[1(18.02)(193 - 80) + 982(18.02)]$$
$$= 18,670 \text{ B.t.u./lb. mole}$$

Eq. (9.88): $\qquad q = \dfrac{H_G - H_F}{H_G - H_L} = \dfrac{18,670 - 792}{18,670 - 1,490} = 1.04$

(NOTE: Had the heat of solution been ignored, $q$ would still calculate to be 1.04 within slide-rule precision.)

c. $\qquad\qquad \dfrac{q}{q - 1} = \dfrac{1.04}{1.04 - 1} = 26$

On Fig. 9.27, plot $x_D$, $x_W$, and $z_F$ at the 45° diagonal, and draw the $q$ line of slope 26. The operating line for minimum reflux in this case passes through the intersection of the $q$ line and the equilibrium curve as shown, assuming the usual simplifying assumptions.

$$\frac{x_D}{R_m + 1} = \frac{0.915}{R_m + 1} = 0.57$$
$$R_m = 0.605 \text{ mole reflux/mole } D$$

d. The minimum number of trays is determined using the 45° diagonal as operating lines (Fig. 9.27). Theoretical stages to the number of 4.9, including the reboiler, are determined. $N_m = 4.9 - 1 = 3.9$.

e. $R = 1.5(0.605) = 0.908$ mole reflux/mole $D$. Distillate: bubble point $= 150°$F., dew point $= 153.5°$F. (Fig. 9.27). $\Delta H_S = -53.5$ B.t.u./lb. mole ("International Critical Tables," vol. V, p. 159). At 153.5°F., $\lambda_A = 468$ B.t.u./lb., $\lambda_B = 1,006$ B.t.u./lb.

Eq. (9.25): $H_D = H_{L0} = 0.65(150 - 80)(31.1) - 53.5 = 1,362$ B.t.u./lb. mole
Eq. (9.26): $H_{G1} = 0.915[0.65(32.04)(153.5 - 80) + 468(32.04)]$
$\qquad\qquad\qquad + (1 - 0.915)[1(18.02)(153.5 - 80) + 1,006(18.02)]$
$\qquad\qquad = 16,790$ B.t.u./lb. mole
Eq. (9.52): $Q_C = 84.4[(0.908 + 1)(16,790) - 0.908(1,362) - 1,362]$
$\qquad\qquad = 2,480,000$ B.t.u./hr. to be removed from condenser (2,470,000 if $\Delta H_S$ is ignored)

Assume $Q_L$ (the heat losses) to be negligible. Heat of solution for the residue $= -120$ B.t.u./lb. mole ("International Critical Tables," vol. V, p. 159).

At 100°F. [Eq. (9.25)], $H_W = 1(100 - 80)(18.08) - 120 = 242$ B.t.u./lb. mole
At 80°F., $H_F = -\Delta H_S$ for the feed $= -400$ B.t.u./lb. mole
Eq. (9.53): $Q_B = 84.4(1,362) + 132.4(242) + 2,480,000 + 0 - 216.8(-400)$
$\qquad\qquad = 2,714,000$ B.t.u./hr. heat into reboiler (2,640,000 if $\Delta H_S$ is ignored)

*f.* Assume equimolal overflow and vaporization.

Eq. (9.47): $L = L_0 = RD = 0.908(84.4) = 76.5$ moles/hr.

Eq. (9.77): $G = D(R + 1) = 84.4(0.908 + 1) = 160.9$ moles/hr.

Eq. (9.88): $\bar{L} = qF + L = 1.04(216.8) + 76.5 = 302.5$ moles/hr.

Eq. (9.89): $\bar{G} = F(q - 1) + G = 216.8(1.04 - 1) + 160.9 = 169.7$ moles/hr.

Refer to Fig. 9.28:

$$\frac{x_D}{R + 1} = \frac{0.915}{0.908 + 1} = 0.480$$

The $y$ intercept 0.480 and enriching and exhausting lines are plotted. Steps are drawn to determine the number of theoretical trays, as shown. The exhausting operating line is used immediately after crossing the operating-line intersection, and the

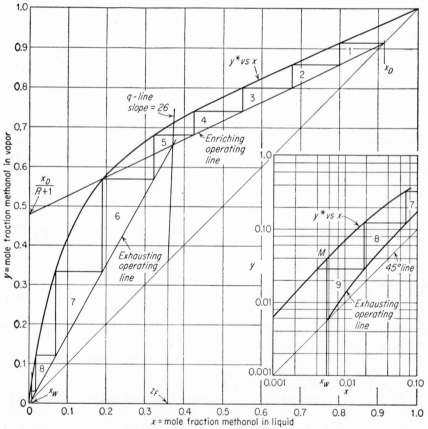

FIG. 9.28. Solution to Illustration 8.    $R = 0.908$ mole reflux/mole distillate product.

feed is therefore to be introduced on the fifth theoretical tray from the top. A total of 8.8 theoretical stages, including the reboiler, is required, and therefore the tower must contain 7.8 theoretical trays. An integral number of theoretical stages can be obtained by very slight adjustment of the reflux ratio, but since a tray efficiency must still be determined and used to obtain the real number of trays, this need not be done.

(NOTE: For cases where the residue composition is very small, it will be necessary to enlarge the scale of the lower left-hand part of the diagram in order to obtain the number of trays. In some cases the graphical determination may still be difficult because of the closeness of the exhausting line and the equilibrium curve. Logarithmic coordinates may then be used to maintain satisfactory separation of the lines, as in the insert of Fig. 9.28. On such a graph, for very low values of $x$, the equilibrium curve will be substantially given by $y^* = \alpha x$, which is a straight line of unit slope. The exhausting operating line will, however, be curved and must be plotted from its equation. In this example, the equation is [Eq. (9.83)]

$$y = \frac{302.5}{169.7} x - \frac{132.4}{169.7} (0.00565) = 1.785x - 0.0044$$

The steps representing theoretical stages are made in the usual manner on these coordinates, continued down from the last made on the arithmetic coordinates.)

The diameter of the tower and the tray design are established through the methods of Chap. 6. Note the substantially different liquid loads in the enriching and exhausting sections. A column of constant diameter for all sections is usually desired for reasons of simplicity in construction and costs. If, however, the discrepancy between liquid or vapor quantities in the two sections is considerable, and particularly if expensive alloy or nonferrous metal is used, different diameters for the two sections may be warranted.

g. Computations for other reflux ratios are easily and quickly made once the diagram and equations have been set up for one value of $R$. These provide data for determining the most economical $R$. The following table lists the important quantities for this separation at various values of $R$:

| $R$ | $L$ | $G$ | $\bar{L}$ | $\bar{G}$ | $Q_C$ | $Q_B$ | No. of theoretical stages (incl. reboiler) |
|---|---|---|---|---|---|---|---|
| $R_m = 0.605$ | 51.0 | 135.4 | 277 | 144.1 | 2,090,000 | 2,324,000 | ∞ |
| 0.65 | 54.8 | 139.2 | 281 | 147.9 | 2,150,000 | 2,384,000 | 14 |
| 0.70 | 59.0 | 143.4 | 285 | 152.1 | 2,210,000 | 2,444,000 | 11.5 |
| 0.80 | 67.5 | 151.9 | 294 | 160.6 | 2,340,000 | 2,574,000 | 10 |
| 0.908 | 76.5 | 160.9 | 303 | 169.7 | 2,480,000 | 2,714,000 | 8.8 |
| 2.0 | 168.8 | 253 | 395 | 262 | 3,900,000 | 4,134,000 | 6.5 |
| 4.0 | 338 | 422 | 564 | 431 | 6,510,000 | 6,744,000 | 5.5 |
| ∞ | ∞ | ∞ | ∞ | ∞ | ∞ | ∞ | $4.9 = N_m + 1$ |

As an alternative to the logarithmic plotting suggested in the illustration, over ranges of concentration where the equilibrium curve can be considered straight, of slope $m = y^*/x$, Fig. 8.15 can be used to determine the number of theoretical stages. In the exhausting section this is particularly useful since, at low concentrations of $A$, the equilibrium curve is substantially given by $y^* = \alpha x$, whence $m = \alpha$. If these methods are used, Eq. (8.24) applies to the exhausting section for the stripping of the more volatile substance $A$ but the enriching section must be considered as an absorber for the less volatile substance $B$, with Eqs. (8.22) and (8.23) applicable.

**Illustration 9.** Repeat the determination of the number of theoretical trays for the example of Illustration 8, at a reflux ratio of 0.908 mole reflux/mole product, without the usual simplifying assumptions.

*Solution.* Neglect heat losses ($Q_{Ln}$ and $\bar{Q}_{Lm} = 0$). $t_0 = 80°F$.

Eq. (9.58): $Q_0 = \dfrac{Q_C}{D} + H_D = \dfrac{2,480,000}{84.4} + 1,362 = 30,760$ B.t.u./mole $D$

Enriching section [Eq. (9.61)],

$$y_{n+1} = \frac{30,760 - H_{G,n+1}}{30,760 - H_{Ln}}\, x_n + 0.915 \left(1 - \frac{30,760 - H_{G,n+1}}{30,760 - H_{Ln}}\right)$$

This equation is used to determine the coordinates of points on the enriching operating line. As an example, take $x_n = 0.80$. $\Delta H_S = -195.8$ B.t.u./lb. mole ("International Critical Tables," vol. V, p. 159). Bubble point = 153.5°F. (Fig. 9.27).

$C_L = 0.66$ ("Chemical Engineers' Handbook," 3d ed., p. 235)
$M_{av} = 0.8(32.04) + 0.2(18.02) = 29.2$ lb./mole
Eq. (9.25): $H_{Ln} = 0.66(153.5 - 80)(29.2) - 195.8 = 1,224$ B.t.u./lb. mole

The approximate value of $y_{n+1}$ will be 0.86 (from the operating line of Fig. 9.28). Vapor dew point = 157°F. (Fig. 9.27). At this temperature, latent heats of vaporization are, for methanol, $\lambda_A = 479$ B.t.u./lb.; for water, $\lambda_B = 1,003.7$ B.t.u./lb.

Eq. (9.26): $H_{G,n+1} = 0.86[0.65(32.04)(157 - 80) + 479(32.04)]$
$+ (1 - 0.86)[1(18.02)(157 - 80) + 1,003.7(18.02)]$
$= 17,320$ B.t.u./lb. mole

Substitution in the enriching-line equation provides $y_{n+1} = 0.862$, which is sufficiently close to 0.86 to make recomputation unnecessary.

For purposes of Eq. (9.66), the value of $H_W$ must be that for the residue product as it leaves the reboiler, and not the value used in Illustration 8 for the over-all enthalpy balance. The residue leaves the reboiler at its bubble point, 210°F., and hence [Eq. (9.25)]

$H_W = 1(210 - 80)(18.08) - 120 = 2,230$ B.t.u./lb. mole

Eq. (9.66): $\bar{Q}_0 = \dfrac{-Q_B}{W} + H_W = \dfrac{-2,714,000}{132.4} + 2,230 = -18,270$ B.t.u./mole $W$

Exhausting section [Eq. (9.69)],

$$y_{m+1} = \frac{\bar{H}_{G,m+1} + 18,270}{\bar{H}_{Lm} + 18,270}\, x_m - 0.00565 \left(\frac{\bar{H}_{G,m+1} + 18,270}{\bar{H}_{Lm} + 18,270} - 1\right)$$

This equation is used in the manner indicated above to compute the coordinates of the exhausting operating line. The results of these calculations are shown in the following table:

| $x_n$ | $y_{n+1}$ | $x_m$ | $y_{m+1}$ |
|-------|-----------|-------|-----------|
| 0.915 | 0.915 | 0.30 | 0.526 |
| 0.80 | 0.862 | 0.20 | 0.352 |
| 0.70 | 0.816 | 0.10 | 0.1770 |
| 0.60 | 0.772 | 0.00565 | 0.00565 |
| 0.50 | 0.727 | | |
| 0.40 | 0.683 | | |

The operating lines may then be plotted on the coordinates of Fig. 9.28 (not shown). The enriching line shows a slight concave-upward curvature, while the exhausting line substantially coincides with the straight line used in the previous illustration. A total of 9.5 theoretical stages (including reboiler) is required, rather than the 8.8 previously determined. (NOTE: The plotting of the operating lines and the graphical comparison of the two sets of data for these illustrations are suggested as a student exercise.)

Some of the discrepancy indicated in the two numbers of trays will be lessened when uncertainties of tray efficiency are taken into account. It should be noted that this particular mixture was chosen because the discrepancy by the two methods could be anticipated to be relatively large, inasmuch as the heat of solution is large and the molal latent heats of vaporization of the components differ considerably (at 193°F., $M_A\lambda_A = 14,430$ B.t.u./lb. mole for methanol and $M_B\lambda_B = 17,700$ B.t.u./lb. mole for water). For binary mixtures containing only organic substances the simplified and the exact methods will ordinarily give closer agreement.

**Reboilers.** The heat-exchanger arrangement to provide the necessary heat and vapor return at the bottom of a fractionator may take several forms. Small fractionators used for pilot-plant work may merely require a jacketed kettle, as shown schematically in Fig. 9.29a, but the heat-transfer surface and the corresponding vapor capacity will necessarily be small. The tubular heat exchanger built into the bottom of the tower (Fig. 9.29b) is a variation which provides larger surface, but cleaning requires shutdown of the distillation operation. This type may also be built with an internal floating head. Both these provide a vapor entering the bottom tray essentially in equilibrium with the residue product, so that the last step of the graphical theoretical-tray computation represents the enrichment owing to the reboiler.

External reboilers of several varieties are commonly used for large installations, and these may be arranged with spares for cleaning. The kettle reboiler (Fig. 9.29c) is probably most frequently used, and it provides a vapor to the column essentially in equilibrium with the residue product. The vertical thermosiphon reboiler of Fig. 9.29d is designed to vaporize all the liquid entering and produce a vapor of the same composition as the residue product. That of Fig. 9.29e receives liquid from the trap-out of the bottom tray, which it partially vaporizes to provide a liquid residue and a vapor essentially in equilibrium. In these arrangements the reservoir at the foot of the fractionator customarily holds 5 to 10 min. flow of liquid to provide for reasonably steady operation of the reboiler.

Reboilers may be heated by steam, heat-transfer oil, or other hot fluids. For some high-boiling liquids, the reboiler may be a fuel-fired furnace.

**Use of Open Steam.** When a water solution is fractionated to give the nonaqueous solute as the distillate and the water is removed as the residue product, the heat required may be provided by the use of open steam at the bottom of the tower. The reboiler is then dispensed with.

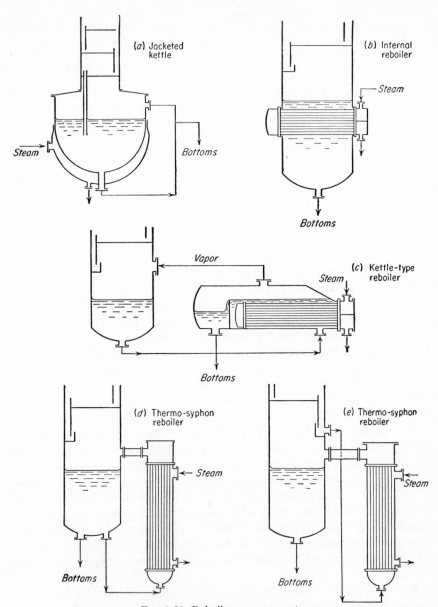

Fig. 9.29. Reboiler arrangements.

For a given reflux ratio and overhead composition, however, more trays will be required in the tower.

Refer to Fig. 9.30. Over-all material balances for both components and for the more volatile substance are

$$F + \bar{G} = D + W \tag{9.100}$$
$$Fz_F = Dx_D + Wx_W \tag{9.101}$$

where $\bar{G}$ is moles/(hr.)(sq. ft.) of steam used. The enriching operating line is located as usual, and the slope of the exhausting line $\bar{L}/\bar{G}$ is related

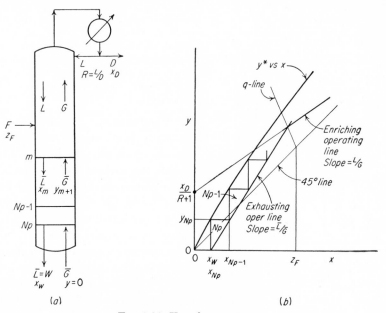

FIG. 9.30. Use of open steam.

to $L/G$ and the feed conditions in the same manner as before. A material balance for the more volatile substance below tray $m$ in the exhausting section is

$$\bar{L}x_m + \bar{G}(0) = \bar{G}y_{m+1} + Wx_W \tag{9.102}$$

and since $\bar{L} = W$ in this case,

$$\frac{\bar{L}}{\bar{G}} = \frac{y_{m+1}}{x_m - x_W} \tag{9.103}$$

The exhausting line therefore passes through the point $(y = 0, x = x_W)$ as shown in Fig. 9.30b. The graphical tray construction must therefore be continued to the $x$ axis of the diagram.

**Illustration 10.** The feed of Illustration 8 is to enter the column at the same temperature as previously and is to be rectified at the same reflux ratio ($R = 0.908$) to give the same distillate product, but with open steam at 1 atm. instead of a reboiler. Determine the quantity of steam required per hour and the number of theoretical trays.

*Solution.* Each of the following quantities is the same as in Illustration 8: $F = 216.8$, $D = 84.4$, $G = 160.9$, $L = 76.5$, $\bar{G} = 169.7$, $\bar{L} = 302.5$ moles/hr.; $x_D = 0.915$, $z_F = 0.360$; $q = 1.04$. Since in this case $W = \bar{L}$, the residue product is $W = 302.5$ moles/hr. The steam required $= \bar{G} = 169.7$ moles/hr.

Eq. (9.101):                    $216.8(0.360) = 84.4(0.915) + 302.5x_W$

$$x_W = 0.00264 \text{ mole fraction methanol}$$

The enriching operating line and $q$ line are plotted as before. The exhausting line is merely an extension of that used in Illustration 8, extending now to the $x$ axis at $x_W$,

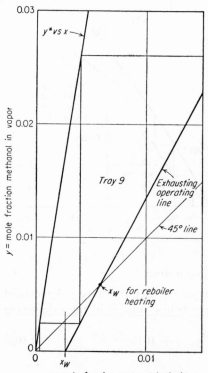

FIG. 9.31. Solution to Illustration 10.

and the lower part of the diagram is shown in Fig. 9.31. The tray construction is a continuation of that obtained previously, and 9.3 theoretical trays are required.

**Condensers.** Condensers are usually conventional tubular heat exchangers, arranged horizontally with the coolant inside the tubes. The condenser may be placed above the tower for gravity flow of the condensed reflux to the top tray. But it is usually more convenient for purposes of construction and cleaning to place the condenser nearer the ground and to return the reflux from an accumulator drum to the top tray by pumping. This procedure also provides more pressure drop for operation of control valves on the reflux line.

The condenser coolant is most frequently water. The pressure of the distillation must then be sufficiently high so that the available cooling water can condense the overhead vapor with an adequate temperature difference to provide reasonably rapid heat-transfer rates. The cost of the fractionator will, however, increase with increased pressure of operation, and in the case of very volatile distillates some low-temperature refrigerant may be used as a coolant.

If the condensate is cooled only to the bubble point, the withdrawn distillate is then usually further cooled in a separate heat exchanger to avoid vaporization loss on storage.

**Partial Condensers.** It is occasionally desired to withdraw a distillate product in the vapor state, especially when the low boiling point of the distillate makes complete condensation difficult. In this case the overhead vapor is cooled sufficiently to condense the necessary liquid reflux and the residual vapor provides the product, as in Fig. 9.32.

A partial condenser may produce any of several results. (1) If time of contact between vapor product and liquid reflux is sufficient, the two

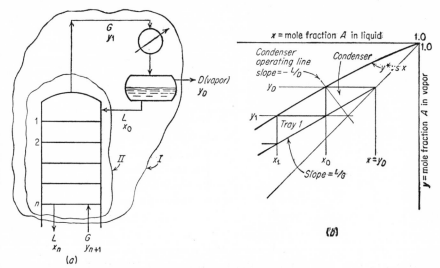

FIG. 9.32. Partial equilibrium condenser.

will be in equilibrium with each other and the condenser provides an equilibrium condensation. (2) If the condensate is removed as rapidly as it forms, a differential condensation may occur. (3) If cooling is very rapid, little mass transfer between vapor and condensate results and the two will have essentially the same composition.

In case the first pertains, the condenser acts as one theoretical stage for the separation. The compositions $y_D$ and $x_0$ may be computed by the methods of equilibrium condensation, as shown in Fig. 9.32b. The enriching operating line is then given as usual by material balances.

Envelope I:

$$G = L + D \tag{9.104}$$
$$Gy_{n+1} = Lx_n + Dy_D \tag{9.105}$$

Envelope II:

$$Gy_{n+1} + Lx_0 = Gy_1 + Lx_n \tag{9.106}$$

In the design of new equipment it is safer to ignore the enrichment which may be obtained by a partial condenser and to include the additional theoretical tray in the column, since it is difficult to ensure that equilibrium condensation will actually occur.

**Cold Reflux.** If the overhead vapor is condensed and cooled below its bubble point so that the reflux liquid is cold, vapor rising from the top tray will be less in quantity than that from tray 2 since some will be condensed to heat the reflux to its boiling point. The net result is an internal reflux ratio $L/G$ greater than that apparently provided by the external reflux ratio.

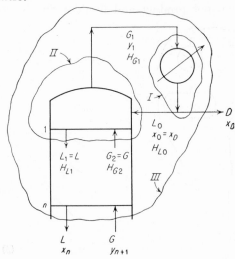

Fig. 9.33. Cold reflux.

Refer to Fig. 9.33. Below the top tray the $L/G$ ratio is constant if the usual simplifying assumptions may be applied. The external reflux ratio is defined as usual,

$$R = \frac{L_0}{D} \tag{9.107}$$

A material balance, envelope I,

$$G_1 = L_0 + D = D(R + 1) \tag{9.108}$$

and the reflux and distillate product compositions are identical, $x_0 = x_D$. A material balance, envelope II,

$$L_0 + G = L + G_1 \tag{9.109}$$

and an enthalpy balance,

$$L_0 H_{L0} + G H_{G2} = L H_{L1} + G_1 H_{G1} \tag{9.110}$$

Assuming that the enthalpies of the saturated vapors, $H_{G1}$ and $H_{G2}$, are identical, Eqs. (9.109) and (9.110) provide

$$L = L_0 \frac{H_{G1} - H_{L0}}{H_{G1} - H_{G1}} \tag{9.111}$$

If an *apparent* reflux ratio $R'$ is defined by

$$\frac{R'}{R' + 1} = \frac{L_1}{G_2} = \frac{L}{G} \tag{9.112}$$

it is easily shown that

$$R' = R \frac{H_{G1} - H_{L0}}{H_{G1} - H_{L1}} \tag{9.113}$$

and, applying Eq. (9.75),

$$R' = R \left[ 1 + \frac{C_{L0} M_{av}(t_{bpR} - t_R)}{(\lambda M)_{av}} \right] \tag{9.114}$$

where $t_R$ is the reflux temperature, $t_{bpR}$ is the reflux bubble point, and $C_{L0}$ is the reflux specific heat. The enriching operating line then becomes (envelope III),

$$y_{n+1} = \frac{R'}{R' + 1} x_n + \frac{x_D}{R' + 1} \tag{9.115}$$

and it is plotted through $(y = x = x_D)$, with a $y$ intercept at $x_D/(R' + 1)$ and a slope $R'/(R' + 1)$.

**Rectification of Azeotropic Mixtures.** Minimum and maximum boiling azeotropic mixtures of the type shown in Figs. 9.7 and 9.10 may be treated by the methods already described, except that it will be impossible to obtain two products of compositions which fall on opposite sides of the azeotropic composition. In the rectification of a minimum-boiling azeotrope (Fig. 9.7), for example, the distillate product may be as close to the azeotropic composition as desired. But the residue product will be either rich in $A$ or rich in $B$ depending upon whether the feed is richer or leaner in $A$ than the azeotropic mixture. In the case of maximum-boiling mixtures (Fig. 9.10) the residue product will always approach the azeotropic composition. These mixtures may sometimes be separated completely by addition of a third substance, as described later.

Insoluble mixtures which form two-liquid-phase azeotropes may, however, be readily separated completely, provided two fractionators are used. This depends upon the fact that the condensed distillate forms two liquid solutions on opposite sides of the azeotropic composition. Consider the separation of the mixture whose vapor-liquid equilibrium diagram is shown in Fig. 9.34, where the feed has the composition $z_F$ and the solubility limits are $x_{RI}$ and $x_{RII}$ at the boiling point. If the feed is introduced into fractionator I of Fig. 9.35, it is evident that the residue product of composition $x_{WI}$ may be as nearly pure $B$ as desired. The enriching section may contain sufficient trays to produce an overhead vapor approaching the azeotropic composition $M$, such as vapor $y_{DI}$. This vapor, when totally condensed to mixture $K$ at its boiling point, will form two insoluble liquids of composition $x_{RI}$ and $x_{RII}$, which may be decanted as shown. The layer which is richer in $B$ is returned to the top tray of column I as reflux. The enriching operating line for column I then passes through the point $(y = y_{DI}, x = x_{RI})$, as shown in Fig. 9.34, and its slope will be the liquid/vapor in the enriching section.

The $A$-rich layer from the decanter (Fig. 9.35) is sent to the top tray of fractionator II, which contains only a stripping or exhausting section. It is clear from Fig. 9.34 that the residue product composition $x_{WII}$ may be as nearly pure $A$ as desired (turn the figure upside down to give it its usual appearance). The overhead vapor from tower II will be of

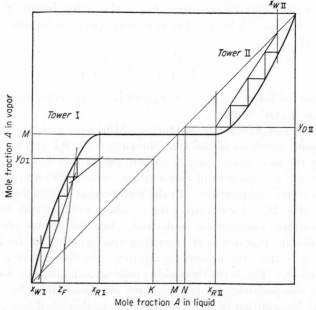

Fig. 9.34. Fractionation of partially miscible mixtures.

composition $y_{DII}$, which, when totally condensed as mixture $N$, produces the same two insoluble liquids as the first distillate. Consequently a common condenser may be used for both towers.

In practice it will be desirable to cool the distillate below its bubble point to prevent excessive loss of vapor from the vent of the decanter. This changes the compositions $x_{RI}$ and $x_{RII}$ slightly, and provides somewhat larger internal reflux ratios. If the feed itself consists of two insoluble liquids, it may be fed to the decanter, whereupon both fractionators then consist of exhausting sections only. When it is desired to remove the last traces of water from a substance such as a hydrocarbon, it is common practice to use only one tower from which the dry hydrocarbon is removed as the residue product. The hydrocarbon-rich layer from the decanter is returned as reflux, but the water-rich layer, which contains very little hydrocarbon, is simply discarded.

**Over-all Tray Efficiency.** As in the case of absorbers, the number of real trays required in a fractionator will generally be different from the number of theoretical trays which are used as the standard for comparison. As before, the simplest approach for design purposes, although the

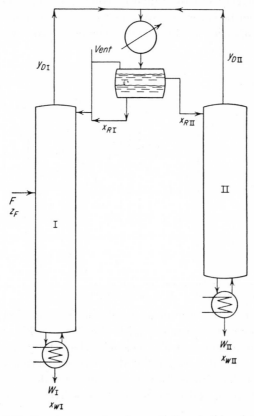

FIG. 9.35. Two-tower system for partially miscible mixtures.

least fundamental, is the over-all tray efficiency **E**, the ratio of the number of theoretical trays in the entire fractionator to the number of real trays required to make the desired separation.

Over-all tray efficiencies for fractionators can be expected generally to be greater than those for absorbers, owing to the lower liquid viscosities which result from the higher temperatures of operation. Figure 9.36 is an empirical correlation[16] of the over-all efficiency of a number of bubble-cap tray fractionators of commercial scale used for separating hydrocarbons and related mixtures. The only variables involved are the relative volatilities of the components of the solution and the liquid viscosity of the feed taken at the average of the reboiler outlet and overhead vapor temperatures. The success of a simple correlation of this sort, which does not reflect variations in rate of liquid or gas flow or in the mechanical design of the trays, depends upon the fact that all the fractionators included in the correlation were designed and operated within the relatively narrow range of conditions representing standard practice, as described, for example, in Chap. 6. Further, the range of the physical properties of the liquids included is not very great. It is

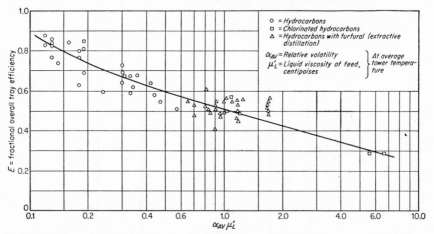

FIG. 9.36. Over-all tray efficiencies for bubble-tray fractionators separating hydrocarbons and similar mixtures. (*After O'Connell.*[16])

found, for example, that the meager data on fractionation of water solutions do not correlate very well with the data of Fig. 9.36 but show instead generally higher over-all efficiencies than the curve would predict.

For these reasons it is suggested that the correlation of Fig. 9.36 be used only for rough estimates, for the conventional designs and conditions described in Chap. 6, and for fractionation of hydrocarbons and similar substances.

**Illustration 11.** A bubble-cap tray fractionator of conventional design is to separate a solution of benzene and toluene at atmospheric pressure. The feed will contain 60 mole %, the distillate 96 mole %, and the residue 25 mole % benzene. A reflux ratio of 2.3 is to be used, and for these conditions 5.3 theoretical plates are required exclusive of the reboiler. Estimate the over-all tray efficiency to be expected and the number of real trays required for the separation.

*Solution.* The temperature at the reboiler (bubble point for $x_W = 0.25$) is 213°F.; that at the top of the column (dew point for $y_1 = 0.96$) is 178°F. The average temperature is therefore $(213 + 178)/2 = 196$°F.

Benzene-toluene solutions are substantially ideal, so that Eq. (9.7) applies. At 196°F., the vapor pressure of benzene $= P_A = 1,050$ mm. Hg; that of toluene $= P_B = 419$ mm. Hg. Therefore $\alpha_{av} = P_A/P_B = 1,050/419 = 2.5$.

The liquid viscosities of benzene and toluene at 196°F. are each 0.3 centipoise, so that for the feed solution $\mu'_L = 0.3$ centipoise, approximately. Therefore $\alpha_{av}\mu'_L = 2.5(0.3) = 0.75$. From Fig. 9.36, $\mathbf{E} = 0.54$. The number of real trays required is estimated to be $5.3/0.54 = 9.8$ or 10 trays.

**Murphree Tray Efficiency.** The logical approach to tray efficiencies, which would permit considerations of tray design, operating conditions, and variations in composition which necessarily occur on each tray, is through the *local*, or *point*, efficiency, but the present state of our knowledge does not now permit general estimates of these. Instead, as in the case of absorbers, the Murphree gas efficiency is recommended as the most practical approach. This is the ratio of the actual enrichment of the gas in passing through a tray using average gas compositions ($y_n - y_{n+1}$) to the enrichment obtained if the gas leaving were in equilibrium ($y_n^*$) with the liquid leaving the tray ($x_n$),

$$\mathbf{E}_G = \frac{y_n - y_{n+1}}{y_n^* - y_{n+1}} \tag{9.116}$$

The student should refer to the discussion of these efficiencies presented in Chap. 8. For present purposes, the empirical relations of Walter and Sherwood[23] [Eqs. (8.26) and (8.27)] are recommended for bubble-cap tray designs, with the substitution of relative volatility in the case of distillation for the gas solubility used for absorbers,

$$\mathbf{E}_G = 1 - e^{-K} \tag{9.117}$$

$$K = \frac{h}{\left(2.5 + \dfrac{0.37\alpha M_L}{\rho_L}\right)\mu'^{0.68}_L b^{0.33}} \tag{9.118}$$

where $h$ = vert. distance from center of bubble-cap slots to top of weir, in.
    $\alpha$ = relative volatility [Eq. (9.2)]
    $M_L$ = mol. wt. of liquid
    $\rho_L$ = liquid density, lb./cu. ft.
    $\mu'_L$ = liquid viscosity, centipoises
    $b$ = width of bubble-cap slot, in.

The equation can be used to estimate variations in tray efficiency with changing conditions from one end of the tower to the other, and the computation of the number of real trays made graphically as shown in Fig. 9.37 and Illustration 12. In special cases where $\mathbf{E}_G$ is essentially constant and the operating line and equilibrium curve are both straight, as sometimes occurs with the exhausting section of a tower handling dilute solutions, Eq. (8.28) may be used.

Tray efficiencies of perforated trays appear to be of the same order of magnitude as those of bubble-cap trays, but as yet insufficient data have been accumulated to permit correlation or generalizations.

**Illustration 12.** The tower for the methanol-water separation of Illustration 8 is to be designed following the conventions of Chap. 6, and the bubble-cap tray arrangement is such that in both enriching and exhausting sections the distance from the center of the cap slots to the top of the weir will be 2.70 in., with triangular slots of average width 0.44 in. Determine the number of trays to be used in the tower.

*Solution.* Consider that part of the tower where $x = 0.5$. From Fig. 9.27, the liquid temperature is 167°F., and the equilibrium vapor composition $y^* = 0.779$. Therefore [Eq. (9.2)],

$$\alpha = \frac{0.779(1 - 0.5)}{0.5(1 - 0.779)} = 3.52$$

The liquid viscosity at this composition and temperature is estimated to be 0.45 centipoise ("Chemical Engineers' Handbook," 3d ed., p. 373), and the liquid density is 53.5 lb./cu. ft.

$$M_L = 0.5(32.04) + 0.5(18.02) = 25.03 \text{ lb./lb. mole}$$
$$h = 2.70 \text{ in.} \qquad b = 0.44 \text{ in.}$$

Eq. (9.118): $\quad K = \dfrac{2.70}{\left[ 2.5 + \dfrac{0.37(3.52)(25.03)}{53.5} \right] (0.45)^{0.68}(0.44)^{0.33}} = 1.95$

Eq. (9.117): $\qquad\qquad E_G = 1 - 1/e^{1.95} = 0.858$

In similar fashion, values of $E_G$ are computed for other concentrations, as follows:

| $x$ | 0 | 0.2 | 0.4 | 0.5 | 0.6 | 0.8 | 0.9 |
|---|---|---|---|---|---|---|---|
| $E_G$ | 0.918 | 0.856 | 0.856 | 0.858 | 0.867 | 0.881 | 0.913 |

The operating diagram, including equilibrium curve and operating lines, is plotted in Fig. 9.37, all identical with Fig. 9.28. The vertical distance between operating lines and equilibrium curve is then divided in accordance with the value of $E_G$ pertaining at each value of $x$ (for example, at $x = 0.2$, the ratio of distances $PT/MT = 0.856$) and the broken curve drawn. This represents the composition of the vapors leaving each real tray. The steps representing the trays are then drawn between operating line and the broken curve, so that at each tray the Murphree gas efficiency is the calculated value corresponding to the prevailing value of $x$. The reboiler, if it may be assumed to provide a vapor in complete equilibrium with the residue, is drawn as a stage of 100% efficiency (see insert, Fig. 9.37).

The construction shows 9.3 real trays required in the tower, and at least 10 trays would therefore be provided, with provisions for introducing the feed onto the sixth tray from the top (the construction should theoretically show an integral number of real trays, which could be arranged for by very slight change in the reflux ratio, but the tray efficiency data do not warrant this refinement.) It is sometimes desirable to build several more than the computed number of trays in a tower, to allow for future changes in the specifications of the product or composition of the feed, since it is more economical to provide for these during the initial construction rather than later. In any case, provisions for introducing the feed onto several trays should be made.

Note that the indicated over-all tray efficiency is $7.8/9.3 = 0.84$, which is within the range to be expected from the available data on methanol-water mixtures [see, for example, Gerster, Koffolt, and Withrow, *Trans. Am. Inst. Chem. Engrs.*, **41**, 393 (1945)].

**Illustration 13.** In the development of a new process, it will be necessary to fractionate 2,000 lb./hr. of an ethanol-water solution containing 0.3 mole fraction ethanol, available at the boiling point. It is desired to produce a distillate containing 0.80 mole fraction ethanol, with a substantially negligible loss of ethanol in the residue.

There is available a column containing 25 identical crossflow bubble-cap trays, 30 in. diameter, with provisions for introduction of the feed only onto the thirteenth tray from the top. The tower is suitable for use at 1 atm. pressure. The tray

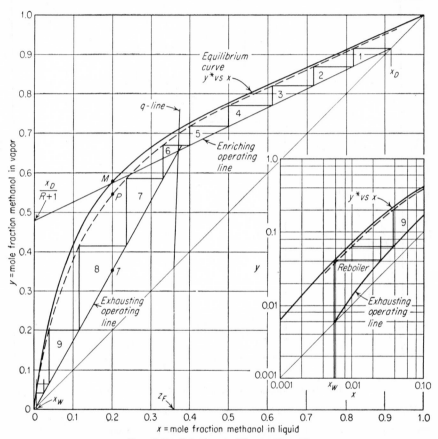

Fig. 9.37. Solution to Illustration 12.

spacing is 18 in. The weir on each tray is 21 in. long, extending 2.25 in. above the tray floor. The bubble-cap slots are 0.25 by 1 in., and the vertical distance from the top of the slots to the top of the weir is 0.75 in. The slot area per tray is 0.5 sq. ft.

It is desired to determine whether this tower is satisfactory for the separation, and if so, what reflux ratios may be used. It may be assumed that adequate condenser and reboiler capacity will be made available if the column is satisfactory.

*Solution.* Mol. wt. of ethanol = 46.05, of water = 18.02. $z_F = 0.30$.

Basis: 100 moles feed (30 moles ethanol, 70 moles water). 30(46.05) = 1,383 lb. ethanol; 70(18.02) = 1,263 lb. water. Total = 2,646 lb.

Basis: 1 hr. Feed contains $2,000(30/2,646) = 22.7$ moles ethanol and $2,000(70/2,646) = 52.9$ moles water; total $= 75.6$ moles.

Equilibrium data for ethanol-water are available in the "Chemical Engineers' Handbook," 3d ed., p. 574. See Fig. 9.38.

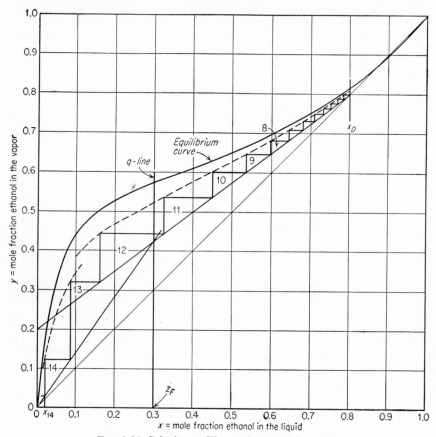

FIG. 9.38. Solution to Illustration 13 at $R = 3.0$.

*Murphree gas efficiencies.* Let $x = 0.50$. $y^* = 0.654$.

Eq. (9.2):  $\alpha = 0.654(1 - 0.5)/(0.5)(1 - 0.654) = 1.89$

The temperature at this liquid composition is 79.8°C. (not shown in Fig. 9.38, but available with the equilibrium data). The liquid viscosity $\mu'_L = 0.5$ centipoise ("Chemical Engineers' Handbook," 3d ed., p. 373), and the density $\rho_L = 49.4$ lb./cu. ft.

$$M_L = 0.5(46.05) + 0.5(18.02) = 32.05 \text{ lb./mole}$$
$$h = 0.75 + 0.5 = 1.25 \text{ in.}$$
$$b = 0.25 \text{ in.}$$

Eq. (9.118): $K = \dfrac{1.25}{\left[ 2.50 + \dfrac{0.37(1.89)(32.05)}{49.4} \right] (0.5)^{0.68}(0.25)^{0.33}} = 1.076$

Eq. (9.117): $\mathbf{E}_G = 1 - 1/e^{1.076} = 0.658$

In similar fashion, values of $E_G$ at other concentrations are calculated as follows:

| $x$...... | 0 | 0.2 | 0.4 | 0.5 | 0.6 | 0.8 |
|---|---|---|---|---|---|---|
| $E_G$..... | 0.712 | 0.661 | 0.654 | 0.658 | 0.658 | 0.68 |

*Tray calculations.* Assume that a reflux ratio $R = 3.0$ is to be used. $x_D = 0.80$; $x_D/(R + 1) = 0.80/(3 + 1) = 0.20$; $q = 1.0$; $q/(q - 1) = \infty$. Refer to Fig. 9.38. The $q$ line and operating lines are located as usual (since the residue will contain negligible ethanol in this case, the stripping-section operating line may be drawn through the origin on this scale of plot). The broken curves representing vapor compositions corresponding to $E_G$ are located as in Illustration 12. Stepwise construction for real trays is started at $x_D$, and the change from enriching to stripping operating line is made at tray 13, corresponding to introduction of feed on the thirteenth tray.

Below tray 14, the construction of trays may be made on logarithmic coordinates in the manner of Fig. 9.37. This will necessitate trial-and-error location of the operating line, since $x_W$ is unknown, so that exactly 25 real trays and 1 reboiler are completed where the stripping operating line crosses the 45° diagonal. In this instance, since at low concentrations the equilibrium curve is essentially straight, it is easier to proceed as follows:

The operating-line intersection occurs at $(x = 0.3, y = 0.425)$, and since $x_W$ may be tentatively taken as zero, $\bar{L}/\bar{G} = 0.425/0.3 = 1.417$ moles/mole. The slope of the equilibrium curve at low concentrations is $m = y^*/x = 8.95$.

$$\therefore A = \bar{L}/m\bar{G} = 1.417/8.95 = 0.1582$$

where $A$ is the absorption factor. The value of $E_G$ at these low concentrations is essentially constant at 0.71, so that the over-all tray efficiency is [Eq. (8.28)]

$$E = \frac{\log\,[1 + 0.71(1/0.1582 - 1)]}{\log\,(1/0.1582)} = 0.848$$

There are 11 real trays from the fifteenth to the twenty-fifth, or $11(0.848) = 9.33$ ideal trays. If the reboiler has an efficiency of 1.00, there will be 10.33 ideal stages below the fourteenth real tray. Applying Eq. (8.24),

$$\frac{x_{14} - x_W}{x_{14} - x_W/m} = \frac{(1/A)^{Np+1} - 1/A}{(1/A)^{Np+1} - 1}$$

From Fig. 9.38, $x_{14} = 0.020$, so that

$$\frac{0.020 - x_W}{0.020 - x_W/8.95} = \frac{(1/0.1582)^{11.33} - (1/0.1582)}{(1/0.1582)^{11.33} - 1}$$
$$x_W = 0.0_81 \text{ mole fractional ethanol in residue}$$

*Quantity computations.* Define quantities in terms of moles/hr.

Eq. (9.19): $75.6 = D + W$
Eq. (9.20): $22.7 = 0.8D + 0.0_81W$
$\qquad\qquad D = 28.4$ moles/hr. $\quad W = 47.2$ moles/hr.
$\qquad\qquad L = RD = 3.0(28.4) = 85.2$ moles/hr.
Eq. (9.77): $\quad G = L + D = 85.2 + 28.4 = 113.6$ moles/hr.
Eq. (9.89): $\quad \bar{G} = G + F(q - 1) = 113.6 + 75.6(1 - 1) = 113.6$ moles/hr.
Eq. (9.85): $\quad \bar{L} = F + L + \bar{G} - G = 75.6 + 85.2 = 160.8$ moles/hr.

In the enriching section, at the top tray, the vapor temperature is 78.2°C. (see equilibrium data, "Chemical Engineers' Handbook," 3d ed., p. 574).

$$\therefore \text{Vapor volumetric rate} = \frac{113.6(359)(273 + 78.2)}{3,600(273)} = 14.58 \text{ cu. ft./sec.}$$

$x_1 = 0.785$ (Fig. 9.38) $\qquad M_L = 0.785(46.05) + 0.215(18.02)$
$$= 40.1 \text{ lb./mole}$$

$\rho_L = 46.5$ lb./cu. ft.

$$\text{Liquid volumetric rate} = \frac{85.2(40.1)}{3,600(46.5)} = 0.0204 \text{ cu. ft./sec.}$$

Similarly,

| Tray No. | Gas rate, cu. ft./sec. | Liquid rate, cu. ft./sec. |
|---|---|---|
| 1 | 14.58 | 0.0204 |
| 12 | 14.81 | 0.0097 |
| 13 | 15.40 | 0.0135 |
| 25 | 15.50 | 0.0135 |

The volumetric vapor rate is largest at the bottom owing to increased temperature, but the volumetric liquid rate is largest at the top owing to the higher molecular weight of the distillate. This prevails at all reflux ratios.

In similar fashion, the following quantities were calculated for other reflux ratios:

| $R$ | $x_W$ | Gas rate, cu. ft./sec. | | Liquid rate, cu. ft./sec. | |
|---|---|---|---|---|---|
| | | Tray 1 | Tray 25 | Tray 1 | Trays 13 and 14 |
| 4.0 | Ca. 0 | 18.2 | 19.4 | 0.0272 | 0.0158 |
| 3.0 | $0.0_81$ | 14.6 | 15.5 | 0.0204 | 0.0135 |
| 2.20 | $0.0_82$ | 11.5 | 12.3 | 0.0148 | 0.0115 |
| 1.91 | $0.0_75$ | 10.5 | 11.2 | 0.0128 | 0.0109 |
| 1.81 | $0.0_63$ | 10.2 | 10.8 | 0.0122 | 0.0106 |
| 1.78 | Ca. 0.3 | | | | |

The smallest value of $R$ which will still produce a distillate $x_D = 0.80$, with 13 enriching trays, is 1.78, but no enrichment will then be given by the stripping section of the tower. At even slightly higher values of $R$, the residue composition rapidly falls to negligible values.

*Capacity of the tower.* The static submergence of the slots = 0.75 in. Assume a liquid seal of 1.5 in., corresponding to a weir head of $1.5 - 0.75 = 0.75$ in. Weir length/tower diam. = $21/30 = 0.7$; weir head/tower diam. = $0.75(12)/30 = 0.30$ in./ft. Use Chap. 6 notation.

Fig. 6.12: $\qquad (W/W_{eff})^{2/3} = 1.06$
By trial, Fig. 6.13, $\qquad k_W = 0.99$
Eq. (6.4): $\qquad 0.75 = 5.38(0.99)(1.06)(q/W)^{2/3}$
$$q/W = 0.0434 \text{ cu. ft./(sec.)(ft.)}$$
$$q = 0.0434(21/12) = 0.0760 \text{ cu. ft. liquid/sec.}$$

This is a reasonable liquid volumetric rate and is greater than any of those listed in the previous tabulation. Liquid rate will not therefore limit the capacity of the tower.

At tray 1, av. mol. wt. of vapor $= 0.8(46.05) + 0.2(18.02) = 40.5$ lb./mole, temp. $= 78.2°C.$, $\rho_G = 40.5(273)/(359)(273 + 78.2) = 0.0876$ lb./cu. ft., $\rho_L = 46.5$ lb./cu. ft.

By Fig. 6.4, $K = 0.14$ (Chap. 6 notation).

Eq. (6.1):        $V = 0.14[(46.5 - 0.0876)/0.0876]^{0.5} = 3.22$ ft./sec.

Similarly at tray 25, av. mol. wt. $= 18.02$, temp. $= 100°C.$, $\rho_G = 0.0368$ lb./cu. ft., $\rho_L = 59.6$ lb./cu. ft., and $V = 5.63$ cu. ft./sec.

The percentage increase in permissible vapor velocity, from the top to the bottom of the tower, is greater than the percentage increase in volumetric flow rate of vapor (see above tabulation). Therefore top vapor rate controls the tower capacity. The cross-sectional area of the tower is $\pi(30)^2/4(144) = 4.90$ sq. ft., and the permissible top vapor rate is therefore $4.90(3.22) = 15.8$ cu. ft./sec.

In addition, the slot velocity should not exceed approximately $12/\rho_G^{0.5}$ (Table 6.1), which at tray 1 is $12/0.0876^{0.5} = 40.5$ ft./sec., or a volumetric rate $40.5(0.5) = 20.3$ cu. ft./sec. Therefore the superficial vapor velocity controls the tower capacity. Neither should the slot velocity be lower than about $3.4/\rho_G^{0.5}$ for reasons of maintaining tray efficiency (Table 6.1), which at tray 25 is $3.4/0.0368^{0.5} = 17.75$ ft./sec., corresponding to $17.75(0.5) = 8.88$ cu. ft./sec. vapor rate. This is exceeded at even the lowest reflux ratios.

Therefore, the desired separation can be made in the available tower, with negligible loss of ethanol in the residue. The maximum reflux ratio which ought to be used (by interpolation in the above table for a top vapor rate of 15.8 cu. ft./sec.) is 3.4 moles reflux per mole product, but negligible ethanol loss will result at values of $R$ as low as 1.81 or 1.90.

(Additional computations of flooding and pressure drop may be made provided details of the tray layout are known.)

## CONTINUOUS-CONTACT EQUIPMENT (PACKED TOWERS)

Packed towers, filled with the various types of packings described in Chap. 6, are commonly used in small-scale, semiworks, or pilot-plant distillation. They are also used extensively in bench-scale work, for which extremely efficient packings have been devised, capable of producing the equivalent of very many theoretical stages in packed heights of only a few feet or more. For reasons of cost and perhaps also uncertainties in design, packed towers have not been used extensively for large-scale fractionators.

**Height Equivalent to a Theoretical Plate.** As in the case of absorbers (see Chap. 8) we may use the concept of the height equivalent to a theoretical plate (H.E.T.P.) in the design of, and in expressing the performance characteristics of, packed-tower fractionators. This is the height of packing which, under specified conditions of operation, will provide the separation equivalent to that of one theoretical plate. In the design of new equipment, the number of theoretical plates required for a separation is computed by the methods described previously, and this is multiplied by the appropriate H.E.T.P. to obtain the necessary packed height. The method is subject to the same limitations and objections that were described in Chap. 8 for absorbers, since it ignores the fundamental difference which exists between the stepwise contact of gas and liquid in a tray tower and the continuous contact of the streams in a packed tower.

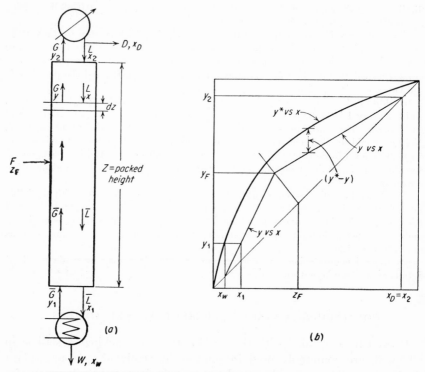

FIG. 9.39. Fractionation in a packed tower.

The transfer unit, consequently, would seem to be the more logical approach. Especially in the case of very efficient laboratory packed columns, however, where mixtures of low relative volatility are distilled at essentially total reflux, the number of transfer units and theoretical stages will be very nearly identical. This is because the equilibrium curve for such mixtures is very flat and therefore nearly parallel to the operating lines. In these cases, therefore, H.E.T.P. is a satisfactory characterization of packing performance.

**The Transfer Unit. Principal Diffusional Resistance in the Gas.**
Figure 9.39$a$ shows a schematic drawing of a packed-tower fractionator.

As in the case of tray towers, it must be provided with a reboiler at the bottom, a condenser at the top, and means for returning liquid reflux and reboiled vapor, as well as means for introducing the feed. The last may be accomplished by providing a short unpacked section at the point where the feed is to be introduced, and especially if the feed is liquid by providing adequate liquid distribution over the top of the exhausting section (see Chap. 6).

The principles of material and enthalpy balances, equimolar overflow and vaporization, location of operating lines, and $q$ line are all equally applicable to packed towers as to tray towers. The equations for the operating lines in the previous section are all applicable directly, with the exception that the tray-number subscripts may be omitted. The operating lines are then simply the relation between $y$ and $x$, the bulk gas and liquid compositions, prevailing at each horizontal section of the tower. As before, the change from enriching- to exhausting-section operating line is made at the point where the feed is actually introduced, and for new designs the shortest column will result, for a given reflux ratio, if this is done at the $q$ line.

As a result of the dispersion of the liquid over the packing in a thin film, the total interfacial surface exposed between the phases through which the counterdiffusion of the more and less volatile substance occurs is $S$ sq. ft./sq. ft. cross section of tower. For a packed height of $Z$ ft. (or $Z$ cu. ft. packing/sq. ft. cross section), this equals the product of $a$ sq. ft. interfacial surface/cu. ft. packing by $Z$. The quantity $a$, which depends greatly on the rates of liquid and gas flow, is not to be confused with the dry packing surface $a_p$ (see Chap. 6). In the differential height $dZ$ of packing shown in Fig. 9.39, the interfacial surface is

$$dS = a\,dZ \qquad\qquad (9.119)$$

The quantity of substance $A$ in the vapor passing through the differential section of the tower is $Gy$ moles/(hr.)(sq. ft.), and the rate of mass transfer of $A$ to the vapor is therefore $d(Gy)$, or $G\,dy$ since the molar vapor rate is constant throughout the enriching section. If over-all mass-transfer coefficients are satisfactory (see Chap. 5), this may be described as

$$G\,dy = K'_y(y^* - y)\,dS = K'_y a(y^* - y)\,dZ \qquad (9.120)$$

where $y^* - y$ is the over-all gas-phase concentration driving force at the section of the tower in question. This will be the vertical distance between the equilibrium curve and the operating line at any value of $x$, as in Fig. 9.39b. The coefficient $K'_y$ is used (see Chap. 3) since in fractionation the principle of equimolar counterdiffusion of the more and less volatile substances prevails so long as the usual simplifying assumptions pertain. The coefficient is ordinarily combined with the area term as $K_y'a$, since except in such cases as wetted-wall towers the value of $a$ cannot conveniently be determined separately. Equation (9.120) may be rearranged to read

$$\frac{dy}{y^* - y} = \frac{K_y'a\ dZ}{G} \tag{9.121}$$

whereupon the left-hand portion is seen to be the number of times the driving force $y^* - y$ must divide into the change in vapor composition. This is a measure of the difficulty of the separation and in integrated form is the number of over-all gas transfer units $N_{tOG}$,

$$N_{tOG} = \int_{y_1}^{y_2} \frac{dy}{y^* - y} \tag{9.122}$$

The height of packing $Z$ is related to the number of transfer units through an experimentally determined quantity, the height of a transfer unit $H_{tOG}$,

$$Z = N_{tOG}H_{tOG} \tag{9.123}$$

The integral of Eq. (9.122) is shown with limits covering the entire range of concentrations prevailing in the tower, but in practice it will be desirable to evaluate $N_{tOG}$ separately for the enriching section by integrating from $y_2$ to $y_f$, the value at the point of introducing the feed (not necessarily the point of operating-line intersection), and for the exhausting section by integrating from $y_f$ to $y_1$. From Eqs. (9.121) and (9.123),

$$H_{tOG} = \frac{G}{K_y'a} = \frac{G}{K_G'aP_t} \tag{9.124}$$

where $G$ is the prevailing molal gas mass velocity ($\bar{G}$ for the exhausting section).

The integral of Eq. (9.122) is ordinarily evaluated graphically by plotting $1/(y^* - y)$ as ordinate against $y$ as abscissa and determining the area under the resulting curve. Alternatively, the graphical stepwise method (see Fig. 8.23 and Illustration 14) may be used in regions where the equilibrium curve and operating line are both reasonably straight.

**Illustration 14.** Determine the number of transfer units $N_{tOG}$ required for the methanol-water fractionation of Illustration 8.

*Solution.* The equilibrium curve and operating diagram (Fig. 9.28), used in Illustration 8 are satisfactory for present purposes. At various values of $x$, values of $y$ from the operating lines and $y^*$ from the equilibrium curve are read, and the tabulation below is made.

| $x$ | $y$ | $y^*$ | $\dfrac{1}{y^* - y}$ |
|---|---|---|---|
| $x_2 = x_D = 0.915$ | $y_2 = 0.915$ | 0.965 | 20.0 |
| 0.8 | 0.860 | 0.915 | 18.20 |
| 0.7 | 0.812 | 0.870 | 17.25 |
| 0.6 | 0.765 | 0.825 | 16.68 |
| 0.5 | 0.717 | 0.779 | 16.14 |
| 0.4 | 0.670 | 0.729 | 16.95 |
| 0.37 | $y_f = 0.655$ | 0.710 | 18.20 |
| 0.3 | 0.528 | 0.665 | 7.30 |
| 0.2 | 0.351 | 0.579 | 4.39 |
| 0.1 | 0.175 | 0.418 | 4.12 |
| 0.05 | 0.086 | 0.270 | 5.44 |
| $x_1 = 0.025$ | $y_1 = 0.040$ | 0.160 | 8.33 |

Note that the value of $y_1$, the composition of vapor entering the packed tower, is given by point $M$ on Fig. 9.28, thus allowing for the enrichment given by the reboiler. The curve to be integrated is plotted in Fig. 9.40. The area under the curve between

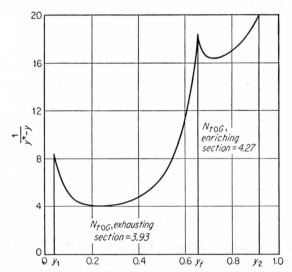

FIG. 9.40. Solution to Illustration 14 by graphical integration.

$y_2$ and $y_f$ is 4.27; hence $N_{tOG}$ for the enriching section is 4.27. The area under the curve between $y_f$ and $y_1$ is 3.93; hence $N_{tOG}$ for the exhausting section is 3.93. The total number of transfer units is $4.27 + 3.93 = 8.20$.

The stepwise graphical construction of Fig. 9.41 is an alternative method. On this figure, equilibrium curve and operating line are located as usual. The broken curve is drawn everywhere halfway *vertically* between the two (for example, distances $AB = BC$). Construction for the enriching section is started at point $D$, and the first step is drawn so that lines $FE = ED$, and the step continued to the operating line at $G$. The step $GFD$ is one transfer unit (for proof, see Chap. 8). In this way,

4+ transfer units are seen to be required for the enriching section and 3+ for the exhausting section of the column. In this case, the stepwise construction and the graphical integration do not give exactly identical results because of the relatively great curvature of the equilibrium curves. Graphical integration is preferred.

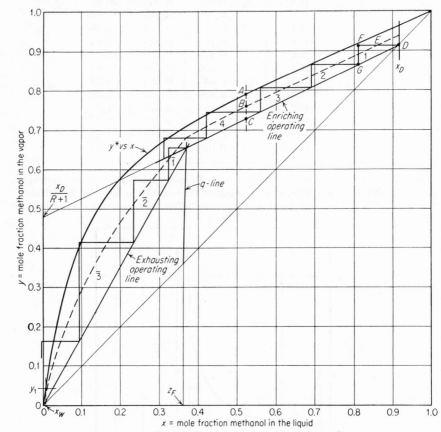

FIG. 9.41. Graphical construction of transfer units.

**Total Reflux, Constant Relative Volatility.** At total reflux, or infinite reflux ratio, the operating lines coincide with the 45° diagonal on the operating diagram, so that $y = x$. If the relative volatility [Eq. (9.2)] is constant, as it will nearly be for ideal solutions formed from close-boiling constituents, the equality of $y$ and $x$ and Eq. (9.2) may both be substituted in Eq. (9.122) to yield[6]

$$N_{tOG} = \frac{1}{\alpha - 1} \ln \frac{y_2(1 - y_1)}{y_1(1 - y_2)} + \ln \frac{1 - y_1}{1 - y_2} \qquad (9.125)$$

This equation is particularly useful in bench-scale laboratory work for evaluating the performance of very efficient packings of small $H_{tOG}$.

**Principal Diffusional Resistance in the Liquid.** Particularly in the case of the exhausting sections of columns operating at low concentrations of the more volatile substance, the principal diffusional resistance may reside within the liquid rather than within the gas. In these cases, it is more appropriate to compute the number of transfer units in terms of liquid concentrations,

$$N_{tOL} = \int_{x_1}^{x_2} \frac{dx}{x - x^*} = \frac{Z}{H_{tOL}} \tag{9.126}$$

$$H_{tOL} = \frac{L}{K'_x a} \tag{9.127}$$

where the subscripts $OL$ denote an over-all resistance in terms of liquid concentration gradients. Equation (9.126) is evaluated by graphical integration of a curve of $1/(x - x^*)$ against $x$ between the appropriate limits. Data for the curve, in turn, are obtained from the operating diagram by choosing values of $y$ and reading corresponding values of $x$ on the operating line and $x^*$ on the equilibrium curve. The concentration difference $x - x^*$, in other words, is the horizontal difference between operating line and equilibrium curve on the operating diagram.

**Special Cases.** When operating line and equilibrium curve are both straight, the number of transfer units may be computed analytically by use of a logarithmic average concentration gradient, as in Eq. (8.50). In such situations, furthermore, enriching sections may be considered as absorbers for the *less* volatile substance and calculated through Eq. (8.52), while Eq. (8.53) may be used for exhausting sections by considering them as strippers for the *more* volatile substance.

**Heights of Transfer Units.** For computation of the packing height required for a given rectification, experimental data for the height of a transfer unit must be at hand. These may be obtained by pilot-plant studies on relatively small-scale equipment, using the same system and conditions of operation expected to pertain in the large plant. The precautions respecting tower diameter, packing size, and effects, and liquid distribution discussed in Chap. 8 must, of course, be observed. Under comparable conditions it is then expected that the same values of $H_{tOG}$ and $H_{tOL}$ obtained in the pilot-plant study would apply to the large installation.

As in the case of gas absorption, the resistance to mass transfer in distillation is divided between that in the gas and that in the liquid. Adapting Eq. (5.22) to the present circumstances,

$$\frac{1}{K'_y a} = \frac{1}{k'_y a} + \frac{m}{k'_x a} \tag{9.128}$$

and this may be written as

$$\frac{G}{K_y'a} = \frac{G}{k_y'a} + \frac{mG}{L}\frac{L}{k_x'a} \tag{9.129}$$

The term on the left-hand side of Eq. (9.129) is $H_{toG}$, and by analogy the terms on the right may be considered as the individual contributions to the over-all height of a transfer unit residing in each phase,

$$H_{toG} = H_{tG} + \frac{mG}{L} H_{tL} = H_{tG} + \frac{H_{tL}}{A} \tag{9.130}$$

In a similar fashion, starting with Eq. (5.23), we obtain

$$H_{toL} = H_{tL} + \frac{L}{mG} H_{tG} = H_{tL} + A H_{tG} \tag{9.131}$$

Equations (9.130) and (9.131) are then used to compute the appropriate over-all $H_t$'s, provided individual values of $H_{tG}$ and $H_{tL}$ may be estimated.

The available experimental data on distillation, unfortunately, are not nearly sufficiently complete to permit estimation of these with assurance. In the case of distillation it is experimentally very difficult to choose conditions such that the entire diffusional resistance lies in either one or the other phase, as was the case for absorption.[7,18] The relative size of individual phase contributions depends upon the group $mG/L$, but the variation in $m$ and in $L/G$ possible in distillation is much more severely restricted than in gas absorption. In the enriching section of a fractionator, for example, $m$ is ordinarily less than 1.0, but the group $G/L$ necessarily exceeds 1.0, so that the combined group $mG/L$ cannot be made either completely insignificant or of controlling significance. The same conditions, but in reverse, prevail in the exhausting section. For the present, the available evidence seems to show that $H_{tG}$ and $H_{tL}$ for distillation can be computed from the correlations for gas absorption and stripping, the principal difficulty from a practical point of view being that the $L/G$ ratios used in the absorption-stripping experimental work are very different from those ordinarily prevailing in distillation.

In the complete absence of pertinent data, therefore, it is recommended that the correlations represented by Eqs. (8.59) and (8.60), together with Tables 8.1 and 8.2, be used to compute $H_{tL}$ and $H_{tG}$. Values of over-all $H_t$'s should be computed separately for enriching and exhausting sections owing to the different values of $L$, $G$, and $m$ which prevail in the two sections.

In order to allow for widely varying values of $L$, $G$, $m$, temperature, and physical properties of fluids in a fractionator, one might determine the packed height by the relation

$$Z = \int_{y_1}^{y_2} H_{toG}\, dN_{toG} = \int_{y_1}^{y_2} \left( H_{tG} + \frac{mG}{L} H_{tL} \right) \frac{dy}{y^* - y} \tag{9.132}$$

evaluating the integral graphically. The presently available data do not warrant such a detailed computation, however.

**Illustration 15.** The methanol-water fractionator of Illustrations 8 and 14 is to be a tower packed with 1.5-in. Berl saddles. Compute the height of packing required.

*Solution.* From the data of Illustration 8, at a reflux ratio $R = 0.908$, the following tabulation is made:

| Position | Gas rate | | Liquid rate | |
|---|---|---|---|---|
| | $\dfrac{\text{Moles}}{\text{Hr.}}$ | $\dfrac{\text{Lb.}}{\text{Hr.}}$ | $\dfrac{\text{Moles}}{\text{Hr.}}$ | $\dfrac{\text{Lb.}}{\text{Hr.}}$ |
| Enriching section: | | | | |
| Top.............. | 160.9 | 5,000 | 76.5 | 2,380 |
| Bottom........... | 160.9 | 4,370 | 76.5 | 1,780 |
| Exhausting section: | | | | |
| Top.............. | 169.7 | 4,610 | 302.5 | 7,040 |
| Bottom........... | 169.7 | 3,070 | 302.5 | 5,480 |

In order to ensure sufficient wetting of the packing, the cross-sectional area of the tower will be based on the lowest liquid rate, and a minimum mass velocity of 400 lb. liquid/(hr.)(sq. ft.) $= L'$ will be used. Larger liquid rates could be used, but they would lead to gas rates beyond the correlations for $H_{tG}$.

Therefore cross section of tower $= 1,780/400 = 4.45$ sq. ft., corresponding to a diameter of 2.38 ft., or 2 ft. 4.5 in. This cross section must be checked for loading and flooding at the four positions of the above tabulation by the methods of Chap. 6. It was found that everywhere conditions are below loading.

Consider the circumstances at the bottom of the enriching section. $t = 170°F.$ (350°K.), $x = 0.370$, $y = 0.655$. $L' = 400$, $G' = 4,370/4.45 = 982$ lb./(hr.)(sq. ft.). Gas diffusivity will be estimated by Eq. (2.23). $T = 350°K.$, $M_A = 32.04$, $M_B = 18.02$, $P_t = 1$ atm.

For methanol, normal boiling point (n.b.p.) $= 377.7°K.$, and critical vol. $= 118$ cu. cm./gm. mole. By Eq. (2.25), $\epsilon/k = 525°K.$ By Eq. (2.26), $r = 4.09$ A.

For water, n.b.p. $= 373°K.$, and critical vol. $= 55.8$ cu. cm./gm. mole. Therefore $\epsilon/k = 518°K.$, $r = 3.18$ A.

For the mixture, $\epsilon_{AB}/k = [525(518)]^{0.5} = 521$ A, $kT/\epsilon = {}^{350}\!/_{521} = 0.672$, and $f(kT/\epsilon) = 0.397$ (Fig. 2.3). By Eq. (2.23), $D = 0.344$ sq. cm./sec. The average molecular weight of the gas is 27.2, whence

$$\rho_G = (27.2/22,400)({}^{273}\!/_{350}) = 0.000948 \text{ gm./cu. cm.}$$

The viscosity of both water and methanol vapors $= 0.0115$ centipoise; hence $\mu = 0.000115$ gm./(cm.)(sec.), or poise.

$$\therefore \text{Sc}_G = \mu/\rho D = 0.000115/(0.000948)(0.344) = 0.353$$

From Table 8.2, for 1.5-in. Berl saddles, $\alpha = 5.05$, $\beta = 0.32$, $\gamma = 0.45$.

Eq. (8.60):     $$H_{tG} = \frac{5.05(982)^{0.32}(0.353)^{0.5}}{400^{0.45}} = 1.84 \text{ ft.}$$

The diffusivity of methanol in dilute solution in liquid water at 15°C. (288°K.) = $1.28(10^{-5})$ sq. cm./sec. (Table 2.3). The viscosity of water at 15°C. = 1.1404 centipoises and at 170°F. = 0.370 centipoise.

Eq. (2.38): $$F = \frac{350}{D(0.370)} = \frac{288}{1.28(10^{-5})(1.1404)}$$

$$D \text{ at } 170°F. = 4.8(10^{-5}) \text{ sq. cm./sec.}$$
$$= 4.8(10^{-5})(3.87) = 18.6(10^{-5}) \text{ sq. ft./hr.}$$

The effect of concentration on the liquid diffusivity will be ignored. For $x = 0.37$ and $t = 170°F.$, $\mu_L = 0.45$ centipoise $= 0.45(2.42) = 1.09$ lb./(ft.)(hr.) and $\rho_L = 55$ lb./cu. ft.

$$\therefore \text{Sc}_L = \mu/\rho D = 1.09/(55)(18.6)(10^{-5}) = 106.6$$

From Table (8.1), for 1.5-in. Berl saddles, $\phi = 0.00625$, $\eta = 0.28$.

Eq. (8.59): $$H_{tL} = 0.00625 \left(\frac{400}{1.09}\right)^{0.28} (106.6)^{0.5} = 0.336 \text{ ft.}$$

At $x = 0.37$, $m = dy^*/dx$ (tangent to the equilibrium curve) = 0.594. Therefore $mG/L = 0.594(160.9)/76.5 = 1.248$.

Eq. (9.130): $$H_{tOG} = 1.84 + 1.248(0.336) = 2.26 \text{ ft.}$$

In a similar fashion, at the top of the enriching section, $H_{tOG} = 2.03$ ft., whence the average for the enriching section is $(2.26 + 2.03)/2 = 2.15$ ft. For the enriching section, $N_{tOG} = 4.27$ (Illustration 14). The height of the enriching-section packing [Eq. (9.123)] = $4.27(2.15) = 9.2$ or 10 ft.

Similarly for the exhausting section, $H_{tOG}$ at the top = 1.18 ft. and at the bottom = 2.30 ft., av. = 1.74 ft. Since $N_{tOG} = 3.93$ (Illustration 14), the exhausting-section packed height = $3.93(1.74) = 6.85$ or 7 ft.

The total indicated packed height is therefore $10 + 7 = 17$ ft. The tower shell, however, would be made taller than this. One foot of unirrigated packing may be placed above the top reflux entry to act as an entrainment separator, with 1 ft. of unpacked height at each of the following points: above and below the entrainment-separator section, at the point of introducing the feed, and below the exhausting section, for introducing the reboiled vapor. In addition, allow a 10-min. hold-up of liquid at the bottom of the tower as a feed reservoir for the reboiler. Since the density of the liquid here is 57.5 lb./cu. ft. and its rate of flow 5,480 lb./hr., this amounts to a tower height of $5,480(^{10}\!/_{60})(1/57.5)(1/4.45) = 3.5$ ft. The total height of the shell is then 25.5 ft.

## BATCH RECTIFICATION—BINARY SYSTEMS

The rectification or fractionation of a batch of solution is necessarily an unsteady-state operation. It is ordinarily carried out on relatively small amounts of solutions where continuous operation is unwarranted from the point of view of cost. A typical batch fractionator consists of a heated kettle into which the batch of solution to be rectified is placed, surmounted by a plate or packed tower, as in Fig. 9.29a. The column must be fitted with a condenser and provisions for returning reflux and withdrawing distillate at the top, but no liquid is withdrawn from the

kettle during the distillation. At the end of the operation, after the
desired portion of the charge has been distilled, the residual liquid is
withdrawn from the kettle and a new batch may be charged. The discussion which follows will neglect effect of the hold-up, or quantity of
liquid and vapor necessarily present in the column and condenser, and is
therefore applicable when the amount of any component in the batch is
large (at least 10 times) in comparison with the hold-up. The discussion

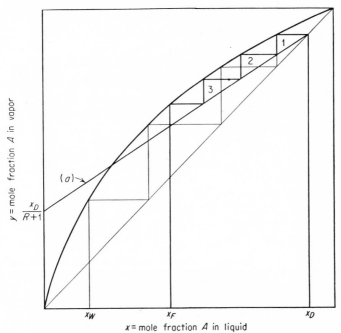

Fig. 9.42. Batch rectification at varying reflux ratio and constant distillate composition.

is in terms of theoretical plates, but interpretation in terms of transfer
units is easily made.

**Varying Reflux Ratio, Constant Distillate Composition.** If it is desired
to obtain a distillate of fixed composition, heat may be applied to the
kettle so as to boil vapor up the column, and when condensate first flows
from the condenser, reflux may be returned and distillate withdrawn at
such rates as to obtain exactly the desired overhead composition. Refer
to Fig. 9.42. The fractionator consists entirely of an enriching section.
Assuming that the principles of equimolal overflow and vaporization may
be applied, the operating line is straight, of slope $R/(R + 1) = L/G$ and
intercept $x_D/(R + 1)$, as for continuous fractionation. If $x_F$ is the initial
composition of the liquid in the kettle and $x_D$ is the desired distillate

composition, the initial reflux ratio and hence the initial slope of the operating line must be chosen so that exactly the number of ideal stages to which the apparatus is equivalent can be drawn over the composition range $x_D$ to $x_F$. In the figure, if the column contained the equivalent of three theoretical plates, with one theoretical plate for the action of the kettle, the initial reflux ratio corresponds to operating line (a). As soon, however, as any measurable amount of distillate, which is richer in the more volatile substance, is withdrawn, the liquid in the kettle must necessarily become leaner, so that the location of the residual-liquid composition $x_W$ on the graph immediately moves toward the origin. This will necessitate an immediate increase in reflux ratio if the same number of theoretical stages is to produce the same distillate composition. The reflux ratio, in other words, must be continuously increased at a rate depending upon the rate of withdrawal of distillate, and if the boil-up rate of the vapor is maintained constant, the rate of withdrawal of distillate must be correspondingly decreased.

Ultimately the entire condensate is returned as reflux (total reflux), the rate of distillate withdrawal has fallen to zero, and the composition of the residual liquid in the kettle has reached its ultimate value, shown on the figure as $x_W$ when the 45° diagonal is the operating line. If distillation is to proceed further, the composition of the withdrawn distillate must become smaller in terms of the more volatile substance. Such a distillate may be collected separately from the first, to provide a second "cut."

The total quantity of distillate $D$ moles and the amount of liquid $W$ moles remaining in the kettle for an initial charge $F$ moles may be calculated by material balance. For any value of residue composition $x_W$,

$$D = F - W \tag{9.133}$$
$$Dx_D = Fx_F - Wx_W \tag{9.134}$$

The more theoretical plates in the column, the lower the final value of $x_W$ may be, and the greater will be the ultimate yield of distillate of fixed composition.

The total quantity of vapor $G$ moles to be boiled up through the tower during the distillation, which is related to the heat requirement of the operation, may also be calculated. For a differential time,

$$dG = dL + dD = \frac{dL}{dG}\,dG + dD = \frac{R}{R+1}\,dG + dD \tag{9.135}$$

$$G = \int_0^G dG = \int_0^D \frac{dD}{1 - \dfrac{R}{R+1}} \tag{9.136}$$

From Eqs. (9.133) and (9.134),

$$D = \frac{Fx_F - Fx_W}{x_D - x_W} \tag{9.137}$$

$$dD = \frac{F(x_F - x_D)\, dx_W}{(x_D - x_W)^2} \tag{9.138}$$

Equation (9.136) therefore becomes[2]

$$G = F(x_D - x_F) \int_{x_{Wf}}^{x_F} \frac{dx_W}{(x_D - x_W)^2 \left(1 - \dfrac{R}{R+1}\right)} \tag{9.139}$$

where $x_{Wf}$ is the residue composition when the operation is stopped. The equation is integrated graphically.

**Illustration 16.** Fifty pound moles (approx. 500 gal.) of a solution of carbon disulfide ($A$) in carbon tetrachloride ($B$) is charged to the kettle of a batch fractionator

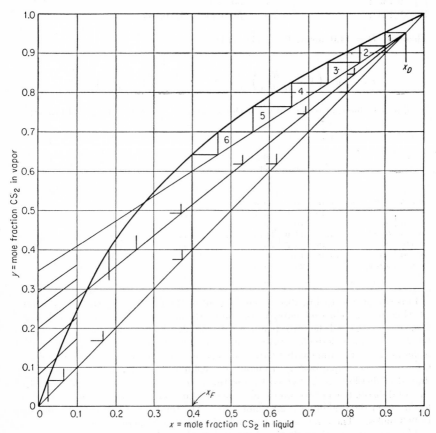

FIG. 9.43. Solution to Illustration 16.

and is to be distilled at 1 atm. The composition of the charge is $x_F = 0.40$ mole fraction carbon disulfide, $CS_2$. The column above the kettle is known to be equivalent to 6 theoretical trays. It is desired to withdraw a distillate of constant composition $x_D = 0.95$ mole fraction $CS_2$. The limitations of the column cross section, condenser, and heating-surface capacity require that the vapor boil-up rate be 10 moles/hr. Determine the time of distillation and the distillate yield for various values of residue composition.

*Solution.* Vapor-liquid equilibrium data at 1 atm. pressure are plotted in Fig. 9.43. The column, together with the kettle, is equivalent to seven theoretical stages. The uppermost operating line on the figure is located by trial so that exactly seven steps may be drawn between $x_D = 0.95$ and the feed composition $x_F = 0.40$. This represents the initial reflux ratio. Other operating lines of greater slope are drawn as shown, and for each the residual-liquid composition is determined at seven steps from $x_D$.

Consider the operating line whose $y$ intercept is 0.20. Then $x_D/(R+1) = 0.95/(R+1) = 0.20$, whence $R = 3.75$ moles reflux/mole distillate. The residue composition for this reflux ratio (from the figure) is $x_W = 0.185$.

Eq. (9.133): $$D = 50 - W$$
Eq. (9.134): $$D(0.95) = 50(0.40) + W(0.185)$$

Therefore $D = 14.0$ moles, $W = 36.0$ moles.

$$\frac{1}{(x_D - x_W)^2 \left(1 - \dfrac{R}{R+1}\right)} = \frac{1}{(0.95 - 0.185)^2 \left(1 - \dfrac{3.75}{4.75}\right)} = 8.15$$

In similar fashion, at other values of the $y$ intercept, the following are obtained:

| (1) $\dfrac{x_D}{R+1}$ | (2) $x_W$ | (3) $R$ | (4) $D$, moles | (5) $W$, moles | (6) $\dfrac{1}{(x_D-x_W)^2\left(1-\dfrac{R}{R+1}\right)}$ | (7) $G$, moles | (8) Time, hr. | (9) Av. rate of distillate, $D$ moles/hr. |
|---|---|---|---|---|---|---|---|---|
| 0.345 | 0.40 = $x_F$ | 1.75 | 0 | 50.0 | 9.08 | 0 | 0 | |
| 0.292 | 0.312 | 2.16 | 6.9 | 43.1 | 7.77 | 19.55 | 1.96 | 3.52 |
| 0.250 | 0.258 | 2.80 | 10.3 | 39.7 | 7.92 | 32.4 | 3.24 | 3.18 |
| 0.200 | 0.185 | 3.75 | 14.0 | 36.0 | 8.15 | 49.3 | 4.93 | 2.84 |
| 0.140 | 0.126 | 5.79 | 16.6 | 33.4 | 9.95 | 64.3 | 6.43 | 2.58 |
| 0.080 | 0.079 | 10.88 | 18.4 | 31.6 | 15.63 | 80.6 | 8.06 | 2.18 |
| 0 | 0.026 | ∞ | 20.2 | 29.8 | ∞ | ∞ | ∞ | 0 |

In accordance with Eq. (9.139), column (6) of the table is plotted against column (2) (Fig. 9.44). For each entry in the table, the area under the curve is determined between $x = 0.4$ and the corresponding value of $x_W$. Each of these areas is multiplied by $F(x_D - x_F) = 50(0.95 - 0.40) = 27.5$ to give the corresponding value of $G$ [column (7)]. The time of distillation, exclusive of start-up time, is given by dividing $G$ by the rate of vapor boil-up, 10 moles/hr. [column (8)]. The average rate of withdrawal of distillate is $D$ divided by the time. For example, at the end of 4.93 hr. the total distillate collected up to that time is 14.0 moles, and the average rate of collection from the beginning is 2.84 moles/hr. The total vapor boiled up to that time is 49.3 moles. The time does not include the starting-up period, however.

The average rate of distillation falls off only slowly in this example up to 8.06 hr.

but will then fall off very rapidly with only a small increase in the ultimate distillate yield and great increase in the heat requirement.

**Constant Reflux Ratio, Varying Distillate Composition.** An alternative method of operating the batch still involves keeping the reflux ratio constant during the entire distillation. The initial distillate is therefore rich in the more volatile component, the more so the greater the reflux ratio for a fixed number of trays, as at $x_{D1}$ in Fig. 9.45. As distillate is withdrawn and the liquid in the kettle becomes leaner in the more volatile component, the distillate will also become leaner,

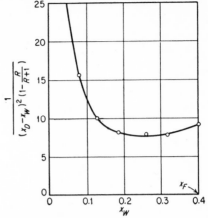

FIG. 9.44. Graphical integration for Illustration 16.

such as the distillate $x_{D2}$ at residue $x_W$ in the figure. The operating lines (a) and (b) in the figure are parallel, since the reflux ratio and hence $L/G$ are

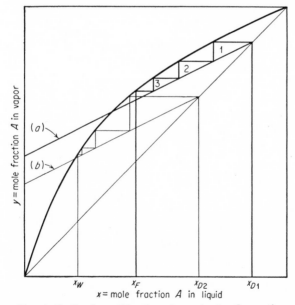

FIG. 9.45. Batch rectification at constant reflux ratio.

constant. The distillate liquid may then be composited to give an average composition between the initial and final values.

If at any time there are $W$ moles of residue of composition $x_W$ and this is reduced by removal of $dW$ moles of composition $x_D$, then a material balance for component $A$ is

$$Wx_W = x_D\,dW + (W - dW)(x_W - dx_W) \qquad (9.140)$$

Ignoring second-order differentials, this becomes[21]

$$\ln\frac{F}{W} = \int_W^F \frac{dW}{W} = \int_{x_{Wf}}^{x_F} \frac{dx_W}{x_D - x_W} \qquad (9.141)$$

which may be evaluated graphically to obtain either $W$ or $x_{Wf}$. Since the reflux ratio is fixed, the total moles of vapor boil-up is simply

$$G = D(R + 1) \qquad (9.142)$$

where $D$ is the total moles of distillate. The average distillate composition may be obtained by material balances.

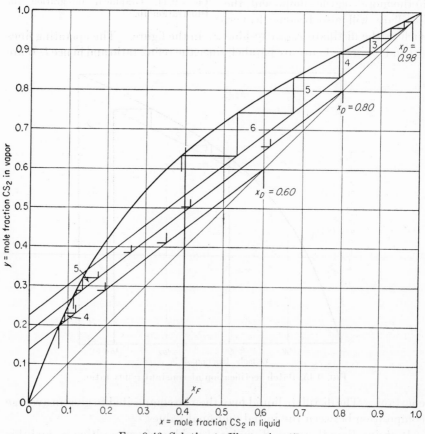

FIG. 9.46. Solution to Illustration 17.

**Illustration 17.** Suppose the batch distillation of Illustration 16 had been conducted at a constant reflux ratio $R = 3.4$ moles reflux/mole distillate and had been continued until the residue composition was $x_{Wf} = 0.079$. [NOTE: This is the same as the average reflux ratio of Illustration 16, $R = (G/D) - 1 = 80.6/18.4 - 1 = 3.4$.] Compute the quantity of distillate and its average composition and the vapor boil-up quantity.

*Solution.* The vapor-liquid equilibrium data are replotted in Fig. 9.46. Let $x_D = 0.98$. Therefore $x_D/(R + 1) = 0.98/(3.4 + 1) = 0.223$, which is the $y$ intercept of the uppermost operating line on the figure. Construction of seven stages shows $x_W$ to be 0.390. In similar fashion,

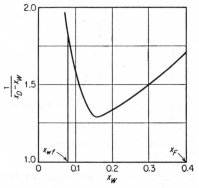

| $x_D$ | $\dfrac{x_D}{R+1}$ | $x_W$ | $\dfrac{1}{x_D - x_W}$ |
|---|---|---|---|
| 0.98 | 0.223 | 0.390 | 1.698 |
| 0.95 | 0.216 | 0.210 | 1.352 |
| 0.90 | 0.204 | 0.150 | 1.283 |
| 0.85 | 0.193 | 0.135 | 1.400 |
| 0.80 | 0.182 | 0.115 | 1.460 |
| 0.70 | 0.159 | 0.094 | 1.650 |
| 0.65 | 0.148 | 0.084 | 1.768 |
| 0.60 | 0.136 | 0.077 | 1.912 |

FIG. 9.47. Solution to Illustration 17.

The last two columns are plotted against each other (Fig. 9.47), and in accordance with Eq. (9.141) the area under the curve between $x_F = 0.40$ and $x_{Wf} = 0.079$ is determined to be $0.4815 = \ln(50/W)$. $W = 30.9$ moles, and $D = F - W = 50 - 30.9 = 19.1$ moles.

Eq. (9.142):      $G = D(R + 1) = 19.1(3.4 + 1) = 84.0$ moles

$$\text{Av. distillate composition} = \frac{Dx_D}{D} = \frac{Fx_F - Wx_W}{D} = \frac{50(0.4) - 30.9(0.079)}{19.1}$$

$$= 0.919 \text{ mole/fraction CS}_2$$

**Hold-up.** Consider a batch fractionator with negligible hold-up and equivalent to a very large number of theoretical plates. If the column is used to separate a binary mixture by operation at some very high reflux ratio, the distillate can be nearly pure, more volatile component $A$ until nearly all the $A$ has been removed, and the residue nearly pure $B$. The distillation may then be continued with collection of the distilled $B$ in a separate receiver. Under these circumstances a plot of per cent of the charge distilled against composition will result in a curve such as (a) (Fig. 9.48). Such a separation, where a very high percentage of the $A$ is recovered as a high-purity product, is said to be *sharp*. Suppose, on the other hand, that the moles of hold-up in the column are an appreciable percentage of the moles of $A$ in the charge. It will then be possible to collect a distillate of nearly pure $A$ until some percentage $D$ (Fig.

9.48) has been removed.   At this time the only remaining component $A$ is that retained in the column, where the hold-up material varies in composition from nearly pure $A$ at the top to nearly pure $B$ at the bottom.   Continuation of the distillation necessarily requires withdrawal of a mixture of $A$ and $B$, until the $A$ in the hold-up has all been distilled, as at $E$ (Fig. 9.48), and curve $B$ results.   The separation is said to be *sloppy.*

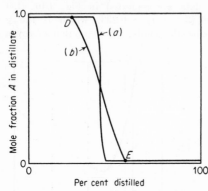

FIG. 9.48. Batch rectification of a binary mixture.

For this reason, packed towers, which generally have lower hold-up than comparable plate towers, are frequently preferred for batch-distillation work.   In the laboratory, efficient packed columns capable of sharp separation[4] can be used for analysis of the charge mixture, and distillation curves of the type corresponding to (*a*) (Fig. 9.48) can be approached, despite finite hold-up, by intermittent withdrawal of distillate.   In this method, the fractionator is operated at total reflux until the upper portion of the column contains substantially pure $A$, which is then withdrawn at low reflux ratio.   When measurable amounts of $B$ appear in the distillate, operation at total reflux is resumed until again the upper portion of the column contains substantially only $A$, and so on.

## CONTINUOUS RECTIFICATION—MULTICOMPONENT SYSTEMS

The detailed consideration of multicomponent systems is outside the province of this book, and the student is referred instead to an excellent and thorough review of the subject.[19]   It is nevertheless useful to consider briefly the nature of the problems involved in such operations, since they occur so frequently in practical work.

Consider the continuous separation of a ternary solution consisting of components $A$, $B$, and $C$ whose relative volatilities are in that order ($A$ most volatile).   In order to obtain the three substances in substantially pure form, either of the schemes of Fig. 9.49 may be used.   According to scheme (*a*), the first column is used to separate $C$ as a residue from the rest of the solution.   The residue is necessarily contaminated with a small amount of $B$ and with an even smaller amount of $A$, although if relative volatilities are reasonably large, the amount of the latter may be exceedingly small.   The distillate, which is necessarily contaminated with at least a small amount of $C$, is then fractionated in a second column to provide nearly pure $A$ and $B$. According to scheme ($b$), the first tower provides nearly pure $A$ directly, and the residue is separated in the second. Which of the two schemes would be used depends upon the relative difficulty of the separation according to the two methods, but generally scheme ($b$) will be the more economical since it requires only one vaporization of substance $A$.

An important principle to be emphasized is that a single fractionator cannot separate more than one component in reasonably pure form from a multicomponent solution and that a total of $n - 1$ fractionators will be

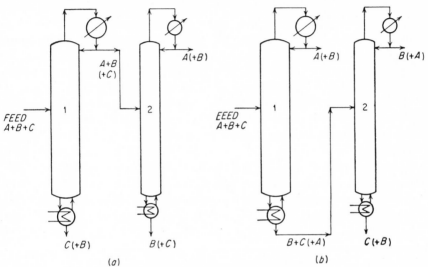

Fig. 9.49. Separation of a ternary system.

required for complete separation of a system of $n$ components. It might at first be thought, for example, that the component of intermediate volatility $B$ would tend to concentrate in reasonably pure form in the central parts of the first tower, from which it might be withdrawn as a *side stream*, thus allowing pure $A$ and pure $C$ to be withdrawn as distillate and residue, respectively. But this cannot occur. The feed tray of column 1, scheme ($a$), for example, will necessarily contain all three components in proportions not far from those prevailing in the feed itself. Trays immediately above the feed will therefore also contain appreciable quantities of all three substances, with the proportion of $C$ gradually diminishing as we go higher in the enriching section. Similarly, trays immediately below the feed necessarily contain large proportions of all substances, with decreasing amounts of $A$ and $B$ as we penetrate more deeply into the exhausting section. While side streams are indeed sometimes withdrawn from fractionating towers, these streams must be further processed if they are to provide pure products.

A second important principle is that the complete composition of both products and the yields of the various components in each may not be specified arbitrarily, even aside from the obvious material-balance considerations. Consider the first tower of scheme (a) (Fig. 9.49), for example. If it is desired that the distillate contain substantially all of the $A$ and 95 per cent of the $B$ originally present in the feed, the fraction of the $C$ which will also enter the distillate will be very small. But the actual amount will be automatically determined by the particular reflux ratio and corresponding number of trays used in the tower to satisfy the specifications respecting $A$ and $B$, together with the equilibrium relationship. Changing the reflux ratio and the corresponding number of trays will result in a corresponding change in the fraction of $C$ in the distillate. As a general rule only two component concentrations or yields may be arbitrarily assigned for multicomponent systems, just as in the case of binaries, and the remainder are controlled by the fractionator.

The general principles of design of multicomponent fractionators are the same in many respects as those for binary systems, but the dearth of adequate vapor-liquid equilibrium data imposes severe restrictions on their direct application. Relatively few ternary systems have been thoroughly investigated, and for more complex mixtures there are substantially no complete data at all. Ternary systems sometimes form ternary azeotropes, the occurrence of which is not obviously indicated by azeotropic formation in the binary systems formed from the same components. Ternary azeotropes furthermore need not necessarily boil at either the lowest or the highest temperature for the system. Considerations such as these emphasize the danger of attempting new designs without adequate equilibrium data or pilot-plant study, particularly for systems whose components are chemically dissimilar. Rational designs for really complex systems, containing up to 10 or more components, can be attempted only for solutions such as those found in the low-boiling products of the petroleum industry. These are solutions of the low-molecular-weight hydrocarbons, for which it may be assumed that the liquid phase is ideal or for which empirical corrections for departure from ideality may be applied. Lack of information on tray efficiencies for the various components also represents a real obstacle in design.

Granted that equilibrium data are available or may be assumed from the ideal nature of the solutions, the calculation of the number of ideal trays for such systems follows a logical extension of the principles established for binary systems. For example, starting with the overhead vapor composition, the equilibrium data provide the composition of the liquid on the first tray. If the principle of equimolal vaporization and overflow may be applied, the operating-line equation for the enriching section [Eq. (9.79)] may be written for each component appearing in the product, since each has its separate concentration.    Solving each of these provides the composition from the second tray, and so on from tray to tray.    The computations must be made analytically since the equilibrium data cannot generally be shown graphically.    Allowance for unequal molal overflow may be made by use of heat as well as material balances for each tray, and special techniques are introduced to permit calculation when all the components do not appear in appreciable amounts in both distillate and residue.    For each separation there is a minimum number of theoretical trays corresponding to total reflux, and a minimum reflux ratio for which an infinite number of trays are required.    Reflux ratios and numbers of theoretical trays must be large for sharp separations (high yield at high concentrations for one or a group of components in one of the products) but may be smaller for sloppy separations.

Multicomponent rectification finds its most complex applications in the field of petroleum refining.    Petroleum products such as gasoline, naphthas, kerosenes, gas oils, fuel oils, and lubricating oils are each mixtures of hundreds of hydrocarbons, so many that their identity and actual number cannot readily be established.    Fortunately, it is not usually specific substances that are desired in these products, but rather *properties*, so that specifications may be made as to boiling range, specific gravity, viscosity, and the like.    Fractionators for these products cannot be designed by the detailed methods just described but must instead be based upon laboratory studies in small-scale equipment.    As an example which effectively illustrates the many variations from the basic procedures which may be employed, consider the schematic diagram of a topping plant for the initial distillation of a crude oil (Fig. 9.50).    The crude oil, after preliminary heat exchange with several of the products from the plant, is passed through the tubes of a gas-fired furnace, the tube-still heater. Here a portion of the oil is vaporized somewhat larger in amount than that ultimately to be taken as vaporized products.    The mixture of liquid and vapor then enters the large bubble-tray tower.    Open steam is introduced at the bottom to strip the last traces of volatile substances from the residue product, and this steam passes up the column, where it lowers the effective pressure and hence the temperature of the distillation.    The steam and most volatile substances (crude gasoline) leaving the top tray are condensed, the water separated, and the gasoline sent to storage. Reflux in the scheme shown here is provided by withdrawing a portion of the liquid from the top tray and returning it after it has been cooled. The cold liquid condenses some of the rising vapors to provide internal reflux.    Several trays down from the top of the tower, a side stream may be withdrawn which will contain the hydrocarbons characteristic of a desired naphtha product.    Since the components of the more volatile gasoline are also present at this point, the liquid is steam-stripped in a short auxiliary bubble-tray tower, the steam and vaporized gasoline being sent back to the main fractionator. The stripped naphtha is then withdrawn to storage. In similar fashion kerosene and gas oil cuts may be withdrawn, but each must be separately steam-stripped. The individual steam strippers are frequently built into a single shell, as shown, for reasons of economy, so that from the outside the multipurpose nature

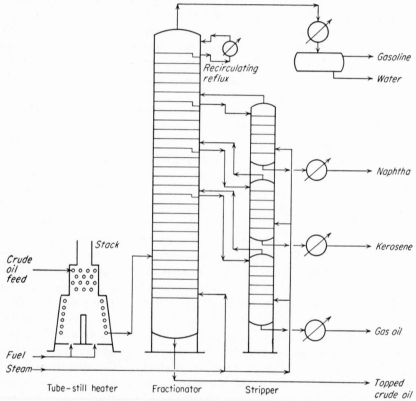

Fig. 9.50. Schematic arrangement, petroleum topping plant.

of the smaller tower is not readily evident. The withdrawn products must ordinarily be further processed before they are considered finished.

The design, method of operation, and number of products from topping units of this sort may vary considerably from refinery to refinery. Indeed, any individual unit will be built for maximum flexibility of operation, with, for example, multiple nozzles for introducing the feed at various trays and multiple side-stream withdrawal nozzles, to allow for variations in the nature of the feed and in the products to be made.

**Azeotropic Distillation.** This is a special case of multicomponent distillation used for separation of binary mixtures which are either difficult or impossible to separate by ordinary fractionation. If the relative volatility of a binary mixture is very low, the continuous rectification of the mixture to give nearly pure products will require high reflux ratios and correspondingly high heat requirements, as well as towers of large cross section and numbers of trays. In other cases the formation of a binary azeotrope may make it impossible to produce nearly pure products by ordinary fractionation. Under these circumstances a third component, sometimes called an "entrainer," may be added to the binary mixture

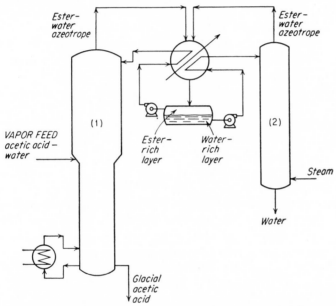

FIG. 9.51. Azeotropic distillation of acetic acid–water with butyl acetate.[17]

to form a new low-boiling azeotrope with one of the original constituents, whose volatility is such that it may be easily separated from the other original constituent.

As an example of such an operation, consider the flow sheet of Fig. 9.51 for the azeotropic separation of acetic acid–water solutions, using butyl acetate as entrainer.[17] Acetic acid may be separated from water by ordinary methods, but only at great expense owing to the low relative volatility of the constituents despite their fairly large difference in boiling points at atmospheric pressure (n.b.p. acetic acid = 118.1°C., n.b.p. water = 100°C.). Butyl acetate is only slightly soluble in water and consequently forms a heteroazeotrope with it (b.p. = 90.2°C.). Therefore if at least sufficient butyl acetate is added to the top of the distillation column (1) to form the azeotrope with all the water in the binary feed, the azeotrope may be readily distilled from the high-boiling acetic acid which leaves as a residue product.    The heteroazeotrope on condensation forms two insoluble liquid layers, one nearly pure water but saturated with ester, the other nearly pure ester saturated with water.    The latter is returned to the top of the column as reflux and is the source of the entrainer in the column.    The former may be stripped of its small entrainer content in a second small column (2).    The separation of the heteroazeotrope from acetic acid is readily done, so that relatively few trays are required in the principal tower.    On the other hand, heat must be supplied, not only to vaporize the water in the overhead distillate, but to vaporize the entrainer as well.    The operation may also be done batchwise, in which case sufficient entrainer is charged to the still kettle, together with the feed, to azeotrope the water.    The azeotrope is then distilled overhead.

Sometimes the new azeotrope which is formed contains all three constituents.    The dehydration of ethanol-water mixture with benzene as added substance is an example.    Dilute ethanol-water solutions may be continuously rectified to give at best mixtures containing 89.4 mole per cent ethanol at atmospheric pressure, since this is the composition of the minimum-boiling azeotrope in the binary system.    By introducing benzene into the top of a column fed with an ethanol-water mixture, the ternary azeotrope containing benzene (53.9 mole %), water (23.3 mole %), ethanol (22.8 mole %), boiling at 64.9°C., is readily separated from the ethanol (b.p. = 78.4°C.) which leaves as a residue product.    In this case also the azeotropic overhead product separates into two liquid layers, one rich in benzene which is returned to the top of the column as reflux, the other rich in water which is withdrawn.    Since the latter contains appreciable quantities of both benzene and ethanol, it must be separately rectified.    The ternary azeotrope contains nearly equal molar proportions of ethanol and water, and consequently dilute ethanol-water solutions must be given a preliminary rectification to produce substantially the alcohol-rich binary azeotrope which is used as a feed.

In still other cases the new azeotrope which is formed does not separate into two insoluble liquids, and special means for separating it, such as liquid extraction, must be provided, but this is less desirable.

It is clear that the choice of entrainer is a most important consideration.    The added substance should preferably form a low-boiling azeotrope with only one of the constituents of the binary mixture it is desired to separate, preferably the constituent present in the minority so as to reduce the heat requirements of the process.    The new azeotrope must be of sufficient volatility to make it readily separable from the remaining constituent and so that inappreciable amounts of entrainer will appear in the residue product.    It should preferably be lean in entrainer content, to reduce the amount of vaporization necessary in the distillation.    It should preferably be of the heterogeneous-liquid type, which then simplifies greatly the recovery of the entrainer.    In addition, a satisfactory entrainer must be (a) cheap and readily available, (b) chemically stable and inactive toward the solution to be separated, (c) noncorrosive toward common construction materials, (d) nontoxic, (e) of low latent heat of vaporization, (f) of low freezing point to facilitate storage and outdoor handling, and (g) of low viscosity to provide high tray efficiencies.

**Extractive Distillation.**    This is a multicomponent-rectification method similar in purpose to azeotropic distillation.    To a binary mixture which

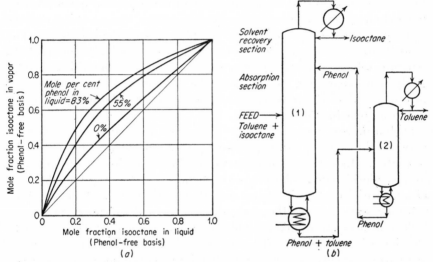

Fig. 9.52. Extractive distillation of toluene-isooctane with phenol.    [*Vapor-liquid equilibria from Drickamer, Brown, and White, Trans. Am. Inst. Chem. Engrs.,* **41,** 555 (1945).]

is difficult or impossible to separate by ordinary means a third component, termed a "solvent," is added which alters the relative volatility of the original constituents, thus permitting the separation.    The added solvent is, however, of low volatility and is itself not appreciably vaporized in the fractionator.

As an example of such an operation, consider the process of Fig. 9.52. The separation of toluene (b.p. = 110.8°C.) from paraffin hydrocarbons of approximately the same molecular weight is either very difficult or impossible, owing to low relative volatility or azeotropism, yet such a separation is necessary in the recovery of toluene from certain petroleum hydrocarbon mixtures.    Using isooctane (b.p. = 99.3°C.) as an example of a paraffin hydrocarbon, Fig. 9.52a shows that isooctane in this mixture is the more volatile, but the separation is obviously difficult. In the presence of phenol (b.p. = 181.4°C.), however, the isooctane relative volatility increases, so that, with as much as 83 mole per cent phenol in the liquid, the separation from toluene is relatively easy. A flow sheet for accomplishing this is shown in Fig. 9.52b, where the binary mixture is introduced more or less centrally into the extractive distillation tower (1), and phenol as the solvent is introduced near the top so as to be present in high concentration upon most of the trays in the tower. Under these conditions isooctane is readily distilled as an overhead product, while toluene and phenol are removed as a residue. Although phenol is relatively high-boiling, its vapor pressure is nevertheless sufficient so that its appearance in the overhead product must be prevented. The solvent-recovery section of the tower, which may be relatively short, serves to separate the phenol from the isooctane. The residue from the tower must be rectified in the auxiliary tower (2) to separate toluene from the phenol which is recycled, but this is a relatively easy separation. In practice, the paraffin hydrocarbon is a mixture rather than the pure substance isooctane, but the principle of the operation remains the same.

Such a process depends upon the difference in departure from ideality between the solvent and the components of the binary mixture to be separated. In the example given, both toluene and isooctane separately form nonideal liquid solutions with phenol, but the extent of the non-ideality with isooctane is greater than that with toluene. When all three substances are present, therefore, the toluene and isooctane themselves behave as a nonideal mixture and their relative volatility becomes high. Considerations of this sort form the basis for the choice of an extractive-distillation solvent. If, for example, a mixture of acetone (b.p = 56.4°C.) and methanol (b.p. = 64.7°C.), which form a binary azeotrope, were to be separated by extractive distillation, a suitable solvent could probably be chosen from the group of aliphatic alcohols.[20] Butanol (b.p. = 117.8°C.), since it is a member of the same homologous series but not far removed, forms substantially ideal solutions with methanol, which are themselves readily separated. It will form solutions of positive deviation from ideality with acetone, however, and the acetone-methanol vapor-liquid equilibria will therefore be substantially altered in ternary mixtures. If butanol forms no azeotrope with acetone, and if it alters the vapor-liquid equilibrium of acetone-methanol sufficiently to destroy the azeotrope in this system, it will serve as an extractive-distillation solvent. When both substances of the binary mixture to be separated are themselves chemically very similar, a solvent of an entirely different chemical nature will be necessary. Acetone and furfural, for example, are useful as extractive-distillation solvents for separating the hydrocarbons butene-2 and n-butane.

Generally the requirements of a satisfactory extractive-distillation solvent are:

1. High selectivity, or ability to alter the vapor-liquid equilibria of the original mixture sufficiently to permit its easy separation, with, however, use of only small quantities of solvent.

2. High capacity, or ability to dissolve the components in the mixture to be separated. It frequently happens that substances which are incompletely miscible with the mixture are very selective; yet if sufficiently high concentrations of solvent cannot be obtained in the liquid phase, the separation ability cannot be fully developed.

3. Low volatility in order to prevent vaporization of the solvent with the overhead product and to maintain high concentration in the liquid phase.

4. Separability. The solvent must be readily separated from the mixture to which it is added, and particularly it must form no azeotropes with the original substances.

5. The same considerations of cost, toxicity, corrosive character, chemical stability, freezing point, and viscosity apply as for entrainers for azeotropic distillation.

Extractive distillation is usually more desirable a process than azeotropic distillation since no large quantities of solvent must be vaporized. Furthermore, a greater choice of added component is possible since the process is not dependent upon the accident of azeotropic formation. It cannot be conveniently carried out in batch operations, however.

Azeotropic and extractive-distillation equipment can be designed using the general methods for multicomponent distillation, but these are beyond the scope of this book. Detailed discussion is, however, available.[1,5,11,19,20]

## LOW-PRESSURE DISTILLATION

Many organic substances cannot be heated to temperatures which even approach their normal boiling points without chemical decomposition. If such substances are to be separated by distillation, then the pressure and the corresponding temperature must be kept low. The time of exposure of the substances to the distillation temperature must also be kept to a minimum, since the extent of thermal decomposition will thereby be reduced. For distillation under absolute pressures of the order of several lb./sq. in., packed towers may be used, bubble trays can be designed with pressure drops approaching 0.05 lb./sq. in. (2.6 mm. Hg), and other simpler designs such as the shower tray of Fig. 9.53 for which the pressure drops are of the order of 0.015 lb./sq. in. (0.75 mm. Hg) are possible.

In the distillation of many natural products, such as the separation of vitamins from animal and fish oils as well as the separation of many synthetic industrial products such as plasticizers, the temperature may not exceed perhaps 200 to 300°C., where the vapor pressures of the substances may be a fraction of a millimeter of mercury. The conventional equipment is, of course, wholly unsuitable for such separations, not only because the pressure drop would result in high temperatures at the bottom of columns, but also because of the long exposure time to the prevailing temperatures resulting from high hold-up.

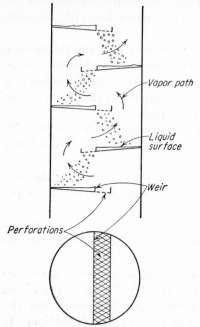

**Molecular Distillation.** This is a form of very-low-pressure distillation, conducted at absolute pressures of the order of 0.003 mm. Hg, suitable for the heat-sensitive substances described above.

The rate at which evaporation takes place from a liquid surface is given by the Langmuir equation,

Fig. 9.53. Shower tray for low-pressure distillation.[14]

$$N_A' = 1006 p_A \left( \frac{1}{2\pi M R'' T} \right)^{0.5} \qquad (9.143)$$

where $N_A'$ = gm. moles substance $A$ evaporated/(sec.)(sq. cm.)

$\quad p_A$ = partial pressure of $A$, atm.

$\quad M_A$ = mol. wt. of $A$

$\quad R''$ = universal gas const., 82.07 cu. cm. (atm.)/(gm. mole)(°K.)

$\quad T$ = abs. temp., °K.

At ordinary pressures the net rate of evaporation is, however, very much less than this, owing to the fact that the evaporated molecules are reflected back to the liquid after collisions occurring in the vapor. By reducing the absolute pressure to values used in molecular distillation, the mean free path of the molecules becomes very large, of the order of 1 cm. If the condensing surface is then placed at a distance from the vaporizing liquid surface not exceeding a few centimeters, very few molecules will return to the liquid and the net rate of evaporation of each substance of a binary mixture will approach that given by Eq. (9.143). The vapor composition, or the composition of the distillate, will now be different from that given by ordinary equilibrium vaporization, and the ratio of the constituents in the distillate will approach

$$\frac{N_A'}{N_B'} = \frac{\text{moles of } A}{\text{moles of } B} = \frac{p_A/M_A^{0.5}}{p_B/M_B^{0.5}} \qquad (9.144)$$

If this ratio is to be maintained, however, the surface of the liquid must be rapidly renewed, since otherwise the ratio of constituents in the surface will change as evaporation proceeds. The vigorous agitation or boiling present during ordinary distillations is absent under conditions of molecular distillation, and in most devices the liquid is caused to flow in a thin film over a solid surface, thus continually renewing the surface but at the same time maintaining low hold-up of liquid.

Figure 9.54 shows a device which is used industrially for accomplishing a molecular distillation.[12] The degassed liquid to be distilled is introduced continuously at the bottom of the inner surface of the rotor, a

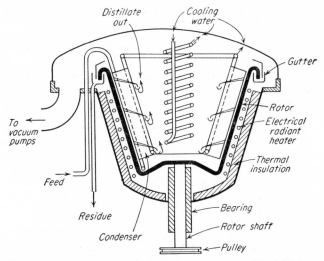

Fig. 9.54. Schematic section, centrifugal molecular still of Hickman.[12]

rotating conical-shaped surface. The rotor may be as large as 5 ft. in diameter at the top and may revolve at speeds of 400 to 500 r.p.m. A thin layer of liquid to be distilled, 0.05 to 0.1 mm. thick, then spreads over the inner surface and travels rapidly to the upper periphery under the action of centrifugal force. Heat is supplied to the liquid through the rotor by radiant electrical heaters, and the vaporized material is condensed upon the water-cooled louver-shaped condenser. This is maintained at temperatures sufficiently low to prevent reevaporation or reflection of the vaporized molecules. The residue liquid is caught in the collection gutter at the top of the rotor, and the distillate is drained from the collection troughs on the condenser. Each product is pumped from the still body, which is evacuated to the low pressures necessary for molecular distillation, and the time of residence of the substances in the still may be as low as several seconds or less. Such a device is capable of handling 50 to 250 gal./hr. of liquid to be distilled and gives a separation of 80 to 95 per cent of that indicated by Eq. (9.144). Multiple distillations are necessary for multistage separation effects.

## NOTATION FOR CHAPTER 9

$a$ = interfacial surface, sq. ft./cu. ft.
$A$ = more volatile component of a binary mixture
= absorption factor = $L/mG$, dimensionless
$b$ = width of bubble-cap slot, in.
$B$ = less volatile component of a binary mixture
$C$ = heat capacity at constant pressure, B.t.u./(lb.)(°F.)
$d$ = differential operator
$D$ = quantity of distillate, lb. moles/(hr.)(sq. ft. tower cross section)
= quantity of distillate, total lb. moles (batch distillation)
$e$ = 2.7183
$E$ = over-all tray efficiency as a fraction = number of theoretical trays/number of real trays, dimensionless
$E_G$ = Murphree gas efficiency as a fraction. Defined by Eq. (9.116)
$f$ = function
$F$ = quantity of feed, lb. moles/(hr.)(sq. ft. tower cross section)
= quantity of feed, total lb. moles (batch distillation)
$G$ = superficial vapor rate, lb. moles/(hr.)(sq. ft. tower cross section)
= vapor quantity, total lb. moles (batch distillation)
$G'$ = superficial vapor rate, lb./(hr.)(sq. ft. tower cross section)
$h$ = vertical distance from center of bubble-cap slot to top of weir, in.
$H$ = enthalpy, B.t.u./lb. mole of solution
$H_{tG}$ = gas-film height of a transfer unit, ft.
$H_{tL}$ = liquid-film height of a transfer unit, ft.
$H_{tOG}$ = over-all height of a transfer unit, gas, ft.
$H_{tOL}$ = over-all height of a transfer unit, liquid, ft.
$\Delta H_S$ = integral heat of solution, B.t.u./lb. mole of solution
$k'_x a$ = liquid-film mass-transfer coefficient, lb. moles/(hr.)(cu. ft.) (mole fraction)
$k'_y a$ = gas-film mass-transfer coefficient, lb. moles/(hr.)(cu. ft.)(mole fraction)
$K$ = defined by Eq. (9.118)
$K'_G a$ = over-all gas mass-transfer coefficient, lb. moles/(hr.)(cu. ft.)(atm.)
$K'_x a$ = over-all liquid mass-transfer coefficient, lb. moles/(hr.)(cu. ft.)(mole fraction)
$K'_y a$ = over-all gas mass-transfer coefficient, lb. moles/(hr.)(cu. ft.)(mole fraction)
log = common logarithm
ln = natural logarithm
$L$ = superficial liquid rate, lb. moles/(hr.)(sq. ft. tower cross section)
$L'$ = superficial liquid rate, lb./(hr.)(sq. ft. tower cross section)
$L_0$ = external reflux rate, lb. moles/(hr.)(sq. ft. tower cross section)
$m$ = slope of the equilibrium curve, mole fraction in gas/mole fraction in liquid
= $dy^*/dx$. If constant, $m = y^*/x$
$M$ = molecular weight, lb./lb. mole
$N_p$ = number of theoretical trays
$N'$ = rate of evaporation, gm. moles/(sec.)(sq. cm.) [Eqs. (9.143), (9.144)]
$N_m$ = minimum number of theoretical trays
$N_{tOG}$ = number of over-all gas transfer units
$N_{tOL}$ = number of over-all liquid transfer units
$p$ = partial pressure, atm.

$p^*$ = equilibrium partial pressure, atm.

$P$ = vapor pressure of a pure substance, atm.

$P_t$ = total pressure, atm.

$q$ = defined by Eq. (9.88)

$Q$ = net heat added, B.t.u./(hr.)(sq. ft. tower cross section)

$Q_B$ = heat added at reboiler, B.t.u./(hr.)(sq. ft. tower cross section)

$Q_C$ = heat removed at condenser, B.t.u./(hr.)(sq. ft. tower cross section)

$Q_L$ = total heat loss, B.t.u./(hr.)(sq. ft. tower cross section)

$Q_0$ = defined by Eq. (9.58)

$\bar{Q}_0$ = defined by Eq. (9.66)

$R$ = reflux ratio, moles reflux returned to top of tower/mole distillate withdrawn

$R'$ = apparent reflux ratio, defined by Eq. (9.112)

$R''$ = universal gas constant, 82.07 cu. cm. (atm.)/(gm. mole)(°K.) [Eq. (9.143)]

$R_m$ = minimum reflux ratio, moles reflux returned to top of tower/mole distillate withdrawn

$S$ = interfacial surface, sq. ft./sq. ft. tower cross section

$t$ = temperature, °F.

$t_0$ = base temperature for enthalpy balance, °F.

$T$ = absolute temperature, °K. [Eq. (9.143)]

$W$ = quantity of residue, lb. moles/(hr.)(sq. ft. tower cross section)

= quantity of residue, total lb. moles (batch distillation)

$x$ = concentration of $A$ in the liquid, mole fraction

$x^*$ = concentration of $A$ in the liquid in equilibrium with a vapor of mole fraction $y$, mole fraction

$x_D$ = concentration of $A$ in the liquid distillate, mole fraction

$x_F$ = concentration of $A$ in the liquid feed, mole fraction

$x_W$ = concentration of $A$ in the residue, mole fraction

$x_{Wf}$ = concentration of $A$ in the final residue, mole fraction

$y$ = concentration of $A$ in the vapor, mole fraction

$y^*$ = concentration of $A$ in the vapor in equilibrium with a liquid of mole fraction $x$, mole fraction

$y_D$ = concentration of $A$ in the vapor distillate, mole fraction

$y_f$ = concentration of $A$ in the vapor at the point where the feed is introduced into the column, mole fraction

$y_F$ = concentration of $A$ in the vapor feed, mole fraction

$z$ = average concentration of $A$ in a solution or mixture, mole fraction

$z_F$ = average concentration of $A$ in the feed, mole fraction

$Z$ = height of packing, ft.

$\alpha$ = separation factor or relative volatility, defined by Eq. (9.2), dimensionless

$\alpha_{JC}$ = relative volatility of component $J$ with respect to component $C$

$\lambda$ = latent heat of vaporization, B.t.u./lb.

$\mu'_L$ = liquid viscosity, centipoises

$\pi$ = 3.1416

$\rho_L$ = liquid density, lb./cu. ft.

$\Sigma$ = summation

Subscripts:

av = average

$A$ = more volatile substance; component $A$

$B$ = less volatile substance; component $B$

$D$ = distillate

$F$ = feed
$G$ = gas
$L$ = liquid
$m$ = from tray $m$
$n$ = from tray $n$
$W$ = residue
1 = bottom of tower (for packed towers); tray 1 (for tray towers)
2 = top of tower (for packed towers); tray 2 (for tray towers)

Superscripts:

\* = equilibrium
− over quantity = stripping or exhausting section of a tower

## REFERENCES

1. Benedict, M., and L. C. Rubin: *Trans. Am. Inst. Chem. Engrs.*, **41**, 353 (1945).
2. Bogart, M. J. P.: *Trans. Am. Inst. Chem. Engrs.*, **33**, 139 (1937).
3. Brown, G. G., and H. Z. Martin: *Trans. Am. Inst. Chem. Engrs.*, **35**, 679 (1939).
4. Carney, T. P.: "Laboratory Fractional Distillation," The Macmillan Company, New York, 1949.
5. Chambers, J. M.: *Chem. Eng. Progr.*, **47**, 555 (1951).
6. Chilton, T. H., and A. P. Colburn: *Ind. Eng. Chem.*, **27**, 205 (1935).
7. Deed, D. W., P. W. Schutz, and T. B. Drew: *Ind. Eng. Chem.*, **39**, 766 (1947).
8. Dodge, B. F.: "Chemical Engineering Thermodynamics," McGraw-Hill Book Company, Inc., New York, 1944.
9. Fenske, M. R.: *Ind. Eng. Chem.*, **24**, 482 (1932).
10. Gilliland, E. R.: *Ind. Eng. Chem.*, **32**, 1220 (1940).
11. Hachmuth, K. H.: *Chem. Eng. Progr.*, **48**, 523, 570, 617 (1952).
12. Hickman, K. C. D.: *Ind. Eng. Chem.*, **39**, 686 (1947).
13. Horsley, L. H.: Azeotropic Data, *Advances in Chem. Ser.* 6 (1952).
14. Kraft, W. W.: *Ind. Eng. Chem.*, **40**, 807 (1948).
15. McCabe, W. L., and E. W. Thiele: *Ind. Eng. Chem.*, **17**, 605 (1925).
16. O'Connell, H. E.: *Trans. Am. Inst. Chem. Engrs.*, **42**, 741 (1946).
17. Othmer, D. F.: *Chem. Met. Eng.*, **42**, 356 (1935).
18. Peck, R. E., and E. F. Wagner: *Trans. Am. Inst. Chem. Engrs.*, **41**, 737 (1945).
19. Robinson, C. S., and E. R. Gilliland: "Elements of Fractional Distillation," 4th ed., McGraw-Hill Book Company, Inc., New York, 1950.
20. Scheibel, E. G.: *Chem. Eng. Progr.*, **44**, 927 (1948).
21. Smoker, E. H., and A. Rose: *Trans. Am. Inst. Chem. Engrs.*, **36**, 285 (1940).
22. Underwood, A. J. V.: *Trans. Inst. Chem. Engrs.*, **10**, 112 (1932).
23. Walter, J. F., and T. K. Sherwood: *Ind. Eng. Chem.*, **33**, 493 (1941).

## PROBLEMS

**1.** Solutions of methanol and ethanol are substantially ideal. (*a*) Compute the vapor-liquid equilibria for this system at 1 and at 5 atm. abs. pressure, and plot $xy$ and $txy$ diagrams at each pressure. (*b*) For each pressure compute relative volatilities, and determine an average value. (*c*) Using Eq. (9.2) with the average volatilities, compare the values of $y^*$ at each value of $x$ so obtained with those computed directly from vapor pressures.

**2.** A 1,000-lb. batch of nitrobenzene is to be steam-distilled from a very small amount of a nonvolatile impurity, insufficient to influence the vapor pressure of the nitrobenzene. The operation is to be carried out in a jacketed kettle fitted with a condenser and distillate receiver. Saturated steam at 5 lb./sq. in. gauge is introduced into the kettle jacket for heating. The nitrobenzene is charged to the kettle at 80°F., and it is substantially insoluble in water.

*a.* Liquid water at 80°F. is continuously introduced into the nitrobenzene in the kettle, so as always to maintain a liquid water level. The mixture is distilled at atmospheric pressure. (1) At what temperature does the distillation proceed? (2) How much water is vaporized? (3) How much steam must be condensed in the kettle jacket? Neglect the heat required to bring the still up to operating temperature. The heat capacity of nitrobenzene is 0.33 B.t.u./(lb.)(°F.), and its latent heat of vaporization may be determined by the methods of Chap. 7.

*b.* Superheated steam at 210.5°F. instead of liquid water is introduced into the nitrobenzene beneath the liquid surface. The batch is kept at 210.5°F. by condensing steam in the kettle jacket, and liquid water is prevented from accumulating by carrying out the distillation at 50 mm. Hg abs. The vapors rising from the kettle have a relative saturation of nitrobenzene of 80%. How much steam (superheated and that in the jacket) is now required?

**3.** A mixture contains 40 mole % methanol, 35 mole % ethanol, and 25 mole % *n*-propanol. Liquid solutions of these substances are substantially ideal. Assuming the applicability of the perfect-gas law, for a total pressure of 1 atm. abs. compute:

*a.* The bubble point and the equilibrium vapor composition
*b.* The dew point and the equilibrium liquid composition

**4.** Vapor-liquid equilibrium data at 1 atm. abs. and heats of solution for the system acetone (*A*)–water (*B*), in addition to heat-capacity and latent-heat data for acetone, are as follows:

| $x$ mole fraction acetone in liquid | Integral ht. soln. at 59°F., B.t.u./lb. mole soln. | $y^*$ equil. mole fraction acetone in vapor | Vapor-liquid temp., °F. | Ht. capacity at 63°F., B.t.u./(lb. soln.)(°F.) |
|---|---|---|---|---|
| 0.00 | 0 | 0.00 | 212 | 1.00 |
| 0.01 | ....... | 0.253 | 197.1 | 0.998 |
| 0.02 | −81.0 | 0.425 | 187.8 | 0.994 |
| 0.05 | −192.3 | 0.624 | 168.3 | 0.985 |
| 0.10 | −287.5 | 0.755 | 151.9 | 0.96 |
| 0.15 | −331 | 0.798 | 146.2 | 0.93 |
| 0.20 | −338 | 0.815 | 143.9 | 0.91 |
| 0.30 | −309 | 0.830 | 141.8 | 0.85 |
| 0.40 | −219 | 0.839 | 140.8 | 0.80 |
| 0.50 | −150.5 | 0.849 | 140.0 | 0.75 |
| 0.60 | −108.6 | 0.859 | 139.1 | 0.70 |
| 0.70 | ....... | 0.874 | 138.1 | 0.66 |
| 0.80 | ....... | 0.898 | 136.8 | 0.61 |
| 0.90 | ....... | 0.935 | 135.5 | 0.57 |
| 0.95 | ....... | 0.963 | 134.6 | 0.55 |
| 1.00 | ....... | 1.000 | 133.7 | |

| $t$, °F.................................................. | 68 | 100 | 150 | 200 | 212 |
|---|---|---|---|---|---|
| Ht. capacity acetone, B.t.u./(lb.)(°F.).......... | 0.53 | 0.54 | 0.56 | 0.58 | |
| Latent ht. vaporization, B.t.u./lb.............. | 242 | 233 | 219 | 206 | 203 |

A liquid mixture containing 60 mole % acetone, 40 mole % water, at 80°F., is to be continuously flash-vaporized at 1 atm. pressure, to vaporize 30 mole % of the feed.

a. What will be the composition of the products and the temperature in the separator?

b. How much heat, B.t.u./lb. mole of feed, is required?

c. If the products are each cooled to 80°F., how much heat, B.t.u./lb. mole of feed, must be removed from each?

**5.** A liquid mixture containing 60 mole % acetone, 40 mole % water, at 80°F., is to be continuously flash-vaporized at 1 atm. pressure. If 7,800 B.t.u./lb. mole is added to the feed, compute the composition of the vapor and liquid products, the fraction vaporized, and the equilibrium temperature.

**6.** A saturated vapor at 1 atm. pressure, containing 50 mole % acetone and 50 mole % water, is subject to equilibrium condensation to yield 50 mole % of the feed as a liquid. Compute the equilibrium vapor and liquid compositions, the equilibrium temperature, and the heat to be removed, B.t.u./lb. mole feed.

**7.** The ideal liquid mixture containing 40 mole % methanol, 35 mole % ethanol, 25 mole % n-propanol is flash-vaporized to vaporize 60 mole % of the feed. Determine the compositions of the liquid and vapor products and their equilibrium temperature.

**8.** The liquid solution of Prob. 4 is differentially distilled at 1 atm. pressure to vaporize 30 mole % of the feed. Compute the composition of the composited distillate and the residue. Compare with the results of Prob. 4.

**9.** The liquid solution of Prob. 4 is to be differentially distilled at 1 atm. pressure to produce a composited vapor composition of 84 mole % acetone. What percentage of the feed must be vaporized, and what is the residue composition?

**10.** The ideal solution containing 10 mole % methanol, 80 mole % ethanol, and 10 mole % n-propanol is to be differentially distilled at 1 atm. pressure. The first 20 mole % of vapor will be discarded, following which a "heart cut" of 60 mole % will be distilled and separately retained. The 20 mole % of residue will be discarded. Compute the yield of ethanol in the heart cut and the composition of this product.

**11.** a. Integrate Eq. (9.40) for the case where $m = y^*/x = $ const.

b. Derive Eqs. (9.43) and (9.44).

c. Integrate Eq. (9.42) for the case of constant relative volatility.

**12.** A solution of carbon tetrachloride and carbon disulfide containing 50% by wt. of each is to be continuously fractionated at atmospheric pressure at the rate of 4,000 lb./hr. The distillate product is to contain 95 wt. % carbon disulfide, the residue 0.5%. The feed will be 30 mole % vaporized. A total condenser will be used, and reflux will be returned at the boiling point. Equilibrium data are available in the "Chemical Engineers' Handbook," 3d ed., p. 574. Make the usual simplifying assumptions.

a. Determine the quantities of products, lb./hr. and lb. moles/hr.

b. Determine the minimum reflux ratio.

c. Determine the minimum number of theoretical trays required, graphically and by means of Eq. (9.99).

d. Determine the number of theoretical trays required at a reflux ratio equal to twice the minimum, and the position of the feed tray.

e. Estimate the over-all tray efficiency for a bubble-tray tower of conventional design, the number of real trays, and the tray on which the feed is to be introduced.

f. Estimate the quantities, cu. ft./sec., of liquid and vapor at the extremities of the tower and at the feed tray.

g. Using the distillate temperature as base temperature, determine the enthalpy of the feed, the products, and the vapor entering the condenser. Determine the heat to be removed from the condenser and that to be added at the reboiler. Latent heats and specific heats are available in the "Chemical Engineers' Handbook," 3d ed., pp. 218, 228.

**13.** Five thousand pounds per hour of an acetone-water solution, containing 25 wt. % acetone, is to be fractionated at 1 atm. pressure. It is desired to recover 99.5 % of the acetone in the distillate, at a concentration of 99 wt. %. The feed will be available at 80°F. and will be preheated by heat exchange with the residue product from the fractionator, which in turn will be cooled to 125°F. The distilled vapors will be condensed and cooled to 100°F. by cooling water entering at 80°F. and leaving at 105°F. The reflux will be returned at 100°F. Steam at 5 lb./sq. in. gauge will be supplied to the reboiler. Bubble-cap trays of conventional design will be used, and the distance from the center of the slots to the top of the weir has been set at 2.50 in., the slot width at 0.40 in.

*a.* Make the usual simplifying assumptions, and determine the minimum reflux ratio (moles cold reflux/mole distillate).

*b.* At a reflux ratio of 1.8 moles cold reflux/mole distillate, determine the steam and cooling-water requirements.

*c.* Make the usual simplifying assumptions, and determine the number of real bubble-cap trays required under the conditions of part *b*.

*d.* Repeat (*c*) without making the usual simplifying assumptions.

**14.** The separation of Prob. 13 is to be carried out with open steam at atmospheric pressure instead of with a reboiler, and at a reflux ratio of 1.8 moles cold reflux/mole distillate. The feed is to be preheated by heat exchange with the residue, which is to be cooled to 125°F. as before. Determine the steam requirement and the number of real bubble-cap trays under these conditions. Make the usual simplifying assumptions.

**15.** A solution of carbon tetrachloride and carbon disulfide containing 50% of each component by weight is to be continuously fractionated to give a distillate and a residue analyzing 95.0 and 0.5 wt. % carbon disulfide, respectively. Feed will be available as liquid at the bubble point, and reflux will be returned at the bubble point.

There is available a bubble-cap tray tower of conventional design suitable for use at atmospheric pressure. The diameter is 30 in., and it contains 26 identical cross-flow trays at a spacing of 20 in. A feed nozzle is available only for the tenth tray from the top. Each tray contains an 18-in.-long straight weir, extending 2.5 in. from the tray floor. The slot area is 0.6 sq. ft. per tray, and the static submergence is 0.5 in. Adequate condenser and reboiler will be supplied.

The listed products represent the minimum purities acceptable, and higher purities at the expense of additional heat load or reduced capacity are not warranted. Estimate the largest quantity of feed, lb./hr., which the column may be reasonably expected to handle.

**16.** An aqueous solution of furfural contains 4 mole % furfural. It is to be continuously rectified to give products containing 0.5 mole % and 99.5 mole % furfural, respectively. Feed is liquid at the boiling point, and the distillation pressure is to be 1 atm. abs. Arrange a scheme for the separation, and determine the number of theoretical trays required for a vapor boil-up of 1.25 times the minimum for an infinite number of trays. Equilibrium data are available in the "Chemical Engineers' Handbook," 3d ed., p. 574.

**17.** Design a tower packed with 1.5-in. stoneware Raschig rings for the separation of Prob. 12 at twice the minimum reflux ratio. It is agreed that nowhere shall the vapor velocity exceed 50% of that which will cause flooding in the tower.

**18.** One thousand pounds per hour of an aniline-water solution containing 7 wt. % aniline is to be continuously steam-stripped in a tower packed with 1-in. Berl saddles with open steam to remove 99% of the aniline.   The feed will be available at the boiling point.   The condensed overhead vapor will be decanted at 98.5°C. and the water-rich layer returned to the column.   The aniline-rich layer will be withdrawn as distillate product.   The quantity of steam used will be 1.3 times the minimum quantity.   The tower is to be designed for 50% of the vapor flooding rate.   Make the usual simplifying assumptions, and design the tower.   (NOTE: Calculate $N_{tOL}$ and $H_{tOL}$.)

Data: At 98.5°C., the solubility of aniline in water is 7.02 and 89.90 wt. % aniline. The vapor-liquid equilibra at 745 mm. Hg, at which pressure the tower is to be operated, are as follows [Griswold *et al.*, *Ind. Eng. Chem.*, **32**, 878 (1940)]:

| $x$ = mole fraction aniline | 0.002 | 0.004 | 0.006 | 0.008 | 0.010 | 0.012 | Two liquid phases (98.5°C.) |
|---|---|---|---|---|---|---|---|
| $y^*$ = mole fraction aniline | 0.01025 | 0.0185 | 0.0263 | 0.0338 | 0.03575 | 0.03585 | 0.0360 |

**19.** Two thousand pounds of an acetone-water solution containing 40 mole % acetone is to be rectified in a batch apparatus consisting of a kettle and a column. The column contains the equivalent of four theoretical trays and has a negligible hold-up.   A distillate containing 95 mole % acetone will be withdrawn, and the operation will be carried on at varying reflux ratio until 90% of the ultimate distillate yield (of the required composition, with this apparatus) is obtained.   Reflux will be returned at the bubble point, and the operation will be conducted at 1 atm. pressure. Calculate the number of pound moles of vapor which must be formed during the distillation.

**20.** Six thousand pounds of an acetone-water solution containing 40 mole % acetone is to be batch-rectified at 1 atm. pressure.   The available apparatus consists of a kettle of 2,000 lb. capacity, surmounted by a column of negligible hold-up equivalent to four theoretical plates.   The kettle is charged with 2,000 lb. of the feed and distilled at a constant reflux ratio equal to 2 moles reflux/mole distillate, the reflux being returned at the bubble point.   The residue is allowed to accumulate in the kettle, but, for each pound of distillate withdrawn, 1 lb. of new feed is introduced until the entire 6,000 lb. of solution has been charged and 4,000 lb. of distillate has been collected.   Compute the compositions of the composited distillate and of the final residue.

# PART III

# LIQUID-LIQUID OPERATIONS

Liquid extraction, the only operation in this category, is basically very similar to the operations of gas-liquid contact described in the previous part. The creation of a new insoluble liquid phase by addition of a solvent to a mixture accomplishes in many respects the same result as the creation of a new phase by the addition of heat in distillation operations, for example, or by addition of gas in desorption operations.

Certain minor differences in the operations nevertheless make it expedient to provide a separate treatment for liquid extraction. The considerably greater change in mutual solubility of the contacted liquid phases which may occur during passage through a cascade of stages requires somewhat different techniques of computation than are necessary for gas absorption or stripping. The considerably smaller differences in density of the contacted phases and their relatively low interfacial tension, as compared with the corresponding gas-liquid systems, require consideration in the design of apparatus. The larger number of variables which apparently influence the rate of mass transfer in countercurrent equipment makes the correlation of design data much more difficult. For these reasons separate treatment is desirable, at least for the present.

# LIQUID LIQUID OPERATIONS

CHAPTER 10

# LIQUID EXTRACTION

Liquid extraction, sometimes called solvent extraction, is the separation of the constituents of a liquid solution by contact with another insoluble liquid. If the substances comprising the original solution distribute themselves differently between the two liquid phases, a certain degree of separation will result and this may be enhanced by use of multiple contacts or their equivalent in the manner of gas absorption and distillation.

A simple example will indicate the scope of the operation and some of its characteristics. If a solution of acetic acid in water is agitated with a liquid such as ethyl acetate, some of the acid but relatively little water will enter the ester phase. Since at equilibrium the densities of the aqueous and ester layers are different, they will settle on cessation of agitation and may be decanted from each other. Since now the ratio of acid to water in the ester layer is different from that in the original solution and also different from that in the residual water solution, a certain degree of separation will have occurred. This is an example of stagewise contact, and it may be carried out either in batch or in continuous fashion. The residual water may be repeatedly extracted with more ester to reduce still further the acid content, or we may arrange a countercurrent cascade of stages. Another possibility is to use some sort of countercurrent continuous-contact device, where discrete stages are not involved. The use of reflux, as in distillation, may enhance still further the ultimate separation.

In all such operations, the solution which is to be extracted is called the *feed,* and the liquid with which the feed is contacted is the *solvent.* The solvent-rich product of the operation is called the *extract,* and the residual liquid from which solute has been removed is the *raffinate.*

More complicated processes may use two solvents to separate the components of a feed. For example, a mixture of *p*- and *o*-nitrobenzoic acids may be separated by distributing them between the insoluble liquids chloroform and water. The chloroform preferentially dissolves the para isomer and the water the ortho isomer. This is called *double-solvent,* or *fractional,* extraction.

361

**Field of Usefulness.** No matter what the complications of the flow sheet, there are certain characteristics common to all extraction operations which influence greatly its field of usefulness. The solute removed by an extraction process is obtained in the form of a new solution which ordinarily must itself be separated, both for obtaining the desired solute and also for recovery of the solvent. This separation will usually be another of the mass-transfer operations such as distillation, or the like. In addition, the so-called insoluble liquids are nevertheless usually sufficiently soluble that recovery of some solvent from the raffinate is also necessary.

It follows that extraction as a separation technique will generally be useful under the following circumstances:

1. Where the combined extraction and solvent recovery operations are more economical than direct separation procedures. This may occur, for example, in the separation of a valuable organic substance from dilute aqueous solution. The solvent quantity, latent heat of vaporization, and difficulty of solvent separation being less in each case than the corresponding values for water, the combined extraction-solvent recovery operations may be cheaper than direct distillation. This may also be the case where it might be necessary to make a distillation at very low pressures and temperatures in order to avoid thermal decomposition. In the separation of long-chain fatty acids from vegetable oils, for example, either high-vacuum distillation or extraction with liquid propane which may be removed from the products at low temperature may be chosen on the basis of ultimate cost.

2. Where simpler methods fail. The separation of azeotropic mixtures, where direct distillation will not give a complete separation, is an example of this. In other instances, extraction has been especially useful in separating the components of complex mixtures according to chemical type, where the components of different chemical type have similar boiling points. This is exemplified by the separation of mixtures of aromatic from paraffin hydrocarbons by preferential extraction of the former with liquid sulfur dioxide.

## EQUIPMENT

There are two major categories of equipment for liquid extraction:

1. Single-stage equipment, which provides one stage of contact in a single device or combination of devices. In such an apparatus, the liquids are mixed, extraction occurs, and the insoluble liquids are settled and separated. A cascade of such stages may then be arranged.

2. Multistage equipment, where the equivalent of many stages may be incorporated into a single device or apparatus. This is the more important category.

## SINGLE-STAGE EQUIPMENT

A single stage must provide facilities for mixing the insoluble liquids and for settling and decanting the emulsion or dispersion which results. In batch operation, mixing together with settling and decanting may take place in the same or in separate vessels. In continuous operation, different vessels are required.

**Mixers.** For efficient extraction, the mixing device must bring about intimate contact of the liquids. This usually requires that one liquid be dispersed in the form of small droplets into the other and that sufficient time of contact ("holding time") be provided to allow extraction to take place. The smaller the droplets and the larger their number, the greater will be the interfacial area produced, the more rapid will be the interphase mass transfer, and the less holding time will be required. It is, however, essential that the dispersion not be made so fine that subsequent settling is too slow.

To effect the dispersion requires the expenditure of mechanical work or power upon the system. The mere application of large amounts of power through some mixing device will not necessarily ensure adequate mixing, however. The mixing effectiveness, which may be loosely defined as the degree of dispersion produced per unit of power applied, depends greatly upon the design of the mixing device. As yet no really adequate measurements of this have been made, and we must rely instead on the stage efficiency as indication of the success of the mixing. This will include the influence of degree of dispersion, holding time, and rate of diffusion upon the operation as a whole. It is known, however, that the degree of dispersion which results from the application of a fixed amount of power through a given mixer depends upon the properties of the liquids involved, including their densities, viscosities, and interfacial tension.

There are two major varieties of mixers, agitated vessels and flow mixers.

**Agitated Vessels.** These consist of a vessel to contain the liquids and a mechanical agitator to provide the mixing, as in Fig. 10.1. In such vessels strong vertical currents within the liquid are necessary to ensure that the heavy liquid will not stratify at the bottom. Radial rather than circular motion is desired, since the latter tends to stratify the liquids by centrifugal force, causing the heavy liquid to be flung to the side wall of the vessel. The circulation currents developed will depend upon the vessel shape, the presence of baffles, and the design, location, and speed of the agitation impeller.

The vessels are ordinarily vertical cylinders, circular rather than rectangular in cross section. They should be fitted with internal baffles, which are necessary to provide vertical liquid currents and to prevent rotational swirl and vortices. For this application the baffles may be simply vertical strips attached to the vessel wall, as shown in the figure.

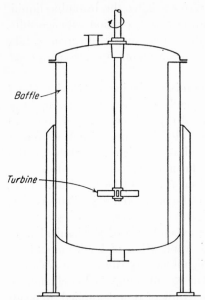

FIG. 10.1. Agitated vessel for batch or continuous extraction.

Impellers of many designs are effective, and Fig. 10.2 shows several of these. Marine-type impellers should be rotated in such a manner as to cause downward flow against the tank bottom. Turbine-type impellers provide principally radial flow and depend upon the baffles for effective vertical mixing currents. Ring baffles which may be built around the turbine are effective but usually result in such extensive shear of the liquids that stable emulsions may result; they are generally avoided in this service. The impeller diameter is usually about one-third that of the vessel, and the shaft is best placed along the vessel axis.

*Batch Operation.* For batch operation the vessel may be covered to prevent evaporation of the contents, but ordinarily there will be an air space above the liquids. The liquid depth is best kept equal to or somewhat greater than the vessel diameter.

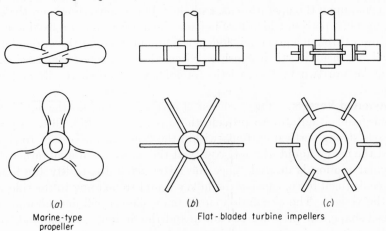

(a)
Marine-type
propeller

(b)          (c)
Flat-bladed turbine impellers

FIG. 10.2. Mixing impellers.

Impellers may be placed between one impeller diameter above the bottom of the tank and a similar distance below the liquid surface, but for highest mixing effectiveness they should be below the interface of the settled liquids after agitation is stopped.[14]  It has been established that four equally spaced vertical baffles, arranged radially, of length equal to the liquid depth and width equal to one-tenth the tank diameter provide a "fully baffled" condition.[12]  Less baffling may invite swirl and vortexing, with consequent ineffective use of power, while additional baffling produces no great advantage.  Estimates of the power required for various impeller designs may be made from the correlation of Rushton et al.[18]

The agitated vessel itself may be used for settling the liquids, and after agitation has been stopped and stratification has occurred, the more dense liquid may be withdrawn from the bottom.

*Continuous Operation.*  The two liquids to be contacted are continuously introduced into the bottom of the vessel, and the emulsion or dispersion is withdrawn at the top, with continuous agitation.  There is no air space in the vessel under these conditions, and the flow of liquids past the top surface of the vessel produces different circulation currents from those in the case of a partly filled vessel.  The minimum conditions for fully baffled agitation are known to be more extensive than in the case of a partly filled vessel[7] but have not yet been established.

In most well-designed agitated vessels, the mixing is very effective and the agitated contents are very uniformly mixed throughout.  The average concentration in each of the two phases is almost the same as that in the effluent liquids, and consequently the concentration-difference driving force for interphase mass transfer is relatively small.  For this reason, several vessels in series may be used, or a single vessel may be divided into two or three smaller compartments by horizontal plates with central openings for passage of liquid from one compartment to the next.  Extensive mixing in the direction parallel to the axis of the tank is thus prevented, and only in the final compartment are the concentrations substantially the same as in the effluent liquids.

**Flow Mixers.**  The power required for dispersion by flow mixers, or "line mixers," comes from pumping the liquids through the device.  They have small volumes and consequently provide little holding time.  They are especially useful for liquids of low viscosity and low interfacial tension, for which dispersion is not difficult.

Several types are shown in Fig. 10.3.  Jet mixers depend for their action upon impingement of one liquid, which is caused to flow through a small opening, upon the other when both are pumped into the mixer.  Mixing nozzles and orifices bring about mixing and dispersion by causing great turbulence when both liquids are pumped through the device.  Each of these devices is effective and inexpensive to install but may incur high pressure drop and consequently may be expensive to operate.

**Emulsions.** The mixture of liquids issuing from any mixing device, an emulsion, consists of small droplets of one liquid dispersed throughout a continuum of the other. The stability, or permanence, of the emulsion is of the utmost importance in liquid extraction, since it is necessary to separate the phases at each extraction stage. Stable emulsions, those

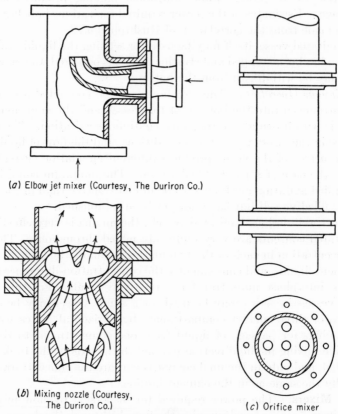

(*a*) Elbow jet mixer (Courtesy, The Duriron Co.)

(*b*) Mixing nozzle (Courtesy,
The Duriron Co.)

(*c*) Orifice mixer

Fig. 10.3. Flow mixers.

which do not settle and coalesce rapidly, must be avoided. For an emulsion to "break," or separate into its phases in bulk, both sedimentation and coalescence of the dispersed phase must occur.

The rate of sedimentation of a quiescent emulsion is the more rapid if the size of the droplets and the density difference of the liquids are large and if the viscosity of the continuous phase is small. Stable emulsions, those which settle only over long periods of time, are usually formed when the diameter of the dispersed droplets is of the order of 1 to 1.5 microns, whereas dispersions of particle diameter 1 mm. or larger usually sedimentate rapidly.

Coalescence of the settled droplets is the more rapid the higher the interfacial tension. Interfacial tension is ordinarily low for liquids of high mutual solubility and is lowered by the presence of emulsifying or wetting agents. In addition, high viscosity of the continuous phase hinders coalescence by reducing the rate at which the residual film between drops is removed. Dust particles, which usually accumulate at the interface between liquids, also hinder coalescence.

In the case of an unstable emulsion, after agitation has stopped, the mixture settles and coalesces rapidly into two liquid phases unless the viscosity is high. The appearance of a sharply defined interface between

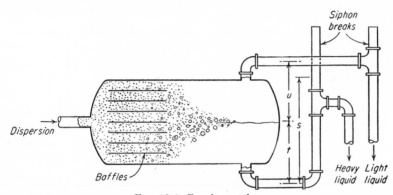

Fig. 10.4. Gravity settler.

the phases (primary break) is usually very rapid, but one of the phases, ordinarily that in the majority, may remain clouded by a very fine fog or haze, a dispersion of the other phase. The cloud will eventually settle and leave the clouded phase clear (secondary break), but this may take a considerable time. The primary break of an unstable emulsion is usually so rapid that merely stopping agitation for a very short time, a matter of minutes, is sufficient to bring it about. In continuous multistage operation, it is usually impractical to hold the mixture between stages long enough to attain the secondary break.

**Settlers.** In continuous extraction, the dispersion from the mixer is allowed to flow through a vessel of sufficient size so that the time of residence is great enough to permit primary break. The cross section of such a device should be large so that turbulence is reduced to a minimum. An empty vessel may be employed, but baffles are often included, as in Fig. 10.4. Horizontal baffles reduce turbulence and also the distance through which the dispersed droplets must settle before coalescence. Other more elaborate devices are also in use.[20]

Neglecting the pressure drop for flow through the exit pipes, which should be kept to a minimum, the level of the interface within the settler

(Fig. 10.4) will adjust itself so that

$$s\rho_H = t\rho_L + u\rho_H \tag{10.1}$$

For operation under pressure and with elimination of the siphon vents, a liquid-level controller activated by the interface position and operating a regulating valve in the exit pipe for the heavy liquid may be used.

Continuous centrifuges are sometimes used for decreasing the settling time, but they will not influence in any way the rate of coalescence of the settled dispersed phase. The latter may be assisted by causing the emulsion to flow through a bed of porous substance which is preferentially wetted by the dispersed phase. Glass fibers, steel wool, and coarse wire

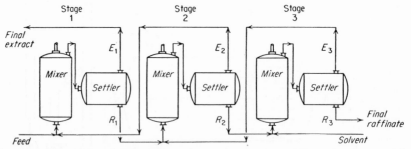

FIG. 10.5. Flow sheet of three-stage countercurrent mixer-settler extraction cascade.

mesh have been successfully used as coalescers, and these should be placed upstream from the settling vessel.

**Multistage Extraction.** A continuous multistage extraction plant will consist of the required number of stages arranged according to the desired flow sheet. Each stage will consist of at least a mixer and a settler, as in the countercurrent plant of Fig. 10.5. The liquids will generally be pumped from one stage to the next, but occasionally gravity flow can be arranged if sufficient headroom is available.

### MULTISTAGE EQUIPMENT

When the contacted liquids are made to flow countercurrently through a single piece of equipment, the equivalent of as many stages may be had as desired. In such devices the countercurrent flow is produced by virtue of the difference in densities of the liquids, and with few exceptions the equipment takes the form of a vertical tower which may or may not contain internal devices to influence the flow pattern. As in the case of gas-liquid contact, the cross-sectional area for flow is governed by the quantity of liquids to be handled and the limiting velocities, while the length of the flow path is a function of the number of stages required.

Depending upon the nature of the internal structure, the equipment may be of the stagewise or continuous-contact type.

**Spray Towers.** These, the simplest of the continuous-contact devices, consist merely of an empty vertical shell with provisions for introducing and removing the liquids. Refer to Fig. 10.6a, where operation is shown with the light liquid dispersed. Heavy liquid enters at the top, fills the tower completely (continuous phase), and flows out at the bottom. Light liquid enters at the bottom through a distributor which disperses

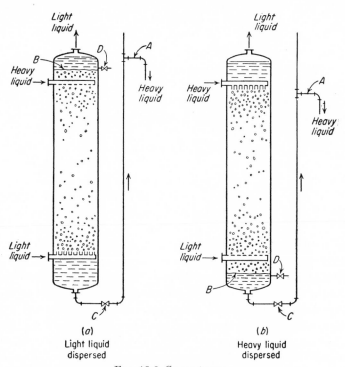

(a) Light liquid dispersed

(b) Heavy liquid dispersed

FIG. 10.6. Spray tower.

it into small droplets. These rise through the downward-flowing heavy liquid and coalesce into a layer at the top. The heavy liquid is shown leaving through a looped pipe $A$, and the head of heavy liquid at the bottom of the pipe (static pressure + friction resulting from flow) must balance the head of combined light and heavy liquids in the tower. In this manner the interface $B$ is maintained in the position shown. The position of the interface may be regulated by the elevation of $A$, but it is more satisfactorily controlled in large-scale equipment by the valve $C$, which may be operated by a liquid-level controller actuated by the position of the interface itself. The tap $D$ is used periodically to withdraw scum and dust particles which accumulate at the interface and interfere with coalescence of the droplets of dispersed liquid. The exit streams from this and other types of countercurrent towers are frequently passed through settlers of the sort shown in Fig. 10.4, to remove entrained droplets from the product liquids.

By reducing the height of pipe $A$ or by opening the valve $C$ the interface may be lowered to the position shown in Fig. 10.6$b$. The heavy liquid is now dispersed and the light liquid continuous. As an additional alternative the interface may be located more or less centrally in the tower. Usually that liquid is dispersed which must flow in the largest volume rate, since in this way the largest interfacial surface will result for a given drop size.

The spray tower is inexpensive to build, easy to keep clean, and has high flow capacities. The freedom with which the continuous phase can circulate from top to bottom leads to a reduced extraction efficiency by destruction of the true countercurrent concentration differences between the phases, however. The towers will be most efficient if the length/diameter ratio is large, and to produce this effect for large quantities of liquids, several narrow towers in parallel may be used. Alternatively internal vertical partitions may be built into a single shell.

Consider operation as it is shown in Fig. 10.6$a$. The linear velocity of heavy liquid must be kept below the rising velocity of the light droplets; else the latter will be swept out through the bottom pipe. Suppose, however, the heavy liquid is kept fixed at some moderate flow rate, while the rate of flow of dispersed liquid is slowly increased. Droplets will form at the distributor more and more frequently and will tend to crowd each other as they rise. The reduction in the available space for flow of heavy liquid causes it to move at higher linear velocities, which in turn reduces the rate of rise of the droplets. The hold-up of dispersed phase, or the fraction of the active volume of the tower occupied by the dispersed liquid, will therefore increase. Increased pressure drop for flow of light liquid out the top of the tower tends to lower the interface $B$. This may be counteracted at moderate rates of flow by increasing the pressure drop through valve $C$ by closing it slightly. But as the rate is increased further, the tower will tend to fill with light liquid, large eddy currents develop, and the flow regime in the tower becomes very chaotic. Large quantities of light liquid may be carried out pipe $A$, the tower is *flooded*, and satisfactory operation is impossible. Reduced area for flow at the liquid distributors frequently aggravates the situation. The flooded condition may actually be brought about by increasing the flow rate of either phase, and for each rate of flow of light liquid there is a rate for the heavy liquid which results in flooding. The same conditions can arise in the tower of Fig. 10.6$b$.

The tower design due to Elgin[2] (Fig. 10.7) alleviates much of the difficulty owing to restricted flow area at the points of introducing the liquids, and much higher flow rates are possible than with straight-sided towers. As shown, it is arranged for light liquid dispersed, but it may be turned upside down for dispersing the heavy liquid. With such a tower, flooding is characterized by high hold-up of dispersed phase in the column, with the mass of drops extending down to the top of the flared, funnel-shaped base. Operation at flooding can actually be tolerated, but at somewhat higher rates of flow the mass of drops will extend to the lowest and widest part of the flared section and the limit of flow will have been reached.

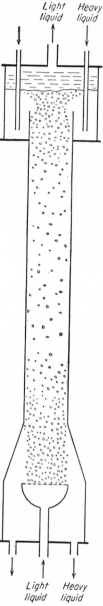

**Limiting Flow Rates in Spray Towers.** Minard and Johnson,[15] in studying the flow capacities of a 4-in.-diameter laboratory extraction spray tower of the Elgin design, observed that for any system

$$V_{Cf}^{1/2} + b V_{Df}^{1/2} = n \qquad (10.2)$$

where $V_{Cf}$ and $V_{Df}$ are the superficial linear velocities of the continuous and dispersed liquids at flooding and $b$ and $n$ are constants. Flooding was defined as that velocity which caused the mass of dispersed-phase droplets to extend to the base of the flared end of the tower. The quantities $b$ and $n$ were related empirically to the physical properties of the liquids and the drop diameters $d_p$. By very slight adjustment of the empirical constants, insufficient to cause significant variation in the calculated velocities, their empirical expression may be written in simpler form,†

$$V_{Cf} = \frac{10,000\ \Delta\rho^{0.28}}{[0.483\mu_C^{'0.075}\rho_C^{0.5} + d_p^{0.056}\rho_D^{0.5}(V_D/V_C)^{0.5}]^2} \qquad (10.3)$$

or
$$V_{Cf} = \frac{10,000\ \Delta\rho^{0.28}}{\rho_C[0.483\mu_C^{'0.075} + d_p^{0.056}(L_D/L_C)^{0.5}]^2} \qquad (10.4)$$

In view of the small size of the experimental tower and of the definition of flooding used, it would seem particularly wise to employ rather generous safety factors in applying this to larger equipment, especially if the flared inlet section is not used. Flow rates corresponding to 30 to 40 per cent of the flooding values calculated by the above equations are suggested.

**Drop Formation.** The drops of dispersed liquid should, for highest flow capacities, be reasonably uniform in size so as to prevent coalescence during passage through the tower. The distributor used for drop formation may be a drilled perforated

Fig. 10.7. Spray tower of Elgin.[2]

† It is customary to use superficial velocities $V$ expressed on an hourly basis [cu. ft./-(hr.)(sq. ft.) or ft./hr.], and these are used throughout this chapter except in the empirical equation (10.5). Mass rates are indicated by $L$ lb./(hr.)(sq. ft.).

plate, provided that the dispersed phase does not preferentially wet the plate.   But to avoid wetting and consequent nonuniformity of drop size, it is best to use small nozzles which project from the flat surface to form the droplets.   These may be punched in a flat plate in the manner of Fig. 10.8, if desired.   Small nozzle diameters result in small drop size and consequently large interfacial surface and extraction rates, but also low flooding velocities and possible plugging if there is a chance of solids being suspended in the liquids.   They should not be smaller than about 0.1 in., and to avoid excessively large drops not over 0.25 in.

When the dispersed phase issues from a nozzle or perforated plate which is not preferentially wetted by the dispersed liquid, drop size will be uniform up to nozzle or perforation velocities of 0.3 ft./sec.   At higher velocities, "streamers," or jets of dispersed liquid, issue from the nozzles, and these break up at some distance from the nozzle into drops of nonuniform size.   The following empirical expresson will permit calculation of drop volumes for nozzle velocities up to 0.3 ft./sec., or the volumes of

Fig. 10.8. Punched perforations for dispersed phase.[13]

the largest drops in the range of velocities 0.3 to 1.0 ft./sec., when nozzles or perforations up to 0.31 in. diameter are used,[9]

$$v_p + 0.01255 v_p^{2/3} \frac{\rho_D V_O'^2}{\Delta \rho} = 1.41(10^{-4}) \frac{\sigma' d_O}{\Delta \rho} + \frac{0.0556 d_O^{1.12} V_O'^{0.547} \mu_C'^{0.279}}{\Delta \rho^{1.5}} \qquad (10.5)$$

where $V_O'$ indicates the nozzle velocity in ft./sec.   Figure 10.9, developed from this equation on the assumption that the drops are spherical, will permit determination of the drop diameter $d_p$ without trial-and-error computation.

**Illustration 1.**   Isopropyl ether is to be used to extract acetic acid from water in a spray tower of the Elgin design.   The flow rates are to be 180 cu. ft. ether/hr. and 120 cu. ft. aqueous solution/hr.   The physical properties are aqueous-phase density = 63.0 lb./cu. ft., viscosity = 3.1 centipoises; ether-phase density = 45.6 lb./cu. ft.; interfacial tension = 13 dynes/cm.   Determine the diameter of the tower to be used.

*Solution.*   The ether phase will be dispersed, not only because it will flow in the largest volume, but because it is desirable to have the hold-up of this very flammable liquid small.

In order to ensure uniform drop size, the velocity of the ether through the distributor nozzles will be kept to 0.3 ft./sec.   Therefore 180/3,600(0.3) = 0.167 sq. ft. total nozzle cross section.   The diameter of the nozzles will be set at $\frac{3}{16}$ in., which is sufficiently large to avoid plugging.   The internal cross section of each nozzle is 0.000191 sq. ft.   Therefore 0.167/0.000191 = 875 nozzles in the distributor.

$\sigma' = 13.0$ dynes/cm., $d_o = 3/16(12) = 0.01561$ ft., $\mu_C' = 3.1$ centipoises, $\rho_C = 63.0$ lb./cu. ft., $\rho_D = 45.6$ lb./cu. ft., $\Delta \rho = 63.0 - 45.6 = 17.4$ lb./cu. ft., $V_O' = 0.3$ ft./sec.

$$\frac{\sigma' d_O}{\Delta \rho} + \frac{396 d_O^{1.12} V_O'^{0.547} \mu_C'^{0.279}}{\Delta \rho^{1.5}} = \frac{13.0(0.01561)}{17.4} + \frac{396(0.01561)^{1.12}(0.3)^{0.547}(3.1)^{0.279}}{17.4^{1.5}}$$
$$= 0.0615$$
$$\frac{\rho_D V_O'^2}{\Delta \rho} = \frac{45.6(0.3)^2}{17.4} = 0.236$$

Fig. 10.9:
$$d_p = 0.0235 \text{ ft.}$$
$$\frac{V_D}{V_C} = \frac{180}{120} = 1.5$$

Eq. (10.3): $V_{Cf} = \dfrac{10,000(17.4)^{0.28}}{[0.483(3.1)^{0.075}(63.0)^{0.5} + (0.0235)^{0.056}(45.6)^{0.5}(1.5)^{0.5}]^2}$
$$= 187 \text{ ft./hr.}$$

For 40% of flooding, use $V_C = 0.4(187) = 74.8$ ft./hr. Cross section of tower = $120/74.8 = 1.60$ sq. ft., corresponding to a diameter of 1.43 ft.

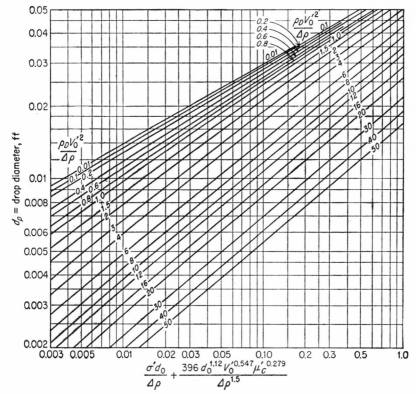

FIG. 10.9. Drop diameters for dispersion of insoluble liquids through nozzles and perforations.

Nozzles can be drilled or punched in a distributor plate, placed at the corners of squares 0.5 in. on each side.

**Packed Towers.** Towers filled with the random packings used for gas-liquid contact are employed extensively for liquid extraction. The packing serves several purposes: (1) it increases the degree of turbulence of the continuous phase, (2) by hindering the movement of the drops of dispersed liquid it continually distorts their shape and results in exposure of fresh surface to contact with the continuous liquid, and (3) it prevents the vertical recirculation of the continuous phase which gives rise to the poor extraction efficiencies of spray towers.

A typical packed tower for extraction is shown schematically in Fig. 10.10. The tower may be straight-sided as shown or fitted with expanded sections at the point of introduction of the dispersed phase as in Fig. 10.11. Either light or heavy liquids may be the dispersed phase.

The nature of the liquid flow in such towers requires that the choice of packing, arrangement of dispersed-phase distributor, and the design of the packing supports be given careful attention. If the dispersed phase preferentially wets the packing, it will

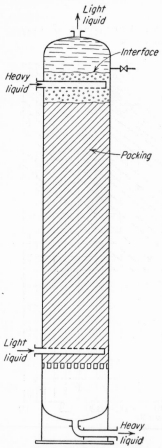

FIG. 10.10. Packed extraction tower, light liquid dispersed.

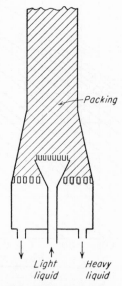

FIG. 10.11. Elgin-type packed tower, dispersed-phase inlet.

pass through in rivulets on the packing, not as droplets, and the interfacial surface between the phases will be relatively small. For this reason the packing material must be such that it is preferentially wetted by the continuous phase, whereupon the dispersed-phase droplets will retain their identity as they rise or fall through the packed bed. Under these circumstances the average diameter of the droplets in the packing is independent of the size of the drops at formation, provided the latter are above a rather small minimum size.[11] The perforations in the dispersed-phase distributor may therefore be made sufficiently large (say $\frac{3}{16}$ to $\frac{1}{4}$ in. diameter for packings of 1 in. size or larger) to ensure against plugging with suspended solids which may be present. In cases where the material of the packing support is not preferentially wetted by the dispersed-phase droplets and where the distributor is placed below the support (in the case of light liquid dispersed) the drops will have difficulty in entering the packing, and premature flooding may result. For this reason it is always desirable to embed the dispersed-phase distributor in the packing, as shown in Figs. 10.10 and 10.11. Intermediate packing supports such as those used in gas absorbers may for this reason lead to reduced flow capacities also. As in the case of gas-liquid towers the packing size should be smaller than one-eighth of the tower diameter, in order to ensure reproducible packing density in the tower.

**Flooding in Packed Towers.** Flooding in packed towers is generally characterized by increased hold-up of dispersed phase in the packing (30 to 80 per cent at flooding[8]) and a layer of dispersed phase builds up on the packing, unable to enter at the rate at which it is supplied. For each packing and system, it has been found that the quantity $V_{Cf}^{1/2} + V_{Df}^{1/2}$ equals some constant value, so that the permissible rate of flow of dispersed phase increases as the rate of the continuous phase decreases. Crawford and Wilke,[5] working with a tower of the Elgin type packed with Raschig rings, Berl saddles, and spheres in the size range 0.25 to 1.5 in., were able to correlate the value of the constant with the packing and liquid properties, and their results are shown in Fig. 10.12. It is interesting to note that the ordinate in this figure is a form of Reynolds number. Towers should be designed for flow rates not exceeding 40 to 50 per cent of the flooding values, especially if straight-sided towers are used.

**Illustration 2.** The extraction of Illustration 1 is to be performed in a tower packed with 1-in. stoneware Raschig rings, ether dispersed. Determine the diameter of tower to be used.

*Solution.* For 1-in. stoneware rings, $\epsilon = 0.685$, and $a_p/\epsilon^3 = 164$ (Table 6.2). Consequently $a_p = 164(0.685)^3 = 52.6$. Other quantities required are listed in Illustration 1.

$$\frac{\mu_C'}{\Delta\rho}\left(\frac{\sigma}{\rho_C}\right)^{0.2}\left(\frac{a_p}{\epsilon}\right)^{1.5} = \frac{3.1}{17.4}\left(\frac{13}{63.0}\right)^{0.2}\left(\frac{52.6}{0.685}\right)^{1.5} = 87.5$$

The ordinate at flooding from Fig. 10.12 is 221.

$$V_{Cf} = \frac{221a_p\mu_C'}{\left[1+\left(\dfrac{V_D}{V_C}\right)^{0.5}\right]^2 \rho_C} = \frac{221(52.6)(3.1)}{(1+1.5^{0.5})^2(63.0)} = 115.5 \text{ ft./hr.}$$

For 40% of flooding, use $V_C = 0.4(115.5) = 46.2$ ft./hr. The tower cross section is therefore $120/46.2 = 2.60$ sq. ft., corresponding to a diameter of 1.82 ft.

**Baffle Towers.** Baffle towers for liquid extraction may be of the disk-and-doughnut type (Fig. 6.19), or they may be fitted with segmental baffles. There is substantially no information regarding their effectiveness. It would be expected that their capacity for handling liquids would be intermediate between spray and packed towers. They are free of the tendency toward recirculation of the continuous phase, which limits the usefulness of spray towers, and clogging in the presence of suspended solids, which may make packed towers undesirable.

**Perforated-plate Towers.** Perforated-plate, or sieve-plate, towers have proved very effective, both with respect to liquid-handling capacity and

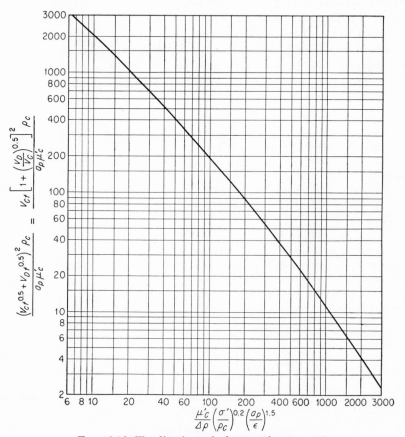

FIG. 10.12. Flooding in packed extraction towers.[5]

efficiency of extraction. A tower of simple design is shown in Fig. 10.13, where the general arrangement of plates and downspouts is much the same as for gas-liquid contact except that no weir is required. The figure shows the tower arranged for light liquid dispersed. Light liquid passes through the perforations, and the bubbles rise through the heavy continuous phase and coalesce into a layer which accumulates beneath each plate. The heavy liquid flows across each plate through the rising droplets and passes through the downspouts to the plate below. By turning the tower as shown upside down, the downspouts become "upspouts" and carry the light liquid from plate to plate, while the heavy liquid flows through the perforations and is dispersed into drops. As an alternative, the heavy liquid may be dispersed in one part of the tower and the light liquid in the other, while the principal interface is maintained in the central portion of the tower. Interface taps to remove scum accumulating at the interface may be included between each tray, or special by-passes may be arranged.[13]

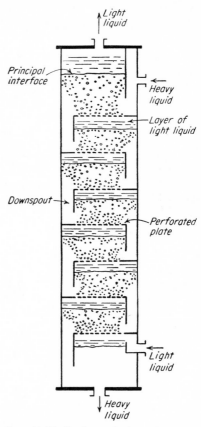

Perforation diameters of ⅛ to ¼ in. may be used, and these may either be drilled or punched (Fig. 10.8) to eliminate wetting of the plate by the dispersed liquid which interferes with drop formation. The best velocity of liquid through the perforations ought to be established by pilot-plant tests, but in the absence of experimental information it is recommended that it be kept within the range 0.4 to 1.0 ft./sec. At lower velocities the diameter of the tower will be unnecessarily large, and all perforations may not operate, while at higher velocities the many fine droplets which form will be likely to be carried from tray to tray through the downspout by the continuous phase. At the recommended velocities the liquid flowing through the perforations will probably "stream,"

FIG. 10.13. Perforated-plate extractor, arranged for light liquid dispersed.

and droplets will not form at the perforations, but rather at the end of jets which extend from the plate.

The tower will flood if excessive quantities of dispersed-phase droplets are carried through the downspout, entrained in the continuous phase. The velocity of the liquid in the downspouts, $V_d$, should therefore be lower than the settling velocity of all except the smallest droplets, those smaller than $\frac{1}{32}$ in. diameter, for example.[13] The settling velocity of the drops may be estimated approximately through Stokes' law, which applies to rigid isolated spheres settling in laminar flow,

$$V_p = \frac{g\,\Delta\rho\,d_p^2}{18\mu_C} \qquad (10.6)$$

The plate spacing should be sufficient so that (1) the "streamers" of dispersed liquid from the perforations break up into drops before coalescing into the layer of liquid on the next plate, (2) the linear velocity of the continuous liquid is not greater than that in the downspout, to avoid excessive entrainment, and (3) the tower may be entered through hand- or manholes in the sides for cleaning.

The tower will also flood if the dispersed liquid accumulates to a depth greater than the length of the downspout. The depth of dispersed liquid accumulating on each tray is determined by the pressure drop required for counterflow of the liquids,[3]

$$h = h_C + h_D \tag{10.7}$$

where $h$ is the total thickness of the layer, while $h_C$ and $h_D$ are the contributions from the flow of each liquid. The head required for the dispersed phase $h_D$ is that necessary to overcome interfacial tension effects at the perforations $h_\sigma$ plus that necessary to cause flow through the orifices $h_O$,

$$h_D = h_\sigma + h_O \tag{10.8}$$

The value of $h_O$ may be computed from the usual orifice equation with a coefficient of 0.67,

$$h_O = \frac{(V_O^2 - V_D^2)\rho_D}{2g_C(0.67)^2 \, \Delta\rho} \tag{10.9}$$

Up to perforation velocities where streaming occurs, usually about 0.4 ft./sec., $h_\sigma$ may be estimated as

$$h_\sigma = \frac{6\sigma}{d_p \, \Delta\rho} \tag{10.10}$$

For perforation velocities greater than 1.0 ft./sec., $h_D = h_O$ for all practical purposes, and for intermediate velocities the value of $h_D$ may be approximated in the manner of Illustration 3.

The head required for flow of the continuous phase $h_C$ includes losses owing to (1) friction in the downspout, which is ordinarily negligible, (2) contraction and expansion upon entering and leaving the downspout, which are substantially equal to 0.5 and 1.0 "velocity heads," respectively, and (3) the two abrupt changes in direction, which are each equivalent to 1.47 velocity heads. The value of $h_C$ is therefore substantially 4.5 velocity heads, or

$$h_C = \frac{4.5V_d^2\rho_C}{2g_C \, \Delta\rho} \tag{10.11}$$

**Illustration 3.** Design a perforated tray tower for the extraction of Illustration 1' with ether as the dispersed phase.

*Solution.* The perforations will be made $\frac{3}{16}$ in. diameter. $d_O = 3/16(12) = 0.01561$ ft., and the area of each perforation $= \pi(0.01561)^2/4 = 0.000191$ sq. ft. A perforation velocity of 0.7 ft./sec. will be used, and $V_O' = 0.7$ ft./sec., $V_O = 0.7(3,600) = 2,520$ ft./hr.

For 180 cu. ft. ether/hr., $180/2,520(0.000191) = 372$ perforations per plate. If placed on corners of $\frac{3}{4}$-in. equilateral triangles, 1.265 sq. ft. of the tower cross section must be devoted to perforations.

The velocity of the aqueous phase in the downspout will be set at the settling velocity of ether droplets of $\frac{1}{32}$ in. diameter. Therefore $d_p = 1/32(12) = 0.0026$ ft. $\mu_C = 3.1(2.42) = 7.5$ lb./(ft.)(hr.), $g = 4.17(10^8)$, $\Delta\rho = 17.4$ lb./cu. ft.

Eq. (10.6): $\qquad V_p = \dfrac{4.17(10^8)(17.4)(0.0026)^2}{18(7.5)} = 364$ ft./hr. $= V_d$

For 120 cu. ft./hr. of aqueous liquid, the downspout cross-sectional area is therefore $120/364 = 0.330$ sq. ft., and the tower cross section devoted to downspouts and perforations $= 2(0.330) + 1.265 = 1.925$ sq. ft. Keeping the perforations at least 1 in. from the walls of the tower (to allow for a ring plate support) and 1 in. from the downspouts brings the total cross section of the tower to 2.30 sq. ft., corresponding to a diameter of 1.71 ft. Therefore $V_D = 180/2.30 = 78.3$ ft./hr.; $V_C = 120/2.30 = 52.2$ ft./hr. For a tower arranged as in Fig. 10.13, the segmental downspouts are formed of chords 16.5 in. long, set at 6.1 in. from the tower center. The distance between

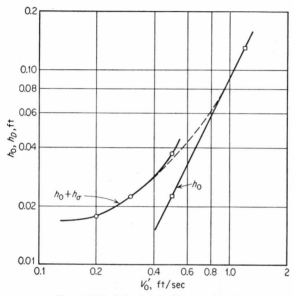

FIG. 10.14. Solution to Illustration 3.

downspout plates is therefore 12.2 in. The distance between trays will be set at 12 in., which will permit cleaning through handholes in the shell, and the downspouts will extend 6 in. below each plate.

Suppose the perforation velocity were $V_0' = 0.2$ ft./sec. Therefore the abscissa for Fig. 10.9 becomes

$$\frac{13(0.01561)}{17.4} + \frac{396(0.01561)^{1.12}(0.2)^{0.547}(3.1)^{0.279}}{17.4^{1.5}} = 0.041$$

and $\rho_D V_0'^2/\Delta\rho = 45.6(0.2)^2/17.4 = 0.105$. From Fig. 10.9, $d_p = 0.022$ ft. $\sigma = 13.0(6.85)(10^{-5}) = 0.00089$ lb./ft.

Eq. (10.10):  $h_\sigma = \dfrac{6\sigma}{d_p \, \Delta\rho} = \dfrac{6(0.00089)}{0.022(17.4)} = 0.01395$ ft.

Eq. (10.9):  $h_o = \dfrac{\{[0.2(3,600)]^2 - (78.3)^2\}45.6}{2(4.17)(10^8)(0.67)^2(17.4)} = 0.0036$ ft.

Eq. (10.8):  $h_D = h_\sigma + h_o = 0.01395 + 0.0036 = 0.01755$ ft.

Similarly,

| $V_O'$ | $h_\sigma$ | $h_O$ | $h_D$ |
|---|---|---|---|
| 0.2 | 0.01395 | 0.0036 | 0.01755 |
| 0.3 | 0.01395 | 0.00815 | 0.0221 |
| 0.5 | 0.01395 | 0.0228 | 0.0368 |
| 1.0 | . . . . . . . | 0.0910 | 0.0910 |
| 1.2 | . . . . . . . | 0.130 | 0.130 |

These values are plotted in Fig. 10.14. The calculated data are plotted as unbroken lines. Between perforation velocities of 0.4 and 1.0 ft./sec., the broken curve was sketched in to provide values of $h_D$ in the region where these cannot be calculated. From the figure, at

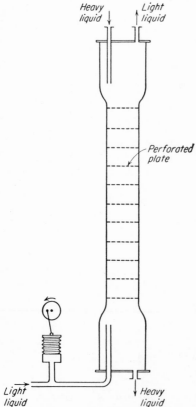

$$V_O' = 0.7 \text{ ft./sec.,} \quad h_D = 0.052 \text{ ft.}$$

Eq. (10.11): $\quad h_C = \dfrac{4.5(364)^2 63}{2(4.17)(10^8)17.4}$
$$= 0.00259 \text{ ft.}$$

Eq. (10.7): $\quad h = h_C + h_D = 0.0026$
$$+ 0.052 = 0.055 \text{ ft., or } 0.66 \text{ in.}$$

The tower will therefore not flood.

Bubble-cap tray towers, so successful for gas-liquid contact, have not been found useful for liquid extraction owing probably to the small differences in density of the liquid phases, which provide insufficient head for liquid flow, and to the low interfacial tensions.

**Pulse Columns.** The device shown in Fig. 10.15 is a very effective countercurrent extractor, at least in small sizes.[4] The perforated plates, which have no downspouts, are drilled with holes so small (of the order of 0.04 in. diameter) that ordinarily flow of the liquids would not occur. A rapid pulsating motion is superimposed upon one of the liquids by the mechanically

FIG. 10.15. Pulse column.

driven flexible diaphragm, however, and this alternately forces light and heavy liquids through the perforations. Each of the liquids is at one time or another dispersed in the other. Pulse amplitudes may be in the range 0.2 to 0.9 in. and frequencies from 15 to 75

per minute.   Packed columns may also be pulsed[6] to give enhanced
extraction rates owing to the agitation and smaller size of dispersed-phase
droplets which result.   These have been operated at as many as 1,000
pulses per minute.   For both types of equipment, the flow capacities are
lower than for conventional perforated-plate and packed towers.

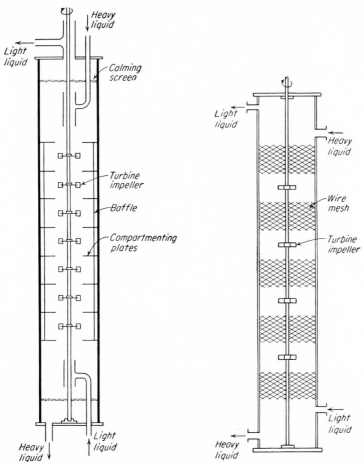

FIG. 10.16. Agitated compartmented
extractor.[16]

FIG. 10.17. Agitated extractor.[19]

**Agitated Countercurrent Extractors.**   The column of Fig. 10.16[16] uses
mechanically driven turbine mixers to disperse and mix the liquids in
each section and depends upon the horizontal baffles which separate the
sections to prevent mixing in the vertical direction.   The column of Fig.
10.17,[19] on the other hand, consists of alternate agitated spaces and sections packed with a wire mesh of high void content (97 to 98%) which

act as coalescing zones. Both devices are very effective extractors. The permissible flow rates, which depend upon agitator speeds, are smaller than those of conventional spray, perforated plate, and packed towers, however.

**Centrifugal Extractors.** The problem of obtaining the equivalent of many stages in equipment of small height and volume has led to several types of mechanically driven extractors, where the density difference responsible for the flow of liquids is enhanced by centrifugal force.

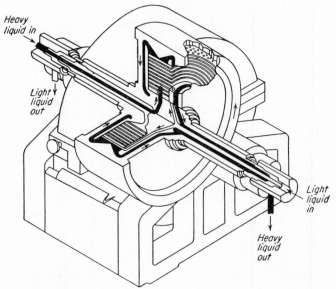

Fig. 10.18. Podbielniak centrifugal extractor (schematic). (*Courtesy of Podbielniak, Inc.*)

The *Podbielniak* extractor is one of these which has had extensive application. One design, shown schematically in Fig. 10.18, consists of a perforated plate wrapped in a spiral about a horizontal shaft which is rapidly rotated (2,000 to 5,000 r.p.m.). The liquids are pumped into the device through the shaft, and the heavy liquid is led to the center of the spiral, while the light liquid is led to the periphery. The liquids then flow countercurrently through the spiral, with some dispersion of one into the other resulting from flow through the perforations. The liquids are then removed through the shaft. The machines are also built with perforated concentric rings rather than spirals, and provision for handling suspended solids may also be had. They are especially useful for liquids which tend to emulsify easily, for those with small density differences, and where very small holding time is essential, as in some pharmaceutical applications. They are available in capacities ranging up to 25,000 gal./hr., with hold-up time of the order of seconds, and containing the equivalent of many theoretical stages, depending upon the system and operating conditions.

The *Luwesta* (or *Centri-Westa*) centrifugal extractor (Fig. 10.19) is a three-stage device built on a vertical rotating shaft through which the liquids are introduced and removed. The liquids are mixed by causing

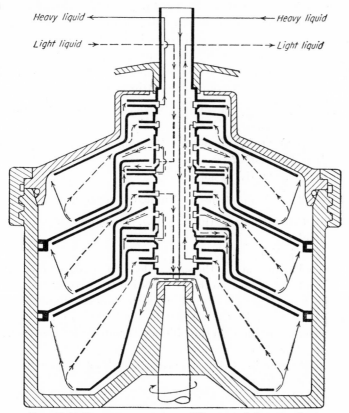

Fig. 10.19. Luwesta extractor.    (*Courtesy of Centrico, Inc.*)

them to flow through small openings in the shaft at each stage, as shown. The heavy liquid is thrown to the periphery and passes to the next stage, while the light liquid is collected at the shaft. Speeds up to 3,800 r.p.m. are used, and capacities up to 3,800 gal./hr. are possible.

## TERNARY LIQUID EQUILIBRIA

Extraction involves the use of systems composed of at least three substances, and in most cases all three components appear in appreciable concentrations in both insoluble liquid phases. The following notation scheme will be used to describe the concentrations and amounts of these ternary mixtures, for purposes of discussing both equilibria and material balances.

## Notation Scheme

1. $A$ and $B$ are pure, substantially insoluble liquids, and $C$ is the distributed solute. Mixtures to be separated by extraction are composed of $A$ and $C$, and $B$ is the extracting solvent.

2. The same letter will be used to indicate the quantity of a solution or mixture and the location of the mixture on a phase diagram. Quantities are measured in pounds for batch operations, lb./(hr.)(sq. ft. apparatus cross section) for continuous operation. Thus,

$E$ = lb./(hr.)(sq. ft.) of solution $E$, an extract, shown on a phase diagram by point $E$

$R$ = lb./(hr.)(sq. ft.) of solution $R$, a raffinate, shown on a phase diagram by point $R$

$B$ = lb./(hr.)(sq. ft.) of solvent $B$

Solvent-free ($B$-free) quantities are indicated by primed letters. Thus,

$E'$ = lb. $B$-free solution/(hr.)(sq. ft.), shown on a phase diagram by point $E$

$E = E'(1 + N_E)$

3. $x$ = weight fraction $C$ in the solvent-lean ($A$-rich), or raffinate, liquids

$y$ = weight fraction $C$ in the solvent-rich ($B$-rich), or extract, liquids

$x' = x/(1 - x)$ = lb. $C$/lb. non-$C$ in the raffinate liquids

$y' = y/(1 - y)$ = lb. $C$/lb. non-$C$ in the extract liquids

$X$ = weight fraction $C$ in the raffinate liquids on a $B$-free basis, lb. $C$/- (lb. $A$ + lb. $C$)

$Y$ = weight fraction $C$ in the extract liquids on a $B$-free basis, lb. $C$/- (lb. $A$ + lb. $C$)

$N$ = weight fraction $B$ on a $B$-free basis, lb. $B$/(lb. $A$ + lb. $C$)

Subscripts identify the solution or mixture to which the concentration terms refer. Stages are identified by number. Thus, $x_3$ = wt. fraction $C$ in the raffinate from stage 3, $Y_3$ = wt. fraction $C$ ($B$-free basis) in the extract from stage 3, etc. For other solutions identified by a letter on a phase diagram, the same letter is used as an identifying subscript. Thus, $x_M$ = wt. fraction $C$ in the mixture $M$.

An asterisk specifically identifies equilibrium concentrations where the condition of equilibrium is emphasized. Thus, $y_E^*$ = wt. fraction $C$ in the equilibrium solution $E$.

4. Throughout the discussion of equilibria, material balances, and stagewise calculations, mole fractions, mole ratios, and pound moles

may be consistently substituted for weight fractions, weight ratios, and pounds, respectively.

**Equilateral Triangular Coordinates.**    These are used extensively in the chemical literature to describe graphically the concentrations in ternary systems.    It is the property of an equilateral triangle that the sum of the perpendicular distances from any point within the triangle to the three sides equals the altitude of the triangle.    We may therefore let the altitude represent 100 per cent composition and the distances to the three sides the per cents or fractions of the three components.    Refer to Fig. 10.20.    Each apex of the triangle represents one of the pure components, as marked.    The perpendicular distance from any point such as $K$ to the base $AB$ represents the percentage of $C$ in the mixture at $K$, the distance to the base $AC$ the percentage of $B$, and that to the base $CB$ the percentage of $A$. Thus $x_K = 0.4$.    Any point on a side of the triangle represents a binary mixture.    Point $D$, for ex-

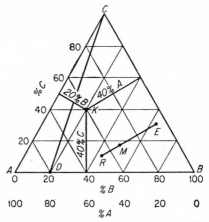

Fig. 10.20. Equilateral triangular coordinates.

ample, is a binary containing 80% $A$, 20% $B$.    All points on the line $DC$ represent mixtures containing the same ratio of $A$ to $B$ and may be considered as mixtures originally at $D$ to which $C$ has been added.    If $R$ lb. of a mixture at point $R$ is added to $E$ lb. of a mixture at $E$, the new mixture is shown on the straight line $RE$ at point $M$, such that

$$\frac{R}{E} = \frac{\text{line } ME}{\text{line } RM} = \frac{x_E - x_M}{x_M - x_R} \tag{10.12}$$

Alternatively the composition corresponding to point $M$ can be computed by material balances, as will be shown later.    Similarly, if a mixture at $M$ has removed from it a mixture of composition $E$, the new mixture is on the straight line $EM$ extended in the direction away from $E$, and located at $R$ so that Eq. (10.12) applies.

Equation (10.12) is readily established.    Refer to Fig. 10.21, which again shows $R$ lb. of mixture at $R$ added to $E$ lb. of mixture at $E$.    Let $M$ represent the pounds of new mixture as well as the composition on the figure.    Line $RL$ = wt. fraction $C$ in $R$ = $x_R$, line $MO$ = wt. fraction $C$ in $M$ = $x_M$, and line $ET$ = wt. fraction $C$ in $E$ = $x_E$.    A total material balance,

$$R + E = M$$

A balance for component $C$,

$$R(\text{line } RL) + E(\text{line } ET) = M(\text{line } MO)$$
$$Rx_R + Ex_E = Mx_M$$

Eliminating $M$,

$$\frac{R}{E} = \frac{\text{line } ET - \text{line } MO}{\text{line } MO - \text{line } RL} = \frac{x_E - x_M}{x_M - x_R}$$

But line $ET$ − line $MO$ = line $EP$, and line $MO$ − line $RL$ = line $MK$ = line $PS$. Therefore

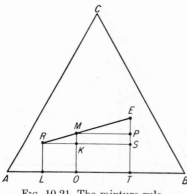

$$\frac{R}{E} = \frac{\text{line } EP}{\text{line } PS} = \frac{\text{line } ME}{\text{line } RM}$$

The following discussion is limited to those types of systems which most frequently occur in liquid-extraction operations. For a complete consideration of the very many types of systems which may be encountered, the student is referred to one of the more comprehensive texts on the phase rule.[17]

FIG. 10.21. The mixture rule.

**Systems of Three Liquids, One Pair Partially Soluble.** This is the most commonly encountered type of system in extraction, and typical examples are water $(A)$–chloroform $(B)$–acetone $(C)$, and benzene $(A)$–water $(B)$–acetic acid $(C)$. The triangular coordinates are used as *isotherms*, or diagrams at constant temperature. Refer to Fig. 10.22a. Liquid $C$ dissolves completely in $A$ and $B$, but $A$ and $B$ dissolve only to a limited extent in each other to give rise to the saturated liquid solutions at $L$ $(A$-rich) and at $K$ $(B$-rich). The more insoluble are the liquids $A$ and $B$, the nearer the apexes of the triangle will points $L$ and $K$ be located. A binary mixture $J$, anywhere between $L$ and $K$, will separate into two insoluble liquid phases of compositions at $L$ and $K$, the relative amounts of the phases depending upon the position of $J$, according to the principle of Eq. (10.12).

Curve $LRPEK$ is the binodal solubility curve, indicating the change in solubility of the $A$- and $B$-rich phases upon addition of $C$. Any mixture outside this curve will be a homogeneous solution of one liquid phase. Any ternary mixture underneath the curve, such as $M$, will form two insoluble, saturated liquid phases of equilibrium compositions indicated by $R$ $(A$-rich) and $E$ $(B$-rich). The line $RE$ joining these equilibrium compositions is a tie line, which must necessarily pass through point $M$ representing the mixture as a whole. There are an infinite number of tie lines in the two-phase region, and only a few are shown. They are rarely parallel and usually change their slope slowly in one direction as shown. In a relatively few systems the direction of the tie-line slope changes, and one tie line will be horizontal. Such systems are said to be "solutropic." Point $P$, the *plait point*, the last of the tie lines and the point where the $A$-rich and $B$-rich solubility curves merge, is ordinarily not at the maximum value of $C$ on the solubility curve.

The percentage of $C$ in solution $E$ is clearly greater than that in $R$, and it is said that in this case the distribution of $C$ favors the $B$-rich phase. This is conveniently shown on the distribution diagram (Fig. 10.22$b$), where the point $E$, $R$ lies above the diagonal $y = x$. The ratio

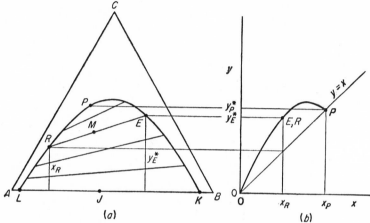

FIG. 10.22. System of three liquids, $A$ and $B$ partially soluble.

$y^*/x$, the *distribution coefficient*, is in this case greater than unity. The concentrations of $C$ at the ends of the tie lines, when plotted against each other, give rise to the distribution curve shown. Should the tie lines on Fig. 10.22$a$ slope in the opposite direction, with $C$ favoring $A$ at equilibrium, the distribution curve will lie below the diagonal. The distribution curve may be used for interpolating between tie lines when only a few have been experimentally determined. Other methods of interpolation are also available.[20]

*Effect of Temperature.* To show the effect of temperature in detail requires a three-dimensional figure, as in Fig. 10.23$a$. In this diagram, temperature is plotted vertically, and the isothermal triangles are seen to be sections through the prism. For most systems of this type, the mutual solubility of $A$ and $B$ increases with increasing temperature, and, above some temperature $t_4$, the critical solution temperature, they dissolve completely. The increased solubility at higher temperatures influences the ternary equilibria considerably, and this is best shown by projection of the isotherms onto the base triangle as in Fig. 10.23$b$. Not only does the area of heterogeneity decrease at higher temperatures, but the slopes of the tie lines may also change.   Liquid-extraction operations, which depend upon the formation of insoluble liquid phases, must be carried on at temperatures below $t_4$.   Other temperature effects, which are less common, are also known.[17,20]

*Effect of Pressure.*   Except at very high pressures, the influence of pressure on the liquid equilibrium is so small that it may generally be ignored.   All the diagrams shown are therefore to be considered as having been plotted at sufficiently high pressure to maintain a completely

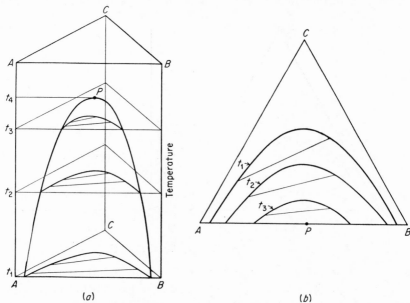

(a)                                                   (b)

Fig. 10.23. Effect of temperature on ternary equilibria.

condensed system, i.e., above the vapor pressures of the solutions.   However, should the pressure be sufficiently reduced so that it becomes less than the vapor pressure of the solutions, a vapor phase will appear and the liquid equilibrium will be interrupted.   Such an effect on a binary solubility curve of the type $APB$ of Fig. 10.23a is shown in Fig. 9.8.

**Systems of Three Liquids, Two Pairs Partially Soluble.**   This type is exemplified by the system chlorobenzene $(A)$–water $(B)$–methyl ethyl ketone $(C)$, where $A$ and $C$ are completely soluble, while the pairs $A$-$B$ and $B$-$C$ show only limited solubility.   Refer to Fig. 10.24a, a typical isotherm.   At the prevailing temperature, points $K$ and $J$ represent the mutual solubilities of $A$ and $B$ and points $H$ and $L$ those of $B$ and $C$. Curves $KRH$ ($A$-rich) and $JEL$ ($B$-rich) are the ternary solubility curves, and mixtures outside the band between these curves form homogeneous single-phase liquid solutions.   Mixtures such as $M$, inside the hetero-

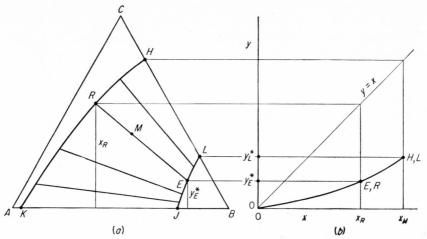

FIG. 10.24. System of three liquids, *A-B* and *B-C* partially soluble.

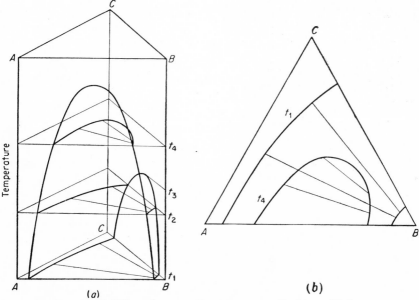

FIG. 10.25. Effect of temperature on ternary liquid equilibria.

geneous area, form two liquid phases at equilibrium at $E$ and $R$, joined on the diagram by a tie line. The corresponding distribution curve is shown in Fig. 10.24*b*.

*Effect of Temperature.* Increased temperature usually increases the mutual solubilities and at the same time influences the slope of the tie lines. Figure 10.25 is typical of the effect that may be expected. Above the critical solution temperature of the binary *B-C* at $t_3$, the system is similar to the first type discussed. Other temperature effects are also possible.[17,20]

**Systems of Two Partially Soluble Liquids and One Solid.** When the solid does not form compounds such as hydrates with the liquids, the

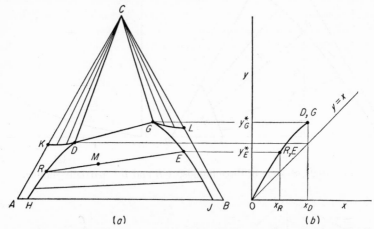

(a)                    (b)

FIG. 10.26. System of two partially soluble liquids ($A$, $B$) and one solid ($C$).

system will frequently have the characteristics of the isotherm of Fig. 10.26, an example of which is the system naphthalene ($C$)–aniline ($A$)–isooctane ($B$). Solid $C$ dissolves in liquid $A$ to form a saturated solu-

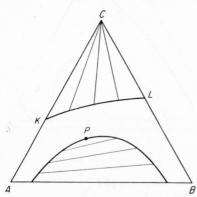

FIG. 10.27. System of two partially soluble liquids ($A$, $B$) and one solid ($C$).

tion at $K$ and in liquid $B$ to give the saturated solution at $L$. $A$ and $B$ are soluble only to the extent shown at $H$ and $J$. Mixtures in the regions $AKDH$ and $BLGJ$ are homogeneous liquid solutions. The curves $KD$ and $GL$ show the effect of adding $A$ and $B$ upon the solubilities of the solid. In the region $HDGJ$ two liquid phases form: if $C$ is added to the insoluble liquids $H$ and $J$ to give a mixture $M$, the equilibrium liquid phases will be $R$ and $E$, joined by a tie line. All mixtures in the region $CDG$ consist of three phases, solid $C$, and saturated liquid solutions at $D$ and $G$. Liquid-extraction operations are usually confined to the region of the two liquid phases, which is that corresponding to the distribution curve shown.

Increased temperature frequently changes these systems to the configuration shown in Fig. 10.27.

**Other Coordinates.**   Because the equilibrium relationship can rarely be expressed algebraically with any convenience, extraction computations must usually be made graphically on a phase diagram.   The coordinate scales of equilateral triangles are necessarily always the same, and in order to be able to expand one concentration scale relative to the other, rectangular coordinates may be used.   One of these is formed by plotting concentrations of $B$ as abscissa against concentrations of $C$ ($x$ and $y$) as ordinate, as in Fig. 10.28$a$.   Unequal scales may be used in order to expand the plot as desired.   Equation (10.12) applies for mixtures on Fig. 10.28$a$, regardless of any inequality of the scales.

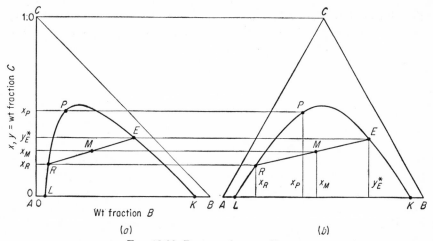

FIG. 10.28. Rectangular coordinates.

Another rectangular-coordinate system involves plotting as abscissa the weight fraction of $C$ on a $B$-free basis, $X$ and $Y$ in the $A$-rich and $B$-rich phases, respectively, against the $B$ concentration on a $B$-free basis, $N$, as ordinate, as shown in Fig. 10.29$a$.   The numerical relationship between this and the triangular coordinates shown in Fig. 10.29$b$ for comparison is not direct, but the appearances of the two diagrams are somewhat similar, as shown.   The mixture rule on these rectangular coordinates is

$$\frac{R'}{E'} = \frac{\text{line } ME}{\text{line } RM} = \frac{Y_E - X_M}{X_M - X_R} = \frac{N_E - N_M}{N_M - N_R} \qquad (10.13)$$

where $R'$ and $E'$ are the $B$-free weights of these mixtures.

**Choice of Solvent.**   There is usually a wide choice among liquids to be used as solvents for extraction operations.   It is unlikely that any particular liquid will exhibit all the properties considered desirable for extraction, and some compromise is usually necessary.   The following are the quantities to be given consideration in making a choice:

**1. *Selectivity.*** The effectiveness of solvent $B$ for separating a solution of $A$ and $C$ into its components is measured by comparing the ratio of $C$ to $A$ in the $B$-rich phase to that in the $A$-rich phase at equilibrium. The ratio of the ratios, the separation factor, or selectivity, $\beta$, is analogous to the relative volatility of distillation. If $E$ and $R$ are the equilibrium phases,

$$\beta = \frac{(\text{wt. fraction } C \text{ in } E)/(\text{wt. fraction } A \text{ in } E)}{(\text{wt. fraction } C \text{ in } R)/(\text{wt. fraction } A \text{ in } R)}$$
$$= \frac{y_E^*(\text{wt. fraction } A \text{ in } R)}{x_R(\text{wt. fraction } A \text{ in } E)} \quad (10.14)$$

For all useful extraction operations the selectivity must exceed unity, the more so the better. If the selectivity is unity, no separation is possible.

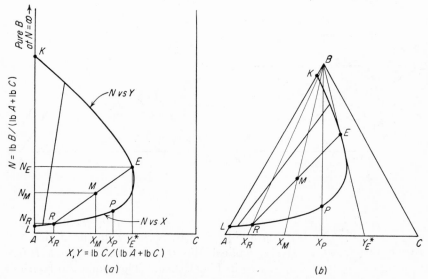

FIG. 10.29. Rectangular coordinates, solvent-free basis.

Selectivity usually varies considerably with solute concentration, and in systems of the type shown in Fig. 10.22 it will be unity at the plait point. In some systems it passes from large values through unity to fractional values, and these are analogous to azeotropic systems of distillation.

**2. *Distribution Coefficient.*** This is the ratio $y^*/x$ at equilibrium. While it is not necessary that the distribution coefficient be larger than 1, large values are very desirable since less solvent will then be required for the extraction.

**3. *Insolubility of Solvent.*** Refer to Fig. 10.30. For both systems shown, only those $A$-$C$ mixtures between $D$ and $A$ can be separated by use of the solvents $B$ or $B'$, since mixtures richer in $C$ will not form two liquid phases with the solvents. Clearly the solvent in Fig. 10.30$a$, which is the more insoluble of the two, will be the more useful.

4. *Recoverability.* It is always necessary to recover the solvent for reuse, and this must ordinarily be done by another of the mass-transfer operations, most frequently distillation. If distillation is to be used, the solvent should form no azeotrope with the extracted solute and mixtures should show high relative volatility for low-cost recovery. That substance in the extract, either solvent or solute, which is present as the

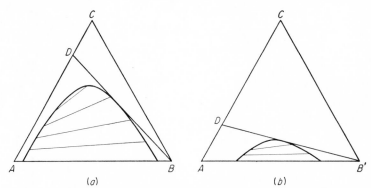

Fig. 10.30. Influence of solvent solubility on extraction.

lesser quantity should be the more volatile in order to reduce heat costs. If the solvent must be volatilized, its latent heat of vaporization should be small.

5. *Density.* A difference in densities of the saturated liquid phases is necessary, both for stagewise and continuous-contact equipment operation. The larger this difference the better. In systems of the type shown in Fig. 10.22, the density difference for equilibrium phases will become less as $C$ concentrations increase and will be zero at the plait point. It may reverse in sign before reaching the plait point, in which case continuous-contact equipment cannot be specified to operate at the concentrations at which the density difference passes through zero.

6. *Interfacial Tension.* The larger the interfacial tension, the more readily will coalescence of emulsions occur, but the more difficult will the dispersion of one liquid in the other be. Coalescence is usually of greater importance, and interfacial tension should therefore be high. Interfacial tension between equilibrium phases in systems of the type shown in Fig. 10.22 falls to zero at the plait point.

7. *Chemical Reactivity.* The solvent should be stable chemically and inert toward the other components of the system and toward the common materials of construction.

8. *Viscosity, Vapor Pressure, and Freezing Point.* These should be low for ease in handling and storage.

The solvent should be *nontoxic, nonflammable,* and of *low cost.*

## STAGEWISE CONTACT

Extraction in equipment of the stage type may be carried on according to a variety of flow sheets, depending upon the nature of the system

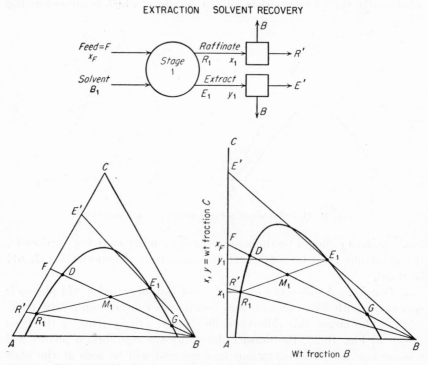

FIG. 10.31. Single-stage extraction, followed by solvent recovery.

and the extent of separation desired. In the discussion which follows it is to be understood that each stage is a *theoretical* or *ideal* stage, such that the effluent extract and raffinate solutions are in equilibrium with each other. Each stage must include facilities for contacting the insoluble liquids and separating the product streams. A combination of a mixer and a settler may therefore constitute a stage, and in multistage operation these may be arranged in cascades as desired. In the case of countercurrent multistage operation, it is also possible to use towers of the multistage type, as described earlier.

**Single-stage Extraction.** This may be a batch or a continuous operation. Refer to Fig. 10.31. The flow sheet shows the extraction stage and the solvent-recovery operations as well. Feed $F$ lb. (if a batch operation) or $F$ lb./(hr.)(sq. ft.) (if a continuous operation) contains substances $A$ and $C$ at wt. fraction $C = x_F$. This is contacted with $B_1$ lb. [or lb./(hr.)(sq. ft.)] of solvent $B$, to give the equilibrium extract $E_1$ and raffinate $R_1$, each measured in pounds or lb./(hr.)(sq. ft.). This completes the extraction operation. Solvent recovery then involves the separate removal of solvent $B$ from each product stream to give the solvent-free products $E'$ and $R'$.

The operation may be followed on either of the phase diagrams as shown. Adding $B_1$ to $F$ produces in the extraction stage a mixture $M_1$, which on settling forms the equilibrium phases $E_1$ and $R_1$ joined by the tie line through $M_1$. A total material balance on the extractor is

$$F + B_1 = M_1 = R_1 + E_1 \qquad (10.15)$$

and point $M_1$ may be located on the line $FB$ by the mixture rule of Eq. (10.12), but it is usually more satisfactory to locate $M_1$ by calculating its $C$ concentration. Thus, a $C$ balance provides

$$Fx_F = M_1 x_{M1} \qquad (10.16)$$

and

$$x_{M1} = \frac{Fx_F}{M_1} = \frac{Fx_F}{F + B_1} \qquad (10.17)$$

Alternatively the amount of solvent necessary to provide a given location for $M_1$ on the line $FB$ can be computed,

$$B_1 = \frac{F(x_F - x_{M1})}{x_{M1}} \qquad (10.18)$$

Since two insoluble phases must be formed for extraction operations, the point $M_1$ must lie within the heterogeneous-liquid area, as shown. The minimum amount of solvent which can be used is thus found by locating $M_1$ at $D$, which will then provide an infinitesimal amount of extract, and the maximum amount of solvent is found by locating $M_1$ at $G$, which provides an infinitesimal amount of raffinate.

The quantities of extract and raffinate may be computed by the mixture rule of Eq. (10.12), or by a material balance for substance $C$,

$$E_1 y_1 + R_1 x_1 = M_1 x_{M1} \qquad (10.19)$$

$$E_1 = \frac{M_1(x_{M1} - x_1)}{y_1 - x_1} \qquad (10.20)$$

and $R_1$ can be determined through Eq. (10.15).

Removal of solvent from $E_1$ and $R_1$ provides $E'$ and $R'$ on the base $AC$, and the entire operation has thus separated the feed $F$ into the products $R'$ and $E'$. The weights of the latter may be found by the mixture rule or by the balances,

$$F = R' + E' \tag{10.21}$$

$$E' = \frac{F(x_F - x'_R)}{x'_E - x'_R} \tag{10.22}$$

The maximum percentage of $C$ in the extract $E_1$ will result when the minimum solvent is used ($M_1$ at $D$), but the maximum in the final product $E'$ will result when the solvent-removal operation is represented by a line $E'B$ tangent to the solubility curve. The maximum concentration of $A$ in $R'$ or in $R_1$ will result when the maximum solvent is used ($M_1$ at $G$).

Computations for systems having two insoluble-liquid pairs are made in exactly the same manner, as shown in Fig. 10.32, and Eqs. (10.15) to

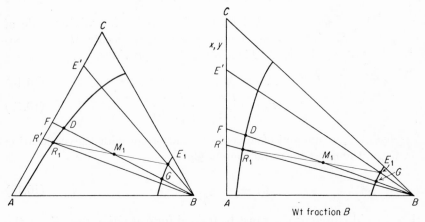

Fig. 10.32. Single-stage extraction and solvent recovery.

(10.22) all apply. The maximum purities of final extract $E'$ and final raffinate $R'$ are seen, however, to be limited by the location of the feed $F$. Minimum solvent ($M_1$ at $D$) provides maximum purity of extract, and maximum solvent ($M_1$ at $G$) provides maximum purity of raffinate.

All the computations may also be made on the solvent-free basis, as in the upper part of Fig. 10.33, if the nature of this diagram makes it convenient. Since solvent $B_1$ is represented by $N = \infty$ and addition of solvent to the feed does not change the solvent-free concentration, the addition of solvent to feed is represented by a vertical line through $F$. Products $E_1$ and $R_1$ lie on a tie line through point $M_1$ representing the mixture in the extractor as a whole. Removal of solvent from the products is shown by vertical lines, as at $E_1E'$ and $R_1R'$.

Material balances may be made as before, but $B$-free weights must be used. Thus, $F = F'$, $R'_1 = R'$, $E'_1 = E'$. A total material ($B$-free) balance is

$$F' = M'_1 = R'_1 + E'_1 \qquad (10.23)$$

A balance for $C$,

$$F'X_F = M'_1 X_{M1} \qquad (10.24)$$

or

$$X_F = X_{M1} \qquad (10.25)$$

A balance for $B$,

$$B_1 = N_{M1}F' \qquad (10.26)$$

or

$$N_{M1} = \frac{B_1}{F} \qquad (10.27)$$

Equations (10.25) and (10.27) permit location of $M_1$ on the diagram. By similar balances there are obtained

$$\frac{R'_1}{E'_1} = \frac{R'}{E'} = \frac{Y_1 - X_{M1}}{X_{M1} - X_1} \qquad (10.28)$$

and

$$E'_1 = E' = \frac{M'_1(X_{M1} - X_1)}{Y_1 - X_1} \qquad (10.29)$$

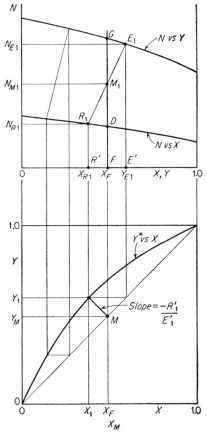

Whichever phase diagram is the most convenient to work with is used. Usually the solvent-free coordinates are most convenient for systems containing two pairs of insoluble liquids.

The lower part of Fig. 10.33 shows a transformation of the computations to $X$, $Y$ coordinates. The tie lines provide the equilibrium curve $Y^*$ vs. $X$, and the extraction is shown by the operating line of slope $-R'_1/E'_1$. The resemblance to the flash-vaporization diagram (Fig. 9.13) is obvious, with the addition of solvent to the feed replacing the addition of heat.

Fig. 10.33. Single-stage extraction, solvent-free coordinates.

**Illustration 4.** One hundred pounds of a solution of acetic acid ($C$)–water ($A$) containing 30% acetic acid is to be extracted in a single stage with 120 lb. of isopropyl ether ($B$) at 20°C. Compute the weights and compositions of the products.

*Solution.* The equilibrium data at 20°C. are listed below [from *Trans. Am. Inst. Chem. Engrs.*, **36**, 628 (1940), with permission]. The horizontal rows give the concentrations in equilibrium solutions.

| Water layer | | | Isopropyl ether layer | | |
|---|---|---|---|---|---|
| Wt. % acetic acid 100$x$ | Water | Isopropyl ether | Acetic acid 100$y^*$ | Water | Isopropyl ether |
| 0.69 | 98.1 | 1.2 | 0.18 | 0.5 | 99.3 |
| 1.41 | 97.1 | 1.5 | 0.37 | 0.7 | 98.9 |
| 2.89 | 95.5 | 1.6 | 0.79 | 0.8 | 98.4 |
| 6.42 | 91.7 | 1.9 | 1.93 | 1.0 | 97.1 |
| 13.30 | 84.4 | 2.3 | 4.82 | 1.9 | 93.3 |
| 25.50 | 71.1 | 3.4 | 11.40 | 3.9 | 84.7 |
| 36.70 | 58.9 | 4.4 | 21.60 | 6.9 | 71.5 |
| 44.30 | 45.1 | 10.6 | 31.10 | 10.8 | 58.1 |
| 46.40 | 37.1 | 16.5 | 36.20 | 15.1 | 48.7 |

Computations will be made on triangular coordinates, and the data are plotted in Fig. 10.34. The equilibrium concentrations of acid are also plotted in the form of a distribution curve ($x$ vs. $y^*$, not shown) to facilitate tie-line interpolation.

$$F = 100 \text{ lb.} \quad x_F = 0.30 \text{ wt. fraction acid} \quad B_1 = 120 \text{ lb.}$$

Eq. (10.15): $\quad M_1 = 100 + 120 = 220 \text{ lb.}$

Eq. (10.17): $\quad x_{M1} = 100(0.30)/220 = 0.1364$

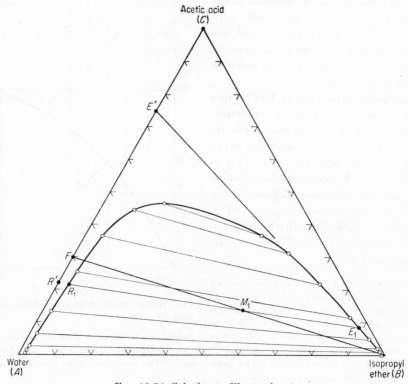

FIG. 10.34. Solution to Illustration 4.

Point $F$ is plotted on the base $AC$ and point $M_1$ on the line $FB$. Equilibrium values of $x_1$ and $y_1$ are obtained from the distribution curve so that a tie line between $E_1$ (at $y_1$) and $R_1$ (at $x_1$) passes through $M_1$. By trial, this results in $x_1 = 0.215$ wt. fraction $C$ in the raffinate and $y_1 = 0.085$ in the extract.

Eq. (10.20): $\qquad E_1 = 220(0.1364 - 0.215)/(0.085 - 0.215) = 133$ lb.
Eq. (10.15): $\qquad R_1 = 220 - 133 = 87$ lb.

The concentration of acid in the final extract and raffinate is found by extending line $BE_1$ to $E'$ and line $BR_1$ to $R'$. Thus $x_{E'} = 0.746$, $X_{R'} = 0.222$ wt. fraction acetic acid.

Eq. (10.22): $\qquad E' = 100(0.30 - 0.222)/(0.746 - 0.222) = 14.9$ lb.
Eq. (10.21): $\qquad R' = 100 - 14.9 = 85.1$ lb.

The extracted acetic acid $= E'x_{E'} = E_1y_1 = 11.2$ lb.

**Multistage Cocurrent Extraction.** This is an extension of single-stage extraction, wherein the raffinate is successively contacted with fresh solvent. It may be carried on in batch or continuous fashion. Refer to Fig. 10.35, which shows the flow sheet for a three-stage extraction. A single raffinate product $R_3$ results, which when freed of its solvent leaves the finished product $R'$. The three extracts may be combined as shown and treated together for solvent removal to provide the final extract $E'$. As many extraction stages as may be desired may be included in the scheme.

Computations are shown here on equilateral triangular coordinates, but the rectangular plot of $x$ and $y$ against weight fraction $B$ may equally well be used, and the relationship and relative positions of construction lines will be the same. The material balance equations (10.15) to (10.20) all apply for the first stage. For any other stage $n$, a total material balance is

$$R_{n-1} + B_n = M_n = R_n + E_n \qquad (10.30)$$

A balance for substance $C$ leads to

$$x_{Mn} = \frac{R_{n-1}x_{n-1}}{M_n} = \frac{R_{n-1}x_{n-1}}{R_{n-1} + B_n} \qquad (10.31)$$

or

$$B_n = \frac{R_{n-1}(x_{n-1} - x_{Mn})}{x_{Mn}} \qquad (10.32)$$

and to

$$E_n = \frac{M_n(x_{Mn} - x_n)}{y_n - x_n} \qquad (10.33)$$

Point $M_n$ is located on line $R_{n-1}B$, and the tie line through $M_n$ provides $E_n$ and $R_n$.

Unequal amounts of solvent may be used in the various stages, and even different temperatures, in which case each stage must be computed with the help of a phase diagram at the appropriate temperature. Mixing of the extracts produces mixture $E$, for which the amount and compo-

400   LIQUID-LIQUID OPERATIONS

sition may be determined by material balances.   $E'$ is located by extending the line $BE$ to the $AC$ base.   Similarly $R'$ is located by extending a line from $B$ through the point representing the raffinate from the final stage.   Any purity of $A$ in the raffinate $R'$ may be obtained, limited only by the number of stages which are to be employed.

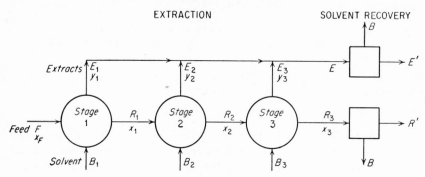

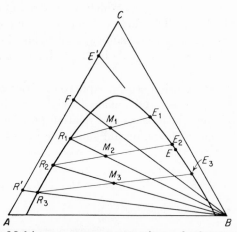

FIG. 10.35. Multistage cocurrent extraction and solvent recovery.

The calculations are also easily followed on the $B$-free coordinate diagram of Fig. 10.36.   As before, Eqs. (10.23) to (10.29) describe the first stage, and, for any other stage $n$, a nonsolvent material balance is

$$R'_{n-1} = M'_n = R'_n + E'_n \qquad (10.34)$$

A balance for $C$ is

$$X_{Mn} = X_{R,n-1} \qquad (10.35)$$

and for solvent $B$

$$R'_{n-1}N_{R,n-1} + B_n = M'_n N_{Mn} \qquad (10.36)$$

The last equations locate point $M$ for that stage.   The extract and raffinate leaving the stage are located by a tie line through $M_n$, and a $C$

balance provides

$$E'_n = \frac{M'_n(X_{Mn} - X_n)}{Y_n - X_n} \tag{10.37}$$

The raffinate product is then computed through Eq. (10.34). The solvent-free products are shown at points $E'$ and $R'$ on the diagram.

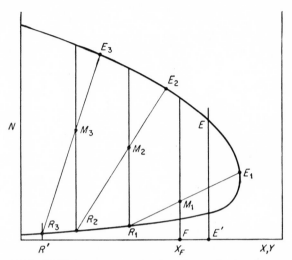

FIG. 10.36. Multistage cocurrent extraction and solvent recovery.

**Illustration 5.** One hundred pounds of a solution of acetic acid ($C$) and water ($A$) containing 30% acid is to be extracted three times with isopropyl ether ($B$) at 20°C., using 40 lb. of solvent in each stage. Determine the compositions and quantities of the various streams.

*Solution.* Equilibrium data listed in Illustration 3 are plotted on the rectangular coordinates of Fig. 10.37.

*Stage 1.* $F = 100$ lb., $x_F = 0.30$, $B_1 = 40$ lb. Point $F$ is plotted as shown.

Eq. (10.15):          $M_1 = 100 + 40 = 140$ lb.
Eq. (10.17):          $x_{M1} = 100(0.30)/140 = 0.214$

Point $M_1$ is located on line $FB$. With the help of a distribution curve, the tie line passing through $M_1$ is located as shown, and $x_1 = 0.258$, $y_1 = 0.117$ wt. fraction acetic acid.

Eq. (10.20):   $E_1 = 140(0.214 - 0.258)/(0.117 - 0.258) = 43.6$ lb.
Eq. (10.15):   $R_1 = 140 - 43.6 = 96.4$ lb.

  *Stage 2.*  $B_2 = 40$ lb.

Eq. (10.30):       $M_2 = R_1 + B_2 = 96.4 + 40 = 136.4$ lb.
Eq. (10.31):       $x_{M2} = R_1 x_1/M_2 = 96.4(0.258)/136.4 = 0.1822$

Point $M_2$ is located on line $R_1B$, and the tie line $R_2E_2$ through $M_2$ located as before. $x_2 = 0.227$, $y_2 = 0.095$.

Eq. (10.33):    $E_2 = M_2(x_{M2} - x_2)/(y_2 - x_2)$
$$= 136.4(0.1822 - 0.227)/(0.095 - 0.227) = 46.3 \text{ lb.}$$
Eq. (10.30):    $R_2 = M_2 - E_2 = 136.4 - 46.3 = 90.1 \text{ lb.}$

*Stage 3.* In a similar manner, $B_3 = 40$, $M_3 = 130.1$, $x_{M3} = 0.1572$, $x_3 = 0.20$, $y_3 = 0.078$, $E_3 = 45.7$, and $R_3 = 84.4$.

The ether content of the final raffinate (from the figure) is 0.03 wt. fraction, and consequently $R' = 84.4(1 - 0.03) = 81.8 \text{ lb.}$ The acid content of the final raffinate is $0.20(84.4) = 16.88 \text{ lb.}$

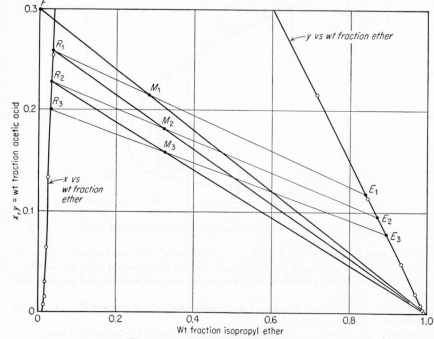

Fig. 10.37. Solution to Illustration 5.

The mixed extract $E = E_1 + E_2 + E_3 = 43.6 + 46.3 + 45.7 = 135.6 \text{ lb.}$, and its acid content $= E_1y_1 + E_2y_2 + E_3y_3 = 43.6(0.117) + 46.3(0.095) + 45.7(0.078) = 13.09 \text{ lb.}$ The solvent content of the mixed extracts may be found by multiplying each extract weight by its weight fraction solvent, as read from the figure,

$$43.6(0.842) + 46.3(0.871) + 45.7(0.894) = 117.6 \text{ lb. solvent in } E$$

Note that, by dividing the 120 lb. of solvent used in Illustration 4 into three smaller batches of the same total solvent content, the total extracted acid has been increased from 11.2 to 13.09 lb.

*Insoluble Liquids.* When the extraction solvent and feed solution are insoluble and remain so at all concentrations of the distributed solute which are encountered in the operation, the computations may be simplified. For this purpose, the equilibrium concentrations are plotted as in

Fig. 10.38, $x' = x/(1 - x)$ against $y' = y/(1 - y)$. Since the liquids $A$ and $B$ are insoluble, there are $A$ lb. of this substance in all raffinates. Similarly, the extract from each stage contains all the solvent fed to that stage. A material balance for substance $C$ about any stage $n$ is then

$$Ax'_{n-1} = B_n y'_n + Ax'_n \tag{10.38}$$

$$-\frac{A}{B_n} = \frac{y'_n}{x'_n - x'_{n-1}} \tag{10.39}$$

This is the operating-line equation for stage $n$, of slope $-A/B_n$, passing through the points $(x'_{n-1}, y' = 0)$ and $(x'_n, y'_n)$. The construction for a

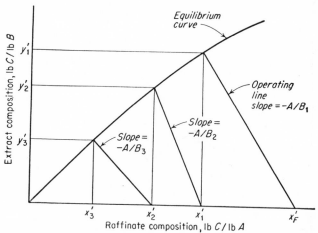

FIG. 10.38. Multistage cocurrent extraction, insoluble solvent.

three-stage plant is shown on Fig. 10.38, where for each stage a line is drawn of slope appropriate to that stage. Each operating line intersects the equilibrium curve at the raffinate and extract compositions.

**Illustration 6.** Nicotine ($C$) in a water ($A$) solution containing 1% nicotine is to be extracted with kerosene ($B$) at 20°C. Water and kerosene are essentially insoluble. (*a*) Determine the percentage extraction of nicotine if 100 lb. of feed solution is extracted once with 150 lb. solvent. (*b*) Repeat for three ideal extractions using 50 lb. solvent each.

*Solution.* Equilibrium data are provided by Claffey *et al.*, *Ind. Eng. Chem.*, **42**, 166 (1950), and expressed as lb. nicotine/lb. liquid they are as follows:

| $x' = \dfrac{\text{lb. nicotine}}{\text{lb. water}}\dots$ | 0 | 0.001011 | 0.00246 | 0.00502 | 0.00751 | 0.00998 | 0.0204 |
|---|---|---|---|---|---|---|---|
| $y'^* = \dfrac{\text{lb. nicotine}}{\text{lb. kerosene}}\dots$ | 0 | 0.000807 | 0.001961 | 0.00456 | 0.00686 | 0.00913 | 0.01870 |

*a.* $x_F = 0.01$ wt. fraction nicotine, $x'_F = 0.01/(1 - 0.01) = 0.0101$ lb. nicotine/lb. water. $F = 100$ lb. $A = 100(1 - 0.01) = 99$ lb. water. $A/B = {}^{99}\!/_{150} = 0.66$.

Refer to Fig. 10.39, which shows the equilibrium data and the point $F$ representing the composition of the feed. From $F$, line $FD$ is drawn of slope $-0.66$, intersecting the equilibrium curve at $D$, where $x_1' = 0.00425$ and $y_1' = 0.00380$ lb. nicotine/lb. liquid. The nicotine removed from the water is therefore $99(0.0101 - 0.00425) = 0.580$ lb., or $58\%$ of that in the feed.

*b.* For each stage, $A/B = {}^{99}\!/_{50} = 1.98$. The construction is started at $F$, with operating lines of slope $-1.98$. The final raffinate composition is $x_3' = 0.0034$, and the nicotine extracted is $99(0.0101 - 0.0034) = 0.663$ lb., or $66.3\%$ of that in the feed.

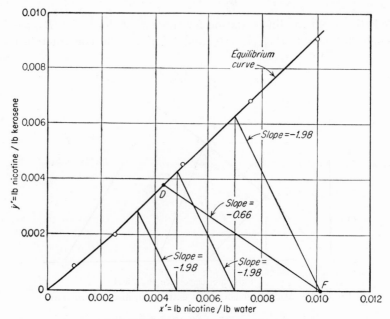

FIG. 10.39. Solution to Illustration 6.

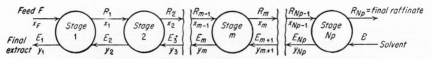

FIG. 10.40. Countercurrent multistage extraction.

**Continuous Countercurrent Multistage Extraction.** The flowsheet for this type of operation is shown in Fig. 10.40. Extract and raffinate streams flow from stage to stage in countercurrent and provide two final products, raffinate $R_{Np}$ and extract $E_1$. For a given degree of separation, this type of operation requires fewer stages for a given amount of solvent, or less solvent for a fixed number of stages, than the cocurrent methods described above.

The graphical treatment is developed in Fig. 10.41 on rectangular coordinates. Construction on the equilateral triangle is identical with this.   A total material balance about the entire plant is

$$F + B = E_1 + R_{Np} = M \tag{10.40}$$

Point $M$ may be located on line $FB$ through a balance for substance $C$,

$$Fx_F = E_1 y_1 + R_{Np} x_{Np} = M x_M \tag{10.41}$$

$$x_M = \frac{Fx_F}{M} = \frac{Fx_F}{F + B} \tag{10.42}$$

Equation (10.40) indicates that $M$ must also lie on line $R_{Np}E_1$, as shown.

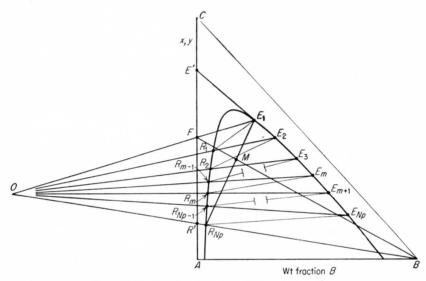

FIG. 10.41. Countercurrent multistage extraction.

Rearrangement of Eq. (10.40) provides

$$F - E_1 = R_{Np} - B = 0 \tag{10.43}$$

so that the extended lines $E_1F$ and $BR_{Np}$ must intersect at $O$, as shown. The quantity $O$ thus represents the difference in the flow quantities at the extremities of the plant.   A material balance for stage 1 through $m$ is

$$F + E_{m+1} = E_1 + R_m \tag{10.44}$$

$$F - E_1 = R_m - E_{m+1} = 0 \tag{10.45}$$

so that the difference in flow quantities at a point between any two stages is a constant.   Line $E_{m+1}R_m$ extended must therefore also pass through $O$, as on the figure.

   The graphical construction is now easily followed.   After location of points $F$, $M$, $E_1$, $R_{Np}$, and $O$, a tie line for $E_1$ provides $R_1$, since extract and raffinate from the first theoretical stage are in equilibrium.   A line from $O$ through $R_1$ when extended provides $E_2$, a tie line through $E_2$ provides $R_2$, etc. Points $E'$ and $R'$, representing the solvent-free products, are located as usual by extension of lines from $B$ through $E_1$ and $R_{Np}$, respectively. Any purity of raffinate $R'$ may be obtained for a given amount of solvent, limited only by the number of stages employed.

As the amount of solvent is increased, point $M$ representing the overall plant balance moves toward $B$ on Fig. 10.41 and point $O$ moves farther to the left. At an amount of solvent such that lines $E_1F$ and $BR_{Np}$ are

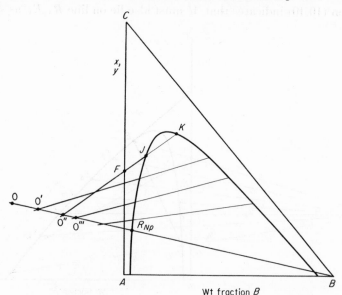

Fig. 10.42. Minimum solvent for countercurrent extraction.

parallel, point $O$ will be at an infinite distance. Greater amounts of solvent will cause these lines to intersect on the right-hand side of the diagram rather than as shown, with point $O$ nearer $B$ for increasing solvent quantities. The interpretation of the difference point is, however, still the same: a line from $O$ intersects the two branches of the solubility curve at points representing extract and raffinate from adjacent stages.

If a line from point $O$ should coincide with a tie line, an infinite number of stages will be required to reach this condition and the position of $O$ corresponds to the minimum solvent/feed ratio which may be used for the specified products. The procedure for determining the minimum amount of solvent is indicated in Fig. 10.42. All tie lines below that marked $JK$ are extended to line $BR_{Np}$, to give intersections such as $O'$, $O''$, and $O'''$. The intersection farthest from $B$ (if on the left-hand side of the diagram) or nearest $B$ (if on the right) represents the difference point for minimum solvent, as at point $O'$ (Fig. 10.42). The actual position of $O$ must be farther from $B$ (if on the left) or nearer to $B$ (if on the right) for a finite number of stages. The larger the amount of solvent, the fewer the number of stages. Usually, but not in the instance shown, the tie lines which when extended pass through $F$, i.e., tie line $JK$, will locate $O'$ for minimum solvent.

When the number of stages is very large, the construction indicated in Fig. 10.43 may be more convenient. A few lines are drawn at random

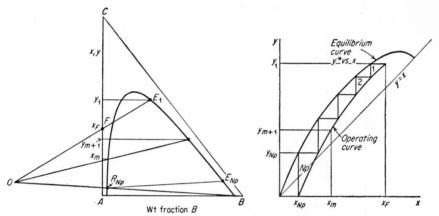

FIG. 10.43. Transfer of coordinates, countercurrent extraction.

from point $O$ to intersect the two branches of the solubility curve as shown, where the intersections do not now necessarily indicate streams between two actual adjacent stages. The $C$ concentrations $x_m$ and $y_{m+1}$ corresponding to these are plotted on $x$, $y$ coordinates as shown to provide an operating curve. Tie-line data provide the equilibrium curve $y^*$ vs. $x$, and the theoretical stages are stepped off in the manner used for gas absorption and distillation.

Figure 10.44 shows the construction for solvent-free coordinates. The solvent-free material balance for the entire plant is

$$F = F' = E_1' + R_{Np}' = M' \qquad (10.46)$$

and point $M$ is located vertically above $F$, since $X_F = X_M$, at $N_M = B/M'$. Line $E_1 R_{Np}$ must pass through $M$. The balance for stages 1 through $m$ is

$$F' + E_{m+1}' = E_1' + R_m' \qquad (10.47)$$
$$F' - E_1' = R_m' - E_{m+1}' = O' \qquad (10.48)$$

and point $O$, the operating point or solvent-free difference point, is common to all stages. It is located at the intersection of line $E_1 F$ extended to the line $X_{Np}$, since $N$ for solvent $B$ is at infinity. A tie line for $E_1$ then locates $R_1$, line $OR_1$ extended locates $E_2$, etc. As the solvent feed ratio is increased, point $O$ will be lower on the graph and the minimum solvent is determined by the lowest point of intersection of all extended tie lines with the line $X_{Np}$. An actual point $O$ must be located below this, corresponding to larger amounts of solvent.

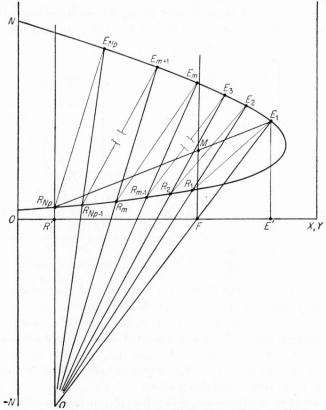

FIG. 10.44. Countercurrent extraction, solvent-free coordinates.

**Illustration 7.** Two thousand pounds per hour of an acetic acid $(C)$–water $(A)$ solution, containing 30% acid, is to be countercurrently extracted with isopropyl ether $(B)$ to reduce the acid concentration to 2% in the solvent-free raffinate product. $(a)$ Determine the minimum amount of solvent which may be used. $(b)$ Determine the number of theoretical stages if 5,000 lb./hr. of solvent is used.

*Solution.* The equilibrium data of Illustration 4 are plotted on triangular coordinates in Fig. 10.45. The tie lines have been omitted for reasons of clarity.

*a.* $F = 2,000$ lb./hr.; $x_F = 0.30$ wt. fraction acetic acid, corresponding to point $F$ on the figure. $R'$ is located on the $AC$ base at 2% acid, and line $BR'$ intersects the water-rich solubility curve at $R_{Np}$, as shown. In this case the tie line $J$ which when extended passes through $F$ provides the conditions for minimum solvent, and this intersects line $R_{Np} B$ on the right of the figure nearer $B$ than any other lower tie line. Tie line $J$ provides the minimum $E_1$ as shown at $y_1 = 0.143$. Line $E_{1,min}R_{Np}$ intersects line $FB$ at $M_{min}$, for which $x_M = 0.114$.

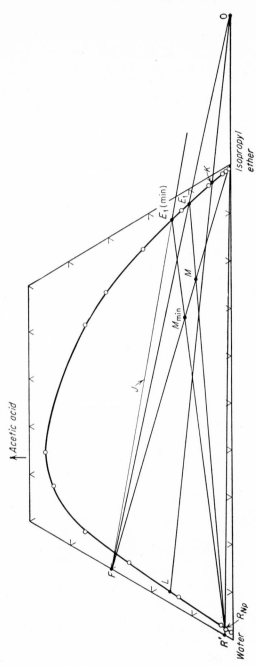

FIG. 10.45. Solution to Illustration 7.

409

Eq. (10.42):

$B_{min} = (Fx_F/x_M) - F = [2,000(0.30)/0.114] - 2,000 = 3,260$ lb./hr., min. solvent rate

     *b.* For $B = 5,000$ lb. solvent/hr. [Eq. (10.42)],

$$x_M = Fx_F/(F + B) = 2,000(0.30)/(2,000 + 5,000) = 0.0857$$

and point $M$ is located as shown on line $FB$. Line $R_{N_p}M$ extended provides $E_1$ at $y_1 = 0.10$. Line $FE_1$ is extended to intersect line $R_{N_p}B$ at $O$. Random lines such as $OKL$ are drawn to provide $y_{m+1}$ at $K$ and $x_M$ at $L$, as follows:

| $y_{m+1}$.... | 0 | 0.01 | 0.02 | 0.04 | 0.06 | 0.08 | $0.10 = y_1$ |
|---|---|---|---|---|---|---|---|
| $x_m$..... | 0.02 | 0.055 | 0.090 | 0.150 | 0.205 | 0.250 | $0.30 = x_F$ |

These are plotted on Fig. 10.46 as the operating curve, along with the tie-line data as the equilibrium curve. There are required 7.6 theoretical stages. The weight of

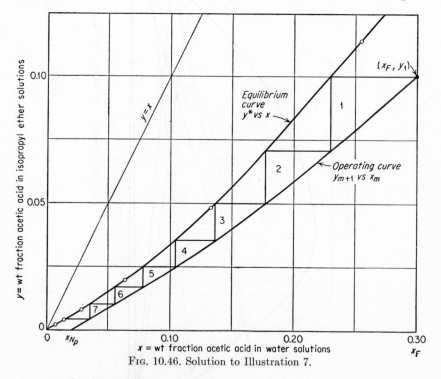

FIG. 10.46. Solution to Illustration 7.

extract may be obtained by an acid balance,

$E_1 = M(x_M - x_{N_p})/(y_1 - x_{N_p}) = 7,000(0.0857 - 0.02)/(0.10 - 0.02) = 5,750$ lb./hr.
and           $R_{N_p} = M - E_1 = 7,000 - 5,750 = 1,250$ lb./hr.

*Insoluble Liquids.* When the liquids $A$ and $B$ are insoluble over the range of solute concentrations encountered, the stage computation is made more simply on $x'$, $y'$ coordinates. For this case, the solvent content of all extracts and the $A$ content of all raffinates are constant. An over-all plant balance for substance $C$ is

$$Ax'_F = Ax'_{Np} + By'_1 \qquad (10.49)$$

or

$$\frac{A}{B} = \frac{y'_1}{x'_F - x'_n} \qquad (10.50)$$

which is the equation of a straight line, the operating line, of slope $A/B$, through points $(y'_1, x'_F)$, $(y' = 0, x'_{Np})$. For stages 1 through $m$, similarly,

$$\frac{A}{B} = \frac{y_1 - y'_{m+1}}{x'_F - x'_m} \qquad (10.51)$$

and Fig. 10.47 shows the construction for stages.

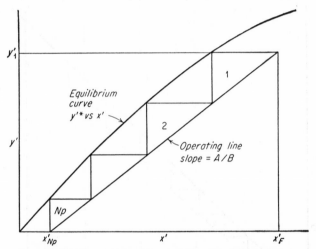

FIG. 10.47. Countercurrent extraction, insoluble solvent.

For the special case where the equilibrium curve is of constant slope $m' = y'^*/x'$, Eq. (8.24) applies,

$$\frac{x'_F - x'_{Np}}{x'_F} = \frac{(m'B/A)^{Np+1} - m'B/A}{(m'B/A)^{Np+1} - 1} \qquad (10.52)$$

where $A/m'B$ is the extraction factor. This may be used in conjunction with Fig. 8.15, with $x'_{Np}/x'_F$ as ordinate and $m'B/A$ as parameter.

**Illustration 8.** One thousand pounds per hour of a nicotine ($C$)–water ($A$) solution containing 1% nicotine is to be countercurrently extracted with kerosene at 20°C. to reduce the nicotine content to 0.1%. (a) Determine the minimum kerosene rate. (b) Determine the number of theoretical stages required if 1,150 lb. of kerosene is used per hour.

*Solution.* The equilibrium data of Illustration 6 are plotted in Fig. 10.48.

*a.* $F = 1{,}000$ lb./hr., $x_F = 0.01$, $A = 1{,}000(1 - 0.01) = 990$ lb. water/hr.

$$x'_F = 0.01/(1 - 0.01) = 0.0101 \text{ lb. nicotine/lb. water}$$
$$x_{Np} = 0.001, \qquad x'_{Np} = 0.001/(1 - 0.001) = 0.001001 \text{ lb. nicotine/lb. water}$$

The operating line starts at point $L$ ($y' = 0$, $x' = 0.001001$) and for infinite stages passes through $K$ on the equilibrium curve at $x'_F$. $y'_K = 0.0093$. Therefore $A/B_{\min}$ $= (0.0093 - 0)/(0.0101 - 0.001001) = 1.021$, and $B_{\min} = A/1.021 = 990/1.021 = 969$ lb. kerosene/hr.

*b.* $B = 1{,}150$ lb./hr., $A/B = 990/1{,}150 = 0.860$.

Eq. (10.50): $\qquad y'_1/(x'_F - x'_{Np}) = y'_1/(0.0101 - 0.001001) = 0.860$
$$y'_1 = 0.00782 \text{ lb. nicotine/lb. kerosene}$$

The operating line is drawn through $(y'_1, x'_F)$, and 8.3 theoretical stages are determined graphically.

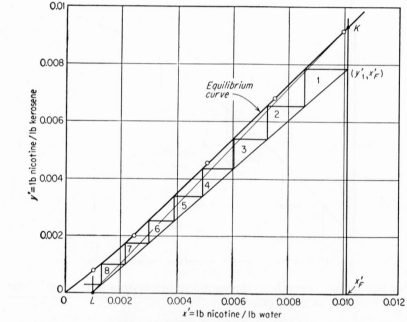

FIG. 10.48. Solution to Illustration 8.

Alternatively, at the dilute end of the system, $m' = dy'^*/dx' = 0.798$, and $m'B/A = 0.798(1{,}150)/990 = 0.928$. At the concentrated end, $m' = 0.953$, and $m'B/A = 0.953(1{,}150)/990 = 1.110$. The average is $[0.928(1.110)]^{0.5} = 1.01$. $x'_{Np}/x'_F = 0.001001/0.0101 = 0.099$, and Fig. 8.15 indicates 8.4 theoretical stages.

## Continuous Countercurrent Extraction with Reflux.

Whereas in ordinary countercurrent operation the richest possible extract product leaving the plant is at best only in equilibrium with the feed solution, the use of reflux at the extract end of the plant can provide a product even richer, as in the case of the rectifying section of a distillation column. Reflux may also be provided at the raffinate end of the extraction cascade, and this is particularly useful for cases where the distribution coefficient is very low.

An arrangement for this is shown in Fig. 10.49. The feed to be separated into its components is introduced more or less centrally into the cascade, through which extract and raffinate liquids are passing countercurrently. The concentration of solute $C$ is increased in the extract-enriching section by countercurrent contact with a raffinate liquid rich in $C$. This is provided by removing the solvent from extract $E_1$ to produce a solvent-free stream $E'$, part of which is removed as extract product

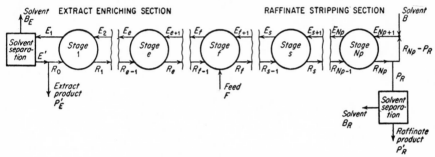

FIG. 10.49. Countercurrent extraction with reflux.

and part returned as reflux $R_0$. In the raffinate-stripping section of the cascade, $C$ is stripped from the raffinate by countercurrent contact with extract liquid containing some $A$. The latter is provided by returning part of the raffinate, after withdrawal of product $P_R$, as reflux to be sent back to the last stage along with fresh solvent. An alternative arrangement, to be used when it is desired to enrich the extract as shown but when the distribution coefficient is not very low, is to omit the raffinate reflux, withdraw all the raffinate $R_{Np}$ as product, and provide only solvent as the extract stream into the last stage.

Graphical treatment will be shown first on triangular coordinates. The construction on the rectangular coordinates of Fig. 10.28 is identical. Consider first the extract-enriching section, as in Figs. 10.49 and 10.50. A material balance about the solvent separator is

$$E_1 = B_E + E' = B_E + P'_E + R_0 \qquad (10.53)$$

Let

$$Q = B_E + P'_E \qquad (10.54)$$

or the net flow out of the system at this end of the plant. Therefore

$$E_1 = Q + R_0 \qquad (10.55)$$

and $Q$ represents a point on line $BP'_E$, with $E_1$ on the line between $Q$ and $R_0$, as shown in Fig. 10.50a.

A material balance about the entire end of the cascade including stage $e$ is

$$E_{e+1} = B_E + P'_E + R_e = Q + R_e \qquad (10.56)$$

and $Q$ is therefore the difference in flow, $E_{e+1} - R_e$. Points on the triangular diagram representing extract and raffinate from adjacent stages must lie on the same line as $Q$, as shown on Fig. 10.50$a$. At the same time, points representing extract and raffinate from the same theoretical stage must lie on a tie line. Stages in the extract-enriching section may therefore be determined by alternate tie lines and construction lines from the difference point $Q$, as shown. If overcrowding on the graph is severe,

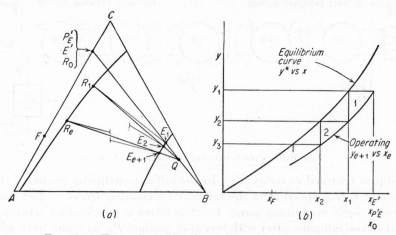

Fig. 10.50. Extraction with reflux. Extract enriching section.

random lines from $Q$ will provide $y$ and $x$ values at the solvent-rich and solvent-lean solubility curves and these may be plotted as the operating line (Fig. 10.50$b$). Together with the equilibrium curve, this provides the means for stepping off ideal stages, as shown. Stage construction in this manner may be continued until the feed stage $f$ is reached.

By the mixture rule,

$$\frac{R_e}{Q} = \frac{\text{line } E_{e+1}Q}{\text{line } R_e E_{e+1}} \qquad (10.57)$$

Further,

$$\text{Line } R_e E_{e+1} + \text{line } E_{e+1}Q = \text{line } R_e Q \qquad (10.58)$$

Combining these provides the internal reflux ratio,

$$\frac{R_e}{E_{e+1}} = \frac{\text{line } E_{e+1}Q}{\text{line } R_e Q} = \frac{y_{e+1} - y_Q}{y_e - y_Q} \qquad (10.59)$$

At the end of the cascade,

$$\frac{B_E}{P'_E} = \frac{\text{line } P'_E Q}{\text{line } QB} \qquad (10.60)$$

and, combining this with Eqs. (10.53) and (10.54), the external reflux ratio is

$$\frac{R_0}{P'_E} = \frac{\text{line } E_1Q}{\text{line } P'_E E_1} \frac{\text{line } P'_E B}{\text{line } QB} = \frac{y_1 - y_Q}{x_{P'E} - y_1} \frac{x_{P'E}}{y_Q} \qquad (10.61)$$

Point $Q$ may then be located on line $R_0B$ to provide the desired reflux ratio.

At the raffinate-stripping end of the cascade, a material balance at the point of introducing solvent is

$$(R_{Np} - P_R) + B = E_{Np+1} \qquad (10.62)$$

Similarly, including the withdrawn product $P_R$,

$$R_{Np} + B = E_{Np+1} + P_R \qquad (10.63)$$

Let

$$W = B - P_R \qquad (10.64)$$
$$\therefore E_{Np+1} = R_{Np} + W \qquad (10.65)$$

A material balance around the entire end of the cascade including stage $s + 1$ is

$$R_s + B = E_{s+1} + P_R \qquad (10.66)$$
$$E_{s+1} = R_s + W \qquad (10.67)$$

These balances may be interpreted graphically as in Fig. 10.51a. Point $W$, a difference point representing the difference between extract and raffinate flow at any point in the cascade between stages, must lie on line $P_RB$ extended. A line from $W$ into the body of the triangle must intersect the two branches of the solubility curve at points representing raffinate and extract from adjacent stages. Alternate tie lines and lines radiating from $W$ therefore permit construction of the stages up to the feed stage. As before, this may be done on the $x$, $y$ coordinates (Fig. 10.51b) if this is more convenient. A switch is made from $Q$ to $W$ as operating point when the feed stage $f$ is reached.

The reflux ratios in this section may be determined in the same manner as in the enriching section.[20] The internal ratio is

$$\frac{R_s}{E_{s+1}} = \frac{\text{line } E_{s+1}W}{\text{line } R_sW} = \frac{y_{s+1} - y_w}{x_s - y_w} \qquad (10.68)$$

and the external ratio is

$$\frac{R_{Np} - P_R}{P_R} = \frac{\text{line } E_{Np+1}B}{\text{line } P_R E_{Np+1}} \frac{\text{line } P_RW}{\text{line } BW} = \frac{y_{Np+1}}{x_{Np} - y_{Np+1}} \frac{x_{Np} - y_w}{-y_w} \qquad (10.69)$$

The fictitious $C$ concentration at point $W$, a negative quantity, may be obtained through a $C$ balance corresponding to Eq. (10.64): $y_w = -P_R x_{Np}/W$.

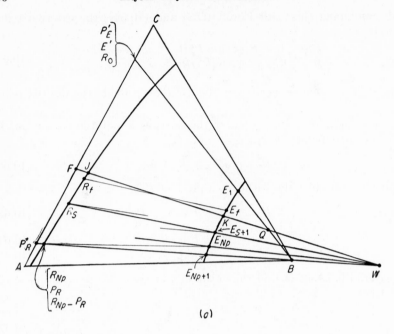

(a)

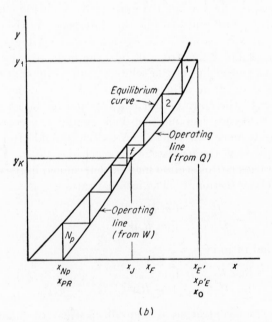

(b)

Fig. 10.51. Extraction with reflux.  Raffinate stripping section.

The reflux ratios at either end of the cascade are interrelated, as in a distillation cascade. At the feed stage,

$$E_{f+1} + R_{f-1} + F = E_f + R_f \tag{10.70}$$

or
$$(E_{f+1} - R_f) + F = E_f - R_{f-1} \tag{10.71}$$

Applying Eq. (10.67) to the quantity in the parentheses on the left-hand side of the equation and Eq. (10.56) to the quantity on the right-hand side, this becomes

$$W + F = Q \tag{10.72}$$

It is seen that $F$, $W$, and $Q$ must lie on the same straight line, as shown in Fig. 10.51$a$.

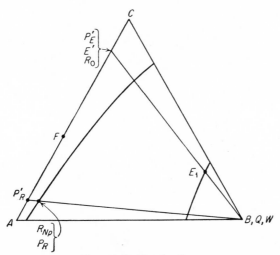

FIG. 10.52. Total reflux.

*Total Reflux.* As the reflux ratios are increased, Eqs. (10.61) and (10.69) indicate that both points $Q$ and $W$ move toward $B$ and consideration of the graphical construction will show that the number of stages required for a given concentration change decreases. When the entire product streams are returned as reflux and the external reflux ratios are therefore infinite, points $Q$ and $W$ coincide at point $B$, as in Fig. 10.52, and the number of stages is the least. The capacity of the plant is now zero, or, interpreted otherwise, the solvent throughput per unit of product or feed is infinite.

*Minimum Reflux Ratio.* If a construction line from either $Q$ or $W$ should coincide with a tie line, the number of stages required to reach this condition would be infinite and a "pinch" would develop. The largest reflux ratio for which this occurs is the minimum permissible reflux ratio.

This may be established as shown in Fig. 10.53. All tie lines above that corresponding to the feed are extended to intersect line $BE'$, and line $FQ'$ is drawn through the intersection $Q'$ closest to $B$. Line $FQ'$ intersects line $P'_RB$ at $W'$. All tie lines below that corresponding to the feed are extended to intersect line $P'_RB$. If these intersections are all farther to the right on the figure than $W'$, then $W'$ and $Q'$ are the operating points for minimum reflux ratio. If the intersections are between

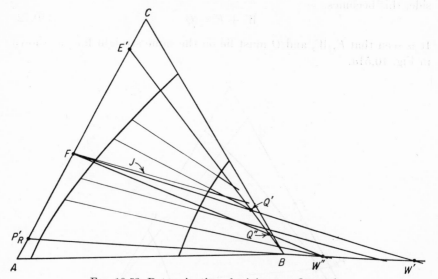

FIG. 10.53. Determination of minimum reflux ratio.

$W'$ and $B$, as shown, then line $FW''$ is drawn through that intersection which is nearest to $B$. Line $FW''$ provides $Q''$ on line $E'B$, and points $Q''$ and $W''$ then become the operating points for minimum reflux ratio. In many cases, the tie line $J$ which passes through $F$ provides both $Q$ and $W$ for minimum reflux.

*Solvent-free Coordinates.* The upper part of Fig. 10.54 shows the graphical construction for a typical case. The principles having been established in the case of triangular coordinates, the corresponding solvent-free relationships are readily set down. Thus, $A + C$ balances at the end of the extract-enriching section are

$$E'_1 = E' = P'_E + R'_0 \tag{10.73}$$

and a $B$ balance,

$$B_E = E'_1 N_{E1} \tag{10.74}$$

Since $Q$ represents the net flow outward from the enriching section of the

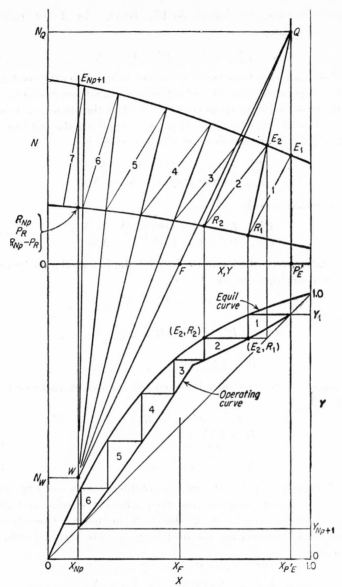

Fig. 10.54. Extraction with reflux, solvent-free coordinates.

plant, both for components $A + C$ and $B$,

$$Q' = P'_E \tag{10.75}$$

$$N_Q = \frac{B_E}{P'_E} \tag{10.76}$$

$$Y_Q = X_{P'E} \tag{10.77}$$

and point $Q$ is located as shown on Fig. 10.54. An $A + C$ balance for all stages through $e$,

$$E'_{e+1} = P'_E + R'_e = Q' + R'_e \tag{10.78}$$

so that lines radiating from point $Q$ cut the solubility curves of Fig. 10.54 at points representing extract and raffinate from adjacent stages. Alternating tie lines and lines from $Q$ then establish the stages, starting with stage 1 and continuing to the feed stage. Applying the mixture rule to Eq. (10.78), the internal reflux ratio at any stage is

$$\frac{R'_e}{E'_{e+1}} = \frac{\text{line } E_{e+1}Q}{\text{line } R_e Q} = \frac{N_Q - N_{E,e+1}}{N_Q - N_{Re}} \tag{10.79}$$

and the external ratio is

$$\frac{R'_0}{P'_E} = \frac{R_0}{P'_E} = \frac{\text{line } QE_1}{\text{line } E_1 P'_E} = \frac{N_Q - N_{E1}}{N_{E1}} \tag{10.80}$$

At the raffinate-product end of the cascade, in exactly the same manner, the relationships are, for $A + C$,

$$R'_{Np} - P'_R = E'_{Np+1} \tag{10.81}$$

and, for $B$,

$$(R'_{Np} - P'_R)N_{R,Np} + B = E'_{Np+1}N_{E,Np+1} \tag{10.82}$$

Therefore

$$B = E'_{Np+1}(N_{E,Np+1} - N_{R,Np}) \tag{10.83}$$

Let $W'$ represent the difference between solvent-free extract and raffinate flow. Then

$$W' = -P'_R = E'_{Np+1} - R'_{Np} = E'_{s+1} - R'_s \tag{10.84}$$

$$N_W = \frac{B - P'_R N_{PR}}{-P'_R} \tag{10.85}$$

$$X_W = X_{PR} \tag{10.86}$$

Lines radiating from point $W$ cut the solubility curves of Fig. 10.54 at raffinate and extract compositions from adjacent stages, and tie lines join those from the same stage, as shown in the figure. Operating point $W$ is thus used after passing the feed stage $f$. The internal reflux ratio at any stage is

$$\frac{R'_s}{E'_{s+1}} = \frac{\text{line } E_{s+1}W}{\text{line } R_s W} = \frac{N_{E,s+1} - N_W}{N_{Rs} - N_W} \tag{10.87}$$

and the external ratio is

$$\frac{R_{Np} - P_R}{P_R} = \frac{\text{line } P_R W}{\text{line } E_{Np+1}P_R} = \frac{N_{PR} - N_W}{N_{E,Np+1} - N_{PR}} \tag{10.88}$$

An over-all plant balance for components $A + C$,

$$F' = F = P'_E + P'_R = Q' - W' \tag{10.89}$$

shows points $F$, $W$, and $Q$ to lie on the same line (Fig. 10.54). Both reflux ratios may not therefore be set independently. The farther $Q$ and $W$ lie away from the $XY$ axis of the graph, the larger the reflux ratios and the fewer the number of stages. When $R_0/P_E'$ is infinite, or for *infinite reflux ratio*, $N_Q$ is infinite and the minimum number of stages result. This is shown in Fig. 10.55, where the radiating lines from $W$ and $B$ are vertical. Infinite stages are required if a line radiating from $Q$ or from $W$ coincides with a tie line, and the greatest reflux ratio for which this occurs is the *minimum reflux ratio*. This may be determined as in Fig. 10.56. Tie lines to the left of $J$ are extended to intersect

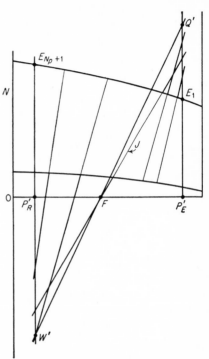

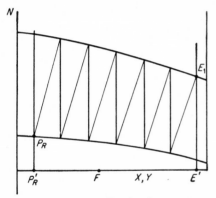

FIG. 10.55. Total reflux.

FIG. 10.56. Determination of minimum reflux ratio.

line $E_{Np+1}P_R'$, and those to the right of $J$ are extended to line $P_E'E_1$. Points $W'$ and $Q'$ representing the minimum reflux ratios are established by selecting the intersection $W'$ or $Q'$ farthest from $N = 0$, consistent with the requirement that $W$, $Q$, and $F$ must be on the same straight line. Frequently tie line $J$, which when extended passes through $F$, will establish the minimum reflux ratio.

The lower portion of Fig. 10.54 shows the graphical treatment transferred to $X$, $Y$ coordinates, and the resemblance to the McCabe-Thiele diagram of distillation is obvious. This provides a convenient method when many stages are required. Random lines from $Q$ and $W$ provide the coordinates of the operating curve, and the tie lines produce the equilibrium curve.

Details of the computations for the case where the solvent contains small amounts of $A$ and $C$, and where the streams $E'$ and $P'_R$ are not solvent-free, are also available.[20]

**Illustration 9.** One thousand pounds per hour of a solution containing 50% ethylbenzene ($A$) and 50% styrene ($C$) is to be separated at 25°C. into products containing 10% and 90% styrene, respectively, with diethylene glycol ($B$) as solvent. (a) Determine the minimum number of theoretical stages. (b) Determine the minimum extract reflux ratio. (c) Determine the number of theoretical stages and the important flow quantities at an extract reflux ratio of 1.5 times the minimum value.

*Solution.* Equilibrium data of Boobar *et al.*, *Ind. Eng. Chem.*, **43**, 2922 (1951), have been converted to a solvent-free basis and are tabulated below.

| Hydrocarbon-rich solutions | | Solvent-rich solutions | |
|---|---|---|---|
| $X$, lb. styrene / lb. hydrocarbon | $N$, lb. glycol / lb. hydrocarbon | $Y^*$, lb. styrene / lb. hydrocarbon | $N$, lb. glycol / lb. hydrocarbon |
| 0 | 0.00675 | 0 | 8.62 |
| 0.0870 | 0.00817 | 0.1429 | 7.71 |
| 0.1883 | 0.00938 | 0.273 | 6.81 |
| 0.288 | 0.01010 | 0.386 | 6.04 |
| 0.384 | 0.01101 | 0.480 | 5.44 |
| 0.458 | 0.01215 | 0.557 | 5.02 |
| 0.464 | 0.01215 | 0.565 | 4.95 |
| 0.561 | 0.01410 | 0.655 | 4.46 |
| 0.573 | 0.01405 | 0.674 | 4.37 |
| 0.781 | 0.01833 | 0.833 | 3.47 |
| 1.00 | 0.0256 | 1.00 | 2.69 |

These are plotted on the solvent-free coordinate system of Fig. 10.57. The tie lines corresponding to these points are not drawn in, for purposes of clarity. $F = 1,000$ lb./hr., $X_F = 0.5$ wt. fraction styrene, $X_{P'E} = 0.9$, $X_{P'R} = 0.1$, all on a solvent-free basis. Point $E_1$ is located as shown. $N_{E1} = 3.10$.

*a.* Minimum theoretical stages are determined by drawing a tie line from $E_1$, a vertical line from $R_1$, a tie line from $E_2$, etc., until the raffinate product is reached, as shown. The minimum number of stages, corresponding to the constructed tie lines, is 9.5.

*b.* The tie line which when extended passes through $F$ provides the minimum reflux ratios, since it provides intersections $Q'$ and $W'$ farthest from the line $N = 0$. From the plot, $N_{Q'} = 20.76$.

Eq. (10.80):    $(R_0/P'_E)_{min} = (20.76 - 3.1)/3.1 = 5.70$ lb. reflux/lb. extract product

*c.* For $R_0/P'_E = 1.5(5.70) = 8.55$ lb. reflux/lb. extract product [Eq. (10.80)],

$$8.55 = (N_Q - 3.1)/3.1$$

and $N_Q = 29.6$. Point $Q$ is plotted as shown. A straight line from $Q$ through $F$ intersects line $X = 0.10$ at $W$. $N_W = -29.6$. Random lines are drawn from $Q$ for concentrations to the right of $F$, and from $W$ for those to the left, and intersections of

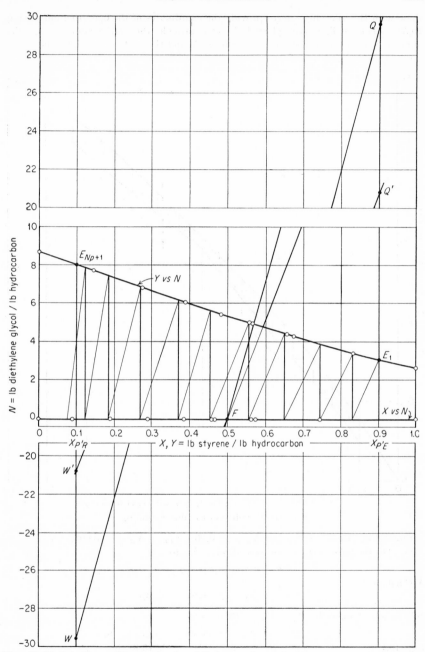

F$_{IG}$. 10.57. Solution to Illustration 9.   Minimum theoretical stages at total reflux and location of operating points.

these with the solubility curves provide the coordinates of the operating curve (Fig. 10.58). The tie-line data plotted directly provide the equilibrium curve. The number of theoretical stages is seen to be 15.5, and the feed is to be introduced into the seventh from the extract-product end of the cascade.

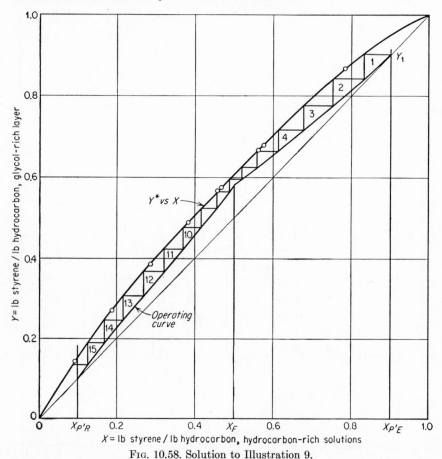

FIG. 10.58. Solution to Illustration 9.

From Fig. 10.57, $Y_{E,Np+1} = X_{R,Np} = 0.10$; $N_{PR} = N_{R,Np} = 0.0082$; $N_{E,Np+1} = 7.95$. On the basis of 1 hr., an over-all plant balance is

$$F = 1,000 = P'_E + P'_R$$

A $C$ balance,

$$FX_X = 500 = P'_E(0.9) + P'_R(0.1)$$

Solving simultaneously, $P'_E = P'_R = 500$ lb./hr.

$$R_0 = R'_0 = 8.55P'_E = 8.55(500) = 4,275 \text{ lb./hr.}$$

Eq. (10.73):    $E'_1 = R_0 + P'_E = 4,275 + 500 = 4,775 \text{ lb./hr.}$

Eq. (10.74):    $B_E = E'_1 N_{E1} = 4,775(3.10) = 14,800 \text{ lb./hr.}$

$$E_1 = B_E + E'_1 = 14,800 + 4,775 = 19,575 \text{ lb./hr.}$$

$$P_R = P'_R(1 + N_{PR}) = 500(1.0082) = 504 \text{ lb./hr.}$$

$$B_R = P_R - P'_R = 504 - 500 = 4 \text{ lb./hr.}$$

Eq. (10.88): $$\frac{R_{Np} - P_R}{P_R} = \frac{0.0082 + 29.6}{7.95 - 0.0082} = 3.728$$

$$R_{Np} = P_R(3.728 + 1) = 504(4.728) = 2,383 \text{ lb./hr.}$$
$$R_{Np} - P_R = 2,383 - 504 = 1,879 \text{ lb./hr.}$$
$$E'_{Np+1} = R'_{Np} - P'_R = 1,879/(1 + 0.0082) = 1,864 \text{ lb./hr.}$$

Eq. (10.83):   $$B = 1,864(7.95 - 0.0082) = 14,804 \text{ lb./hr.}$$
$$E_{Np+1} = E'_{Np+1} + B = 1,864 + 14,804 = 16,670 \text{ lb./hr.}$$

**Economic Balances.**  Several types of economic balances may be made for the various flow sheets just described.  For example, the amount of solute extracted for a fixed solvent/feed ratio increases with increased number of stages, and therefore the value of the unextracted solute may be balanced against the cost of the extraction equipment required to recover it.  The amount of solvent per unit of feed, or reflux ratio in the case of the last flow sheet described, is also subject to economic balance.  For a fixed extent of extraction, the number of stages required decreases as solvent rate or reflux ratio increases.  Since the capacity of the equipment for handling the larger liquid flow must at the same time increase, the cost of equipment must then pass through a minimum.  The extract solutions become more dilute as solvent rate or reflux ratio is increased, and consequently the cost of solvent removal increases.  The total cost, which is the sum of investment and operating costs, must pass through a minimum at the optimum solvent rate or reflux ratio.  In all such economic balances, the cost of solvent recovery will always be a major item and usually must include consideration of recovery from the saturated raffinate product as well as from the extract.

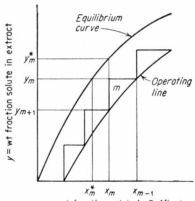

FIG. 10.59. Murphree stage efficiencies.

**Stage Efficiency.**  As in the case of gas-liquid contact, the performance of individual extraction stages can be described in terms of the approach to equilibrium actually realized by the effluent extract and raffinate streams.  The Murphree stage efficiency may be expressed in terms of extract compositions as $E_E$, or in terms of raffinate compositions as $E_R$.  Applying Eq. (5.30) to stage $m$ of the countercurrent cascade of Fig. 10.59, for example,

$$E_E = \frac{y_m - y_{m+1}}{y_m^* - y_{m+1}} \qquad E_R = \frac{x_{m-1} - x_m}{x_{m-1} - x_m^*} \qquad (10.90)$$

where $x_m$ and $y_m$ represent the actual average effluent compositions and $y_{m+1}$ and $x_{m-1}$ those of the streams entering the stage.  Any other consistent set of concentration units may equally well be used. The over-all stage efficiency **E** of a cascade is defined simply as the ratio of the number of ideal stages to the number of real stages required to bring about a given concentration change.

The available experimental data are so meager that few generalizations can be made. Pilot-plant experimentation for new designs is therefore essential. Over-all stage efficiencies for cascades of the mixer-settler type have been reported ranging from 0.75 to 1.0. On the other hand, individual Murphree stage efficiencies of 1.0 are easily obtained with agitated vessels, especially if they are baffled, even with systems of high interfacial tension for which dispersion is difficult.[7,10] It seems quite probable, therefore, that over-all efficiencies as low as the 0.75 occasionally reported for cascades may well be the result of incomplete settling of the liquids between stages.

The few data reported for perforated-tray towers have all been taken from small laboratory devices of only a few inches diameter, and the direct application of these data to the design of large-scale equipment is most risky. Over-all efficiencies range from as low as 0.02 for systems of high interfacial tension which are difficultly dispersed to 1.0 for easily dispersed systems of low interfacial tension, with the bulk of the data falling in the range 0.25 to 0.50. There appears to be little effect of perforation size, up to 0.25 in., for any given system. Tray efficiencies increase with tray spacing, owing to the corresponding increased time of contact of the phases, but there is little improvement for spacing larger than 16 or 18 in. As will be shown later, it appears that the most rapid mass transfer occurs during the formation of droplets, owing probably to the continual formation of new interfacial surface, while that occurring during the passage of the drop through a layer of continuous liquid is slow owing to the relatively stagnant conditions inside the drop. For these reasons very large tray spacings offer no advantage.

Over-all stage efficiencies for agitated equipment of the type shown in Figs. 10.16 and 10.17 depend to some extent on arbitrary definitions as to what constitutes real stages in these devices, and they are perhaps better treated as continuous-contact devices. The centrifugal extractor of Fig. 10.18 has been reported to offer the equivalent of 1 to 13 theoretical stages, depending upon the circumstances of operation.[1]

## CONTINUOUS CONTACT

Countercurrent extraction as shown in Figs. 10.40 and 10.49 may be carried out in any of the continuous-contact devices such as the spray, packed, and agitated towers previously described, as well as in the centrifugal-type extractors.

**Height of a Theoretical Stage.** The performance of any of the continuous-contact devices may be described in terms of the number of theoretical stages to which it is equivalent. By dividing the active height or length by this number, one obtains the height equivalent to a theoretical stage (H.E.T.S.), characteristic of the type of contact under the existing conditions.

$$Z = N_p(\text{H.E.T.S.}) \qquad (10.91)$$

H.E.T.S. may then be used to determine the necessary height for cases where the same method of contact is used under similar circumstances. Owing to the fact that H.E.T.S. incorrectly describes the continuous concentration changes which actually occur in terms of stepwise changes, it is to be expected that for any type of packing H.E.T.S. will be strongly dependent upon such operating conditions as type of system, rates of flow, and concentration. This makes it necessary to have at hand very specific H.E.T.S. data for any contemplated design. Practically, however, H.E.T.S. is widely used owing to its simplicity. The methods described below, which are based on mass-transfer coefficients and transfer units, are theoretically sounder and are therefore preferable.

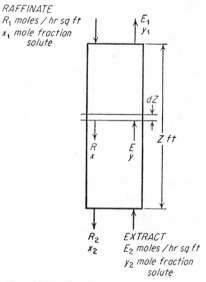

FIG. 10.60. Continuous-contact tower.

**Continuous Contact.** Consider the continuous-contact tower of Fig. 10.60, where extract and raffinate phases flow countercurrently. Although in the diagram the raffinate is shown flowing downward as if it were the more dense phase, it is to be understood that in some instances the solvent-rich, or extract, phase will be the heavier and will therefore enter at the top. In either case, in what follows subscripts 1 will always represent that end of the tower where the raffinate enters and extract leaves, while subscripts 2 will indicate that end where extract enters and raffinate leaves. We are presently unconcerned with the matter of which phase is dispersed and which continuous. It may assist in understanding the action of the tower if one keeps in mind the corresponding gas-absorption operation, where the gas corresponds to a raffinate phase and the liquid to an extract phase.

Throughout this discussion, unless otherwise specifically indicated, $x$ and $y$ *will refer to solute concentrations in terms of mole fractions* in the raffinate and extract phases, respectively, and rates of flow of raffinate $R$ and extract $E$ will be measured in terms of lb. moles/(hr.)(sq. ft. apparatus cross section). Unless otherwise specifically indicated, mass-transfer coefficients will be measured in terms of lb. moles of solute transferred/(hr.)(sq. ft.) (mole-fraction concentration gradient) and will be written as $K_R$ for concentration gradients measured in the raffinate and $K_E$ for those measured in the extract (these correspond to the liquid-phase mass-transfer coefficients $K_x$ of Chap. 3). Owing to the transfer of solute from raffinate to extract and the change in mutual solubility with changing solute concentration, the amounts of the liquids will vary as they flow through the tower. Because of the limitations of our diffusion equations, however, we shall limit the discussion to cases where the distributed solute is the only diffusing substance, although in practice the derived expressions are used for all circumstances.

In the differential height $dZ$ of the tower of Fig. 10.60, the interfacial surface per unit tower cross section is $dS$ sq. ft., and the rate of solute transfer can be described in terms of the over-all mass-transfer coefficients,

$$d(Rx) = d(Ey) = K_R(x - x^*)\, dS = K_E(y^* - y)\, dS \qquad (10.92)$$

where $x^*$ is the raffinate concentration which would be in equilibrium with the bulk extract composition $y$ and $y^*$ is the extract composition which would be in equilibrium with the bulk raffinate composition $x$. The unknown interfacial surface is best described in terms of $a$ sq. ft./cu. ft. of tower, so that

$$dS = a\, dZ \qquad (10.93)$$

and the quantity $a$ is then combined with the mass-transfer coefficients as $K_R a$ and $K_E a$.

**The Transfer Unit. Principal Diffusional Resistance in the Raffinate.** Both $R$ and $X$ vary from one end of the tower to the other, but if the mutual solubility of the liquids $A$ and $B$ does not change, the quantity $R(1 - x)$ should remain constant. Therefore

$$d(Rx) = R(1 - x)\, d\, \frac{x}{1 - x} = \frac{R\, dx}{1 - x} \qquad (10.94)$$

If the solute concentration varies appreciably throughout the length of the tower, the quantity $K_R(1 - x)_M$ should remain more constant than $K_R$ alone, where $(1 - x)_M$ represents the average of the nonsolute concentrations in the bulk of the raffinate and at the interface. Equation

**(10.92)** then becomes

$$\frac{R\,dx}{1-x} = \frac{K_Ra(1-x)_M(x-x^*)\,dZ}{(1-x)_M} \tag{10.95}$$

or

$$\left[\frac{(1-x)_M}{1-x}\right]\frac{dx}{x-x^*} = \frac{K_Ra(1-x)_M\,dZ}{R} \tag{10.96}$$

Neglecting for the moment the quantity in square brackets, the left-hand side of Eq. (10.96) is recognized as the number of times the driving force $x-x^*$ can divide into the change in raffinate composition $dx$, which in integrated form is the over-all number of transfer units, a measure of the difficulty of the separation to be done,

$$N_{tOR} = \int_{x_2}^{x_1}\frac{(1-x)_M}{1-x}\frac{dx}{x-x^*} = \frac{Z}{H_{tOR}} \tag{10.97}$$

where $H_{tOR}$ is the over-all height of a transfer unit. The latter is related to the mass-transfer coefficient,

$$H_{tOR} = \frac{R}{K_Ra(1-x)_M} \tag{10.98}$$

The quantity $(1-x)_M$ is a logarithmic average of the nonsolute concentrations, but in moderately dilute solutions the arithmetic average will serve equally well.

$$(1-x)_M = \frac{(1-x^*)-(1-x)}{\ln\dfrac{1-x^*}{1-x}} \doteq \frac{(1-x^*)+(1-x)}{2} \tag{10.99}$$

Substituting the latter definition into Eq. (10.97) produces

$$N_{tOR} = \int_{x_2}^{x_1}\frac{dx}{x-x^*} + \frac{1}{2}\ln\frac{1-x_2}{1-x_1} \tag{10.100}$$

The integral of Eq. (10.100) is evaluated by determining the area under a curve of $1/(x-x^*)$ as ordinate plotted against $x$ as abscissa. The data for such a curve are in turn taken from an operating diagram such as Fig. 10.43b or 10.51b, keeping in mind that concentrations must be expressed in mole fractions. The operating curve of such diagrams provides the values of $x$, and the equilibrium curve the value of $x^*$ at the same value of $y$. In other words, the horizontal distance between operating and equilibrium curves is the driving force $x-x^*$ of Eq. (10.100).

*Weight Fractions.* If $x$ is defined in terms of weight fractions, the term $\frac{1}{2}\ln\{[x_2(r-1)+1]/[x_1(r-1)+1]\}$ must be added to the right-hand side of Eq. (10.100). In this expression $r$ is the ratio of molecular weights of nonsolute to solute in the raffinate. Operating diagrams in terms of weight fractions may then be used directly.

*Weight Ratios.* For operating diagrams plotted in terms of $x'$ and $y'$, as in Fig. 10.47, the transfer units are computed by means of the following:

$$N_{tOR} = \int_{x_2'}^{x_1'} \frac{dx'}{x' - x'^*} + \frac{1}{2} \ln \frac{1 + rx_2'}{1 + rx_1'} \qquad (10.101)$$

**Principal Diffusional Resistance in the Extract.** Similar treatment of Eq. (10.92) leads to the following expressions for the over-all number of transfer units computed in terms of extract compositions:

$$N_{tOE} = \int_{y_2}^{y_1} \frac{(1 - y)_M}{1 - y} \frac{dy}{y^* - y} = \frac{Z}{H_{tOE}} \qquad (10.102)$$

$$H_{tOE} = \frac{E}{K_E a (1 - y)_M} \qquad (10.103)$$

$$(1 - y)_M = \frac{(1 - y) - (1 - y^*)}{\ln \dfrac{1 - y}{1 - y^*}} \doteq \frac{(1 - y) + (1 - y^*)}{2} \qquad (10.104)$$

$$N_{tOE} = \int_{y_2}^{y_1} \frac{dy}{y^* - y} + \frac{1}{2} \ln \frac{1 - y_2}{1 - y_1} \qquad (10.105)$$

The integral of Eq. (10.105) is evaluated as the area under a curve of $1/(y^* - y)$ as ordinate, $y$ as abscissa, obtained in turn from the operating diagrams Figs. 10.43b and 10.51b plotted in terms of mole fractions. At any value of $x$, the operating curve provides $y$ and the equilibrium curve $y^*$, so that $y^* - y$ is the vertical distance between the curves.

*Weight Fractions.* If $y$ is expressed as weight fraction of solute, so that the operating diagram in terms of weight fractions can be used to obtain the necessary data, thet erm $\frac{1}{2} \ln \{[y_2(r - 1) + 1]/[y_1(r - 1) + 1]\}$ must be added to the right-hand side of Eq. (10.105). Here $r$ is the ratio of molecular weights of nonsolute to solute in the extract.

*Weight Ratios.* For operating diagrams in terms of $x'$ and $y'$, as in Fig. 10.47, the equation becomes

$$N_{tOE} = \int_{y_2'}^{y_1'} \frac{dy'}{y'^* - y'} + \frac{1}{2} \ln \frac{1 + ry_2'}{1 + ry_1'} \qquad (10.106)$$

**Dilute Solutions.** For dilute solutions, only the integral terms of the foregoing equations are important. If in addition the equilibrium-distribution curve and operating line are straight over the range of concentrations involved, it is readily shown in the manner used in Chap. 8 that the logarithmic averages of the terminal concentration differences are applicable:

$$N_{tOR} = \frac{x_1 - x_2}{(x - x^*)_M} \qquad N_{tOE} = \frac{y_1 - y}{(y^* - y)_M} \qquad (10.107)$$

The equivalent expressions in terms of mass-transfer coefficients are

$$R(x_1 - x_2) = E(y_1 - y_2) = K_R a Z(x - x^*)_M = K_E a Z(y - y^*)_M \quad (10.108)$$

If in addition the equivalent of Henry's law applies, so that the equilibrium-distribution curve is a straight line passing through the origin ($m = y^*/x = y/x^* = $ const.), there is obtained, by a procedure exactly similar to that used previously in the case of gas absorption,

$$N_{tOR} = \frac{\ln\left[\dfrac{x_1 - y_2/m}{x_2 - y_2/m}\left(1 - \dfrac{R}{mE}\right) + \dfrac{R}{mE}\right]}{1 - R/mE} \quad (10.109)$$

Equation (10.109) may be used for countercurrent extraction without reflux, or for the raffinate-stripping section of a tower used with reflux, when the appropriate conditions apply. Figure 8.22 represents a graphical solution, provided $(x_2 - y_2/m)/(x_1 - y_2/m)$ is considered the ordinate and $mE/R$ the parameter. Similarly, for the extract-enriching section of a tower used with reflux, the same circumstances provide

$$N_{tOE} = \frac{\ln\left[\dfrac{y_2 - mx_1}{y_1 - mx_1}\left(1 - \dfrac{mE}{R}\right) + \dfrac{mE}{R}\right]}{1 - mE/R} \quad (10.110)$$

which is also solved graphically in Fig. 8.22 provided $(y_1 - mx_1)/(y_2 - mx_1)$ is the ordinate and $R/mE$ the parameter.

For these dilute solutions, Eqs. (10.107), (10.109), and (10.110) may be used with concentrations in terms of weight fractions, in which case $m$ must be defined in these terms as well while $E$ and $R$ are measured in lb./(hr.)(sq. ft.). Weight ratios may also be used. Equations (10.107) and (10.108) are frequently used with concentrations expressed as $c$ lb. moles/cu. ft., in which case the extract and raffinate flow rates are measured in terms of $V$ cu. ft./(hr.)(sq. ft.) and the units of the appropriate mass-transfer coefficients are $K_{LE}$ and $K_{LR}$ lb. moles/(hr.)(sq. ft.)($\Delta c$). The requirements of constant $m$ (in whatever units it is measured) and straight-line operating lines still of course apply.

**Illustration 10.** Determine the number of transfer units $N_{tOR}$ for the extraction of Illustration 7, for the case where 5,000 lb./hr. of solvent are used.

*Solution.* Define $x$ and $y$ in terms of weight fractions acetic acid. $x_1 = x_F = 0.30$; $y_2 = 0$; $x_2 = 0.02$; $y_1 = 0.10$. The operating diagram is already plotted in Fig. 10.46. From this plot, values of $x$ and $x^*$ are taken from the operating line and equilibrium curve at various values of $y$, as follows:

| $x$ | $x^*$ | $\dfrac{1}{x - x^*}$ |
|------|-------|------------|
| 0.30 | 0.230 | 14.30 |
| 0.25 | 0.192 | 17.25 |
| 0.20 | 0.154 | 20.75 |
| 0.15 | 0.114 | 27.8 |
| 0.10 | 0.075 | 40.0 |
| 0.05 | 0.030 | 50.0 |
| 0.02 | 0     | 50.0 |

The area under a curve of $x$ as abscissa against $1/(x - x^*)$ as ordinate (not shown) between $x = 0.30$ and $x = 0.02$ is determined to be 8.40. In these solutions, the mutual solubility of water and isopropyl ether is very small so that $r$ may be taken as $18\!\!\!/_{60} = 0.30$. Eq. (10.100), modified for the use of weight-fraction concentrations:

$$N_{tOR} = 8.40 + \frac{1}{2}\ln\frac{1 - 0.02}{1 - 0.30} + \frac{1}{2}\ln\frac{0.02(0.3 - 1) + 1}{0.30(0.3 - 1) + 1} = 8.46$$

The operating and equilibrium curves are nearly parallel in this case, so that $N_{tOR}$ and $N_p$ are nearly the same. The curvature of the lines makes the simplified methods for $N_{tOR}$ inapplicable, however.

**Illustration 11.** Determine the number of transfer units $N_{tOR}$ for the extraction of Illustration 8, when 1,150 lb./hr. of kerosene is used.

*Solution.* Use weight-ratio concentrations, as in Illustration 8. $x_1' = x_F' = 0.0101$; $y_2' = 0$; $x_2' = 0.001001$; $y_1' = 0.0782$. The calculation may be done through Eq. (10.109) or the equivalent, Fig. 8.22.

$$\frac{x_2' - y_2'/m'}{x_1' - y_2'/m'} = \frac{0.001001}{0.0101} = 0.0909$$

The average $mE/R = m'B/A = 1.01$ (Illustration 8). From Fig. 8.22, $N_{tOR} = 8.8$.

**Illustration 12.** Leibson and Beckmann [*Chem. Eng. Progr.*, **49**, 405 (1953)] extracted diethylamine from water [20.4 cu. ft./(hr.) (sq. ft.)] with toluene [3.05 cu. ft./(hr.)(sq. ft.)] at 30.8°C., toluene dispersed, in a 6-in. I.D. tower packed to a depth of 4 ft. with $\frac{1}{2}$-in. Raschig rings. The observed concentrations of diethylamine, in lb. moles/cu. ft., were water in = 0.01574, out = 0.01450; toluene in = 0, out 0.00860. At this temperature the distribution coefficient = concn. in water/concn. in toluene = 1.156, and water and toluene are substantially insoluble at these diethylamine concentrations. (a) Determine the extraction characteristics of the packing for these conditions. (b) Compute the effluent concentrations if 8 ft. of packing had been used.

*Solution.* a. The water solution is the raffinate and toluene the extract. Define $m'' = c_E^*/c_R = 1/1.156 = 0.865$.

$c_{E1} = 0.00860$, $c_{E2} = 0$, $c_{R1} = 0.01574$, $c_{R2} = 0.01450$ lb. moles diethylamine/cu. ft. Owing to the insolubility of the water and toluene, Eq. (10.108) may be written for this case as

$$V_E(c_{E1} - c_{E2}) = K_{LE}aZ(c_E^* - c_E)_M$$

where    $V_E = 3.05$ cu. ft. extract/(hr.)(sq. ft.), constant at these concentrations
$Z = 4$ ft.
$C_{E1}^* = m''c_{R1} = 0.865(0.01574) = 0.01363$

$$c_{E2}^* = m''c_{R2} = 0.865(0.01450) = 0.01254$$

$$(c_E^* - c_E)_M = \frac{(c_{E2}^* - c_{E2}) - (c_{E1}^* - c_{E1})}{\ln \dfrac{c_{E2}^* - c_{E2}}{c_{E1}^* - c_{E1}}} = \frac{(0.01254 - 0) - (0.01363 - 0.00860)}{\ln \dfrac{0.01254 - 0}{0.01363 - 0.00860}}$$

$$= 0.00825 \text{ lb. mole/cu. ft.}$$

$$\therefore 3.05(0.00860 - 0) = K_{LE}a(4)(0.00825)$$

$$K_{LE}a = 0.795 \text{ lb. mole/(hr.)(cu. ft.)}(\Delta c_E)$$

Applying Eq. (5.24) to this case, $K_{LR}a = m''K_{LE}a = 0.865(0.795) = 0.687$ lb. mole/(hr.)(cu. ft.)($\Delta c_R$).

From Table 3.1, $K_E a = cK_{LE}a$, where $c$ is the molar density, lb. moles/cu. ft., of the extract phase. For these dilute solutions, the density (0.856 gm./cu. cm.) and average molecular weight (92.1) of the extract are the same as those for pure toluene, so that $c = 0.856(62.3)/92.1 = 0.58$ lb. mole/cu. ft. Therefore $K_E a = 0.58(0.795) = 0.461$ lb. mole/(hr.)(cu. ft.)(mole fraction).

$$E = V_E c = 3.05(0.58) = 1.77 \text{ lb. moles extract/(hr.)(sq. ft.)}$$
$$H_{tOE} = E/K_E a = 1.77/0.461 = 3.84 \text{ ft.}$$

Alternatively,

$$H_{tOE} = V_E/K_{LE}a \qquad H_{tOR} = V_R/K_{LR}a = 20.4/0.687 = 29.7 \text{ ft.}$$

b. For 8 ft. of packing let $c_{R2}$ be the exit concentration in the water and $c_{E1}$ the exit concentration in the toluene. Equation (10.109) can be adapted to these units.

$$V_R/m''V_E = 20.4/0.865(3.05) = 7.73$$
$$N_{tOR} = Z/H_{tOR} = 8/29.7 = 0.269$$
$$c_{R1} = 0.01574 \qquad c_{E2} = 0$$
$$\therefore 0.269 = \frac{\ln \left[ \dfrac{0.01574}{c_{R2}} (1 - 7.73) + 7.73 \right]}{1 - 7.73}$$
$$c_{R2} = 0.01400 \text{ lb. mole diethylamine/cu. ft.}$$

A material balance for diethylamine,

$$V_E(c_{E1} - c_{E2}) = V_R(c_{R1} - c_{R2})$$
$$3.05(c_{E1} - 0) = 20.4(0.01574 - 0.01400)$$
$$c_{E1} = 0.01163 \text{ lb. mole/cu.ft.}$$

**Performance of Continuous-contact Equipment.** While over the past 20 years a considerable number of data has been accumulated, taken almost entirely from laboratory-size equipment of a few inches diameter, no satisfactory correlation of them has as yet been possible owing to the very large number of variables which influence extraction rates. For the design of new extractors it is essential that pilot-plant experiments be performed under conditions as nearly like those expected in the large-scale equipment as possible. This discussion will therefore be limited to a brief consideration of the important variables, but no data for design will be presented. Detailed study of many of the data is available elsewhere.[20]

The two-film theory indicates that the over-all resistances to mass transfer are made up of those residing in each of the fluid films. Thus Eq. (5.23) provides the relation between mass-transfer coefficients, and in terms of heights of transfer units we have

$$H_{tOR} = H_{tR} + \frac{R}{mE} H_{tE} \tag{10.111}$$

$$H_{tOE} = H_{tE} + \frac{mE}{R} H_{tR} \tag{10.112}$$

It must be understood that in any equipment of this sort the dispersed phase may be either the extract or the raffinate and either the light or the heavy phase. The resistances to mass transfer in the contacted fluids are likely to depend strongly upon whether the phases in question are dispersed or continuous. It is best therefore to describe the equipment characteristics in terms of mass-transfer coefficients or heights of transfer units written in terms of the continuous or dispersed phase, $K_C a$ and $K_D a$, or $H_{tOC}$ and $H_{tOD}$, so that the resistance equations become

$$H_{tOD} = H_{tD} + \frac{L_D}{mL_C} H_{tC} \tag{10.113}$$

$$H_{tOC} = H_{tC} + \frac{mL_C}{L_D} H_{tD} \tag{10.114}$$

Some work has been done to establish the individual mass-transfer resistances by use of a technique similar to that found useful in humidification work. Thus, by allowing pure water and pure butanol in the absence of a third distributed substance to flow countercurrently through a tower and mutually to saturate each other, values of $H_{tC}$ and $H_{tD}$ can be obtained. A limited number of such studies with spray and packed towers has been made, but insufficient to permit regularization of the data.

*Spray Towers.* These are the simplest of devices; yet the number of variables which appear to influence the rates of mass transfer in such equipment is very great. The physical properties of the fluids important to mass transfer, such as viscosity, density, interfacial tension, and diffusivity, all exert important influences on the extraction rates. All other things being constant, the rate of mass transfer varies depending upon which liquid of a given system is dispersed and which continuous. The interfacial surface between phases exerts a most profound effect, since this quantity appears in the volumetric coefficients $K_C a$ and $K_D a$. The interfacial surface in turn is greatly influenced by the size of the droplets produced by the distributor nozzles (in turn governed by nozzle diameter, velocity of flow, and physical properties of the liquids) and the rate of rise of the droplets, which governs the dispersed-phase hold-up.

As a result, values of the mass-transfer coefficient $K_D a$ for a given system and fixed drop diameter appear to vary directly with hold-up of dispersed phase and in an inverse fashion with drop diameter. It is important, therefore, to disperse the phase flowing in largest quantity, so as to obtain the largest possible interfacial surface.

The direction of extraction also exerts an important influence on the rate of extraction. If, for example, acetic acid is distributed between water and isopropyl ether, at fixed flow rates in a given tower and with the ether dispersed, the rate of extraction will be different depending upon whether the acid is transferred from the water to the ether or in the opposite direction. This is not observed in the case of gas absorption-desorption, where the direction of mass transfer is unimportant. In the case of extraction, the different rates may be the result of variations in physical properties with the change in solute concentrations necessary to cause the change in direction of solute transfer, but this has not yet been clearly established.

The end effects (see Chap. 7) are most important in spray towers There is considerable evidence now accumulated that very appreciable amounts of extraction occur during the formation of liquid droplets at a dispersing nozzle, while relatively little extraction may occur while the droplet rises through considerable depths of continuous liquid. There may also be important extraction phenomena occurring when the droplets coalesce at the end of the spray tower opposite from the spray nozzles. Values of $H_{to}$ are therefore much smaller, and $Ka$'s are correspondingly larger, for short towers than for tall. These effects and the extensive recirculation of continuous phase in towers of large diameter make it most difficult to extend measurements made in small equipment for use in the design of larger equipment.

Typical data from a laboratory tower are shown in Fig. 10.61 for the system acetic acid–isopropyl ether–water, taken with a 2-in.-diameter 4-ft.-tall spray tower fitted with a single $\frac{1}{8}$-in.-diameter nozzle for the dispersed phase. Such plots are typical: $H_{toD}$ usually increases slowly or remains substantially constant with increased ratio $V_D/V_c$, while $H_{toc}$ decreases. For other systems, values of $H_{toc}$ as high as 100 ft. have been reported at low values of $V_D/V_c$.

*Packed Towers.* In addition to the variation in mass-transfer rates to be expected from system to system owing to different physical properties, the following have been noted to influence the extraction rates importantly: (1) choice of dispersed or continuous phase; (2) wetting or nonwetting of the packing by the dispersed phase (see discussion under Flooding in Packed Towers); (3) size and type of packing; (4) height of tower (end effects are important, in other words); (5) direction of extraction; (6) hold-up of dispersed phase; (7) velocity of liquid flow. Within reasonable limits the drop size is independent of diameter of distribution nozzles but depends upon the packing size instead.

The presence of packing prevents extensive recirculation within the continuous phase, increases turbulence, and delays the passage of droplets through the tower so that generally improved rates of extraction are obtained in comparison with those for spray towers. The improvement is reduced, however, if the packing diameter is larger than about one-eighth that of the tower. The smaller the packing, the better the mass

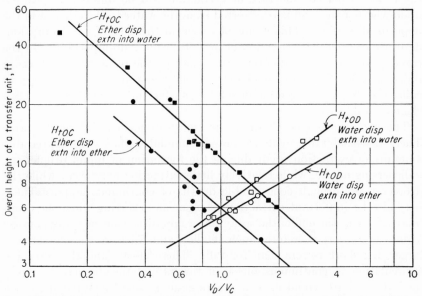

FIG. 10.61. Extraction of acetic acid between water and isopropyl ether in a 2.03-in.-diameter spray tower. [*Data of Elgin and Browning, Trans. Am. Inst. Chem. Engrs.*, **31**, 639 (1935).]

transfer. This is indicated, for example, by the data of Fig. 10.62. Economic considerations would probably put the extraction factor $V_R/mV_E$ in the region of 1 or 2, so that values of $H_{toR}$ are not unreasonably large for the smaller packings. The method of plotting used in this figure derives from a consideration of Eq. (10.111) on the assumption that $H_{tE}$ and $H_{tR}$ are essentially constant. It is generally useful as a correlating device, but it is doubtful that justifiable values of the individual phase resistances can be obtained from the slopes and intercepts of these curves.

By *pulsing* the packed column (see Pulse Columns, above), the values of $Ka$ have been increased many fold and the values of $H_{to}$ correspondingly reduced.[6]

*Agitated Towers.* Equipment of the type shown in Figs. 10.16 and 10.17 offers an additional operational variable which influences the rate of extraction, the degree of agitation. Insufficient data are available from either of these types to permit extensive generalizations, but it appears that they can equal or exceed the performance of packed columns if correctly agitated for the systems handled.[16,19]

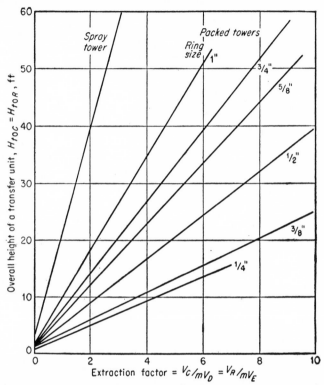

Fig. 10.62. Extraction of diethylamine from water into toluene, toluene dispersed, in a 6-in.-diameter tower. [*Data of Leibson and Beckmann, Chem. Eng. Progr.*, **49**, 405 (1953).]

## MULTICOMPONENT SYSTEMS

Detailed treatment of multicomponent extraction systems is beyond the scope of this book, but it is possible to indicate briefly the nature of some of the separations in such systems, in view of their importance.

**Fractional Extraction.** Two substances may frequently be separated by distributing them simultaneously between two immiscible liquids. If their distribution coefficients are different, then a separation is possible. For example, a mixture of *o*- and *m*-nitroaniline may be separated by adding the mixture to the double-solvent system, benzene-water. The distribution coefficient (concn. in benzene/concn. in water) of the ortho

isomer is greater than that of the meta isomer, and therefore the ratio of
o- to m-nitroaniline in the benzene layer will be greater than in the original
mixture, or in the water layer.   Separations of this sort may be enhanced
by continuous multistage operation.   Thus, benzene and water may be
caused to flow countercurrently through a multistage cascade or a continuous-contact tower, and the mixture of nitroanilines may be introduced more or less centrally into the cascade.   The effluent benzene will
then be rich in the ortho isomer and the effluent water rich in the meta
isomer.   Reflux may also be used in such a device.   Operations of this
sort have been successfully used for previously very difficult processes,

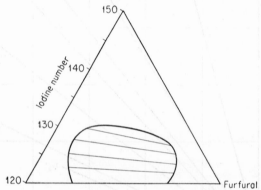

Fig. 10.63. Use of iodine number to characterize a vegetable oil in extraction operations.

such as the separation of the salts of the rare-earth metals from each
other.

**Extraction of Natural Products.**   Many naturally occurring products
are so complex that the number and identity of their components are not
known.   Separation of the components according to chemical type is
often desired, and in such instances simplification of the problem is frequently possible by use of a product property, rather than analysis in
the ordinary sense, as a characterizing quantity.   For example, vegetable
oils such as soybean oil contain a large number of fatty-acid esters of
glycerol, some saturated and others unsaturated to various extents.   The
extent of unsaturation in the mixture may be measured by the "iodine
number," the number of centigrams of iodine absorbed per gram of oil.
This is an additive property, so that the iodine number of a mixture of
equal weights of an oil of iodine number 50 and one of iodine number
100 is 75.   Iodine numbers between 50 and 100 would therefore be an
indication of the relative amounts of the two original oils present in any
mixture of the two.   If it is desired to use a selective solvent such as
liquid propane or furfural to separate the high-iodine-number fractions

from the low, we can use iodine number as one of the coordinate scales of a triangular diagram, as in Fig. 10.63. It is customary to make all the usual stage-type computations on such a diagram.

Similarly in the field of petroleum-lubricant refining, the aromatic portions of the lubricating-oil fractions may be separated from the naphthenic-paraffinic portions by extraction with solvents such as phenol or furfural. For these purposes, diagrams such as Fig. 10.63 can be prepared, using an appropriate additive property such as refractive index or viscosity-gravity constant to characterize the mixture. Viscosity-gravity constant, an empirical quantity relating the viscosity and specific gravity of the fractions, is sufficiently different for aromatic and naphthenic-paraffinic mixtures to permit their ready differentiation. There is some evidence, however, that the use of phase diagrams of this sort obtained from equilibrium measurements of a single-stage type are not entirely satisfactory for predicting properties of products for multistage operation, owing to independent variations of the distribution coefficients of the components of the mixture.

## NOTATION FOR CHAPTER 10

$a$ = interfacial surface, sq. ft./cu. ft. active volume

$a_p$ = surface of packing, sq. ft./cu. ft.

$A$ = component $A$, lb. liquid $A$/(hr.)(sq. ft.) (or lb. in a batch process)

$B$ = component $B$, lb. liquid $B$/(hr.)(sq. ft.) (or lb. in a batch process)

$c$ = concentration of solute, lb. moles/cu. ft. solution

$C$ = component $C$, the distributed solute, lb. substance $C$/(hr.)(sq. ft.) (or lb. in a batch process)

$d$ = differential operator

$d_O$ = orifice or nozzle diameter, ft.

$d_p$ = drop diameter, ft.

$E$ = extract solution, lb. extract/(hr.)(sq. ft.) (or lb. in a batch process), or, in continuous-contact devices, lb. moles/(hr.)(sq. ft.)

$E'$ = solvent-free extract, lb./(hr.)(sq. ft.) (or lb. in a batch process)

$\mathbf{E}$ = over-all stage efficiency, fractional, dimensionless

$\mathbf{E}_E$ = Murphree extract stage efficiency, fractional, dimensionless

$\mathbf{E}_R$ = Murphree raffinate stage efficiency, fractional, dimensionless

$F$ = feed or solution to be extracted, lb. liquid $F$/(hr.)(sq. ft.) (or lb. in a batch process)

$g$ = acceleration due to gravity, ft./hr.$^2$

$g_c$ = conversion factor, 4.17(10$^8$) lb. mass (ft.)/(lb. force)(hr.)$^2$

$h$ = depth of dispersed liquid accumulating on a tray, ft.

$h_C$ = depth of dispersed liquid accumulating on a tray owing to flow of continuous liquid, ft.

$h_D$ = depth of dispersed liquid accumulating on a tray owing to flow of dispersed liquid, ft.

$h_O$ = head required to cause flow through an orifice, ft.

$h_\sigma$ = head required to overcome effect of interfacial tension, ft.

H.E.T.S. = height equivalent to a theoretical stage, ft.

$H_{toC}$ = over-all height of a transfer unit, continuous phase, ft.

$H_{toD}$ = over-all height of a transfer unit, dispersed phase, ft.

$H_{toE}$ = over-all height of a transfer unit, extract phase, ft.

$H_{toR}$ = over-all height of a transfer unit, raffinate phase, ft.

$K_{Ea}$ = over-all extract mass-transfer coefficient, lb. moles/(hr.)(cu. ft.)(mol fraction)

$K_{LEa}$ = over-all extract mass-transfer coefficient, lb. moles/(hr.)(cu. ft.)(lb. moles/cu. ft.)

$K_{LRa}$ = over-all raffinate mass-transfer coefficient, lb. moles/(hr.)(cu. ft.)(lb. moles/cu. ft.)

$K_{Ra}$ = over-all raffinate mass-transfer coefficient, lb. moles/(hr.)(cu. ft.)(mole fraction)

ln = natural logarithm

$L$ = rate of flow; lb./(hr.)(sq. ft.)

$m$ = slope of the equilibrium-distribution curve = $dy^*/dx = dy/dx^*$, dimensionless

$m'$ = slope of the equilibrium-distribution curve = $dy'^*/dx' = dy'/dx'^*$, dimensionless

$M$ = mixture $M$, lb. mixture $M$/(hr.)(sq. ft.) (or lb. in a batch process)

$M'$ = solvent-free mixture $M$, lb./(hr.)(sq. ft.)( or lb. in a batch process)

$n$ = a constant

$N$ = solvent concentration, solvent-free basis, lb. $B$/lb. $(A + C)$

$N_p$ = number of theoretical stages, dimensionless

$N_{toE}$ = over-all number of transfer units, extract phase, dimensionless

$N_{toR}$ = over-all number of transfer units, raffinate phase, dimensionless

$P_E$ = extract product, lb./(hr.)(sq. ft.)

$P_E'$ = solvent-free extract product, lb./(hr.)(sq. ft.)

$P_R$ = raffinate product, lb./(hr.)(sq. ft.)

$P_R'$ = solvent-free raffinate product, lb./(hr.)(sq. ft.)

$Q$ = defined by Eq. (10.54)

$r$ = molecular weight nonsolute/molecular weight solute, dimensionless

$R$ = raffinate solution, lb. raffinate/(hr.)(sq. ft.) (or lb. in a batch process), or, in continuous-contact devices, lb. moles/(hr.)(sq. ft.)

$R'$ = solvent-free raffinate, lb./(hr.)(sq. ft.) (or lb. in a batch process)

$s$ = a distance, Fig. 10.4 and Eq. (10.1), ft.

$S$ = interfacial surface, sq. ft./sq. ft. of tower cross section

$t$ = a distance, Fig. 10.4 and Eq. (10.1), ft.

$u$ = a distance, Fig. 10.4 and Eq. (10.1), ft.

$v_p$ = drop volume, cu. ft.

$V$ = superficial velocity, ft./hr. or cu. ft./(hr.)(sq. ft.)

$V_d$ = superficial velocity in downspout, ft./hr.

$V_O$ = superficial velocity through orifice, ft./hr.

$V_O'$ = superficial velocity through orifice, ft./sec.

$V_p$ = ultimate settling velocity of a drop, ft./hr.

$W$ = defined by Eq. (10.64)

$x$ = concentration of $C$ in $A$-rich, or raffinate, phase, weight fraction (mole fraction for continuous-contact devices)

$x'$ = concentration of $C$ in $A$-rich, or raffinate, phase, lb. $C$/lb. non-$C$

$X$ = concentration of $C$ in $A$-rich, or raffinate, phase, $B$-free basis, lb. $C$/lb. $(A + C)$

$y$ = concentration of $C$ in $B$-rich, or extract, phase, weight fraction (mole fraction for continuous-contact devices)

$y'$ = concentration of $C$ in $B$-rich, or extract, phase, lb. $C$/lb. non-$C$

$Y$ = concentration of $C$ in $B$-rich, or extract, phase, $B$-free basis, lb. $C$/lb. $(A + C)$

$Z$ = active height, ft.

$\beta$ = selectivity of solvent, dimensionless

$\Delta$ = difference

$\epsilon$ = void fraction, dimensionless

$\mu$ = viscosity, lb./(ft.)(hr.)

$\mu'$ = viscosity, centipoises

$\pi$ = 3.1416

$\rho$ = density, lb./cu. ft.

$\sigma$ = interfacial tension, lb./ft. = (dynes/cm.)$(6.85 \times 10^{-5})$

$\sigma'$ = interfacial tension, dynes/cm.

Subscripts:

$C$ = continuous phase

$D$ = dispersed phase

$e$ = stage $e$

$E$ = extract

$f$ = flooding condition

$F$ = feed

$H$ = heavy, or more dense, phase

$L$ = light, or less dense, phase

$m$ = stage $m$

$M$ = pertaining to mixture $M$; logarithmic average

$n$ = stage $n$

$Np$ = last stage of a cascade

$O$ = orifice or nozzle

$s$ = stage $s$

$0$ = entering first stage

$1$ = stage 1; that end of a continuous-contact tower where raffinate enters

$2$ = stage 2; that end of a continuous-contact tower where extract enters

Superscript:

$*$ = equilibrium concentration

## REFERENCES

1. Barson, N., and G. H. Beyer: *Chem. Eng. Progr.*, **49**, 243 (1953).
2. Blanding, F. H., and J. C. Elgin: *Trans. Am. Inst. Chem. Engrs.*, **38**, 305 (1942).
3. Bussolari, R., S. Schiff, and R. E. Treybal: *Ind. Eng. Chem.*, **45**, 2413 (1953).
4. Cohen, R. M., and G. H. Beyer: *Chem. Eng. Progr.*, **49**, 279 (1953).
5. Crawford, J. W., and C. R. Wilke: *Chem. Eng. Progr.*, **47**, 423 (1951).
6. Feick, G., and H. M. Anderson: *Ind. Eng. Chem.*, **44**, 404 (1952).
7. Flynn, A. W.: Thesis, New York University, 1953.
8. Gayler, R., and H. R. C. Pratt: *Trans. Inst. Chem. Engrs.*, **29**, 110 (1951).
9. Hayworth, C. B., and R. E. Treybal: *Ind. Eng. Chem.*, **42**, 1174 (1950).
10. Hixson, A. W., and M. I. Smith: *Ind. Eng. Chem.*, **41**, 973 (1949).

11. Lewis, J. B., I. Jones, and H. R. C. Pratt: *Trans. Inst. Chem. Engrs.*, **29**, 126 (1951).
12. Mack, D. E., and A. E. Kroll: *Chem. Eng. Progr.*, **44**, 189 (1948).
13. Mayfield, F. D., and W. L. Church: *Ind. Eng. Chem.*, **44**, 2253 (1952).
14. Miller, S. A., and C. A. Mann: *Trans. Am. Inst. Chem. Engrs.*, **40**, 709 (1944).
15. Minard, G. W., and A. I. Johnson: *Chem. Eng. Progr.*, **48**, 62 (1952).
16. Oldshue, J. Y., and J. H. Rushton: *Chem. Eng. Progr.*, **48**, 297 (1952).
17. Ricci, J. E.: "The Phase Rule and Heterogeneous Equilibrium," D. Van Nostrand Company, Inc., New York, 1951.
18. Rushton, J. H., E. W. Costich, and H. J. Everett: *Chem. Eng. Progr.*, **46**, 395, 467 (1950).
19. Scheibel, E. G., and A. E. Karr: *Ind. Eng. Chem.*, **42**, 1048 (1950).
20. Treybal, R. E.: "Liquid Extraction," McGraw-Hill Book Company, Inc., New York, 1951.

## PROBLEMS

Problems 1 to 7 refer to the system water ($A$)–chlorobenzene ($B$)–pyridine ($C$) at 25°C. Equilibrium tie-line data, interpolated from those of Peake and Thompson, *Ind. Eng. Chem.*, **44**, 2439 (1952), are in weight per cents.

| Pyridine | Chlorobenzene | Water | Pyridine | Chlorobenzene | Water |
|---|---|---|---|---|---|
| 0 | 99.95 | 0.05 | 0 | 0.08 | 99.92 |
| 11.05 | 88.28 | 0.67 | 5.02 | 0.16 | 94.82 |
| 18.95 | 79.90 | 1.15 | 11.05 | 0.24 | 88.71 |
| 24.10 | 74.28 | 1.62 | 18.90 | 0.38 | 80.72 |
| 28.60 | 69.15 | 2.25 | 25.50 | 0.58 | 73.92 |
| 31.55 | 65.58 | 2.87 | 36.10 | 1.85 | 62.05 |
| 35.05 | 61.00 | 3.95 | 44.95 | 4.18 | 50.87 |
| 40.60 | 53.00 | 6.40 | 53.20 | 8.90 | 37.90 |
| 49.0 | 37.8 | 13.2 | 49.0 | 37.8 | 13.2 |

**1.** Plot the equilibrium data on the following coordinate systems: (*a*) triangular; (*b*) $x$ and $y$ against weight fraction $B$; (*c*) $x$ against $y$.

**2.** Compute the selectivity of chlorobenzene for pyridine at each tie line, and plot selectivity against concentration of pyridine in water.

**3.** It is desired to reduce the pyridine concentration of 2,000 lb. of an aqueous solution from 50 to 2% in a single batch extraction with chlorobenzene. What amount of solvent is required? Solve on triangular coordinates.

**4.** A 2,000-lb. batch of pyridine-water solution, 50% pyridine, is to be extracted with an equal weight of chlorobenzene. The raffinate from the first extraction is to be reextracted with a weight of solvent equal to the raffinate weight, and so on ($B_2$ = $R_1$, $B_3$ = $R_2$, etc.). How many theoretical stages and what total solvent will be required to reduce the concentration of pyridine to 2% in the final raffinate? Solve on triangular coordinates.

**5.** Two thousand pounds per hour of a 50% pyridine–50% water solution is to be continuously and countercurrently extracted with chlorobenzene to reduce the pyridine concentration to 2%. Using the coordinate systems plotted in (*b*) and (*c*) of Prob. 1:

*a.* Determine the minimum solvent rate required, lb./hr.

*b.* If 2,040 lb. solvent/hr. is used, what are the number of theoretical stages and the saturated and solvent-free weights of extract and raffinate?

*c.* Determine the number of transfer units $N_{tOR}$ for the extraction of (*b*).

**6.** The properties of the solutions have not been completely studied, but from those of the pure constituents the following properties are estimated:

| | Density, lb./cu. ft. | Viscosity, centipoises | Interfacial tension, dynes/cm. |
|---|---|---|---|
| Feed............... | 62.1 | 1.0 | 8 |
| Extract............ | 65 | 1.3 | |
| Raffinate.......... | 62.2 | 0.89 | 35 |
| Solvent............ | 68.5 | 1.25 | |

For the extraction of Prob. 5*b* and *c*, chlorobenzene as dispersed phase,

*a.* Estimate the required diameter of a tower packed with 1-in. ceramic rings, operated at 50% of the flooding rates.

*b.* Estimate the required diameter of a spray tower, operated at 40% of flooding, and built with $\frac{3}{16}$-in.-diameter dispersing nozzles.

*c.* Design a perforated tray suitable for the lower part of a tower. Use $\frac{3}{16}$-in.-diameter perforations and a perforation velocity of 0.5 ft./sec. Estimate the depth of dispersed liquid accumulating on the tray.

**7.** Can the separation of Prob. 5 be made by distillation at atmospheric pressure?

**8.** Water-dioxane solutions form a minimum-boiling azeotrope at atmospheric pressure and cannot be separated by ordinary distillation methods. Benzene forms no azeotrope with dioxane and may be used as an extraction solvent. At 25°C., the equilibrium distribution of dioxane between water and benzene [*J. Am. Chem. Soc.*, **66**, 282 (1944)] is as follows:

| Wt. % dioxane in water.............. | 5.1 | 18.9 | 25.2 |
|---|---|---|---|
| Wt. % dioxane in benzene........... | 5.2 | 22.5 | 32.0 |

At these concentrations water and benzene are substantially insoluble. One thousand pounds of a 25% dioxane–75% water solution is to be extracted with benzene to remove 95% of the dioxane.

*a.* Calculate the solvent requirement for a single batch operation.

*b.* If the extraction were done with equal amounts of solvent in five cocurrent stages, how much solvent would be required?

*c.* If the solvent used in (*b*) contained 0.02 lb. dioxane/lb. benzene, what would be the final raffinate composition?

**9.** One thousand pounds per hour of a 25% solution of dioxane in water is to be continuously extracted in countercurrent fashion with benzene to remove 95% of the dioxane. Equilibrium data are given in Prob. 8.

*a.* What is the minimum solvent requirement, lb./hr.?

*b.* If 900 lb./hr. of solvent is used, how many theoretical stages are required? Solve graphically and also through Eq. (10.52) and Fig. 8.15.

*c.* How many transfer units $N_{tOR}$ correspond to the extraction of (*b*)?

**10.** Twenty-four cubic feet per hour of water, containing 0.02 lb. mole diethylamine/-cu. ft., is to be extracted continuously and countercurrently with 27.7 cu. ft. toluene/-

hr. at 30.8°C., in order to remove 90% of the diethylamine. Determine the required height and diameter of a tower packed with ½-in. unglazed porcelain rings, operated at 50% of the flooding velocity.

Equilibrium distribution data are given in Illustration 12 and values of $H_{tOR}$ in Fig. 10.62. The densities and viscosities of the liquids may be taken as those of pure water and toluene, and the interfacial tension is estimated to be 30 dynes/cm.

Problems 11 to 13 refer to the system cottonseed oil $(A)$–liquid propane $(B)$–oleic acid $(C)$ at 98.5°C., 625 lb./sq. in. abs. Smoothed equilibrium tie-line data of Hixson and Bockelmann, *Trans. Am. Inst. Chem. Engrs.*, **38**, 891 (1942), in weight per cents, are as follows:

| Cottonseed oil | Oleic acid | Propane | Cottonseed oil | Oleic acid | Propane |
|---|---|---|---|---|---|
| 63.5 | 0 | 36.5 | 2.30 | 0 | 97.7 |
| 57.2 | 5.5 | 37.3 | 1.95 | 0.76 | 97.3 |
| 52.0 | 9.0 | 39.0 | 1.78 | 1.21 | 97.0 |
| 46.7 | 13.8 | 39.5 | 1.50 | 1.90 | 96.6 |
| 39.8 | 18.7 | 41.5 | 1.36 | 2.73 | 95.9 |
| 31.0 | 26.3 | 42.7 | 1.20 | 3.8 | 95.0 |
| 26.9 | 29.4 | 43.7 | 1.10 | 4.4 | 94.5 |
| 21.0 | 32.4 | 46.6 | 1.0 | 5.1 | 93.9 |
| 14.2 | 37.4 | 48.4 | 0.8 | 6.1 | 93.1 |
| 8.3 | 39.5 | 52.2 | 0.7 | 7.2 | 92.1 |
| 4.5 | 41.1 | 54.4 | 0.4 | 6.1 | 93.5 |
| 0.8 | 43.7 | 55.5 | 0.2 | 5.5 | 94.3 |

**11.** Plot the equilibrium data on the following coordinate systems: $(a)$ $N$ against $X$ and $Y$; $(b)$ $X$ against $Y$.

**12.** One hundred pounds of a cottonseed oil–oleic acid solution containing 25% acid is to be extracted twice in cocurrent fashion, each time with 1,000 lb. of propane. Determine the compositions, per cent by weight, and the weights of the mixed extracts and the final raffinate. Determine the compositions and weights of the solvent-free products. Make the computations on the coordinates plotted in Prob. 11a.

**13.** One thousand pounds per hour of a cottonseed oil–oleic acid solution containing 25% acid is to be continuously separated into products containing 2% and 90% acid (solvent-free compositions) by countercurrent extraction with propane. Make the following computations on the coordinate systems of Prob. 11a and b:

a. What is the minimum number of theoretical stages required?

b. What is the minimum external extract-reflux ratio required?

c. For an external extract-reflux ratio of 4.5, determine the number of theoretical stages, the position of the feed stage, and the quantities, in lb./hr., of the following streams: $E_1$, $B_E$, $E'$, $P'_E$, $R_0$, $P'_R$, $B_R$, $P_R$, $R_{Np}$, $R_{Np} - P_R$, and $B$.

d. What do the equilibrium data indicate as to the maximum purity of oleic acid that could be obtained?

# PART IV

# SOLID-FLUID OPERATIONS

The mass-transfer operations in this category are adsorption, drying, and leaching. Adsorption involves contact of solids with either liquids or gases, with mass transfer in the direction fluid to solid. Drying involves gas-solid, and leaching liquid-solid, contact, with mass transfer in each case in the direction solid to fluid. In many but not all applications, the last two may be considered as special cases of desorption, the reverse of adsorption. Adsorption is thus more general, in principle at least, and is considered first.

Theoretically, at least, the same apparatus and equipment useful for gas-solid or liquid-solid contact in adsorption should also be useful in the corresponding operations of drying and leaching. In practice, however, we find special types of apparatus in all three categories. This is probably the result of many years of development of the practical applications of these operations without the realization that basically they are very similar. For example, we find considerable inventive genius applied to the development of equipment for the continuous gas-solid operations of adsorption, but little application of the results to the problems of drying. Many clever devices have been developed for continuous leaching of solids with liquids, but there is little application of these to the practical problems of adsorption from liquids. Ideal devices have not yet been invented. But we may reasonably expect a reduction in the number of equipment types and greater interapplication among the three operations as the many problems of solids handling are eventually solved.

In developing the quantitative treatment of these operations, particularly the diverse applications of adsorption, considerable simplification results if advantage is taken of the resemblances to the gas and liquid operations previously considered. This introduces many problems of mathematical notation, however, and the student is advised to pay more than ordinary attention to the tables of notation at the end of each chapter. Complete consistency with the notation of the previous chapters seemed impossible to realize.

# CHAPTER 11

# ADSORPTION AND ION EXCHANGE

The adsorption operations exploit the ability of certain solids preferentially to concentrate specific substances from solution onto their surfaces. In this manner, the components of either gaseous or liquid solutions may be separated from each other. A few examples will indicate the general nature of the separations possible and at the same time demonstrate the great variety of practical applications. In the field of gaseous separations, adsorption is used to dehumidify air and other gases, to remove objectionable odors and impurities from industrial gases such as carbon dioxide, to recover valuable solvent vapors from dilute mixtures with air and other gases, and to fractionate mixtures of hydrocarbon gases containing such substances as methane, ethylene, ethane, propylene, and propane. Typical liquid separations include the removal of moisture dissolved in gasoline, decolorization of petroleum products and aqueous sugar solutions, removal of objectionable taste and odor from water, and the fractionation of mixtures of aromatic and paraffinic hydrocarbons.

These operations are all similar in that the mixture to be separated is brought into contact with another insoluble phase, the adsorbent solid, and the unequal distribution of the original constituents between the adsorbed phase on the solid surface and the bulk of the fluid then permits a separation to be made. All the techniques previously found valuable in the contact of insoluble fluids are useful in adsorption. Thus we have batchwise single-stage and continuous multistage separations and separations analogous to countercurrent absorption and stripping in the field of gas-liquid contact and to rectification and extraction with the use of reflux. In addition, the rigidity and immobility of a bed of solid adsorbent particles makes possible useful application of semicontinuous methods which are not at all practicable when two fluids are contacted.

Another solid-liquid operation of great importance is ion exchange, the reversible exchange of ions between certain solids and an electrolyte solution, which permits the separation and fractionation of electrolytic solutes. It is, of course, chemical in nature but involves not only the interaction of the ions with the solid but also diffusion of ions within the solid phase. Although the phenomenon may be more complex than adsorption, the general techniques and the results obtained are very similar.   The special features of ion exchange are considered separately at the end of this chapter.

**Types of Adsorption.**   We must distinguish at the start between two types of adsorption phenomena, physical and chemical.

*Physical adsorption*, or "van der Waals" adsorption, a readily reversible phenomenon, is the result of intermolecular forces of attraction between molecules of the solid and the substance adsorbed.   When, for example, the intermolecular attractive forces between a solid and a gas are greater than those existing between molecules of the gas itself, the gas will condense upon the surface of the solid even though its pressure may be lower than the vapor pressure corresponding to the prevailing temperature.   Such a condensation will be accompanied by an evolution of heat, in amount usually somewhat larger than the latent heat of vaporization and of the order of the heat of sublimation of the gas. The adsorbed substance does not penetrate within the crystal lattice of the solid and does not dissolve in it but remains entirely upon the surface. If, however, the solid is highly porous, containing many fine capillaries, the adsorbed substance will penetrate these interstices if it wets the solid. The equilibrium vapor pressure of a concave liquid surface of very small radius of curvature is lower than that of a large flat surface, and the extent of adsorption is correspondingly increased.   In any case, at equilibrium the partial pressure of the adsorbed substance equals that of the contacting gas phase, and by lowering the pressure of the gas phase or by raising the temperature the adsorbed gas is readily removed or desorbed in unchanged form.   Industrial adsorption operations of the type we shall consider depend upon this reversibility for recovery of the adsorbent for reuse, for recovery of the adsorbed substance, or for the fractionation of mixtures.   Reversible adsorption is not confined to gases but is observed in the case of liquids as well.

*Chemisorption*, or activated adsorption, is the result of chemical interaction between the solid and the adsorbed substance.   The strength of the chemical bond may vary considerably, and identifiable chemical compounds in the usual sense may not actually form, but the adhesive force is generally much greater than that found in physical adsorption.   The heat liberated during chemisorption is usually large, of the order of the heat of chemical reaction.   The process is frequently irreversible, and on desorption the original substance will often be found to have undergone a chemical change.   The same substance which, under conditions of low temperature, will undergo substantially only physical adsorption upon a solid will sometimes exhibit chemisorption at higher temperatures, and both phenomena may occur at the same time.   Chemisorption is of particular importance in catalysis but will not be considered here.

**Nature of Adsorbents.**   Adsorbent solids are usually used in granular form, varying in size from roughly ½ in. in diameter to as small as 50 microns. The solids must possess certain engineering properties depending upon the application to which they are put. If they are used in a fixed bed through which a liquid or gas is to flow, for example, they must not offer too great a pressure drop for flow nor must they easily be carried away by the flowing stream. They must have adequate strength and hardness so as not to be reduced in size during handling or crushed in supporting their own weight in beds of the required thickness. If they are to be transported frequently in and out of bins, they should be free-flowing. These are properties which are readily recognized.

The adsorptive ability of solids is quite another matter. Adsorption is a very general phenomenon, and even common solids will adsorb gases and vapors at least to a certain extent. For example, every student of analytical chemistry has observed with annoyance the increase in weight of a dried porcelain crucible on a humid day during an analytical weighing, owing to the adsorption of moisture from the air upon the crucible surface. But only certain solids exhibit sufficient specificity and adsorptive capacity to make them useful as industrial adsorbents. Since solids are frequently very specific in their ability to adsorb certain substances in large amounts, the chemical nature of the solid evidently has much to do with its adsorption characteristics. But mere chemical identity is insufficient to characterize its usefulness. In liquid extraction, all samples of pure butyl acetate will extract acetic acid from a water solution with identical ability. The same is not true for the adsorption characteristics of silica gel with respect to water vapor, for example. Much depends on its method of manufacture and on its prior history of adsorption and desorption.

Large surface per unit weight seems essential to all useful adsorbents. Particularly in the case of gas adsorption, the significant surface is not the gross surface of the granular particles which are ordinarily used but rather the very much larger surface of the internal pores of the particles. The pores are usually very small, sometimes of the order of a few molecular diameters in width, but their large number provides an enormous surface for adsorption. It is estimated, for example, that a typical gas-mask charcoal has an effective surface of 1,000,000 sq. m./kg.[21] There are many other properties evidently of great importance which are not at all understood, and we must depend largely on empirical observation for recognition of adsorptive ability. The following is a list of the principal adsorbents in general use. For a complete description the student is referred to a more extensive treatment of the subject.[21]

1. *Fuller's earths.* These are natural clays, the American varieties coming largely from Florida and Georgia. They are chiefly magnesium aluminum silicates in the form of the minerals attapulgite and montmorillonite. The clay is heated and dried, during which operation it develops a porous structure, ground, and screened. Commercially available sizes range from coarse granules to fine powders. The clays are

particularly useful in decolorizing, neutralizing, and drying such petroleum products as lubricating oils, transformer oils, kerosenes, and gasolines, as well as vegetable and animal oils. By washing and burning the adsorbed organic matter accumulating upon the clay during use, the adsorbent may be reused many times.

2. *Activated clays.* These are bentonite or other clays which show essentially no adsorptive ability unless activated by treatment with sulfuric or hydrochloric acid. Following such treatment, the clay is washed, dried, and ground to a fine powder. It is particularly useful for decolorizing petroleum products and is ordinarily discarded after a single application.

3. *Bauxite.* This is a certain form of naturally occurring hydrated alumina which must be activated by heating to temperatures varying from 450 to 1500°F. in order to develop its adsorptive ability. It is used for decolorizing petroleum products and for drying of gases and may be reactivated by heating.

4. *Alumina.* This is a hard, hydrated aluminum oxide which is activated by heating to drive off the moisture. The porous product is available as granules or powders, and it is used chiefly as a desiccant for gases and liquids. It may be reactivated for reuse.

5. *Bone char.* This is obtained by the destructive distillation of crushed, dried bones at temperatures in the range 1100 to 1600°F. It is used chiefly in the refining of sugar and may be reused after washing and burning.

6. *Decolorizing carbons.* These are variously made by (a) mixing vegetable matter with inorganic substances such as calcium chloride, carbonizing, and leaching away the inorganic matter, (b) mixing organic matter such as sawdust, etc., with porous substances such as pumice stone, followed by heating and carbonizing to deposit the carbonaceous matter throughout the porous particles, and (c) carbonizing wood, sawdust, and the like, followed by activation with hot air or steam. They are used for a great variety of purposes, including the decolorizing of solutions of sugar, industrial chemicals, drugs, and dry-cleaning liquids, water purification, and refining of vegetable and animal oils.

7. *Gas-adsorbent carbon.* This is made by carbonization of coconut shells, fruit pits, coal, and wood. It must be activated, essentially a partial oxidation process, by treatment with hot air or steam. It is available in granular or pelleted form and is used for recovery of solvent vapors from gas mixtures, in gas masks, and for the fractionation of hydrocarbon gases. It is revivified for reuse by evaporation of the adsorbed gas.

8. *Silica gel.* This is a hard, granular, very porous product made from the gel precipitated by acid treatment of sodium silicate solution. Its moisture content prior to use varies from roughly 4 to 7 per cent, and it is used principally for dehydration of air and other gases, in gas masks, and for fractionation of hydrocarbons. It is revivified for reuse by evaporation of the adsorbed matter.

## ADSORPTION EQUILIBRIA

The great bulk of the experimental data pertaining to adsorption represents equilibrium measurements. Many of them were gathered in an attempt to provide corroboration for one or another of the many theories which have been advanced in an attempt to explain the adsorption phenomena. No one theory has yet been devised which satisfactorily explains even a majority of the observations, and this discussion is therefore limited simply to a description of the more commonly observed adsorption characteristics.  The theories are reviewed elsewhere.[5,21]

## SINGLE GASES AND VAPORS

In many respects the equilibrium adsorption characteristics of a gas or vapor upon a solid resemble the equilibrium solubility of a gas in a

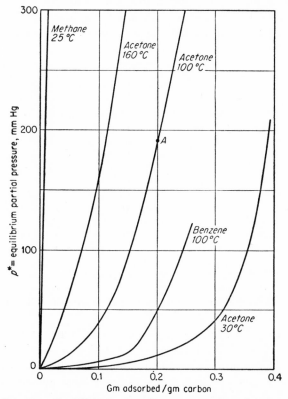

FIG. 11.1. Equilibrium adsorption on an activated carbon.

liquid.   Figure 11.1 shows several equilibrium adsorption isotherms for a particular activated carbon as adsorbent, where the concentration of adsorbed gas (the adsorbate) on the solid is plotted against the equilibrium partial pressure $p^*$ of the vapor or gas at constant temperature. Curves of this sort are analogous to those of Fig. 8.1.   At 100°C., for example, pure acetone vapor at a pressure of 190 mm. Hg is in equilibrium with an adsorbate concentration of 0.2 gm. adsorbed acetone/gm. carbon, point $A$.   Increasing the pressure of the acetone will cause more to be adsorbed, as the rising curve indicates, and decreasing the pressure of the system at $A$ will cause acetone to be desorbed from the carbon. While not determined experimentally in this case, it is known that the 100°C. isotherm for acetone will continue to rise only to a pressure of 2,790 mm. Hg, the saturation vapor pressure of acetone at this temperature. At higher pressures, no acetone can exist in the vapor state at this temperature but instead will condense entirely to a liquid. It will thus be possible to obtain indefinitely large concentrations of the substance on the solid at pressures higher than the vapor pressure, as at point $B$ (Fig. 11.2). However, concentrations in excess of that corresponding to point $B$ indicate liquefaction, but not necessarily adsorption

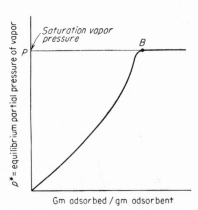

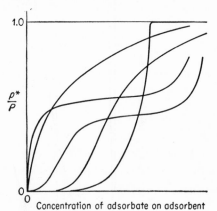

Fig. 11.2. Typical complete adsorption isotherm.

Fig. 11.3. Types of adsorption isotherms for vapors.

of the vapor. Gases above their critical temperature, of course, do not show this characteristic.

Different gases and vapors are adsorbed to different extents under comparable conditions. Thus benzene (Fig. 11.1) is more readily adsorbed than acetone at the same temperature and gives a higher adsorbate concentration for a given equilibrium pressure. As a general rule, vapors and gases are more readily adsorbed the higher their molecular weight and the lower their critical temperature, although chemical differences such as the extent of unsaturation in the molecule also influences the extent of adsorption. The so-called permanent gases are usually adsorbed only to a relatively small extent, as the methane isotherm of Fig. 11.1 indicates.

Adsorption isotherms are not always concave to the pressure axis. The shapes shown in Fig. 11.3 have all been observed for various systems. Here the ordinate is plotted as equilibrium partial pressure $p^*$ divided by the saturation vapor pressure $P$ of the adsorbed substance (actually, the relative saturation) in order to place all the curves on a comparable basis.

It will be recalled that a change of liquid solvent alters profoundly the equilibrium solubility of a gas except in the case of ideal liquid solutions. In a similar fashion the equilibrium curves for acetone, benzene, and methane on silica gel as adsorbent would be entirely different from those of Fig. 11.1. Indeed, differences in the origin and method of preparation of an adsorbent will result in significant differences in the equilibrium adsorption as well. For this reason, many of the data gathered years ago are no longer of practical value, since methods of preparing adsorbents, and consequently the corresponding adsorbent capacities, have improved greatly over the years.

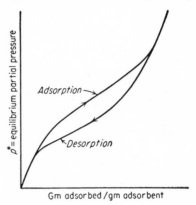

Fig. 11.4. Adsorption isotherm showing hysteresis.

Repeated adsorption and desorption will also frequently alter the characteristics of a particular adsorbent, owing perhaps to progressive changes in the pore structure within the solid.

**Adsorption Hysteresis.** The curves of Fig. 11.1 are true equilibrium curves and therefore represent completely reversible phenomena. The conditions corresponding to point $A$ on the figure, for example, can be obtained either by adsorption onto fresh carbon or by desorption of a sample with an initially higher adsorbate concentration. Occasionally, however, different equilibria result, at least over a part of an isotherm, depending upon whether the vapor is adsorbed or desorbed, and this gives rise to the hysteresis phenomenon indicated in Fig. 11.4. This may be the result of the shape of the openings to the capillaries and pores of the solid or of complex phenomena of wetting of the solid by the adsorbate. In any case, when hysteresis is observed, the desorption equilibrium pressure is always lower than that obtained by adsorption.

**Effect of Temperature.** Since adsorption is an exothermic process, the concentration of adsorbed gas decreases with increased temperature at a given equilibrium pressure, as the several acetone isotherms of Fig. 11.1 indicate.

The reference-substance method of plotting, described in Chap. 8 for gas-liquid solubilities, is conveniently applicable also to adsorption data.[25] As reference substance it is best to use the pure substance being adsorbed, unless the temperatures are above the critical temperature. Figure 11.5, for example, was prepared for the adsorption of acetone vapor on activated carbon with acetone as reference substance. The abscissa of the logarithmic coordinates was marked with the vapor pressure of pure acetone, and the corresponding saturation temperatures were also marked. The equilibrium partial pressure of adsorbate was plotted on the ordinate.

Points of equal temperature for the vapor pressure of pure acetone and the partial pressure of adsorbate were then plotted. Thus, point $A$ of Fig. 11.1 ($p^* = 190$ mm. Hg, 100°C.) was plotted on Fig. 11.5 at $A$, where $P = 2,790$ mm. Hg, the vapor pressure of acetone at 100°C. Points of constant adsorbate concentration (isosteres) form straight lines with few exceptions, and thus only two points are required to establish each.

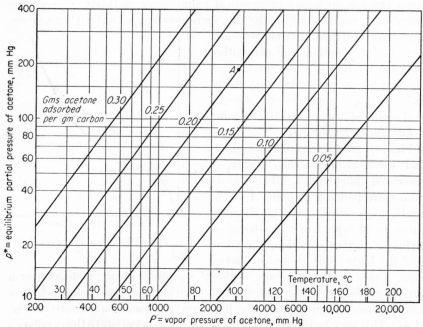

Fɪɢ. 11.5. Reference-substance plot of equilibrium adsorption of acetone on an activated carbon. [*Data of Josefewitz and Othmer, Ind. Eng. Chem.*, **40**, 739 (1948).]

Figure 11.6 shows all the same data plotted in such a manner as to reduce all the measurements to a single curve, thereby permitting considerable extension of meager data. The free energy of compression of 1 mole of a gas from the equilibrium adsorption pressure $p^*$ to the vapor pressure $P$, the "adsorption potential," is $RT \ln (P/p^*)$. In the case of single substances, when this quantity is plotted against adsorbate concentration, a single curve results for all temperatures, at least over a moderate temperature range.[9] The ordinate of Fig. 11.6 is proportional to this quantity. More complex methods of expressing the adsorbate concentration may be used to provide improved and extended correlations of the data.

**Heat of Adsorption.** The *differential heat of adsorption* $(-\bar{H})$ is defined as the heat liberated at constant temperature when unit quantity of vapor is adsorbed upon a large quantity of solid already containing adsorbate. Such a large quantity of solid is used that the adsorbate concentration is unchanged. The *integral heat of adsorption* at any concentration $X$ of adsorbate upon the solid is defined as the enthalpy of

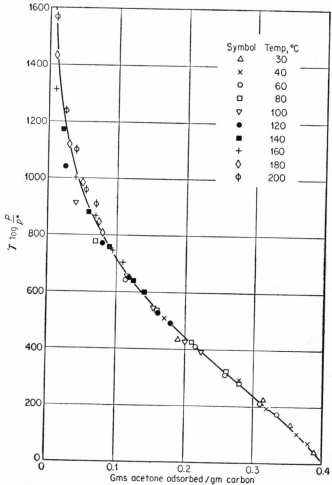

Fig. 11.6. Adsorption of acetone on an activated carbon, 30 to 200°C.

the adsorbate-adsorbent combination minus the sum of the enthalpies of unit weight of pure solid adsorbent and sufficient pure adsorbed substance (before adsorption) to provide the required concentration $X$, all at the same temperature. These are both functions of temperature and adsorbate concentration for any system.

Othmer and Sawyer[25] have shown that plots of the type shown in Fig. 11.5 are useful in estimating the heat of adsorption, which may be calculated in a manner similar to that for the latent heat of vaporization of a pure liquid (see Chap. 7). Thus, the slope of an isostere of Fig. 11.5 is

$$\frac{d \ln p^*}{d \ln P} = \frac{(-\bar{H})M}{\lambda_r M_r} \qquad (11.1)$$

where $\bar{H}$, B.t.u./lb. of vapor adsorbed, is referred to the pure vapor and $\lambda_r$ is the latent heat of vaporization of the reference substance at the same temperature, B.t.u./lb. $M$ and $M_r$ are the molecular weights of the vapor and reference substance, respectively. If $\bar{H}$ is computed at constant temperature for each isostere, then the integral heat of adsorption at this temperature may be computed from the relation

$$\Delta H'_A = \int_0^X \bar{H} \, dX \qquad (11.2)$$

$\Delta H'_A$, B.t.u./lb. of adsorbate-free solid, is referred to the pure vapor, and $X$ is the adsorbate concentration, lb. adsorbate/lb. solid. The integral may be evaluated graphically by determining the area under a curve of $\bar{H}$ against $X$. The integral heat of adsorption referred to solid and the adsorbed substance in the liquid state is $\Delta H_A = \Delta H'_A + \lambda X$, B.t.u./lb. solid. The quantities $\bar{H}$, $\Delta H_A$, and $\Delta H'_A$ are negative quantities if heat is evolved during adsorption.

**Illustration 1.** Estimate the integral heat of adsorption of acetone upon activated carbon at 30°C., as a function of adsorbate concentration.

*Solution.* Refer to Fig. 11.5. The isosteres for various concentrations are straight on this diagram, and their slopes are measured with the help of a millimeter rule. In the accompanying table, column (1) lists the adsorbate concentrate of each isostere and column (2) the corresponding slope. Since in this case the adsorbate and reference substance are the same, $M = M_r$ and consequently $\bar{H} = -\lambda_r$ (slope of isostere). At 30°C., $\lambda_r = \lambda$, the latent heat of vaporization of acetone = 237 B.t.u./lb. Column (3) of the table lists values of $\bar{H}$ calculated in this manner.

| $X, \dfrac{\text{lb. acetone}}{\text{lb. carbon}}$ | Slope of isostere | Differential heat of adsorption, $\bar{H}$, B.t.u./lb. acetone | Integral heat of adsorption, B.t.u./lb. carbon | |
|---|---|---|---|---|
| | | | $\Delta H'_A$, referred to acetone vapor | $\Delta H_A$, referred to acetone liquid |
| (1) | (2) | (3) | (4) | (5) |
| 0.05 | 1.170 | −275 | −12.8 | −0.9 |
| 0.10 | 1.245 | −295 | −27.1 | −3.4 |
| 0.15 | 1.300 | −308 | −42.1 | −6.5 |
| 0.20 | 1.310 | −310 | −57.6 | −10.2 |
| 0.25 | 1.340 | −318 | −73.3 | −14.0 |
| 0.30 | 1.327 | −314 | −89.1 | −18.0 |

Column (3) was plotted as ordinate against column (1) as abscissa (not shown). The area under the curve between $X = 0$ and any value of $X$ is listed in column (4) as the corresponding integral heat of adsorption, referred to acetone vapor. Thus the area under the curve between $X = 0$ and $X = 0.20 = -57.6$. If 0.20 lb. acetone vapor at 30°C. is adsorbed on 1 lb. fresh carbon at 30°C. and the product brought to 30°C., 57.6 B.t.u. will be evolved.

Column (5), the integral heat of adsorption referred to liquid acetone, is computed from the relation $\Delta H_A = \Delta H_A' + \lambda X$. Thus, at $X = 0.20$, $\Delta H_A = -57.6 + 237(0.20) = -10.2$ B.t.u./lb. carbon.

## VAPOR AND GAS MIXTURES

It is necessary to distinguish between mixtures depending upon whether one or several of the components are adsorbed.

**One Component Adsorbed.** In the case of many mixtures, particularly vapor-gas mixtures, only one component is appreciably adsorbed. This would be the circumstance for a mixture of acetone vapor and methane in contact with activated carbon (Fig. 11.1), for example. In such instances, the adsorption of the vapor will be substantially unaffected by the presence of the poorly adsorbed gas, and the adsorption isotherm for the pure vapor will be applicable provided the equilibrium pressure is taken as the *partial* pressure of the vapor in the vapor-gas mixture. The isotherms for acetone (Fig. 11.1) thus apply for mixtures of acetone with any poorly adsorbed gas such as nitrogen, hydrogen, and the like. This is similar to the corresponding case of gas-liquid solubility.

**Binary Gas or Vapor Mixtures, Both Components Appreciably Adsorbed.** When both components of a binary gas or vapor mixture are separately adsorbed to roughly the same extent, the amount of either one adsorbed from the mixture will be affected by the presence of the other. Since such systems are composed of three components when the adsorbent is included, the equilibrium data are conveniently shown in the manner used for ternary liquid equilibria in Chap. 10. For this purpose it is convenient to consider the solid adsorbent as being analogous to liquid solvent in extraction operations. However, adsorption is greatly influenced by both temperature and pressure, unlike liquid solubility, which is scarcely affected by pressure under ordinary circumstances. Equilibrium diagrams are consequently best plotted at constant temperature and constant total pressure, and they are therefore simultaneously *isotherms* and *isobars*.

A typical system is shown in Fig. 11.7 on triangular and rectangular coordinates. The properties of these coordinate systems and the relations between them were considered in detail in Chap. 10. Even though mole fraction is generally a more convenient concentration unit in dealing with gases, the figure is plotted in terms of weight-fraction compo-

sitions since the molecular weight of the adsorbent is uncertain.† Since
the adsorbent is not volatile and does not appear in the gas phase, the
equilibrium gas compositions fall upon one axis of either graph, as shown.
Points $G$ and $H$ represent the adsorbate concentration for the individual
pure gases and the curve $GEH$ that of gas mixtures.   Tie lines such as
line $RE$ join equilibrium compositions of the gas and adsorbate.   The
fact that the tie lines do not, when extended, pass through the adsorbent
apex indicates that under the prevailing conditions the adsorbent can be

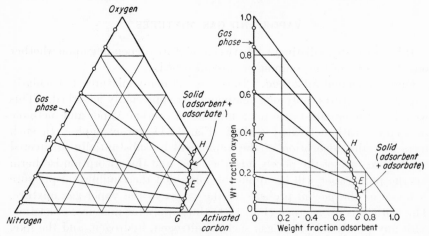

FIG. 11.7. System oxygen–nitrogen–activated carbon, $-150°C.$ and 1 atm., concentrations expressed as weight fractions.   [*Data of Maslan, Altman, and Aberth, J. Phys.
Chem.,* **57,** 106 (1953).]

used to separate the binary gas mixture into its components.   The separation factor, or *relative adsorptivity*, similar to relative volatility in distillation or selectivity in liquid extraction, is obtained by dividing the equilibrium ratio of gas compositions in the adsorbate (as at point $E$) by the
ratio in the gas (as at $R$).   The relative adsorptivity must be larger than
unity if the adsorbent is to be useful for separating the components of
the gas mixture.   In the system of Fig. 11.7 the more strongly adsorbed
of the two pure gases (oxygen) is also selectively adsorbed from any mixture.   This appears to be true for most mixtures, although an inversion
of the relative adsorptivity in some systems (analogous to azeotropism
in distillation) is certainly a possibility.

    Especially when the extent of adsorption is small, it will be more con-
venient to express compositions on an adsorbent-free basis and to plot
them in the manner of Fig. 11.8.   Such diagrams are also analogous to
those used in liquid extraction (Fig. 10.29*a*, for example), and their
properties are outlined in detail in Chap. 10.   The adsorption charac-

† Alternatively, some arbitrary molecular weight could be assigned to the adsorbent.

teristics of the binary gas mixture acetylene-ethylene on silica gel for one temperature and pressure are shown in Fig. 11.8a. In the upper portion of this figure, the gas phase appears entirely along the abscissa of the plot owing to the absence of adsorbent in the gas. The adsorbent-free equilibrium compositions corresponding to the tie lines may be

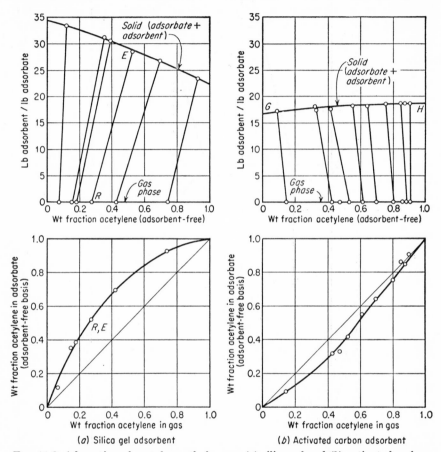

FIG. 11.8. Adsorption of acetylene-ethylene on (a) silica gel and (b) activated carbon, at 25°C., 1 atm. [Data of Lewis et al., J. Am. Chem. Soc., **72**, 1157 (1950).]

plotted in the lower half of the diagram (as at point R, E) to produce a figure analogous to the McCabe-Thiele diagram of distillation. Silica gel selectively adsorbs acetylene from these gas mixtures.

The powerful influence of the adsorbent on the equilibrium is demonstrated with the same gas mixture by Fig. 11.8b, where activated carbon is the adsorbent. Not only is the extent of adsorption greater than for silica gel so that the curve GH is lower than the corresponding curve for silica gel, but in addition the relative adsorptivity is reversed: ethylene

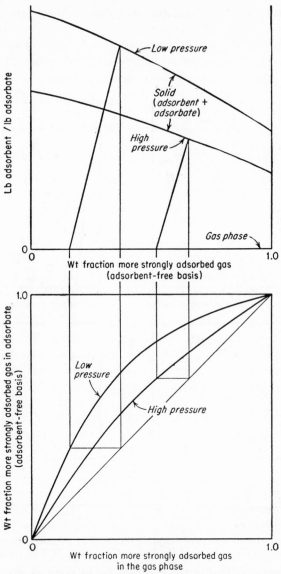

FIG. 11.9. Effect of pressure on adsorption isotherms for binary gas mixtures.

is selectively adsorbed on activated carbon. In both cases, however, that gas which is separately more strongly adsorbed on each adsorbent is selectively adsorbed from mixtures. If a condition corresponding to azeotropism should arise, the curve of the lower half of these figures would cross the 45° diagonal line. In cases such as Fig. 11.8*b*, it will generally be preferable to plot compositions in terms of the more strongly adsorbed gas (ethylene), to keep the appearance of the diagram similar to those used previously in liquid extraction.

**Effect of Change of Pressure or Temperature.** The available data are so meager that generalizations are very difficult to make. Lowering the pressure will of course reduce the amount of adsorbate upon the adsorbent, as shown in the upper half of Fig. 11.9. In those cases investigated over any appreciable pressure range[20] the relative adsorptivity decreased at increased pressure, as shown in the lower part of this figure, just as it does in the case of distillation. It is not known whether this is generally true. Owing to the increased tendency toward liquid condensation in the adsorbent capillaries at higher pressures, the equilibrium may simply be shifting toward the ordinary vapor-liquid equilibrium with increased pressure, and in each of the investigated cases this corresponded to lower separation factor. Increasing the temperature at constant pressure will decrease the amount adsorbed from a mixture and will influence the relative adsorptivity as well, but in a manner for which no generalizations can now be made.

### LIQUIDS

When an adsorbent solid is immersed in a pure liquid, the evolution of heat, known as the heat of wetting, is evidence that adsorption of the liquid does occur. But there is apparently no effective method of measuring the extent of adsorption. No appreciable volume change of the liquid which might be used as a measure of adsorption is ordinarily observed, while withdrawal of the solid and weighing it will not distinguish between the adsorbed liquid and that which is mechanically occluded. This problem does not exist in the case of adsorption of gases, where the change in weight of the solid owing to adsorption is readily measured.

**Adsorption of Solute from Dilute Solution.** When an adsorbent is mixed with a binary solution, adsorption of both solute and solvent occurs. Since the total adsorption cannot be measured, the relative or apparent adsorption of solute is determined instead. The customary procedure is to treat a known volume of solution with a known weight of adsorbent, $V$ cu. ft. solution/lb. adsorbent. As a result of preferential adsorption of solute, the solute concentration of the liquid is observed to fall from the initial value $c_0$ to the final equilibrium value $c^*$ lb. solute/cu. ft. liquid. The apparent adsorption of solute, neglecting any volume change in the solution, is then $V(c_0 - c^*)$ lb. solute adsorbed/lb. adsorbent. This is satisfactory for dilute solutions when the fraction of the original solvent which may be adsorbed is small.

Correction is sometimes made for the volume of the solute apparently adsorbed. Thus, the initial solvent content of the solution is $V(1 - c_0/\rho)$, and on the assumption that no solvent is adsorbed, the volume of residual solution is $V(1 - c_0/\rho)/(1 - c^*/\rho)$. The apparent solute adsorption is then the difference between initial and final solute content of the liquid, $Vc_0 - [V(1 - c_0/\rho)/(1 - c^*/\rho)]c^*$ or $V(c_0 - c^*)/(1 - c^*/\rho)$. This, of course, still neglects solvent adsorption.

The apparent adsorption of a given solute depends upon the concentration of solute, the temperature, the solvent, and the type of adsorbent. Typical isotherms are shown in Fig. 11.10. Isotherms of all the indicated forms have been observed, for example, when a given solute is adsorbed on the same adsorbent, but from different solvents. The extent of adsorption of a given solute practically always decreases at increased temperature and usually is greater the smaller the solubility in the solvent. It is usually reversible, so that the same isotherm results whether solute is desorbed or adsorbed.

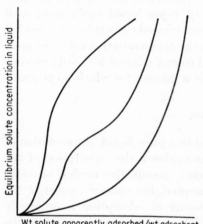

Wt solute apparently adsorbed/wt adsorbent

Fig. 11.10. Typical adsorption isotherms for dilute solutions.

**The Freundlich Equation.** Over a small concentration range, and particularly for dilute solutions, the adsorption isotherms may frequently be described by an empirical expression usually attributed to Freundlich,

$$c^* = k[V(c_0 - c^*)]^n \quad (11.3)$$

where $V(c_0 - c^*)$ is the apparent adsorption per unit weight of adsorbent and $k$ and $n$ are constants.

Other concentration units are frequently used also, and while these will result in different values of $k$, for the dilute solutions for which the equation is applicable the value of $n$ will be unaffected. The form of the equation indicates that plotting the equilibrium solute concentration as ordinate against adsorbate content of the solid as abscissa on logarithmic coordinates will provide a straight line of slope $n$ and intercept $k$. Several typical isotherms are plotted in this manner in Fig. 11.11. The effect of the nature of the solvent on adsorption of benzoic acid on silica gel is shown by curves (a) and (b), which follow Eq. (11.3) excellently over the concentration range shown. The adsorption is less strong from benzene solutions, which is to be expected in view of the higher solubility of the acid in this solvent. Curve (c) of this figure shows the deviation from linearity to be expected over large concentration ranges, although Eq. (11.3) is applicable for the lower concentration ranges. Failure of the data to follow the equation at high solute concentrations may be the result of appreciable adsorption of the

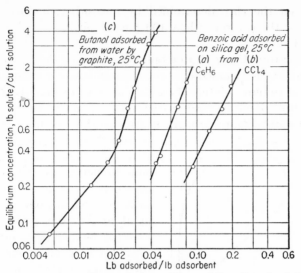

FIG. 11.11. Adsorption from dilute solution.    [*Data of Bartell et al., J. Phys. Chem.,* **33**, 676 (1929); *J. Phys. & Colloid Chem.*, **55**, 1456 (1951).]

solvent which is not taken into account or simply general inapplicability of the expression.

The Freundlich equation is also frequently useful in cases where the actual identity of the solute is not known, as in the adsorption of colored substances from such materials as sugar solutions and mineral or vegetable oils. In such cases, the concentration of solute may be measured by means of a colorimeter or spectrophotometer and expressed in terms of arbitrary units of color intensity, provided that the color scale used varies linearly with the concentration of the responsible solute. Figure 11.12 illustrates the application of this method of plotting the adsorption of colored substances from a petroleum fraction on two adsorbent clays. Here the color concentrations of the solutions are measured on an arbitrary scale, and the concentration of

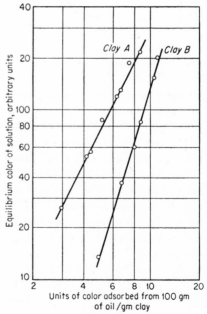

FIG. 11.12. Decolorization of cylinder oil with clay.  [*Data of Rogers et al., Ind. Eng. Chem.*, **18**, 164 (1926).]

adsorbate on the clay determined by measuring the change in color expressed in these terms when 100 gm. of oil is treated with various amounts of clay.

**Adsorption from Concentrated Solutions.** When the apparent adsorption of solute is determined over the entire range of concentrations from pure solvent to pure solute, curves such as those of Fig. 11.13 will result. Curves of the shape marked (a) occur when at all concentrations the solute is adsorbed more strongly relative to the solvent. At increasing solute concentrations, the extent of solute adsorption may actually continue to increase; yet the curve showing apparent solute adsorption necessarily returns to point $E$, since in a liquid consisting of pure solute alone there will be no concentration change on addition of adsorbent. In cases where both solvent and solute are adsorbed to nearly the same extent, the S-shaped curves of type (b) are produced. In the range of concentrations from $C$ to $D$, solute is more strongly adsorbed than solvent. At point $D$, both are equally well adsorbed, and the apparent adsorption falls to zero. In the range of concentrations from $D$ to $E$, solvent is more strongly adsorbed. Consequently, on addition of adsorbent to such solutions, the solute concentration of the liquid increases, and the quantity $V(c_0 - c^*)$ indicates an apparent *negative* solute adsorption.

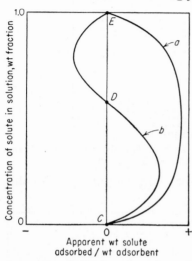

FIG. 11.13. Apparent adsorption of solute from solutions.

The true adsorption of the substances can be estimated only by assuming some mechanism for the process.[2,16] To demonstrate this approach, define the solute as that substance which is more strongly adsorbed when present alone, and express its concentration in solution as $x$ wt. fraction. Let the initial solution be $w$ lb./lb. adsorbent, of composition $x_0$, and let the final equilibrium concentration be $x^*$. Let it further be assumed that the true adsorption of each substance can be described by the Freundlich equation at all concentrations.[2] The true solute adsorption is then $(x^*/k)^{1/n}$ or $k'x^{*n'}$ lb./lb. adsorbent. Similarly the true solvent adsorption is $k''(1 - x^*)^{n''}$. The residual weight of solution is therefore $w - k'x^{*n'} - k''(1 - x^*)^{n''}$. A solute balance then equates the amount adsorbed to the difference in solute contents of the initial and final solutions,

$$k'x^{*n'} = wx_0 - [w - k'x^{*n'} - k''(1 - x^*)^{n''}]x^* \qquad (11.4)$$

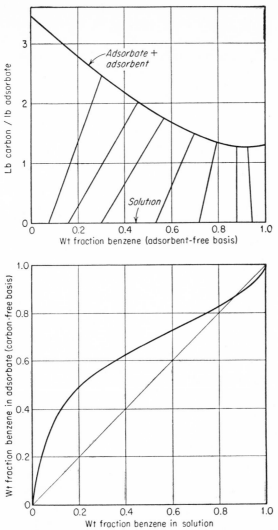

Fig. 11.14. Calculated adsorption of benzene and ethanol by activated carbon. (*Bartell and Sloan.*[2])

This can be solved for the apparent adsorption, which is the ordinarily measured quantity,

$$w(x_0 - x^*) = k'x^{*n'}(1 - x^*) - k''(1 - x^*)^{n''}x^* \qquad (11.5)$$

The constants $k'$, $k''$, $n'$, and $n''$ can be determined from the measurements. It has been demonstrated that Eq. (11.5) can describe curves of the type shown in Fig. 11.13, although quite possibly individual adsorption isotherms other than the Freundlich equation might also be successful in this.[16] Figure 11.14 shows the results calculated by Eq. (11.3) from the apparent adsorption in the system benzene–ethanol–activated carbon. The system gives rise to an S-shaped apparent adsorption isotherm, and it is seen that this results in a situation analogous to azeotropism, with a relative adsorptivity equal to unity at $x = 0.872$ wt. fraction benzene. Different adsorbents might selectively adsorb one of the constituents of the system over all concentration ranges, giving rise to equilibrium diagrams of the sort shown for gases in Fig. 11.8.

## ADSORPTION OPERATIONS

Adsorption is unique in the very diverse nature of its applications. For example, it is applied to such a wide variety of processes as recovery of vapors from dilute mixtures with gases, solute recovery and removal of contaminants from solution, as well as the fractionation of gas and liquid mixtures. The techniques used include both stagewise and continuous-contacting methods, and these are applied to batch, continuous, and semicontinuous operations. Any one of these categories may be used to classify the subject for purposes of study.

The treatment developed here follows the classification outlined in Table 11.1. A broad subdivision is first made according to whether stagewise or continuous-contact methods are employed. Within each of these categories it is possible to recognize operations which are exactly analogous to those already discussed in previous chapters of this book. Thus, when only one component of a fluid mixture (either a gas or a liquid) is strongly adsorbed, the separation of the mixture is analogous for purposes of calculation to gas absorption, where the added insoluble phase is adsorbent in the present case and liquid solvent in the case of absorption. When both components of the fluid (either gas or liquid) are adsorbed strongly, the separation requires a fractionation procedure. The operation is then conveniently considered as being analogous to liquid extraction, where the added insoluble adsorbent corresponds to the use of solvent in extraction. By this means many simplifications in the treatment become possible.

## I. STAGEWISE OPERATION

In industrial practice, stagewise adsorption operations are limited to the treatment of dilute liquid solutions, where the solute to be removed is adsorbed relatively very strongly compared with the remainder of the solution. The operation is frequently called *contact filtration*. Typical process applications include:

1. The collection of valuable solutes from dilute solutions, as, for example, the adsorption onto carbon of iodine from brines, after liberation of the element from its salts by oxidation; and the collection of insulin from dilute solutions

2. The removal of undesirable contaminants from a solution

Owing to the extremely favorable equilibrium distribution of solute toward the adsorbent which is frequently possible, adsorption becomes a powerful tool for the latter purpose, and most industrial applications of stagewise techniques fall into this category. Adsorption of colored substances from aqueous sugar solutions onto carbon, in order to provide a pure product and to assist the crystallization, is a typical example. Similarly, carbon is sometimes used to adsorb odorous substances from potable water, and grease is adsorbed from dry-cleaning liquids. The colors of petroleum and vegetable oils are lightened by treatment with clay.

**Equipment and Methods.** As pointed out in Chap. 1, each stage requires the intimate contact of two insoluble phases for a time sufficient for a reasonable approach to equilibrium, followed by physical

TABLE 11.1. CLASSIFICATION OF ADSORPTION OPERATIONS

| Technique used | Fluids treated | Number of components strongly adsorbed | Relative adsorptivity | Method of operation |
|---|---|---|---|---|
| 1. Stagewise contact | Liquids | One | High | Batch and continuous |
| 2. Continuous contact | | | | |
|   *a.* Steady state (moving bed) | Gases Liquids† | One† All | High Low | Continuous |
|   *b.* Unsteady state (fixed bed) | Gases Liquids | One All | High Low | Semibatch |

† While these categories represent feasible possibilities, they are not generally done on an industrial scale. See text.

separation of the phases. The equipment used in applying these principles to adsorption is varied, depending upon the process application. That shown in Fig. 11.15 is very typical of many installations operated in a batchwise fashion. The liquid to be processed and the adsorbent are intimately mixed in the treating tank at the desired temperature for the required period of time, following which the thin slurry is filtered to separate the solid adsorbent and accompanying adsorbate from the liquid. The equipment is readily adaptable to multistage operation by providing additional tanks and filters as necessary. If the operation is to be made continuous, which is sometimes done in the decolorizing of petroleum lubricating oils, for example, centrifuges or a continuous rotary filter may be substituted for the filter press or the solid may be allowed to settle out by virtue of its higher density when the mixture is passed through a large tank.

The type of adsorbent used depends upon the solution to be treated. Aqueous solutions are frequently treated with activated carbon especially prepared for the purpose at hand, whereas organic liquids such as oils are usually treated with inorganic adsorbents such as clays. Occasionally mixed adsorbents are used. High selectivity for the solute to be removed

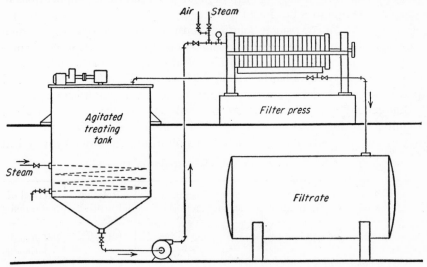

FIG. 11.15. Contact filtration. Schematic arrangement, for single-stage batch treatment of liquids.

is desirable in order to reduce the amount of solid to be added. In any case, the adsorbent is applied in the form of a very finely ground powder, usually at least fine enough to pass entirely through a 200-mesh screen, and frequently very much finer.

The time required for the adsorbent and liquid to come to substantial equilibrium depends principally upon the concentration and particle size of the solid, the viscosity of the liquid, and the intensity of agitation. Agitation should be vigorous in order to ensure rapid contact of the adsorbent particles with all the liquid, and the latter will be the more rapid the larger the solid concentration. The flow regime should be turbulent so that adsorbent particles move relative to the bulk of the liquid, and this is promoted by the presence of baffles in the tank. Rotational motion accompanied by swirl and vortexing merely carries the particles along with the liquid and does not decrease the required time. Moreover, the air introduced by the vortex frequently has a deleterious effect on the solution owing to the oxidation of sensitive organic substances.   The residual concentration of unadsorbed solute still remaining in solution usually varies with time in the manner indicated in Fig. 11.16, falling rapidly at first and approaching the equilibrium value asymptotically.   A practical time for agitation is chosen as at point $A$, where the additional adsorption to be obtained by further contact is insignificant, and this may be of the order of 10 to 30 min.   Agitation should be continued during filtration in order to avoid segregation of the fine and coarser particles of the adsorbent.

The highest convenient temperature should be used during the mixing, since the resulting decreased liquid viscosity increases both the rate of diffusion of solute and the ease with which the adsorbent particles may move through the liquid.   Usually the equilibrium adsorption is decreased to a small extent at higher temperatures, but this is more than compensated for by the increased rate of approach to equilibrium.   Operations are sometimes conducted at the boiling point of the liquid if this temperature will cause no injury to the substances involved. In the clay treatment of petroleum-

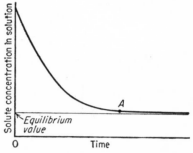

Fig. 11.16. Approach to equilibrium, batch adsorption.

lubricant fractions the adsorbent-oil mixture may be pumped through a tubular furnace to be heated to as much as 250 to 300°F., and for very heavy oils even to 600 to 700°F.   If the adsorbed substance is volatile, however, the equilibrium extent of adsorption will be much more strongly affected by temperature and such material is best handled at ordinary temperatures.

Owing to the large quantity of solution usually treated relative to the amount of adsorption occurring, the temperature rise resulting from release of the heat of adsorption may usually be ignored.

The method of dealing with the spent adsorbent depends upon the particular system under consideration.   The filter cake is usually washed to displace the solution held within the pores of the cake, but relatively little adsorbate will be removed in this manner.   If the adsorbate is the desired product, it may be desorbed by contact of the solid with a solvent other than that which comprises the original solution, one in which the adsorbate is more soluble.   This may be done by washing the cake in the filter or by dispersing the solid into a quantity of the solvent.   If the adsorbate is volatile, it may be desorbed by reduction of the partial pressure of the adsorbate over the solid by passage of steam or warm air through the solid.   In the case of activated carbon adsorbents, care must be taken to avoid too high temperatures in using air for this purpose, in order to avoid combustion of the carbon. In the case of most decolorizing operations, the adsorbate is of no value and is difficultly desorbed. The adsorbent may then be revivified by burning off the adsorbate, followed by reactivation. Usually only a limited number of such revivifications is possible before the adsorbent ability is severely reduced, whereupon the solid is discarded.

**Single-stage Operation.** The schematic flow sheet for this type of operation, when done in either batch or continuous fashion, is shown in

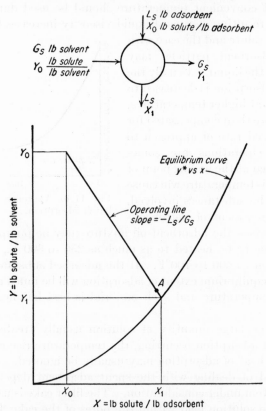

FIG. 11.17. Single-ideal-stage adsorption.

the upper part of Fig. 11.17. Here the circle represents all the equipment and procedures constituting one stage. The operation is essentially analogous to a single-stage gas absorption, where the solution to be treated corresponds to a "gas" and the solid adsorbent to a "liquid." Since the amount of adsorbent used is ordinarily very small with respect to the amount of solution treated, and since the solute to be removed is adsorbed much more strongly than the other constituents present, the adsorption of the latter may be ignored. Furthermore the adsorbent is insoluble in the solution. Adopting a notation scheme similar to that used for gas absorption, the solution to be treated contains $G_s$ lb. unadsorbed substance or solvent, and the adsorbable solute concentration is reduced from $Y_0$ to $Y_1$ lb. solute/lb. solvent. The adsorbent is added to the extent of $L_s$ lb. adsorbate-free solid, and the solute adsorbate content increases from $X_0$ to $X_1$ lb. solute/lb. adsorbent. If fresh adsorbent is used, $X_0 = 0$ and in cases of continuous operation $G_s$ and $L_s$ are measured in terms of lb./hr.†

Equating the solute removed from the liquid to that picked up by the solid,

$$G_s(Y_0 - Y_1) = L_s(X_1 - X_0) \tag{11.6}$$

On $X$, $Y$ coordinates this represents a straight operating line, through points of coordinates $(X_0, Y_0)$ and $(X_1, Y_1)$, of slope $-L_s/G_s$. If the stage is a theoretical or ideal stage, the effluent streams are in equilibrium, so that the point $(X_1, Y_1)$ lies on the equilibrium adsorption isotherm. This is shown on the lower portion of Fig. 11.17. The equilibrium curve should be that obtaining at the final temperature of the operation. If insufficient time of contact is allowed so that equilibrium is not reached, the final liquid and solid concentrations will correspond to some point such as $A$ (Fig. 11.17) but ordinarily equilibrium is approached very closely.

The use of Eq. (11.6) assumes that the amount of liquid mechanically retained with the solid (but not adsorbed) after filtration or settling is negligible. This is quite satisfactory for most adsorption, since the quantity of solid employed is ordinarily very small with respect to that of the liquid treated. If the operation under consideration is *desorption*, and if again the quantity of liquid retained mechanically by the solid is negligible, Eq. (11.6) applies but the operating line lies below the equilibrium curve on Fig. 11.17. In this case, however, it is much more likely that the quantity of liquid retained mechanically with the solid will be an appreciable portion of the total liquid used, and the methods of calculation described in Chap. 13 for leaching should be used.

*Application of the Freundlich Equation.* The Freundlich equation can frequently be applied to adsorption of this type, particularly since small adsorbable solute concentrations are usually involved. This may be written in the following form for the concentration units used here,

$$Y^* = mX^n \tag{11.7}$$

† For the dilute solutions ordinarily used other consistent units may be applied to these terms. Thus, $Y$ may be expressed as lb. solute/lb. solution (or lb. solute/cu. ft. solution) and $G_s$ as lb. (or cu. ft., respectively) of solution. When the adsorbed solute is colored matter whose concentration is measured in arbitrary units, the latter may be considered as $Y$ units of color/lb. or cu. ft. solution and the adsorbate concentration on the solid $X$ as units of color/lb. adsorbent.

and, at the final equilibrium conditions,

$$X_1 = \left(\frac{Y_1}{m}\right)^{1/n} \tag{11.8}$$

Since the adsorbent used ordinarily contains no initial adsorbate and $X_0 = 0$, substitution in Eq. (11.6) yields

$$\frac{L_S}{G_S} = \frac{Y_0 - Y_1}{(Y_1/m)^{1/n}} \tag{11.9}$$

This permits analytical calculation of the adsorbent/solution ratio for a given change in solution concentration, $Y_0$ to $Y_1$.

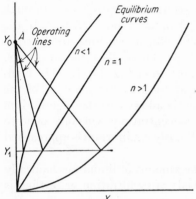

FIG. 11.18. Single-stage adsorption, Freundlich equilibrium curves.

Refer to Fig. 11.18, where three typical Freundlich isotherms are shown. The isotherm is straight for $n = 1$, concave upward for $n > 1$, and concave downward for $n < 1$. If in each case the solution concentration is to be reduced from $Y_0$ to $Y_1$, the three operating lines radiating from point $A$ apply. The slope of the operating line is in each case directly proportional to the adsorbent/solution ratio. It is generally stated[12] that values of $n$ in the range 2 to 10 represent good, 1 to 2 moderately difficult, and less than 1 poor adsorption characteristics. In the case of the last, impractically large adsorbent dosages may be required for appreciable fractional removal of solute.

**Multistage Cocurrent Operation.** The removal of a given amount of solute may be accomplished with greater economy of adsorbent if the solution is treated with separate small batches of adsorbent rather than in a single batch, with filtration between each stage. This method of operation is sometimes called "split-feed" treatment,[11] and it is usually done in batch fashion, although continuous operation is also possible. Economy is particularly important when activated carbon, a fairly expensive adsorbent, is used. The savings are greater the larger the number of batches used but result at the expense of greater filtration and other handling costs. It is therefore rarely economical to use more than two stages. In rare instances, the adsorption may be irreversible so that separate adsorbent dosages may be applied without intermediate filtration at considerable savings in operating costs.[11] This is by far the exception rather than the rule, and when applied to ordinary reversible adsorption it will provide the same end result as if all the adsorbent had been used in a single stage.

A schematic flow sheet and operating diagram for a typical operation of two ideal stages are shown in Fig. 11.19. The same quantity of solution is treated in each stage by amounts of adsorbent $L_{s1}$ and $L_{s2}$ lb. in

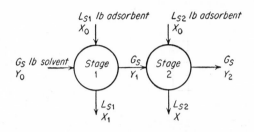

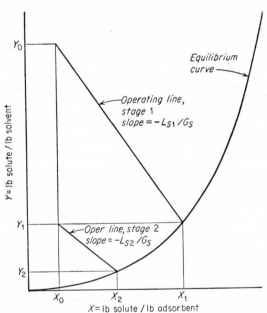

FIG. 11.19. Two-stage cocurrent adsorption.

the two stages, respectively, to reduce the solute concentration of the solution from $Y_0$ to $Y_2$. The material balances are, for stage 1,

$$G_s(Y_0 - Y_1) = L_{s1}(X_1 - X_0) \tag{11.10}$$

and for stage 2,

$$G_s(Y_1 - Y_2) = L_{s2}(X_2 - X_0) \tag{11.11}$$

These provide the operating lines shown on the figure, each of a slope appropriate to the adsorbent quantity used in the corresponding stage.

The extension to large numbers of stages is obvious. If the amounts of adsorbent used in each stage are equal, the operating lines on the diagram will be parallel. The least total amount of adsorbent will require unequal dosages in each stage except for the case where the equilibrium isotherm is linear, and in the general case this can be established only by a trial-and-error computation.

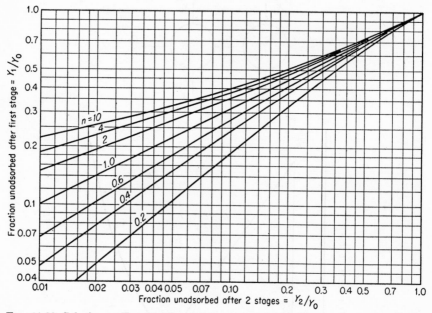

FIG. 11.20. Solution to Eq. (11.15). Minimum total adsorbent, two-stage cocurrent operation.

*Application of the Freundlich Equation.* When the Freundlich expression [Eq. (11.7)] describes the adsorption isotherm satisfactorily and fresh adsorbent is used in each stage ($X_0 = 0$), the least total amount of adsorbent for a two-stage system can be computed directly.[11,30] Thus, for stage 1,

$$\frac{L_{S1}}{G_S} = \frac{Y_0 - Y_1}{(Y_1/m)^{1/n}} \tag{11.12}$$

and, for stage 2,

$$\frac{L_{S2}}{G_S} = \frac{Y_1 - Y_2}{(Y_2/m)^{1/n}} \tag{11.13}$$

The total amount of adsorbent used is

$$\frac{L_{S1} + L_{S2}}{G_S} = m^{1/n}\left(\frac{Y_0 - Y_1}{Y_1^{1/n}} + \frac{Y_1 - Y_2}{Y_2^{1/n}}\right) \tag{11.14}$$

For minimum total adsorbent, $d[(L_1 + L_2)/G_S]/dY_1$ is set equal to zero, and since, for a given case $m$, $n$, $Y_0$, and $Y_2$ are constants, this reduces to

$$\left(\frac{Y_1}{Y_2}\right)^{1/n} - \frac{1}{n}\frac{Y_0}{Y_1} = 1 - \frac{1}{n} \qquad (11.15)$$

Equation (11.15) may be solved for the intermediate concentration $Y_1$,

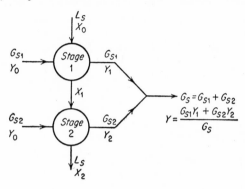

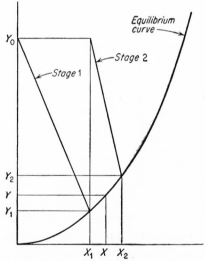

Fig. 11.21. Repeated use of adsorbent, cocurrent operation.

and the adsorbed quantities calculated by Eqs. (11.12) and (11.13). Figure 11.20 permits solutions of Eq. (11.15) without trial and error.

An alternative flow sheet and the corresponding operating diagram are shown in Fig. 11.21, where the same batch of adsorbent is used to treat two batches of solution successively. The solute concentration of the first solution is lowered to a value $Y_1$, less than that ultimately desired, and that of the second to $Y_2$. The two finished solutions are then blended to give the desired ultimate composition $Y$. A solute material balance about the entire plant yields

$$(G_{S1} + G_{S2})Y_0 = G_{S1}Y_1 + G_{S2}Y_2 + L_SX_2 \qquad (11.16)$$

or, since

$$G_SY = G_{S1}Y_1 + G_{S2}Y_2 \qquad (11.17)$$
$$G_S(Y_0 - Y) = L_SX_2 \qquad (11.18)$$

If the same amount of total solution $G_S$ had been treated in a single stage to a final concentration $Y$, sufficient adsorbent would have been used to produce an adsorbate

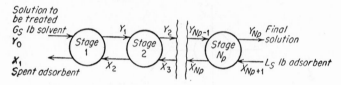

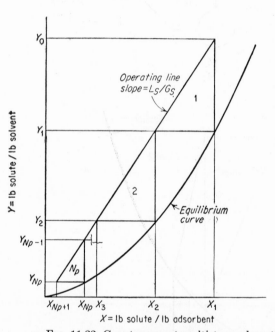

FIG. 11.22. Countercurrent multistage adsorption.

concentration $X$. This amount is larger than $L_S$ of Eq. (11.18), and a savings over single-stage operation is thus obtained. The concentrations and amounts of materials to be used for any given situation can be determined by trial-and-error computation. Even where the Freundlich equation can be written for the isotherm, no simple solution results. In several specific cases studied, the savings for any reasonable ratio of $G_{S1}/G_{S2}$ were not so large as those obtained by the arrangement of Fig. 11.19 or by the countercurrent method described below. The same conclusion was reached in the case of a similar three-stage flow sheet.[26]

**Multistage Countercurrent Operation.** Even greater economy in adsorbent can be obtained by countercurrent operation. The general flow sheet for $N_p$ theoretical stages and an operating diagram are shown in Fig. 11.22, and the initial concentration of adsorbate on the adsorbent is now shown as $X_{Np+1}$. A solute material balance about the $N_p$ stages is

$$G_S(Y_0 - Y_{Np}) = L_S(X_1 - X_{Np+1}) \qquad (11.19)$$

which provides the operating line on the figure, through the coordinates of the terminal conditions $(X_{Np+1}, Y_{Np})$ and $(X_1, Y_0)$ and of slope $L_S/G_S$. The number of theoretical stages required is found by drawing the usual staircase construction between equilibrium curve and operating line in the manner shown. Alternatively the adsorbent/solution ratio for a pre-determined number of stages may be found by trial-and-error location

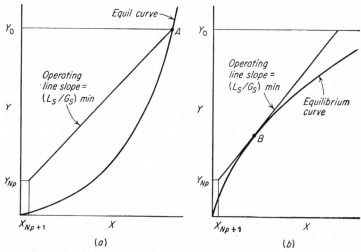

FIG. 11.23. Operating lines and minimum adsorbent/solvent ratio for infinite stages.

of the operating line. If the operation is a *desorption* (corresponding to stripping in gas-liquid contact), the operating line falls below the equilibrium curve.

The minimum adsorbent/solvent ratio will be the largest which results in an infinite number of stages for the desired change of concentration. This corresponds to the operating line of largest slope which touches the equilibrium curve within the specified range of concentrations. For cases where the equilibrium isotherm is straight or concave upward, as in Fig. 11.23a, this will cause a *pinch* at the concentrated end of the cascade, as at point $A$. If the isotherm is concave downward (Fig. 11.23b) the pinch may occur at a point of tangency, as at point $B$, if $Y_0$ is sufficiently large. The situations are entirely analogous to those found in gas absorption (Fig. 8.7).

As the number of stages in a cascade is increased, the amount of adsorbent required at first decreases rapidly but approaches the minimum value only asymptotically. In practice, where intermediate filtration of solid from the liquid must be made between stages, it is rarely economical to use more than two stages in a countercurrent cascade. While theoretically continuous operation is required, actually batch operation is more often the rule. Thus a batch of solution is treated with the once-used adsorbent discharged from a previous treat, and after filtration the adsorbent is discarded or revivified. The filtrate is then treated with the same quantity of fresh adsorbent to provide the finished solution and adsorbent for the next batch of fresh solution. After several cycles have been completed in this manner, the results will be substantially the same as for truly continuous operation, but successful application requires that the amounts and concentrations of the various streams be kept constant at each stage from cycle to cycle.

In small-scale processing, there may be appreciable variation in the amounts of solution to be treated from one batch to the next. Furthermore, long periods of time may pass between batches, so that partially spent adsorbent must be stored between stages. Activated carbon particularly may deteriorate during storage through oxidation, polymerization of the adsorbate, or other chemical change, and in such cases the cocurrent flow sheet may be more practical.

*Application of the Freundlich Equation.* Trial-and-error calculation for the adsorbent/solvent ratio may be eliminated if the equilibrium curve may be conveniently described algebraically. If the equilibrium curve is linear, the Kremser equation [Eq. (8.22) and Fig. 8.15] applies. More frequently the Freundlich expression [Eq. (11.7)] is useful, and fresh adsorbent ($X_{Np+1} = 0$) is used in the last stage.[26] For a typical two-stage cascade (Fig. 11.24) a solute material balance for the entire plant is

$$L_S(X_1 - 0) = G_S(Y_0 - Y_2) \tag{11.20}$$

Applying Eq. (11.7) to the effluents from the first ideal stage,

$$X_1 = \left(\frac{Y_1}{m}\right)^{1/n} \tag{11.21}$$

and combining these,

$$\frac{L_S}{G_S} = \frac{Y_0 - Y_2}{(Y_1/m)^{1/n}} \tag{11.22}$$

The operating line for the second ideal stage is shown on the figure and is given by

$$G_S(Y_1 - Y_2) = L_S X_2 = L_S \left(\frac{Y_2}{m}\right)^{1/n} \tag{11.23}$$

Eliminating $L_S/G_S$ between Eqs. (11.22) and (11.23), there results

$$\frac{Y_0}{Y_2} - 1 = \left(\frac{Y_1}{Y_2}\right)^{1/n}\left(\frac{Y_1}{Y_2} - 1\right) \qquad (11.24)$$

Equation (11.24) may be solved for the intermediate concentration $Y_1$ for specified terminal concentrations $Y_0$ and $Y_2$, and $L_S/G_S$ is then given

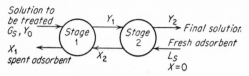

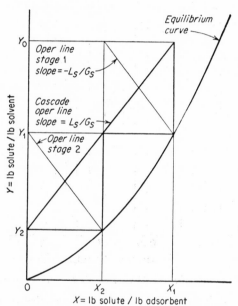

FIG. 11.24. Two-stage countercurrent adsorption.

by Eq. (11.22). Figure 11.25 will assist in the solution of Eq. (11.24). The savings in adsorbent by countercurrent operation over single stage are greater, the greater the value of $n$.

**Illustration 2.** An aqueous solution containing a valuable solute is colored by small amounts of an impurity. Prior to crystallization, the impurity is to be removed by adsorption on a decolorizing carbon which adsorbs only insignificant amounts of the principal solute. A series of laboratory tests were made by stirring various amounts of the adsorbent into batches of the original solution until equilibrium was established, yielding the following data at constant temperature:

| Lb. carbon/lb. soln..... | 0 | 0.001 | 0.004 | 0.008 | 0.02 | 0.04 |
|---|---|---|---|---|---|---|
| Equilibrium color....... | 9.6 | 8.6 | 6.3 | 4.3 | 1.7 | 0.7 |

The color intensity was measured on an arbitrary scale, proportional to the concentration of the colored substance. It is desired to reduce the color to 10% of its original value, 9.6. Determine the quantity of fresh carbon required per 1,000 lb. of solution (a) for a single-stage operation, (b) for a two-stage cocurrent process using the minimum total amount of carbon, and (c) for a two-stage countercurrent operation.

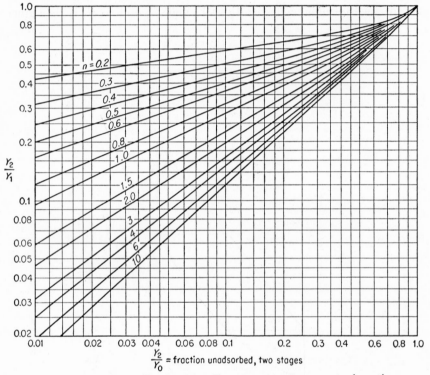

FIG. 11.25. Solution to Eq. (11.24).   Two-stage countercurrent adsorption.

*Solution.* The experimental data must first be converted to a suitable form for plotting the equilibrium isotherm. For this purpose, define $Y$ as units of color per pound of solution and $X$ as units of color adsorbed per pound of carbon. The solutions may be considered as dilute in color, so that operating lines will be straight on $X$, $Y$ coordinates expressed in this manner. The calculations are made in the manner indicated below.

| $\dfrac{\text{Lb. carbon}}{\text{Lb. soln.}}$ | $Y^*$ = equilibrium color, units/lb. soln. | $X$ = adsorbate concn., units/lb. carbon |
|---|---|---|
| 0 | 9.6 | |
| 0.001 | 8.6 | $(9.6 - 8.6)/0.001 = 1,000$ |
| 0.004 | 6.3 | $(9.6 - 6.3)/0.004 = \quad 825$ |
| 0.008 | 4.3 | 663 |
| 0.02 | 1.7 | 395 |
| 0.04 | 0.7 | 223 |

The equilibrium data, when plotted on logarithmic coordinates, provide a straight line, so that the Freundlich equation applies (see Fig. 11.26). The slope of the line is $1.66 = n$, and, at

$$X = 663, \quad Y^* = 4.3$$

Therefore [Eq. (11.7)]

$$m = 4.3/663^{1.66} = 8.91(10^{-5})$$

The Freundlich equation is therefore

$$Y^* = 8.91(10^{-5})X^{1.66}$$

The equilibrium data may also be plotted on arithmetic coordinates (Fig. 11.27).

*a. Single-stage operation.* $Y_0 = 9.6$ units of color/lb. soln.,

$$Y_1 = 0.10(9.6) = 0.96 \text{ unit/lb. soln.}$$

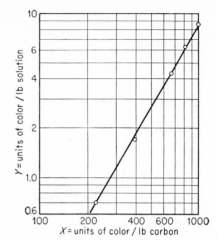

FIG. 11.26. Equilibrium data, Illustration 2.

Let $G_S = 1,000$ lb. soln. Since fresh carbon is to be used, $X_0 = 0$. On Fig. 11.27, point $A$ representing the initial solution and fresh adsorbent is located, and point $B$ is located on the equilibrium curve at the color concentration of the final solution. At $B$, $X_1 = 270$. Therefore [Eq. (11.6)]

$$\frac{L_S}{G_S} = \frac{Y_0 - Y_1}{X_1 - X_0} = \frac{9.6 - 0.96}{270 - 0} = 0.032 \text{ lb. carbon/lb. soln.}$$

and
$$L_S = 0.032(1,000) = 32.0 \text{ lb. carbon/1,000 lb. soln.}$$

Alternatively, since the Freundlich equation applies, use Eq. (11.9):

$$\frac{L_S}{G_S} = \frac{Y_0 - Y_1}{(Y_1/m)^{1/n}} = \frac{9.6 - 0.96}{[0.96/8.91(10^{-5})]^{1/1.66}} = 0.032 \text{ lb. carbon/lb. soln.}$$
$$L_S = 0.032(1,000) = 32.0 \text{ lb. carbon/1,000 lb. soln.}$$

*b. Two-stage cocurrent operation.* The minimum total amount of carbon may be found on Fig. 11.27 by a trial-and-error procedure. Thus, point $C$ on the equilibrium curve is assumed, the operating lines $AC$ and $DB$ drawn, and the values of $L_{S1}$ and $L_{S2}$ computed by Eqs. (11.10) and (11.11). The position of point $C$ is changed until the sum of $L_{S1}$ and $L_{S2}$ is a minimum. The position of $C$ in Fig. 11.27 is the final value, and its coordinates are $(X_1 = 565, Y_1 = 3.30)$. $X_2 = 270$ (at $B$).

Eq. (11.10):
$$L_{S1} = G(Y_0 - Y_1)/(X_1 - X_0) = 1,000(9.6 - 3.30)/(565 - 0) = 11.14 \text{ lb.}$$
Eq. (11.11):
$$L_{S2} = G(Y_1 - Y_2)/(X_2 - X_0) = 1,000(3.30 - 0.96)/(270 - 0) = 8.67 \text{ lb.}$$
$$L_{S1} + L_{S2} = 11.14 + 8.67 = 19.81 \text{ lb. carbon/1,000 lb. soln.}$$

Alternatively, since the Freundlich equation applies, use Fig. 11.20: $Y_2/Y_0 = 0.96/9.6 = 0.10$, $n = 1.66$. From the figure, $Y_1/Y_0 = 0.344$. $Y_1 = 0.344(9.6) = 3.30$.

Eq. (11.12):
$$\frac{L_{S1}}{G_S} = \frac{Y_0 - Y_1}{(Y_1/m)^{1/n}} = \frac{9.6 - 3.30}{[3.30/8.91(10^{-5})]^{1/1.66}}$$
$$= 0.01114 \text{ lb. carbon/lb. soln. into 1st stage}$$

Eq. (11.13): $\dfrac{L_{S2}}{G_S} = \dfrac{Y_1 - Y_2}{(Y_2/m)^{1/n}} = \dfrac{3.30 - 0.96}{[0.96/8.91(10^{-5})]^{1/1.66}}$

$$= 0.00867 \text{ lb. carbon/lb. soln. into 2d stage}$$

Total carbon required $= (0.01114 + 0.00867)1{,}000 = 19.81 \text{ lb.}/1{,}000 \text{ lb. soln.}$

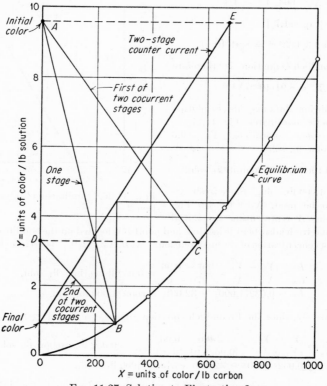

FIG. 11.27. Solution to Illustration 2.

c. *Two-stage countercurrent operation.* $Y_0 = 9.6$, $Y_2 = 0.96$, $X_{Np+1} = 0$. The operating line is located by trial on Fig. 11.27 until two stages may be drawn between operating line and equilibrium curve, as shown. From the figure at $E$, $X_1 = 675$.

Eq. (11.19): $L_S = G_S(Y_0 - Y_2)/(X_1 - X_{Np+1}) = 1{,}000(9.6 - 0.96)/(675 - 0)$
$$= 12.80 \text{ lb. carbon/1,000 lb. soln.}$$

Alternatively, $Y_2/Y_0 = 0.96/9.6 = 0.10$; $n = 1.66$. From Fig. 11.12, $Y_2/Y_1 = 0.217$, and $Y_1 = Y_2/0.217 = 0.96/0.217 = 4.42$.

Eq. (11.22): $\dfrac{L_S}{G_S} = \dfrac{Y_0 - Y_2}{(Y_1/m)^{1/n}} = \dfrac{9.6 - 0.96}{[4.42/8.91(10^{-5})]^{1/1.66}}$

$$= 0.01280 \text{ lb. carbon/lb. soln.}$$

and          $L = 0.01280(1{,}000) = 12.80 \text{ lb. carbon/1,000 lb. soln.}$

**Stage Efficiency.** The resistance to the attainment of equilibrium during batch operation will be the sum of at least the following resistances: (1) The resistance to mass transfer of the solute through the effective liquid film surrounding each adsorbent particle. This may be minimized by maintaining a high degree of turbulence through intensive agitation. (2) The resistance to diffusion of the solute through the liquid in the pores of the solid, from the outside of the particles to the inner surface where adsorption will occur. The liquid in the pores will be stagnant, uninfluenced by the turbulence in the liquid surrounding the particles, and the solute transfer is by a process of molecular diffusion. The path of the diffusion is relatively long and tortuous, and the rate may be described by an effective diffusivity or a pore-shape factor, characteristic of such "structure-sensitive" diffusion (see Chap. 4). (3) The resistance to adsorption itself. This will exist if there is any finite time for the solute molecules to be adsorbed once they have arrived at the point on the surface where they are finally held. For example, it is conceivable that some orientation of the solute molecules with respect to the surface might be required before actual adsorption would occur. For a given system and type of adsorbent, neither the second nor third of these would be under the control of the operator of the process.

The mathematical analysis of these resistances in the unsteady state characteristic of a batch process is very complex, and only a few simple cases have been studied.[8] These indicate that high agitation intensities can readily eliminate the liquid-film resistance as a major factor and that any resistance to adsorption which may have existed is very much smaller than the resistance to diffusion through the pores of the material, which is then the controlling resistance.

Under industrial conditions it is usually possible to reach substantial equilibrium between adsorbent and solution within a reasonable time, and stage efficiencies are therefore essentially unity. For the present at least it will be best to establish the necessary time of contact for this experimentally, using actual samples of the adsorbent and solution to be treated, at the same adsorbent/solution ratio as it is planned to use ultimately. The tests could be made on a small scale provided that for both small-scale test and large-scale operation the intensity of agitation is sufficient substantially to eliminate the resistance of the liquid film surrounding the adsorbent particles. Otherwise large-scale tests would be required.

## II. CONTINUOUS CONTACT

In these operations the fluid and adsorbent are in contact throughout the entire apparatus, without periodic separation of the phases. The operation may be carried out in strictly continuous, steady-state fashion, characterized by movement of the solid as well as the fluid. Alternatively, owing to the rigidity of the solid adsorbent particles, it is also possible to operate advantageously in semicontinuous fashion, characterized by a moving fluid but stationary solid. This results in unsteady-state conditions, where compositions in the system change with time.

## STEADY STATE: MOVING-BED ADSORBERS

Steady-state conditions require continuous movement of both fluid and adsorbent through the equipment at constant rate, with no change in composition at any point in the system with passage of time. If parallel flow of solid and fluid is used, the net result is at best a condition of equilibrium between the effluent streams, or the equivalent of one theoretical stage. It is the purpose of these applications to develop separations equivalent to many stages, however, and hence only countercurrent operation need be considered. At present, these methods are used industrially only for the fractionation of gas mixtures.

**Equipment.** It is only in relatively recent years that satisfactory large-scale devices for the continuous countercurrent contacting of a granular solid and a gas have been developed. These have had to overcome the difficulties of obtaining uniform flow of solid particles and gas without "channeling" or local irregularities, as well as those of introducing and removing the solid continuously into the vessel to be used.

One such device developed specifically for adsorption operations is the *Hypersorber*, shown schematically in its simplest form in Fig. 11.28.[3,15] This is used for fractionation of gas mixtures and has been applied particularly to difficult separations of hydrocarbon gases, using activated carbon as the adsorbent. The Hypersorber consists of a tower down which a compact mass of granular adsorbent flows countercurrently to a gas stream. There are two principal sections to the tower, those directly above and below the point where the feed to be fractionated is introduced. In the section above the point of introducing the feed, the "adsorption" section, the gas is stripped of its more readily adsorbed components, and the product gas taken off at the top of this section is rich in the poorly adsorbed components. Adsorbent passing into the section below the feed contains appreciable amounts of both readily and poorly adsorbed substances, and the adsorbate is enriched in this section by countercurrent contact with a gas stream which removes the more volatile substances. These in turn pass to the upper section of the tower. The adsorbate upon the solid leaving the enriching, or rectifying, section is then rich in the more readily adsorbed components. More complicated construction permits withdrawal of well-fractionated side streams when multicomponent feeds are introduced.[3]

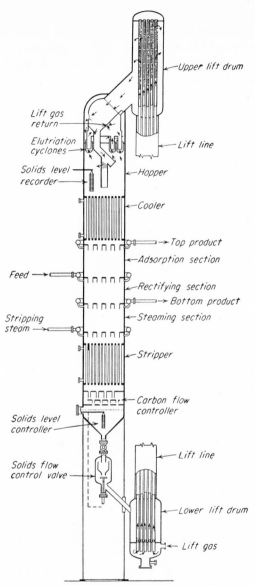

FIG. 11.28. Hypersorber for continuous countercurrent fractionation of a gas into two products. (*Courtesy of Union Oil Co. of California.*)

Certain auxiliary operations are necessary for successful processing. The adsorbent leaving the bottom of the enriching section is stripped of adsorbed gas by heating and contact with steam in the tubular heat exchanger at the lowest part of the tower. The desorbed gas is split into two streams: the bottom product, which is permanently withdrawn, and the reflux stream, which rises through the descending solid in the rectifying section. The hot, freshly stripped adsorbent is then elevated to the top of the tower by means of a gas lift, where it is cooled and introduced into the adsorption section. At the top of this section, a small portion of the gas is allowed to rise through the cooler in order to evaporate moisture from the adsorbent. A portion of this gas in turn is used to

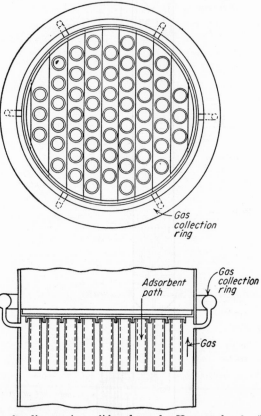

FIG. 11.29. Device for disengaging solid and gas, for Hypersorber.[3]  (*With permission of the American Institute of Chemical Engineers.*)

operate the gas lift for elevating the adsorbent, and the remainder acts as an elutriating agent to remove dust and fines produced by mechanical breakdown of the adsorbent. A small portion of the adsorbent may be continually withdrawn for reactivation, in order to maintain a high level of adsorbent activity.

Figure 11.29 shows the device used for disengaging a product gas stream: the gas collects under the tray and is removed from several points in the tower periphery, while the short pipes carry adsorbent downward through the tray and whatever gas is desired to the upper section. The same device is used for introducing the feed. Figure 11.30 is a schematic representation of the adsorbent flow-controlling device at the bottom of the Hypersorber. The solid must pass through two sets of downcomers, the upper set fixed and the lower set kept in constant reciprocating motion. The adsorbent enters the lower set only when these are in juxtaposition with the upper. The reciprocating motion then carries the entrapped solid to openings in the lower plate, through

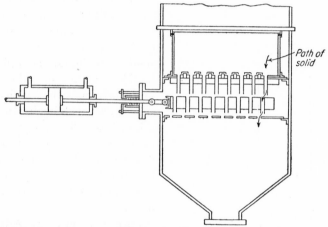

FIG. 11.30. Adsorbent flow-control device for Hypersorber.[15]  (*With permission of the American Institute of Chemical Engineers.*)

which it is discharged. This device successfully produces a rodlike flow of the compacted solids in the tower.

For the hydrocarbon fractionations for which the Hypersorber has thus far been used, a dense, very hard, highly active coconut-shell or fruit-pit carbon is necessary, in the size range 12 to 60 mesh (79 per cent retained on 20- to 30-mesh screens). Attrition losses with such a solid are as low as 0.001 per cent per cycle. Typical of the separations made are the removal of light hydrocarbons such as methane, ethane, and propane from hydrogen for the purpose of making high-purity hydrogen, the recovery of propane and butane from lean gas mixtures, and the purification of ethylene by removal of other hydrocarbons. Such separations could also be made by gas-absorption techniques using a liquid absorbent oil, but the capacity of a highly active carbon (lb. hydrocarbon adsorbed/lb. solid) may be as much as 5 to 90 times as great as a good oil, depending upon the pressure. This in turn means that relatively little solid is required, and heating and cooling costs for recovery of the adsorbent will be less than the corresponding costs for a liquid. On the other hand, the recirculation of solid is costly.

Another less elaborate device for continuous countercurrent flow of granular solids and a gas is that used in the *TCC* catalytic cracking process for petroleum vapors.[24]   While not used for ordinary adsorption operations, this device should be satisfactory for these purposes.

Laboratory and pilot-plant scale towers somewhat similar to those described for gas treatment have been used for treatment of liquids. The difficulty of withdrawing the solid free of liquid at the bottom in a manner so as to provide uniform solids movement over the entire cross section of the tower has not yet been successfully overcome on an industrial scale. Fundamentally, the equipment used for leaching of solids with liquids is applicable to liquid adsorption. Many other quite ingenious devices have been suggested, involving horizontal and upward, as well as downward, movement of the solids through the flowing liquid, but none of these has been permanently successful. Swinton and Weiss[29] review some of these.

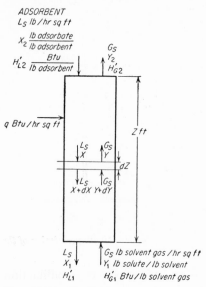

FIG. 11.31. Continuous countercurrent adsorption of one component.

**One Component Adsorbed.** Typical of the processes in this category are those for removal of small quantities of vapors from air and other permanent gases in solvent-recovery operations and the removal of moisture from natural gas.   Actually, continuous apparatus involving a moving bed of adsorbent, which requires mechanical handling and lifting of the solid, is not now used for such processes since it is presently less costly to use the fixed-bed semicontinuous methods to be described later.   It will nevertheless be instructive to consider such operations briefly.

For purposes of computation, the operations are best considered as entirely analogous to gas absorption, with a solid adsorbent replacing the liquid solvent.   Refer to Fig. 11.31.   The notation used resembles that for gas absorption for a binary gas mixture: $G_S$ and $L_S$ are the superficial mass velocities of solute-free gas and adsorbate-free solid, respectively, and solute concentrations are expressed as lb. solute/lb. solute-free substance.   A solute material balance about the entire tower is

$$G_S(Y_1 - Y_2) = L_S(X_1 - X_2) \qquad (11.25)$$

and about the upper part

$$G_S(Y - Y_2) = L_S(X - X_2) \tag{11.26}$$

These establish the operating line on $X$, $Y$ coordinates, a straight line of slope $L_S/G_S$ joining the terminal conditions $(X_1, Y_1)$ and $(X_2, Y_2)$ (Fig. 11.32). The solute concentrations $X$ and $Y$ at any level in the tower fall upon this line. An equilibrium curve appropriate to the system and to the prevailing temperature and pressure may also be plotted on the figure as shown. This will fall below the operating line for adsorption and above for desorption. In the same fashion as for absorbers, the minimum solid/fluid ratio is given by the operating line of maximum slope which anywhere touches the equilibrium curve.

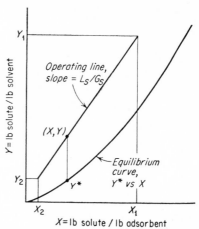

For the purposes of making an enthalpy balance, define the enthalpy of the solid phase at $t_L$°F. as $H'_L$ B.t.u./lb. of adsorbent plus $X$ lb. adsorbate, referred to pure solid adsorbent and to pure solute each at 1 atm. pressure and the reference temperature $t_0$°F., with the solute in its normal state of aggregation at

Fig. 11.32. Continuous countercurrent adsorption of one component.

these conditions. If the pure solute is a liquid at the reference condition, then

$$H'_L = C_L(t_L - t_0) + XC_A(t_L - t_0) + \Delta H_A \tag{11.27}$$

where $C_L$ and $C_A$ are the specific heats of pure adsorbent and pure liquid solute, respectively, B.t.u./(lb.)(°F.), and $\Delta H_A$ is the integral heat of adsorption at $t_0$°F. referred to liquid solute, B.t.u./lb. adsorbent. The enthalpy of the gas at any concentration is $H'_G$ B.t.u./lb. solute-free gas and is given by Eq. (7.19).†

If $q$ represents the net heat added to the adsorber of Fig. 11.31, then an enthalpy balance is

$$L_S H'_{L2} + G_S H'_{G1} + q = G_S H_{G2} + L_S H'_{L1} \tag{11.28}$$

For adiabatic operation, $q = 0$, and, for isothermal operation, $q$ will be negative owing to the evolution of heat during adsorption. The simpli-

† If the solute is a gas at the reference condition, $\Delta H_A$ may be replaced by $\Delta H'_A$, the integral heat of adsorption referred to gaseous solute, and $H'_G$ will then contain only the sensible heat of the components of the gas stream.

fying assumption used in gas absorption, that the temperature of the gas remains substantially constant in adiabatic operations, is unsatisfactory for estimating the temperature of the solid as it passes through the adsorber. The detailed calculations for this are given by Munro and Amundsen[23] and Singer and Wilhelm.[27] The present discussion is limited to isothermal operation.

The resistance to mass transfer of solute from the fluid to the adsorbed state on the solid will include that residing in the gas surrounding the solid particles, that corresponding to the diffusion of solute through the gas within the pores of the solid, and possibly an additional resistance at the time of adsorption. During physical adsorption, the last of these will probably be negligible. If the remaining resistances may be characterized by an over-all gas mass-transfer coefficient based on $a_p$, the outside surface of the solid particles, $K_Y a_p$, then the rate of solute transfer over the differential height of adsorber $dZ$ (Fig. 11.31) may be written in the usual manner as

$$L_S \, dX = G_S \, dY = K_Y a_p (Y - Y^*) \, dZ \qquad (11.29)$$

where $Y^*$ is the equilibrium composition in the gas corresponding to the adsorbate composition $X$. The driving force $Y - Y^*$ is then represented by the vertical distance between operating line and equilibrium curve (Fig. 11.32). Rearranging Eq. (11.29) and integrating define the number of transfer units $H_{tOG}$,†

$$N_{tOG} = \int_{Y_2}^{Y_1} \frac{dY}{Y - Y^*} = \frac{K_y a_p \, dZ}{G_S} = \frac{Z}{H_{tOG}} \qquad (11.30)$$

where
$$H_{tOG} = \frac{G_S}{K_Y a_p} \qquad (11.31)$$

The integral of Eq. (11.30) is ordinarily evaluated graphically and the active height $Z$ determined through knowledge of the height of a transfer unit $H_{tOG}$, characteristic of the system.

The use of an over-all coefficient or over-all height of a transfer unit implies that the resistance to mass transfer within the pores of the solid particles may be considered as a "film resistance"[7] characterized by an individual mass-transfer coefficient $k_S a_p$ or height of a transfer unit $H_{tS}$,

---

† The number of transfer units is more correctly given by

$$N_{tOG} = \int_{p_2}^{p_1} \frac{(P_t - p)_M \, dp}{(P_t - p)(p - p^*)} = \int_{Y_2}^{Y_1} \frac{dY}{Y - Y^*} + \frac{1}{2} \ln \frac{1 + rY_2}{1 + rY_1}$$

where $p$ is the partial pressure of solute, $P_t$ the total pressure, and $r$ the ratio of molecular weights of solvent gas to solute (see Chap. 8). The last term of this expression is quite negligible for the dilute-gas mixtures which would be treated by these methods.

thus,

$$\frac{G_S}{K_Y a_p} = \frac{G_S}{k_Y a_p} + \frac{mG_S}{L_S}\frac{L_S}{k_S a_p} \qquad (11.32)$$

or

$$H_{toG} = H_{tG} + \frac{mG_S}{L_S}H_{tS} \qquad (11.33)$$

where $m = dY^*/dX$, the slope of the equilibrium curve. The resistance within the gas surrounding the particles, $H_{tG}$, or the equivalent mass-transfer coefficient $k_Y a_p$ can be estimated through the correlation represented by curve 7 (Fig. 3.11). There are presently too few experimental data available for over-all $H_{toG}$'s taken on moving beds of solids to permit generalizations, but for fixed beds the indication is that $H_{toG}$ may be as much as three to four times the corresponding value of $H_{tG}$.[13] The resistance within the solid is therefore of major importance.

Owing to the rigidity of each solid particle and to the unsteady-state diffusional conditions existing within each particle as it travels through the adsorber, extension of the film concept to the pores of the particles is open to some question. The mass transfer of solute in the fluid within the pores occurs by the mechanism of molecular diffusion, characterized by an "effective" or diminished diffusivity, or "pore-shape factor," owing to the tortuous paths within the solid (see Chap. 4). The resistance to mass transfer can be expected to be independent of rate of flow of solid or fluid and to increase with increased particle size for any one type of adsorbent. A method of design allowing for the unsteady-state conditions within the solid particles and the varying concentrations of solute at the particle surface as it flows through the adsorber, for the case where the equilibrium curve is linear, has been developed by Kasten and Amundsen.[14]

**Illustration 3.** Eagleton and Bliss[7] have measured the individual resistances to mass transfer residing in the fluid and within the solid during adsorption of water vapor from air by silica gel, using a fixed-bed semicontinuous method of operation. For low moisture contents of the air, they found that

$$k_Y a_p = 188G'^{0.55} \text{ lb. } H_2O/(\text{hr.})(\text{cu. ft.})(\Delta Y)$$

and

$$k_S a_p = 217 \text{ lb. } H_2O/(\text{hr.})(\text{cu. ft.})(\Delta X)$$

where $G'$ is the mass velocity of the gas, lb./(hr.)(sq. ft.). Their silica gel had an apparent bed density of 41.9 lb./cu. ft., an average particle size of 0.068 in. diameter, and the external surface of the particles was 10.58 sq. ft./lb.

It is desired to estimate the height of a continuous countercurrent isothermal adsorber for the drying of air at 80°F., atmospheric pressure, from an initial humidity of 0.005 to a final humidity of 0.0001 lb. water/lb. dry air. The entering gel will be dry. (NOTE: So-called "dry" silica gel must contain a minimum of about 5% water if it is to retain its adsorptive capacity. Moisture measurements as ordinarily reported do not include this.) A gel rate of 500 lb./(hr.)(sq. ft.) and an air rate of 1,000 lb. dry air/(hr.)(sq. ft.) will be used. For the moisture concentrations to be encountered here, the equilibrium adsorption isotherm at 80°F., 1 atm. (see Illustration 6) may be taken as substantially straight and described by the expression $Y* = 0.0185X$.

*Solution.* $Y_1 = 0.005$, $Y_2 = 0.0001$ lb. $H_2O$/lb. dry air. $L_S = 500$ lb./(hr.)(sq. ft.), $G_S = 1,000$ lb./(hr.)(sq. ft.), $X_2 = 0$ lb. $H_2O$/lb. dry gel.

Eq. (11.25):

$$X_1 = G_S(Y_1 - Y_2)/L_S + X_2 = 1,000(0.005 - 0.0001)/500$$
$$= 0.0098 \text{ lb. } H_2O/\text{lb. dry gel}$$
$$Y_2^* = \text{humidity of air in equilibrium with entering gel} = 0$$
$$Y_1^* = 0.0185X_1 = 0.0185(0.0098) = 0.0001815 \text{ lb. } H_2O/\text{lb. dry gel}$$

Since operating line and equilibrium curve will both be straight on $X$, $Y$ coordinates, the average driving force is the logarithmic average [Eqs. (8.49) to (8.50)].

$$Y_1 - Y_1^* = 0.005 - 0.0001815 = 0.00482$$
$$Y_2 - Y_2^* = 0.0001 - 0 = 0.0001$$
$$\text{Av. } \Delta Y = (0.00482 - 0.0001)/\ln{(0.00482/0.0001)} = 0.001217$$
$$N_{tOG} = (Y_1 - Y_2)/\Delta Y = (0.005 - 0.0001)/0.001217 = 4.03$$

If the fixed-bed data are to be used for estimating mass-transfer coefficients for a moving bed of solids, the relative mass velocity of air and solid is appropriate. The linear rate of flow of the solid downward is $500/41.9 = 11.95$ ft./hr., where 41.9 is the apparent density. The density of this substantially dry air at 80°F., 1 atm., is 0.0737 lb./cu. ft., and its superficial linear velocity upward is $1,000/0.0737 = 13,590$ ft./hr. The relative linear velocity of air and solid is $13,590 + 11.95 = 13,602$ ft./hr., and the relative mass velocity of the air is $13,602(0.0737) = 1,004$ lb./(hr.)(sq. ft.) = $G'$.

$$H_{tG} = \frac{G_S}{k_Y a_p} = \frac{G_S}{188G'^{0.55}} = \frac{1,000}{188(1,004)^{0.55}} = 0.118 \text{ ft.}$$

$$H_{tS} = \frac{L_S}{k_S a_p} = \frac{500}{217} = 2.30 \text{ ft.}$$

$$\frac{mG_S}{L_S} = \frac{0.0185(1,000)}{500} = 0.037$$

Eq. (11.33):     $H_{tOG} = 0.118 + 0.037(2.30) = 0.203$ ft.
$$Z = N_{tOG}H_{tOG} = 4.03(0.203) = 0.83 \text{ ft.} \quad Ans.$$

NOTE: Curve 7 (Fig. 3.11) in this case does not give values of $H_{tG}$ which agree with the observed data. Thus, at 80°F., the viscosity of air = 0.018 centipoise, or $0.018(2.42) = 0.0435$ lb./(ft.)(hr.). $d_p = 0.068/12 = 0.00567$ ft., and Re″ = $d_p G/\mu = 0.00567(1,004)/0.0435 = 1.310$. From Fig. 3.11, curve 7, $j_D = (k_y/G_M)$ Sc$^{\frac{2}{3}}$ = 0.154 (Chap. 3 notation).

For air–water vapor, Sc = 0.60. For this gel, $a_p = (10.58 \text{ sq. ft./lb.})(41.9 \text{ lb./cu. ft.}) = 442$ sq. ft./cu. ft. of adsorber volume.

$$H_{tG} = \frac{G_M}{k_y a_p} = \frac{\text{Sc}^{\frac{2}{3}}}{j_D a_p} = \frac{0.6^{\frac{2}{3}}}{0.154(442)} = 0.0104 \text{ ft.}$$

which is only about one-tenth that indicated by the experimental data. Difference in the particle shape and specific surface for the silica gel and for the particles used to establish the curve of Fig. 3.11 may be responsible, in part, at least.

## Two Components Adsorbed. Fractionation. When several components of a gas mixture are appreciably adsorbed, fractionation is required

for their separation and a device such as the Hypersorber may be used. This discussion is confined to binary gas mixtures.

For purposes of computation, it is easiest to recall the similarity between the adsorption operation and continuous countercurrent extraction with reflux. Solid adsorbent as the added insoluble phase is analogous to extraction solvent, the adsorbate is analogous to the solvent-free extract, and the fluid stream is similar to the raffinate. Computations may then be made using the methods and equations of Chap. 10 [Eqs. (10.73) to (10.89) and Figs. 10.54 to 10.56]. Some simplification is possible, however, owing to the complete insolubility of adsorbent in the mixture to be separated.

Refer to Fig. 11.33, a schematic representation of the adsorber. Feed enters at the rate of $F$ lb./- (hr.)(sq. ft.), containing components $A$ and $C$. The adsorbate-free adsorbent enters the top of the tower at the rate of $B$ lb./(hr.)(sq. ft.) and flows countercurrent to the gas entering at the bottom at the rate of $R_1$ lb./(hr.)(sq. ft.). Compositions in the gas stream are expressed as $x$ weight fraction $C$, the more strongly adsorbed substance. $E$ represents the weight of adsorb-

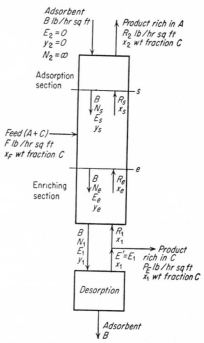

FIG. 11.33. Continuous fractionation.

ent-free adsorbate $A + C$ upon the solid, lb./(hr.)(sq. ft.), and $N$ the ratio, lb. adsorbent/lb. adsorbate. At any point in the adsorber, $B = NE$. The adsorbate composition is expressed as $y$ weight fraction component $C$, on an adsorbent-free basis. Solid leaves the adsorber at the bottom, is stripped of its adsorbate in the desorption section, and the desorbed fluid is split into two streams, the reflux $R_1$ and the $C$-rich product $P_E$. At the top the fluid leaving is the $A$-rich product, $R_2$ lb./(hr.)(sq. ft.). The arrangement is very similar to that shown in Fig. 10.49, except that no raffinate reflux is used. Calculations are made on a phase diagram of the type shown in the upper part of Fig. 11.8$a$, with $N$ plotted as ordinate, $x$ and $y$ as abscissa.

Let $Q$ represent the net adsorbent-free flow downward and out of the adsorber. Then $Q = P_E$, and the coordinates of point $Q$ on the phase diagram are ($N_Q = B/P_E$, $y_Q = x_1$). At the bottom of the adsorber,

$B = N_1 E_1$ and
$$E_1 = E' = P_E + R_1 = Q + R_1 \tag{11.34}$$

An $A$-$C$ balance below section $e$ of the enriching section is
$$E_e = P_E + R_e = Q + R_e \tag{11.35}$$

and, for substance $C$,
$$E_e y_e = P_E x_1 + R_e x_e = Q x_1 + R_e x_e \tag{11.36}$$

while for adsorbent it becomes
$$N_e E_e = N_Q Q = B \tag{11.37}$$

$Q$ therefore represents the difference $E_e - R_e$ for any level in the enriching section. Equations (11.35) and (11.37) provide a measure of the internal reflux ratio,
$$\frac{R_e}{E_e} = \frac{N_Q - N_e}{N_Q} = 1 - \frac{N_e}{N_Q} \tag{11.38}$$

and at the bottom of the tower the external reflux ratio is
$$\frac{R_1}{P_E} = \frac{R_1}{E_1 - R_1} = \frac{N_Q - N_1}{N_1} = \frac{N_Q}{N_1} - 1 \tag{11.39}$$

At the top of the adsorber let $W$ represent the difference between flows of adsorbate and unadsorbed gas, and since $E_2 = 0$, $W = -R_2$. The coordinates of $W$ on the phase diagram are then $(N_W = -B/R_2, x_W = x_2)$. Material balances above section $s$ are then, for $A$ and $C$,
$$R_s = E_s + R_2 = E_s - W \tag{11.40}$$

for $C$,
$$R_s x_s = E_s y_s + R_2 x_2 = E_s y_s - W x_2 \tag{11.41}$$

and for adsorbent,
$$B = N_s E_s = W N_W \tag{11.42}$$

Equations (11.40) and (11.42) provide the internal reflux ratio,
$$\frac{R_s}{E_s} = \frac{N_s - N_W}{-N_W} = 1 - \frac{N_s}{N_W} \tag{11.43}$$

Over-all balances about the entire plant are
$$F = R_2 + P_E \tag{11.44}$$
$$F x_F = R_2 x_2 + P_E x_1 \tag{11.45}$$

The definitions of $W$ and $Q$, together with Eq. (11.45), provide
$$W + F = Q \tag{11.46}$$

The graphical interpretation of these relations on the phase diagram is the same as that for the corresponding situations in extraction and is shown in detail in Illustration 4 below.

Since continuous rather than stagewise contact is used, the height of the adsorber is best computed through the number of transfer units and the height per transfer unit. If the fluid to be separated is a gas,

$$N_{tOG} = \frac{Z}{H_{tOG}} = \int_{p_2}^{p_1} \frac{dp}{p - p^*} = \int_{x_2}^{x_1} \frac{dx}{x - x^*} - \ln \frac{1 + (r - 1)x_1}{1 + (r - 1)x_2} \quad (11.47)$$

where $r = M_A/M_C$ and

$$H_{tOG} = \frac{G}{K_G a_P P_t} \quad (11.48)$$

Equation (11.47) may also be applied separately to the enriching and adsorption sections. It assumes that the counterdiffusion of $A$ and $C$ from and to the solid is equimolar, which is not strictly the case. Further refinement at this time is not warranted, however.

**Illustration 4.** Determine the number of transfer units and adsorbent circulation rate required to separate a gas containing 60% ethylene $C_2H_4$ and 40% propane $C_3H_8$ by volume into products containing 5 and 95% $C_2H_4$ by volume, isothermally at 25°C. and 2.25 atm., using activated carbon as the adsorbent and a reflux ratio of twice the minimum. (NOTE: Hypersorbers customarily operate at reflux ratios closer to the minimum in order to reduce the adsorbent circulation rate. The present value is used in order to make the graphical solution clear.)

*Solution.* Equilibrium data for this mixture at 25°C. and 2.25 atm. have been estimated from the data of Lewis *et al.*, *Ind. Eng. Chem.*, **42**, 1319, 1326 (1950), and are plotted in Fig. 11.34. $C_3H_8$ is the more strongly adsorbed component, and compositions in the gas and adsorbate are expressed as weight fraction $C_3H_8$. Tie lines have been omitted in the upper part of the plot, and the equilibrium compositions are shown instead in the lower part.

Molecular weights are 28.0 for $C_2H_4$ and 44.1 for $C_3H_8$. The feed-gas composition is then $x_F = 0.4(44.1)/[0.4(44.1) + 0.6(28.0)] = 0.512$ wt. fraction $C_3H_8$. Similarly $x_1 = 0.967$, and $x_2 = 0.0763$ wt. fraction $C_3H_8$.

Basis: 100 lb. feed gas.

Eqs. (11.44) and (11.45):
$$100 = R_2 + P_E$$
$$100(0.512) = R_2(0.0763) + P_E(0.967)$$

Solving simultaneously, $R_2 = 51.1$ lb., $P_E = 48.9$ lb.

Point $F$ at $x_F$ and point $E_1$ at $x_1$ are located on the diagram as shown. From the diagram, $N_1$ (at point $E_1$) = 4.57 lb. carbon/lb. adsorbate. The minimum reflux ratio is found as it is for extraction. In this case, the tie line through point $F$ locates $Q_{min}$, and $N_{Qmin} = 5.80$.

$$\left(\frac{R_1}{P_E}\right)_{min} = \frac{5.80}{4.57} - 1 = 0.269 \text{ lb. reflux gas/lb. product}$$
$$(R_1)_{min} = 0.269P_E = 0.269(48.9) = 13.15 \text{ lb.}$$
$$(E_1)_{min} = (R_1)_{min} + P_E = 13.15 + 48.9 = 62.1 \text{ lb.}$$
$$B_{min} = N_1(E_1)_{min} = 4.57(62.1) = 284 \text{ lb. carbon/100 lb. feed}$$

At twice the minimum reflux ratio, $R_1/P_E = 2(0.269) = 0.538$.

Eq. (11.39):
$$0.538 = \frac{N_Q}{4.57} - 1$$
$$N_Q = 7.03 \text{ lb. carbon/lb. adsorbate}$$

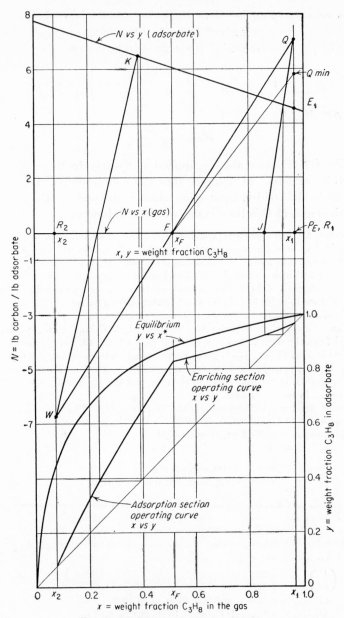

FIG. 11.34. Solution to Illustration 4.

and point $Q$ is located on the diagram.

$$R_1 = 0.538P_E = 0.538(48.9) = 26.3 \text{ lb.}$$
$$E_1 = R_1 + P_E = 26.3 + 48.9 = 75.2 \text{ lb.}$$
$$B = N_1E_1 = 4.57(75.2) = 344 \text{ lb. carbon/100 lb. feed}$$

Point $W$ may be located by extending line $QF$ to intersect the line $x = x_2$. Alternatively, $N_W = -B/R_2 = -344/51.1 = -6.74$ lb. carbon/lb. adsorbate. Random lines such as line $WK$ are drawn from $W$, and the intersections with the equilibrium curves are projected downward in the manner shown to provide the adsorption-section operating curve. Similarly random lines such as line $QJ$ are drawn from $Q$, and intersections projected downward to provide the enriching-section operating curve. The horizontal distance between operating and equilibrium curves on the lower diagram is the driving force $x - x^*$ of Eq. (11.47). The following were determined from the diagram:

| $x$ | $x^*$ | $\dfrac{1}{x - x^*}$ |
|---|---|---|
| $x_1 = 0.967$ | 0.825 | 7.05 |
| 0.90 | 0.710 | 5.26 |
| 0.80 | 0.60 | 5.00 |
| 0.70 | 0.50 | 5.00 |
| 0.60 | 0.43 | 5.89 |
| $x_F = 0.512$ | 0.39 | 8.20 |
| 0.40 | 0.193 | 4.83 |
| 0.30 | 0.090 | 4.76 |
| 0.20 | 0.041 | 6.29 |
| $x_2 = 0.0763$ | 0.003 | 13.65 |

The third column was plotted as ordinate against the first as abscissa, the area under the curve between $x_1$ and $x_F$ was 2.65, and that between $x_F$ and $x_2$ was 2.67. Further, $r = 28.0/44.1 = 0.635$. Applying Eq. (11.47) to the enriching section,

$$N_{tOG} = 2.65 - \ln [1 + (0.635 - 1)0.967]/[1 + (0.635 - 1)0.512]$$
$$= 2.52$$

and to the adsorption section,

$$N_{tOG} = 2.67 - \ln [1 + (0.635 - 1)0.512]/[1 + (0.635 - 1)0.0763]$$
$$= 2.53$$

The total $N_{tOG} = 2.52 + 2.53 = 5.1$.

## UNSTEADY STATE: FIXED-BED ADSORBERS

Owing to the inconvenience and relatively high cost of continuously transporting solid particles as required in steady-state operations, it is frequently found more economical to pass the fluid mixture to be treated through a stationary bed of adsorbent. As increasing amounts of fluid are passed through such a bed, the solid adsorbs increasing amounts of solute and an unsteady state prevails. This technique is very widely used and finds application in such diverse fields as the recovery of valuable solvent vapors from gases, purifying air as with gas masks, dehydration of gases and liquids, decolorizing mineral and vegetable oils, the concentration of valuable solutes from liquid solutions, and many others.

**The Adsorption Wave.** Consider the case of a binary solution, either gas or liquid, containing a strongly adsorbed solute at concentration $c_0$. The fluid is to be passed continuously down through a relatively deep bed of adsorbent initially free of adsorbate. The uppermost layer of solid, in contact with the strong solution entering, at first adsorbs solute rapidly and effectively, and what little solute is left in the solution is substantially all removed by the layers of solid in the lower part of the bed. The effluent from the bottom of the bed is practically solute-free as at $c_a$ in the lower part of Fig. 11.35. The distribution of adsorbate in the solid bed is indicated in the sketch in the upper part of this figure at (a), where the relative density of the horizontal lines in the bed is meant to indicate the relative concentration of adsorbate. The uppermost layer of the bed is practically saturated, and the bulk of the adsorption takes place over a relatively narrow adsorption zone in which the concentration changes rapidly, as shown. As solution continues to flow, the adsorption zone moves downward as a wave, at a rate ordinarily very much more slowly than the linear velocity of the fluid through the bed. At a later time, as at (b) in the figure, roughly half of the bed is saturated with solute, but the effluent concentration $c_b$ is still substantially zero. At (c) in the figure the lower portion of the adsorption zone has just reached the bottom of the bed, and the concentration of solute in the effluent has suddenly risen to an appreciable value $c_c$ for the first time. The system is said to have reached the "break point." The solute concentration in the effluent now rises rapidly as the adsorption zone passes through the bottom of the bed and at (d) has substantially reached the initial value $c_0$. The portion of the effluent concentration curve between positions (c) and (d) is termed the "break-through" curve. If solution continues to flow, little additional adsorption takes place since the bed is for all practical purposes entirely in equilibrium with the feed solution.

If a vapor is being adsorbed adiabatically from a gas mixture in this manner, the evolution of the heat of adsorption causes a temperature wave to flow through the adsorbent bed in a manner somewhat similar to the adsorption wave[19] and the rise in temperature of the bed at the fluid outlet may sometimes be used as a rough indication of the break point. In the case of adsorption from liquids the temperature rise is usually relatively small.

The shape and time of appearance of the break-through curve influence greatly the method of operating a fixed-bed adsorber. The curves generally have an S shape, but they may be steep or relatively flat and in some cases considerably distorted. If the adsorption process were infinitely rapid, the break-through curve would be a straight vertical line in the lower part of Fig. 11.35. The actual rate and mechanism of the

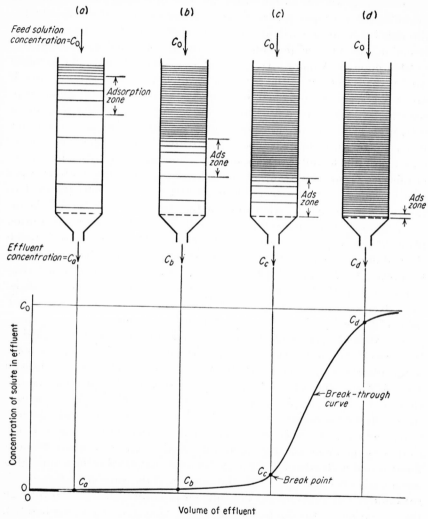

FIG. 11.35. The adsorption wave.

adsorption process, the nature of the adsorption equilibrium, the fluid velocity, the concentration of solute in the feed, and the length of the adsorber bed particularly if the solute concentration in the feed is high, all contribute to the shape of the curve produced for any system. The break point is very sharply defined in some cases and in others poorly defined. Generally the break-point time decreases with decreased bed height, increased particle size of adsorbent, increased rate of flow of fluid through the bed, and increased initial solute content of the feed. There is a critical minimum bed height[17] below which the solute concentration in the effluent will rise rapidly from the first appearance of effluent. In planning new processes it is best to determine the break-point and break-through curve for a particular system experimentally under conditions resembling as much as possible those to be encountered in the process.

**Adsorption of Vapors.** One of the most important applications of fixed-bed adsorbers is in the recovery of valuable solvent vapors. Solids saturated with solvents such as alcohol, acetone, carbon disulfide, benzene, and others may be dried by evaporation of the solvent into an air stream, and the solvent vapor may be recovered by passing the resulting vapor-gas mixture through a bed of activated carbon. The very favorable adsorption equilibrium provided by a good grade of carbon for vapors of this sort permits substantially complete vapor recovery, 99 to 99.8 per cent,[4] from gas mixtures containing as little as 0.5 to 0.05 per cent of the vapor by volume.[6] Air-vapor mixtures of concentration well below the explosive limits may thus be handled. In most such adsorption plants it is necessary to operate with a small drop in pressure through the bed of adsorbent in order to keep power costs low. Therefore granular rather than powdered adsorbents are used, and bed depths are relatively shallow (12 to 36 in.) and large in cross section. The superficial gas velocity may be in the range 0.8 to 1.8 ft./sec. A typical arrangement of the adsorption vessel is shown in Fig. 11.36.

In a typical operation the air-vapor mixture, if necessary cooled to 90 to 100°F. and filtered free of dust particles which might clog the pores of the adsorbent, is admitted to the adsorbent bed. If the break-through curve is steep, the effluent air, substantially free of vapor, may be discharged to the atmosphere until the break point is reached, whereupon the influent stream must be diverted to a second adsorber, while the first is regenerated. On the other hand, if the break-through curve is flat so that at the break point a substantial portion of the adsorbent remains unsaturated with adsorbate, the gas may be permitted to flow through a second adsorber in series with the first until the carbon in the first is substantially all saturated. The influent mixture is then passed through the second and a third adsorber in series, while the first is regenerated. Such operation is relatively unusual, however.

After gas flow has been diverted from an adsorber, the carbon is usually desorbed by admission of low-pressure steam. This lowers the partial pressure of the vapor in contact with the solid and provides by condensation the necessary heat of desorption. The steam-vapor effluent from the carbon is condensed and the condensed solvent recovered by decantation from the water if it is water-insoluble or by rectification if an aqueous solution results.   When desorption is complete, the carbon is saturated with adsorbed water.   This moisture is readily displaced by many vapors and evaporated into the air when the air-vapor mixture is readmitted to the carbon, and indeed much of the heat evolved during adsorption of the vapor may be used in desorbing the water, thus maintaining moderate bed temperatures.   If the moisture interferes with

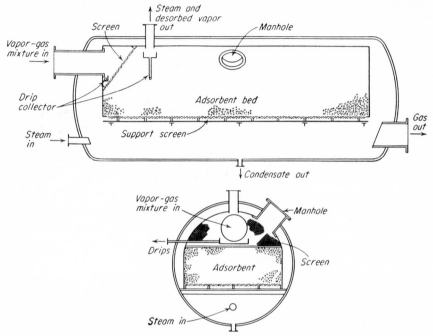

FIG. 11.36. Adsorber for solvent vapors (schematic).   [*Logan, U.S. Patent* 2,180,712 (1939).]

vapor adsorption, the bed may first be dried by admitting heated air and then cooled by unheated air, prior to reuse for vapor recovery. Figure 11.37 shows a typical plant layout arranged for this method of operation.   Mantell[21] provides many other operating details.

Moist gases may be dried of their water content by passing them through beds of activated silica gel, alumina, or bauxite.[1]   Especially if the gases are under appreciable pressures, moderately deep beds are used since the pressure drop will still be only a small fraction of the total pressure.   Towers containing the adsorbent may be as much as 30 ft. tall or more, but in such instances the solid is best supported on trays at intervals of 4 or 5 ft. in order to minimize the compression of the bed resulting from pressure drop.   After the bed has reached the maximum practical moisture content, the adsorbent may be regenerated, either by application of heat by steam coils embedded in the adsorbent or by admitting heated air or gas. Liquids such as gasoline, kerosene, and transformer oil may also be dehydrated by passage through beds of activated alumina. High-temperature (450°F.) steam followed by application of vacuum provided by a steam-jet ejector may be used for regenerating the adsorbent.

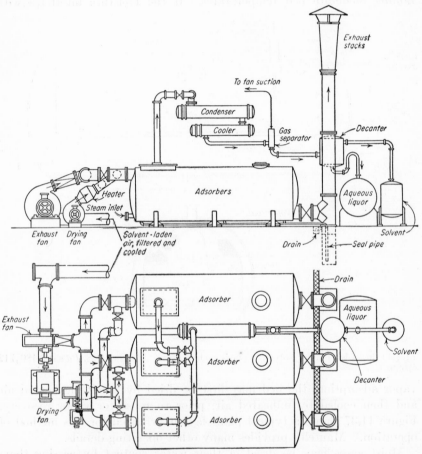

FIG. 11.37. Solvent-recovery adsorption plant. [*After Benson and Courouleau, Chem. Eng. Progr.*, **44**, 466 (1948), *with permission.*]

**Illustration 5.** A solvent recovery plant is to recover 800 lb./hr. of ethyl acetate vapor from a mixture with air at a concentration of 1.8 lb. vapor/1,000 cu. ft. air at 90°F., 1 atm. pressure. The adsorbent will be activated carbon, 6 to 8 mesh (av. particle diam. 0.0091 ft., apparent density of individual particles 45 lb./cu. ft., and apparent density of the packed bed 30 lb./cu. ft.). The carbon is capable of adsorbing 0.45 lb. vapor/lb. carbon up to the break point. The adsorption cycle will be set at 3 hr. to allow sufficient time for regeneration. Determine the amount of carbon required, choose suitable dimensions for the carbon beds, and estimate the pressure drop.

*Solution.* In 3 hr. the vapor to be adsorbed is $3(800) = 2,400$ lb. The carbon required per bed $= 2,400(1/0.45) = 5,330$ lb. Two beds will be necessary, one adsorbing while the other is being regenerated. Total carbon required is $2(5,330) = 10,660$ lb.

The volume of each bed will be $5,330/30 = 178$ cu. ft. If the bed depth is 1.5 ft., the cross section is $178/1.5 = 119$ sq. ft., say 7 by 17 ft., and it may be installed horizontally in a suitable vessel such as that shown in Fig. 11.36.

The pressure drop may be estimated by Eq. (6.26). At 90°F., 1 atm., the viscosity of air $= 0.018$ centipoise, or $0.018(2.42) = 0.0436$ lb./(ft.)(hr.), and the density is $(29/359)(492/550) = 0.0723$ lb./cu. ft. One cubic foot of the bed, weighing 30 lb., contains $30/45 = 0.667$ cu. ft. of solid particles. The fractional void content of the bed (space between particles, but not including pore volume) is $1 - 0.667 = 0.333 = \epsilon$.

The volumetric rate of air flow $= 800(1,000)/1.8 = 445,000$ cu. ft./hr., and the superficial mass velocity $= 445,000(0.0723)/119 = 270$ lb./(hr.)(sq. ft.) (linear velocity $= 1.04$ ft./sec.). The particle Reynolds number $= \text{Re} = d_p G/\mu = 0.0091(270)/0.0436 = 56.3$.

Eq. (6.26) (Chap. 6 notation):

$$\frac{\Delta P}{Z} \frac{g_c' \epsilon^3 d_p \rho_G}{(1 - \epsilon)G''^2} = \frac{150(1 - \epsilon)}{\text{Re}} + 1.75$$

$$\frac{\Delta P \ (4.17)(10^8)(0.333)^3(0.0091)(0.0723)}{1.5(1 - 0.333)(270)^2} = \frac{150(1 - 0.333)}{56.3} + 1.75$$

$$\Delta P = 25.5 \text{ lb./sq. ft., or } 25.5(12/62.4) = 4.9 \text{ in. water}$$

**Adsorption of Liquids. Percolation.** The dehydration of liquids by stationary beds of adsorbent has already been mentioned. In addition, the colors of petroleum products, such as lubricating oils and transformer oils, and of vegetable oils are commonly reduced by percolation through beds of decolorizing clays; sugar solutions are deashed and decolorized by percolation through bone char; and many other liquid-treating operations use these semibatch methods.

In such service, the bed of adsorbent is commonly called a "filter." It may be installed in a vertical cylindrical vessel fitted with a dished or conical bottom, of diameter ranging up to as much as 15 ft. and height up to 30 ft. In the case of decolorizing clays, the beds may contain as much as 50 tons of adsorbent. The granular adsorbent is supported on a screen or blanket, in turn supported by a perforated plate.

The liquid flow is ordinarily downward, either under the force of gravity alone or under pressure from above. At the start of the operation, the adsorbent bed is frequently allowed to "soak" for a time in the first portions of the feed liquid, in order to displace air from the adsorbent particles before the percolation is begun. In decolorizing operations, the concentration of impurity in the initial effluent liquid is usually much smaller than the specifications of the product require, and the break-through curve is frequently rather flat. Consequently it is common practice to allow the effluent liquid to accumulate in a receiving tank below the filter and to blend or composite it until the blended liquid reaches the largest acceptable concentration of impurity. In this way, the largest possible adsorbate concentration may be accumulated upon the solid.

When the solid requires revivification, the flow of liquid is stopped and the liquid in the filter drained. The solid may then be washed in place with an appropriate solvent (e.g., water in the case of sugar-refining filters, naphtha in the case of petroleum products). If necessary the solvent is then removed by admission of steam, following which the solid may be dumped from the filter and reactivated by burning or other suitable procedure, depending upon the nature of the adsorbent.

**Chromatography.** Consider for the moment of a solution containing two solutes which it is desired to separate. If a small portion of the solution is percolated through a tall bed of suitable adsorbent, both solutes will be adsorbed in the uppermost portion of the bed and the lower part of the column will be substantially free of adsorbate. The effluent will be substantially free of both solutes. If now fresh solvent ("eluent"), either the same as that in the original solution or another, is percolated downward through the adsorbent bed, the solute which is least strongly adsorbed will be preferentially desorbed from its position in the upper part of the column. It will, however, be readsorbed in the lower part of the bed upon coming into contact with the unsaturated adsorbent there. The two original solutes are now effectively separated into two adsorption bands† and may be recovered individually by breaking the adsorbent column at a point between the bands. Alternatively by judicious use of eluent it is possible to wash the solutes out of the column one at a time. These methods have come into considerable prominence in the last 15 years as analytical devices, and more recently important industrial operations have used these techniques or variants of them. The *Arosorb* process, for example, separates aromatic hydrocarbons such as benzene and toluene from saturated hydrocarbons of the same boiling range by essentially chromatographic adsorption on silica gel.[10] Two eluents are used to separate the adsorbed hydrocarbons: liquid butane or pentane first removes the less readily adsorbed saturated hydrocarbons of the original mixture, and xylene may be used to elute the adsorbed aromatics.

**Rate of Adsorption in Fixed Beds.** The design of a fixed-bed adsorber, and the prediction of the length of the adsorption cycle between revivifications, requires knowledge of the percentage approach to saturation at the break point, as shown in Illustration 5. This in turn requires the

---

† The adsorption bands in some cases have different colors, depending upon the chemical nature of the solutes, and this has given rise to the terms "chromatographic adsorption" and "chromatography."

designer to predict the time of the break point and the shape of the break-through curve. The unsteady-state circumstances of fixed-bed adsorption and the many factors which influence the adsorption make such computations for the general case most formidable problems, and the mathematics for exact solutions have been established for only a few special cases.[13,17] The following simplified treatment due to Michaels[22] is readily used but is limited to adsorption from dilute feed mixtures and to cases where the equilibrium adsorption isotherm is concave to the solution-concentration axis, where the adsorption zone is constant in

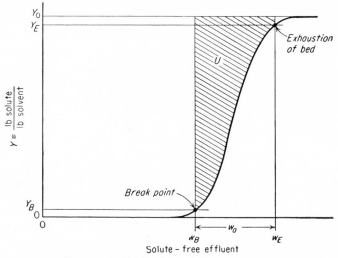

FIG. 11.38. Idealized break-through curve.

height as it travels through the adsorption column, and where the height of the adsorbent bed is large relative to the height of the adsorption zone. Many industrial applications fall within these restrictions. The development here is in terms of adsorption from a gas, but it is equally applicable to treatment of liquids.

Consider the idealized break-through curve of Fig. 11.38. This results from the flow of a solvent gas through an adsorbent bed at the rate of $G_S$ lb./(hr.)(sq. ft.), entering with an initial solute concentration $Y_0$ lb. solute/lb. solvent gas. The total solute-free effluent after any time is $w$ lb./sq. ft. of bed cross section. The break-through curve is steep, and the solute concentration in the effluent rises rapidly from essentially zero to that in the incoming gas. Some low value $Y_B$ is arbitrarily chosen as the break-point concentration, and the adsorbent is considered as essentially exhausted when the effluent concentration has risen to some arbitrarily chosen value $Y_E$, close to $Y_0$. We are concerned principally with the quantity of effluent $w_B$ at the break point and the shape of the curve between $w_B$ and $w_E$.   The total effluent accumulated during the appearance of the break-through curve is $w_a = w_E - w_B$.   The adsorption zone, of constant height $Z_a$ ft., is that part of the bed in which the concentration change from $Y_B$ to $Y_E$ is occurring at any time.

Let $\theta_a$ be the time required for the adsorption zone to move its own height down the column, after the zone has been established.   Then

$$\theta_a = \frac{w_a}{G_S} \qquad (11.49)$$

Let $\theta_E$ be the time required for the adsorption zone to establish itself and move out of the bed.   Then

$$\theta_E = \frac{w_E}{G_S} \qquad (11.50)$$

If the height of the adsorbent bed is $Z$ ft. and if $\theta_F$ is the time required for the formation of the adsorption zone,

$$Z_a = Z \frac{\theta_a}{\theta_E - \theta_F} \qquad (11.51)$$

The quantity of solute removed from the gas in the adsorption zone from the break point to exhaustion is $U$ lb. solute/sq. ft. of bed cross section.   This is given by the shaded area of Fig. 11.38, which is

$$U = \int_{w_B}^{w_E} (Y_0 - Y)\, dw \qquad (11.52)$$

If, however, all the adsorbent in the zone were saturated with solute, it would contain $Y_0 w_a$ lb. solute/sq. ft.   Consequently at the break point, when the zone is still within the column, the fractional ability of the adsorbent in the zone still to adsorb solute is

$$f = \frac{U}{Y_0 w_a} = \frac{\int_{w_B}^{w_E} (Y_0 - Y)\, dw}{Y_0 w_a} \qquad (11.53)$$

If $f = 0$, so that the adsorbent in the zone is essentially saturated, the time of formation of the zone at the top of the bed $\theta_F$ should be substantially the same as the time required for the zone to travel a distance equal to its own height, $\theta_a$.   On the other hand, if $f = 1.0$, so that the solid in the zone contains essentially no adsorbate, the zone-formation time should be very short, essentially zero.   These limiting conditions, at least, are described by

$$\theta_F = (1 - f)\theta_a \qquad (11.54)$$

Equations (11.51) and (11.54) provide

$$Z_a = Z \frac{\theta_a}{\theta_E - (1 - f)\theta_a} = Z \frac{w_a}{w_E - (1 - f)w_a} \qquad (11.55)$$

The adsorption column, $Z$ ft. tall and of unit cross-sectional area, contains $Z\rho_s$ lb. adsorbent, where $\rho_s$ is the apparent packed density of the solid in the bed. If this were all in equilibrium with the entering gas and therefore completely saturated at an adsorbate concentration $X_T$ lb. adsorbate/lb. solid, the adsorbate weight would be $Z\rho_s X_T$ lb. At the break point, the adsorption zone of height $Z_a$ ft. is still in the column

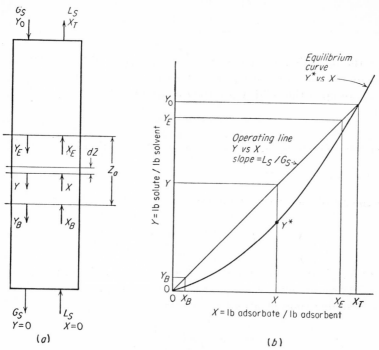

FIG. 11.39. The adsorption zone.

at the bottom, but the rest of the column, $Z - Z_a$ ft., is substantially saturated. At the break point, therefore, the adsorbed solute is $(Z - Z_a)\rho_s X_T + Z_a\rho_s f X_T$ lb. The fractional approach to saturation of the column at the break point is therefore

$$\text{Degree of saturation} = \frac{(Z - Z_a)\rho_s X_T + Z_a\rho_s f X_T}{Z\rho_s X_T} = \frac{Z - (1 - f)Z_a}{Z}$$

$$(11.56)$$

In the fixed bed of adsorbent, the adsorption zone in reality moves downward through the solid, as we have seen. Imagine instead, however, that the solid moves upward through the column countercurrent to the fluid at sufficient velocity so that the adsorption zone remains stationary within the column, as in Fig. 11.39a. Here the solid leaving at the top of the column is shown in equilibrium with the entering gas, and all solute is shown as having been removed from the effluent gas. This would, of course, require an infinitely tall column, but our concern will be primarily with the concentrations at the levels corresponding to the extremities of the adsorption zone. The operating line over the entire tower is

$$G_S(Y_0 - 0) = L_S(X_T - 0) \qquad (11.57)$$

or
$$\frac{L_S}{G_S} = \frac{Y_0}{X_T} \qquad (11.58)$$

Since the operating line passes through the origin of Fig. 11.39$b$, at any level in the column the concentration of solute in the gas $Y$ and of adsorbate upon the solid $X$ are then related by

$$G_S Y = L_S X \qquad (11.59)$$

Over the differential height $dZ$, the rate of adsorption is

$$G_S \, dY = K_Y a_p (Y - Y^*) \, dZ \qquad (11.60)$$

For the adsorption zone, therefore,

$$N_{tOG} = \int_{Y_B}^{Y_E} \frac{dY}{Y - Y^*} = \frac{Z_a}{H_{tOG}} = \frac{Z_a}{G_S/K_Y a_p} \qquad (11.61)$$

where $N_{tOG}$ is the over-all number of gas transfer units in the adsorption zone. For any value of $Z$ less than $Z_a$, assuming $H_{tOG}$ remains constant with changing concentrations,

$$\frac{Z \text{ at } Y}{Z_a} = \frac{w - w_B}{w_a} = \frac{\displaystyle\int_{Y_B}^{Y} \frac{dY}{Y - Y^*}}{\displaystyle\int_{Y_B}^{Y_E} \frac{dY}{Y - Y^*}} \qquad (11.62)$$

Equation (11.62) should permit plotting the break-through curve by graphical evaluation of the integrals.

In addition to the restrictions outlined at the beginning, the success of this analysis largely hinges upon the constancy of $K_Y a_p$ or $H_{tOG}$ for the concentrations within the adsorption zone. This will, of course, depend upon the relative constancy of the resistances to mass transfer in the fluid and within the pores of the solid. Illustration 6 demonstrates the method of using the equations in a typical case.

**Illustration 6.**   Air at 80°F., 1 atm., with a humidity of 0.00267 lb. water/lb. dry air is to be dehumidified by passage through a fixed bed of the silica gel used in Illustration 3.   The depth of the adsorbent bed is to be 2 ft.   The air will be passed through the bed at a superficial mass velocity of 95.5 lb./(hr.)(sq. ft.), and the adsorption will be assumed to be isothermal. The break point will be considered as that time when the effluent air has a humidity of 0.0001 lb. water/lb. dry air, and the bed will be considered exhausted when the effluent humidity is 0.0024 lb. water/lb. dry air. Mass-transfer coefficients are given in Illustration 3 for this gel. Estimate the time required to reach the break point.

*Solution.* The equilibrium data are plotted in Fig. 11.40. The gel is initially "dry," and the effluent air initially of so low a humidity as to be substantially dry,

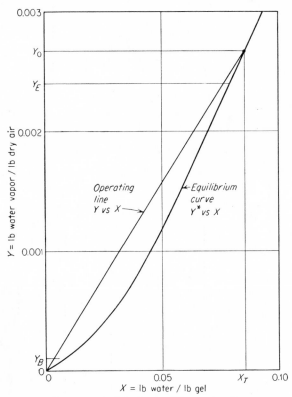

FIG. 11.40. Solution to Illustration 6.

so that the operating line passes through the origin of the figure. The operating line is then drawn to intersect the equilibrium curve at $Y_0 = 0.00267$ lb. water/lb. dry air. $Y_B = 0.0001$, $Y_E = 0.0024$ lb. water/lb. dry air.

In the accompanying table, column (1) lists values of $Y$ on the operating line between $Y_B$ and $Y_E$ and column (2) the corresponding values of $Y^*$ taken from the equilibrium curve at the same value of $X$. From these the data of column (3) were computed. A curve (not shown) of column (1) as abscissa, column (3) as ordinate was prepared and integrated graphically between each value of $Y$ in the table and $Y_B$, to give in column (4) the numbers of transfer units corresponding to each value of $Y$ (thus, for example, the area under the curve from $Y = 0.0012$ to $Y = 0.0001$ equals 4.438). The total number of transfer units corresponding to the adsorption zone is $N_{tOG} = 9.304$, in accordance with Eq. (11.61).

| (1) $Y$, lb. H$_2$O lb. dry air | (2) $Y^*$, lb. H$_2$O lb. dry air | (3) $\dfrac{1}{Y - Y^*}$ | (4) $\displaystyle\int_{Y_B}^{Y} \dfrac{dy}{Y - Y^*}$ | (5) $\dfrac{w - w_B}{w_a}$ | (6) $\dfrac{Y}{Y_0}$ |
|---|---|---|---|---|---|
| $Y_B = 0.0001$ | 0.00003 | 14,300 | 0 | 0 | 0.0374 |
| 0.0002 | 0.00007 | 7,700 | 1.100 | 0.1183 | 0.0749 |
| 0.0004 | 0.00016 | 4,160 | 2.219 | 0.2365 | 0.1498 |
| 0.0006 | 0.00027 | 3,030 | 2.930 | 0.314 | 0.225 |
| 0.0008 | 0.00041 | 2,560 | 3.487 | 0.375 | 0.300 |
| 0.0010 | 0.00057 | 2,325 | 3.976 | 0.427 | 0.374 |
| 0.0012 | 0.000765 | 2,300 | 4.438 | 0.477 | 0.450 |
| 0.0014 | 0.000995 | 2,470 | 4.915 | 0.529 | 0.525 |
| 0.0016 | 0.00123 | 2,700 | 5.432 | 0.584 | 0.599 |
| 0.0018 | 0.00148 | 3,130 | 6.015 | 0.646 | 0.674 |
| 0.0020 | 0.00175 | 4,000 | 6.728 | 0.723 | 0.750 |
| 0.0022 | 0.00203 | 5,880 | 7.716 | 0.830 | 0.825 |
| $Y_E = 0.0024$ | 0.00230 | 10,000 | 9.304 | 1.000 | 0.899 |

By dividing each entry in column (4) by 9.304, the values in column (5) were determined in accordance with Eq. (11.62). Column (6) was obtained by dividing each

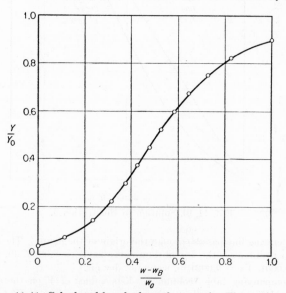

Fig. 11.41. Calculated break-through curve for Illustration 6.

entry in column (1) by $Y_0 = 0.00267$, and column (6) plotted against column (5) provides a form of the break-through curve (Fig. 11.41). Equation (11.53) may be written as

$$f = \frac{\displaystyle\int_{w_B}^{w_E} (Y_0 - Y)\, dw}{Y_0 w_a} = \int_0^{1.0} \left(1 - \frac{Y}{Y_0}\right) d\,\frac{w - w_B}{w_a}$$

from which it is seen that $f$ equals the entire area above the curve of Fig. 11.41 up to $Y/Y_0 = 1.0$. By graphical integration, $f = 0.530$.

The mass-transfer rates are given in equation form in Illustration 3. For a mass velocity of air equal to 95.5 lb./(hr.)(sq. ft.), $k_Y a_p = 188(95.5)^{0.55} = 2{,}310$ lb. $H_2O/$(hr.)(cu. ft.)($\Delta Y$), and $k_S a_p = 217$ lb. $H_2O/$(hr.)(cu. ft.)($\Delta X$).

From Fig. 11.40, $X_T = 0.0858$ lb. water/lb. gel.

Eq. (11.58): $\qquad L_S = Y_0 G_S / X_T = 0.00267(95.5)/0.0858 = 2.97$

The average slope of the equilibrium curve is $\Delta Y/\Delta X = 0.0185$, whence $mG_S/L_S = 0.0185(95.5)/2.97 = 0.595$.

Eqs. (11.32) and (11.33):

$$H_{tG} = \frac{G_S}{k_Y a_p} = \frac{95.5}{2{,}310} = 0.0413 \text{ ft.}$$

$$H_{tS} = \frac{L_S}{k_S a_p} = \frac{2.97}{217} = 0.0137 \text{ ft.}$$

$$H_{tOG} = H_{tG} + \frac{mG_S}{L_S} H_{tS} = 0.0413 + 0.595(0.0137) = 0.0495 \text{ ft.}$$

Eq. (11.61): $\qquad Z_a = N_{tOG} H_{tOG} = 9.304(0.0495) = 0.460 \text{ ft.}$

The height of the bed $= Z = 2$ ft. Therefore, [Eq. (11.56)]:

$$\text{Degree of bed saturation at break point} = \frac{Z - (1 - f)Z_a}{Z}$$

$$= \frac{2 - (1 - 0.53)(0.460)}{2}$$

$$= 0.892, \text{ or } 89.2\%$$

The bed contains 2 cu. ft. gel/sq. ft. of cross section, and since the packed density is 41.9 lb./cu. ft. (Illustration 3), the weight of gel is $2(41.9) = 83.8$ lb./sq. ft. At 89.2% of equilibrium with the incoming air, the gel contains $83.8(0.892)(0.0858) = 6.40$ lb. water/sq. ft. of cross section. The air introduces $95.5(0.00267) = 0.255$ lb. water/(hr.)(sq. ft.), and hence the break point occurs at $6.40/0.255 = 25.1$ hr. after air is admitted initially, and $w_B = 25.1(95.5) = 2{,}400$ lb. air/sq. ft. of cross section.

If the entire bed were in equilibrium with the entering gas, the adsorbed water would be $83.8(0.0858) = 7.18$ lb./sq. ft., and hence $w_a = (7.18 - 6.40)/0.00267 = 292$ lb. air/sq. ft.

NOTE: The circumstances of this calculation correspond to those of run S2 of Eagleton and Bliss,[7] whose observed break-through curve corresponds very closely to the calculated curve of Fig. 11.41. These authors observed that 180 lb. of air/sq. ft. of bed cross section flowed through while the effluent humidity rose from $Y/Y_0 = 0.1$ to $0.8$, whereas the curve of Fig. 11.41 predicts this amount to be $(0.79 - 0.17)(292) = 181$ lb./sq. ft.

## ION EXCHANGE

Ion-exchange operations are essentially metathetical chemical reactions between an electrolyte in solution and an insoluble electrolyte with which the solution is contacted. The mechanisms of these reactions and the techniques used to bring them about resemble those of adsorption so closely that for most engineering purposes ion exchange may simply be considered as a special case of adsorption.

**Principles of Ion Exchange.** The ion-exchange solids first used were porous, natural or synthetic minerals containing silica, the zeolites, such as the mineral $Na_2O \cdot Al_2O_3 \cdot 4SiO_2 \cdot 2H_2O$, for example. Positively charged ions (cations) of a solution which are capable of diffusing through the pores will exchange with the $Na^+$ ions of such a mineral, and the latter is therefore called a cation exchanger. For example,

$$Ca^{++} + Na_2R \rightarrow CaR + 2Na^+$$

where R represents the residual material of the zeolite. In this manner "hard" water containing $Ca^{++}$ may be softened by contact with the zeolite, the less objectionable $Na^+$ replacing the $Ca^{++}$ in solution and the latter becoming immobilized in the solid. The reaction is reversible, and after saturation with $Ca^{++}$ the zeolite may be regenerated by contact with a solution of salt,

$$CaR + 2NaCl \rightarrow Na_2R + CaCl_2$$

Later certain carbonaceous cation exchangers were manufactured by treating substances such as coal with reagents such as fuming sulfuric acid, and the like. The resulting exchangers can be regenerated to a hydrogen form, HR, by treatment with acid rather than salt. Thus, hard water containing $Ca(HCO_3)_2$ would contain $H_2CO_3$ after removal of the $Ca^{++}$ by exchange, and since the carbonic acid is readily removed by degasification procedures, the total solids content of the water may be reduced in this manner. Early applications of ion exchangers using these principles were largely limited to water-softening problems.

In 1935, synthetic resinous ion exchangers were introduced. For example, certain synthetic, insoluble polymeric resins containing sulfonic, carboxylic, or phenolic groups can be considered as consisting of an exceedingly large anion and a replaceable or exchangeable cation.[18] These make exchanges of the following type possible,

$$Na^+ + HR \rightleftharpoons NaR + H^+$$

and different cations will exchange with the resin with different relative ease. The $Na^+$ immobilized in the resin may be exchanged with other cations or with $H^+$, for example, much as one solute may replace another adsorbed upon a conventional adsorbent. Similarly synthetic, insoluble polymeric resins containing amine groups and anions may be used to exchange anions in solution. The mechanism of this action is evidently not so simple as in the case of the cation exchangers, but for present purposes it may be considered simply as an ion exchange. For example,

$$RNH_3OH + Cl^- \rightleftharpoons RNH_3Cl + OH^-$$
$$H^+ + OH^- \rightarrow H_2O$$

where $RNH_3$ represents the immobile cationic portion of the resin. Such resins may be regenerated by contact with solutions of sodium carbonate or hydroxide. The synthetic ion-exchange resins are available in a variety of formulations of different exchange abilities, usually in the form of fine, granular solids or beads, 16 to 325 mesh. The individual beads are frequently nearly perfect spheres.

**Techniques and Applications.** All the operational techniques ordinarily used for adsorption are used also for ion exchange. Thus we have batch or stagewise treatment of solutions and semibatch or fixed-bed operations, and, at least in the laboratory, continuous countercurrent treatment has been used. Fixed-bed percolations are most common. Chromatographic methods have been used for fractionation of multicomponent ionic mixtures.

In addition to the water-softening applications mentioned above, the complete deionization of water may be accomplished by percolation first through a cation exchanger and then through an anion exchanger. By using a bed formed of an intimate mixture of equivalent amounts of a strong cationic and a strong anionic exchange resin, simultaneous removal of all ions at neutrality is possible. For purposes of regeneration, such mixed-bed resins are separated by hydraulic classification through particle size and density differences for the two resin types, and these are regenerated separately.[18] The ion exchangers have also been used for treatment and concentration of dilute waste solutions. Perhaps the most remarkable application of exchange resins has been to the separation of the rare-earth metals, using chromatographic techniques.[28]

**Equilibria.** The equilibrium distribution of an ion between an exchange solid and a solution can be described graphically by plotting isotherms in much the same manner used for ordinary adsorption. Various empirical equations for these isotherms, such as the Freundlich equation [Eq. (11.3)], have sometimes been applied to them. It is also possible to apply equations of the mass-action type to the exchange reaction. For example, for the cationic exchange

$$Na^+ + R^-H^+ \rightleftharpoons R^-Na^+ + H^+$$
$$\text{(soln.)} \quad \text{(solid)} \quad \text{(solid)} \quad \text{(soln.)}$$

the mass-action-law constant is

$$\alpha = \frac{[R^-Na^+]_{solid}[H^+]_{soln.}}{[R^-H^+]_{solid}[Na^+]_{soln.}} = \left[\frac{Na^+}{H^+}\right]_{solid}\left[\frac{H^+}{Na^+}\right]_{soln.} \quad (11.63)$$

where the square brackets [ ] indicate the use of some suitable equilibrium-concentration unit. The quantity $\alpha$ is thus seen to be an expression of relative adsorptivity, in this case of relative adsorptivity of $Na^+$ to $H^+$. Since the solution and the solid remain electrically neutral during the exchange process, we can write

$$\alpha = \frac{X}{X_0 - X}\frac{c_0 - c^*}{c^*} = \frac{X/X_0}{1 - X/X_0}\frac{1 - c^*/c_0}{c^*/c_0} \quad (11.64)$$

where $c_0$ is in this case the initial concentration of $Na^+ + H^+$ in the solution and consequently the total of these at any time, $c^*$ the equilibrium $Na^+$ concentration after exchange, $X$ the equilibrium concentration of $Na^+$ in the solid, and $X_0$ the concentration if all $H^+$ were replaced by $Na^+$, all expressed as equivalents per unit volume or mass. In the general case for any system, the relative adsorptivity $\alpha$ at a given temperature varies with total cationic concentration $c_0$ in the solution and also with $c$. In some cases, $\alpha$ has been found to be essentially constant with varying $c$ at fixed $c_0$.

**Rate of Ion Exchange.** The rate of ion exchange depends, like ordinary adsorption, upon rates of the following individual processes: (1) diffusion of ions from the bulk of the liquid to the external surface of an exchanger particle; (2) inward diffusion of ions through the solid to the site of exchange; (3) exchange of the ions; (4) outward diffusion of the released ions to the surface of the solid; (5) diffusion of the released ions from the surface of the solid to the bulk of the liquid. Too few data are available for generalizations respecting these. In some instances, the kinetics of the exchange reaction (3) may be controlling, but in others the rate of reaction is apparently very rapid in comparison with the rate of diffusion. The diffusion rates can be described by appropriate mass-transfer coefficients for equi-equivalent counterdiffusion through the solid and through the liquid, and in some instances at least it appears that the resistance to diffusion in the liquid phase may be controlling.

For cases where the exchange reactions are rapid in comparison with the rates of mass transfer, the methods of design developed for conventional adsorbers may be applied to ion-exchange operations directly. Some modification of the units of the terms in the various equations may be desirable, owing to the customary use of concentrations expressed as equivalents per unit volume in the c.g.s. system. The following example illustrates this:

**Illustration 7.** A synthetic ion-exchange resin in bead form is to be used for collecting and concentrating the copper in a dilute waste solution. The feed contains $CuSO_4$ at a concentration of 20 milligram equivalents (meq.) $Cu^{++}$/liter and is to be treated at the rate of 10,000 gal./hr. A continuous system is planned: the solution to be treated and regenerated resin will flow countercurrently through a vertical tower, where 99% of the $Cu^{++}$ of the feed will be exchanged; the resin will be regenerated in a second tower by countercurrent contact with 2 N sulfuric acid. The necessary data are provided by Selke and Bliss, *Chem. Eng. Progr.*, **47**, 529 (1951).

*For collection of $Cu^{++}$.* A superficial liquid velocity of 2.2 liters/(hr.)(sq. cm.) will be used for which the mass-transfer rate is 2.0 meq. $Cu^{++}$/(hr.)(gm. resin) (meq. $Cu^{++}$/liter). The regenerated resin will contain 0.30 meq. $Cu^{++}$/gm., and 1.2 times the minimum resin/solution ratio will be used.

*For regeneration of the resin.* The superficial liquid velocity will be 0.17 liter/(hr.) (sq. cm.), for which the mass-transfer rate is 0.018 meq. $Cu^{++}$/(hr.)(gm. resin)(meq. $Cu^{++}$/liter). The acid will be utilized to the extent of 70%.

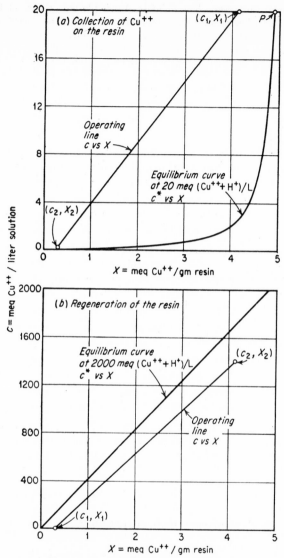

FIG. 11.42. Solution to Illustration 7.

Compute the necessary rates of flow of resin and the amount of resin hold-up in each tower.

*Solution.* Equilibria for the $Cu^{++}-H^+$ exchange are provided by Selke and Bliss at two concentration levels, 20 and 2,000 meq. cation/liter. These are shown in Fig. 11.42a and b, respectively.

*Collection of* $Cu^{++}$. Feed soln. = 10,000(3.785) = 37,850 liters/hr. $c_1 = 20$ meq. $Cu^{++}$/liter, $c_2 = 0.01(20) = 0.20$ meq. $Cu^{++}$/liter. $Cu^{++}$ exchanged = 37,850(20 − 0.20) = 750,000 meq./hr.

$X_2 = 0.30$ meq. $Cu^{++}$/gm. The point $(c_2, X_2)$ is plotted on Fig. 11.42a. For the minimum resin/solution ratio and an infinitely tall tower, the operating line passes also through point $P$ at $X = 4.9$ on this figure, corresponding to equilibrium with $c_1$. The minimum resin rate is then $750,000/(4.9 - 0.30) = 163,000$ gm./hr. For 1.2 times the minimum, the resin rate is $1.2(163,000) = 196,000$ gm./hr., or 430 lb./hr. A copper balance,

$$750,000 = 196,000(X_1 - 0.30)$$
$$X_1 = 4.12 \text{ meq. } Cu^{++}/\text{gm. resin}$$

The point $(c_1, X_1)$ is plotted on Fig. 11.42a, and the operating line may be drawn as a straight line at these low concentrations.

The quantity of resin in the tower may be obtained by application of the rate equation written in a form appropriate to the units of the quantities involved. Adapting Eq. (11.29) to this case, we have

$$V\, dc = \frac{K'_L a_p}{\rho s} (c - c^*)\, d(SZ\rho s)$$

where $V$ = liters liquid/hr.
  $c$ = concn. $Cu^{++}$, meq./liter, in the soln.
  $c^*$ = concn. $Cu^{++}$ in the soln. at equilibrium with the resin
$K'_L a_p / \rho s$ = over-all liquid mass-transfer coefficient, meq./(hr.)(gm. resin)(meq./liter)
  $K'_L$ = over-all liquid mass-transfer coefficient, meq./(hr.)(sq. ft.)(meq./liter)
  $a_p$ = surface of resin particles, sq. ft./cu. ft.
  $\rho s$ = packed density of resin, gm./cu. cm.
$(SZ\rho s)$ = gm. resin in tower
  $S$ = cross section of tower, sq. cm.
  $Z$ = height of tower, cm.
Rearranging this equation and integrating,

$$SZ\rho s = \frac{V}{K'_L a_p / \rho s} \int_{c_2}^{c_1} \frac{dc}{c - c^*}$$

For values of $c$ on the operating line between $c_1$ and $c_2$, the corresponding values of $c^*$ from the equilibrium curve at the same value of $X$ are obtained as follows:

| $c\ldots\ldots$ | 20 | 16 | 12 | 8 | 4 | 2 | 1 | 0.2 |
|---|---|---|---|---|---|---|---|---|
| $c^*\ldots\ldots$ | 2.4 | 1.9 | 0.5 | 0.25 | 0.10 | 0.05 | 0.02 | 0 |
| $\dfrac{1}{c - c^*}$ | 0.0568 | 0.0710 | 0.0870 | 0.129 | 0.256 | 0.513 | 1.02 | 5.0 |

A curve (not shown) of $1/(c - c^*)$ as ordinate, $c$ as abscissa, is plotted and integrated graphically between the limits $c_1$ and $c_2$. The area under the curve is 5.72. (NOTE: This is the number of transfer units $N_{tOL}$.) Substituting in the integrated equation,

$$\text{Resin hold-up} = SZ\rho s = \frac{37,850(5.72)}{2.0} = 108,300 \text{ gm., or } 239 \text{ lb.}$$

*Regeneration of resin.* $Cu^{++}$ to be exchanged = 750,000 meq./hr., requiring as many meq. $H^+$/hr. For a 70% utilization of acid, the acid feed must contain 750,000/0.70 = 1,071,000 meq. $H^+$/hr., or 1,071,000/2,000 = 536 liters/hr. of 2 N acid.
$c_1 = 0$, $c_2 = 750,000/536 = 1,400$ meq. $Cu^{++}$/liter. $X_1 = 0.30$, $X_2 = 4.12$ meq.

$Cu^{++}$/gm. resin. The points $(c_1, X_1)$ and $(c_2, X_2)$ are plotted on Fig. 11.42*b* and the operating line drawn. Integration of the rate equation for this case, where both operating and equilibrium lines are straight, provides

$$V(c_2 - c_1) = \frac{K'_L a_p}{\rho s} (SZ\rho s)(c^* - c)_m$$

where $(c^* - c)_m$ is the logarithmic average of the driving forces at the extremities of the tower and the other symbols have the same meaning as before.

$$c_1^* - c_1 = 120 - 0 = 120 \qquad c_2^* - c_2 = 1,700 - 1,400 = 300 \text{ meq. } Cu^{++}/\text{liter}$$
$$(c^* - c)_m = (300 - 120)/\ln(300/120) = 196.5 \text{ meq. } Cu^{++}/\text{liter}$$

Substituting in the rate equation,

$$750,000 = 0.018(SZ\rho s)(196.5)$$
$$SZ\rho s = 212,000 \text{ gm., or } 476 \text{ lb., resin hold-up in regeneration tower}$$

The resin should be water-rinsed before reintroducing it into the adsorption tower. The $Cu^{++}$ in the effluent solution has been concentrated $1,400/20 = 70$ times, equivalent to the evaporation of 9,857 gal. of water/hr. from the original solution.

## NOTATION FOR CHAPTER 11

$a_p$ = external surface of solid particles, sq. ft./cu. ft. of packed volume

$B$ = rate of adsorbent flow in continuous fractionators, lb. adsorbate-free solid/(hr.)(sq. ft.)

$c$ = solute concentration in solution, lb./cu. ft. or, in the case of ion exchange, equivalents/unit volume

$C_A$ = heat capacity of adsorbed solute, B.t.u./(lb.)(°F.)

$C_L$ = heat capacity of adsorbent, B.t.u./(lb.)(°F.)

$d$ = differential operator

$d_p$ = particle diameter, ft.

$E$ = rate of flow of adsorbate, lb./(hr.)(sq. ft.)

$f$ = fractional ability of adsorbent zone to adsorb solute, dimensionless

$F$ = feed rate, lb./(hr.)(sq. ft.)

$G$ = total rate of flow of gas, lb. moles/(hr.)(sq. ft.)

$G'$ = total rate of flow of gas, lb./(hr.)(sq. ft.)

$G_S$ = solvent in solution, or unadsorbed gas, lb. in a batch process or lb./-(hr.)(sq. ft.) in a continuous process

$\bar{H}$ = differential heat of adsorption, B.t.u./lb. adsorbate

$H'_G$ = enthalpy of gas, B.t.u./lb. solute-free gas

$H'_L$ = enthalpy of solid and adsorbed solute, B.t.u./lb. adsorbate-free solid

$H_{tG}$ = height of gas-film transfer unit, ft.

$H_{tOG}$ = over-all height of gas transfer unit, ft.

$H_{tS}$ = height of solid transfer unit, ft.

$\Delta H_A$ = integral heat of adsorption, B.t.u./lb. adsorbent, referred to liquid adsorbate

$\Delta H'_A$ = integral heat of adsorption, B.t.u./lb. adsorbent, referred to vapor adsorbate

$k, k', k''$ = constants

$k_Y$ = gas-film mass-transfer coefficient, lb./(hr.)(sq. ft.)(lb. solute/lb. solvent gas)

$K_G$ = over-all gas mass-transfer coefficient, lb. moles/(hr.)(sq. ft.)(atm.)

$K_Y$ = over-all gas mass-transfer coefficient, lb./(hr.)(sq. ft.)(lb. solute/lb. solvent gas)

ln = natural logarithm

log = common logarithm

$L_S$ = adsorbate-free adsorbent, lb. in a batch process or lb./(hr.)(sq. ft.) in a continuous process

$m$ = constant

   = in Eqs. (11.32) and (11.33), slope of the equilibrium adsorption isotherm = $dY^*/dX$, dimensionless

$M$ = molecular weight, lb./lb. mole

$n, n', n''$ = constants

$N$ = adsorbent concentration, lb. adsorbate-free adsorbent/lb. adsorbate

$N_p$ = number of theoretical stages in a cascade, dimensionless

$N_{tOG}$ = over-all number of gas transfer units, dimensionless

$p$ = partial pressure, atm., unless otherwise indicated

$P$ = vapor pressure, atm., unless otherwise indicated

$P_E$ = product rich in the more strongly adsorbed substance, lb./(hr.)(sq. ft.)

$P_t$ = total pressure, atm.

$q$ = heat added to an adsorber, B.t.u./(hr.)(sq. ft.)

$Q$ = adsorbent-free flow downward in the enriching section of a fractionator, lb./(hr.)(sq. ft.)

$r$ = molecular weight poorly adsorbed gas/molecular weight strongly adsorbed gas, dimensionless.

$R$ = rate of flow of gas in a continuous fractionator, lb./(hr.)(sq. ft.)

   = gas constant, (cu. ft.)(atm.)/(lb. mole)(°R.)

   = nonexchanged portion of an ion exchanger

Re = Reynolds number, dimensionless

Sc = Schmidt number, dimensionless

$t_L$ = adsorbent temperature, °F.

$t_0$ = base temperature for enthalpy computation, °F.

$T$ = absolute temperature, °R. (°K. on Fig. 11.6)

$U$ = solute adsorbed in the adsorption zone, fixed-bed adsorbers, lb./(hr.)(sq. ft.)

$V$ = quantity of solution, cu. ft. solution/lb. adsorbent

$w$ = in a batch process, quantity of solution, lb. solution/lb. adsorbent

   = in a semibatch process, quantity of effluent from fixed-bed adsorber lb. solute-free effluent/(hr.)(sq. ft.)

$w_a = w_E - w_B$

$w_B$ = quantity of effluent from fixed-bed adsorber at the break point, lb. solute-free effluent/(hr.)(sq. ft.)

$w_E$ = quantity of effluent from fixed-bed adsorber at bed exhaustion, lb. solute-free effluent/(hr.)(sq. ft.)

$W$ = difference between flow of adsorbate and unadsorbed fluid upward in a continuous fractionator, lb./(hr.)(sq. ft.)

$x$ = concentration of more strongly adsorbed substance in the fluid, weight fraction

$X$ = adsorbate concentration, lb. solute adsorbed/lb. adsorbent, or, for ion exchange, equivalents/unit mass or volume

$X_T$ = adsorbate concentration of a fixed-bed adsorber, when in equilibrium with entering fluid, lb. solute/lb. adsorbent

$y$ = composition of adsorbate, weight fraction more strongly adsorbed substance, adsorbent-free basis

$Y$ = concentration of solute in fluid, lb. solute/lb. solvent

$Y_B$ = concentration of solute in effluent from fixed-bed adsorber at the break point, lb. solute/lb. solvent

$Y_E$ = concentration of solute in effluent from fixed-bed adsorber at bed exhaustion, lb. solute/lb. solvent

$Z$ = active height of adsorber, ft.

$Z_a$ = height of adsorption zone in fixed-bed adsorber, ft.

$\alpha$ = mass-action-law constant or relative adsorptivity, dimensionless

$\Delta$ = difference

$\theta$ = time, hr.

$\theta_a$ = time required for adsorption zone to move a distance $Z_a$ through the fixed bed, hr.

$\theta_E$ = time required to reach bed exhaustion, hr.

$\theta_F$ = time of formation of adsorption zone, hr.

$\lambda$ = latent heat of vaporization, B.t.u./lb.

$\rho$ = fluid density, lb./cu. ft.

$\rho s$ = apparent packed density of an adsorbent bed, lb. solid/cu. ft. packed space

Subscripts:

$e$ = within the enriching section of a continuous fractionator

$F$ = pertaining to the feed

$r$ = reference substance

$s$ = within the stripping section of a continuous fractionator

$0$ = initial

$1$ = stage 1, or bottom of a continuous adsorber

$2$ = stage 2, or top of a continuous adsorber

Superscript:

$*$ = equilibrium

## REFERENCES

1. Amero, R. C., J. W. Moore, and R. G. Capell: *Chem. Eng. Progr.*, **43,** 349 (1947).
2. Bartell, F. E., and C. K. Sloan: *J. Am. Chem. Soc.*, **51,** 1643 (1929).
3. Berg, C.: *Trans. Am. Inst. Chem. Engrs.*, **42,** 665 (1946); *Chem. Eng. Progr.*, **47,** 585 (1951).
4. Browning, F. M.: *Chem. Eng.*, **59**(10), 158 (1952).
5. Brunauer, S.: "Adsorption of Gases and Vapors," Princeton University Press, Princeton, N.J., 1943.
6. Courouleau, P. H., and R. E. Benson: *Chem. Eng.*, **55**(3), 112 (1948).
7. Eagleton, L. C., and H. Bliss: *Chem. Eng. Progr.*, **49,** 543 (1953).
8. Edeskuty, F. J., and N. R. Amundsen: *J. Phys. Chem.*, **56,** 148 (1952); *Ind. Eng. Chem.*, **44,** 1698 (1952).
9. Goldman, F., and M. Polanyi: *Z. physik. Chem.*, **132,** 321 (1928).
10. Harper, J. I., J. L. Olsen, and F. R. Shuman: *Chem. Eng. Progr.*, **48,** 276 (1952).
11. Helbig, W. A.: In J. Alexander, ed., "Colloid Chemistry," vol. VI, p. 814, Reinhold Publishing Corporation, New York, 1946.

12. ———: *Chem. Eng.*, **59**(10), 153 (1952).

13. Hougen, O. A., and W. R. Marshall: *Chem. Eng. Progr.*, **43**, 197 (1947).

14. Kasten, P. R., and N. R. Amundsen: *Ind. Eng. Chem.*, **44**, 1704 (1952).

15. Kehde, H., R. G. Fairfield, J. C. Frank, and L. W. Zahnstecher: *Chem. Eng. Progr.*, **44**, 575 (1948).

16. Kipling, J. J., and D. A. Tester: *J. Chem. Soc.*, 1952, p. 4123.

17. Klotz, I. M.: *Chem. Rev.*, **39**, 241 (1946).

18. Kunin, R., and R. J. Meyers: "Ion Exchange Resins," John Wiley & Sons, Inc., New York, 1950.

19. Ledoux, E.: "Vapor Adsorption," Chemical Publishing Company, Inc., New York, 1945.

20. Lewis, W. K., E. R. Gilliland, B. Chertow, and W. P. Cadogan: *Ind. Eng. Chem.*, **42**, 1319 (1950).

21. Mantell, C. L.: "Adsorption," 2d ed., McGraw-Hill Book Company, Inc., New York, 1951.

22. Michaels, A. S.: *Ind. Eng. Chem.*, **44**, 1922 (1952).

23. Munro, W. D., and N. R. Amundsen: *Ind. Eng. Chem.*, **42**, 1481 (1950).

24. Newton, R. H., G. S. Dunham, and T. P. Simpson: *Trans. Am. Inst. Chem. Engrs.*, **41**, 215 (1945).

25. Othmer, D. F., and F. G. Sawyer: *Ind. Eng. Chem.*, **35**, 1269 (1943).

26. Sanders, M. T.: *Ind. Eng. Chem.*, **20**, 791 (1928).

27. Singer, E., and R. H. Wilhelm: *Chem. Eng. Progr.*, **46**, 343 (1950).

28. Spedding, F. A., *et al.*: *J. Am. Chem. Soc.*, **69**, 2777, 2786, 2812 (1947); **72**, 2349, 2354 (1950).

29. Swinton, E. A., D. E. Weiss, *et al.*: *Australian J. Appl. Science*, **4**, 316, 510, 519, 530, 543 (1953).

30. Walker, W. H., W. K. Lewis, W. H. McAdams, and E. R. Gilliland: "Principles of Chemical Engineering," 3d ed., p. 511, McGraw-Hill Book Company, Inc., New York, 1937.

## PROBLEMS

**1.** The equilibrium adsorption of acetone vapor on an activated carbon at 30°C. is given by the following data:

| Gm. adsorbed/gm. carbon | 0 | 0.1 | 0.2 | 0.3 | 0.35 |
|---|---|---|---|---|---|
| Partial pressure acetone, mm. Hg | 0 | 2 | 12 | 42 | 92 |

The vapor pressure of acetone at 30°C. is 283 mm. Hg.

A liter flask contains air and acetone vapor at 1 atm. and 30°C., with a relative saturation of the vapor of 35%. Two grams of fresh activated carbon is introduced into the flask, and the flask is sealed. Compute the final vapor concentration at 30°C. and the final pressure. Neglect the adsorption of air.

**2.** A solution of washed, raw cane sugar, 48% sucrose by weight, is colored by the presence of small quantities of impurities. It is to be decolorized at 80°C. by treatment with an adsorptive carbon in a contact filtration plant. The data for an equilibrium adsorption isotherm were obtained by adding various amounts of the carbon to separate batches of the original solution and observing the equilibrium color reached in each case. The data, with the quantity of carbon expressed on the basis of the sugar content of the solution, are as follows:

| Lb. carbon/lb. dry sugar... | 0 | 0.005 | 0.01 | 0.015 | 0.02 | 0.03 |
|---|---|---|---|---|---|---|
| % of color removed........ | 0 | 47 | 70 | 83 | 90 | 95 |

The original solution has a color concentration of 20, measured on an arbitrary scale, and it is desired to reduce the color to 2.5% of its original value.

*a.* Convert the equilibrium data to a form suitable for adsorption calculations. Do they follow the Freundlich equation? If so, what are the equation constants?

*b.* Calculate the necessary dosage of fresh carbon, per 1,000 lb. of solution, for a single-stage process.

*c.* Calculate the necessary carbon dosages per 1,000 lb. of solution for a two-stage cocurrent treatment, using the minimum total amount of fresh carbon.

*d.* Calculate the necessary carbon dosage per 1,000 lb. of solution for a two-stage countercurrent treatment.

**3.** The sugar refinery of Prob. 2 must treat also a raw cane sugar solution, 48 wt. % sucrose, of original color 50, based on the same color scale used in Prob. 2. The color

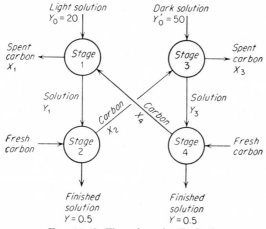

Fɪɢ. 11.43. Flow sheet for Prob. 3e.

scale is such that colors are additive, i.e., equal weights of solution of color 20 and color 50 will give a solution of color $(20 + 50)/2 = 35$. The same adsorption isotherm describes the color removal of the darker solution as that of Prob. 2. Equal quantities of the dark solution and that of Prob. 2 must both be decolorized to a color 0.5.

*a.* In a single-stage process, will it be more economical of carbon first to blend the original solutions and to treat the blend, or to treat each separately to color 0.5 and to blend the finished products?

*b.* Repeat for a two-stage cocurrent treatment, fresh carbon in each stage, arranged for the minimum carbon in each case.

*c.* Repeat for a countercurrent two-stage treatment.

*d.* The following treating scheme was suggested: The light-colored solution is to be treated in a two-stage countercurrent plant to the final desired color. The spent carbon from this operation is to be used to treat an equal weight of the dark solution, and the carbon is then revivified. The residual dark solution is then finished to the desired final color with the necessary amount of fresh carbon. Sketch a flow sheet and an operating diagram (freehand) for the entire process. Determine whether there is any savings of carbon over that for the arrangement of part *c.*

*e.* Determine whether the scheme of Fig. 11.43 offers any economies of carbon.

**4.** Prove that for cocurrent two-stage treatment of liquid solutions by contact filtration, when the adsorption isotherm is linear, the least total adsorbent results if the amounts used in each stage are equal.

**5.** For adsorption from dilute liquid solutions in stagewise countercurrent operations, where the Freundlich equation describes the adsorption equilibrium, derive analytical expressions in terms of $n$, $m$, $Y_0$, and $Y_{Np}$ for the minimum adsorbent/-solvent ratio when fresh adsorbent is used. Cover both cases of Fig. 11.23.

**6.** Nitrogen dioxide, $NO_2$, produced by a thermal process for fixation of nitrogen is to be removed from a dilute mixture with air by adsorption on silica gel in a continuous countercurrent adsorber. The gas entering the adsorber at the rate of 1,000 lb./-hr. contains 1.5% $NO_2$ by volume, and 90% of the $NO_2$ is to be removed. Operation is to be isothermal at 25°C., 1 atm. The entering gel will be free of $NO_2$. The equilibrium adsorption isotherm at this temperature is given by the following data [Foster and Daniels, *Ind. Eng. Chem.*, **43**, 986 (1951)]:

| Partial pressure $NO_2$, mm. Hg........ | 0 | 2 | 4 | 6 | 8 | 10 | 12 |
|---|---|---|---|---|---|---|---|
| Gm. $NO_2$/100 gm. gel.............. | 0 | 0.4 | 0.9 | 1.65 | 2.60 | 3.65 | 4.85 |

*a.* Calculate the minimum weight of gel required per hour.

*b.* For twice the minimum gel rate, calculate the number of transfer units required.

*c.* A superficial air rate of 300 lb./(hr.)(sq. ft.) is to be used. Assume that the characteristics of the gel are the same as those described in Illustration 3. Modify the gas-film mass-transfer coefficient of Illustration 3 so that it will apply to the transfer of $NO_2$ rather than water. Modify the solid-phase mass-transfer coefficient to apply for $NO_2$ on the assumption that the transfer in the pores of the solid is by molecular diffusion through the gas filling the pores. The diffusivity of $NO_2$ in air is estimated to be 0.136 sq. cm./sec. at 25°C., 1 atm.

Estimate the value of $H_{tOG}$, and calculate the corresponding height of the adsorber.

**7.** Lewis *et al.*, *J. Am. Chem. Soc.*, **72**, 1157 (1950), report the following for the simultaneous adsorption of acetylene and ethylene from mixtures of the two on silica gel at 1 atm., 25°C. (reprinted with permission of the American Chemical Society):

| Mole fraction ethylene in adsorbate | Mole fraction ethylene in gas, at equilibrium | Mg. moles mixture adsorbed/gm. adsorbent |
|---|---|---|
| 0.0686 | 0.2422 | 1.622 |
| 0.292 | 0.562 | 1.397 |
| 0.458 | 0.714 | 1.298 |
| 0.592 | 0.814 | 1.193 |
| 0.630 | 0.838 | 1.170 |
| 0.864 | 0.932 | 1.078 |

A gas containing equimolar amounts of acetylene and ethylene is to be fractionated in a continuous countercurrent adsorber, to yield products containing 98% and 2% acetylene by volume. Assume the temperature to remain constant at 25°C. and the pressure to be 1 atm. Calculate the number of transfer units and the gel circulation rate per 1,000 cu. ft. feed gas, using 1.2 times the minimum gel circulation rate.

**8.** The sulfur content of an oil is to be reduced by percolation through a bed of adsorbent clay. Laboratory tests with the clay and oil in a representative percolation filter show the following instantaneous sulfur contents of the effluent oil as a function of the total oil passing through the filter [adapted from Kaufman, *Chem. Met. Eng.*, **30**, 153 (1924)]:

| Bbl. oil/ton clay | 0 | 10 | 20 | 50 | 100 | 200 | 300 | 400 |
|---|---|---|---|---|---|---|---|---|
| % sulfur | 0.011 | 0.020 | 0.041 | 0.067 | 0.0935 | 0.118 | 0.126 | 0.129 |

Assume that the specific gravity of the oil is unchanged during the percolation. The untreated oil has a sulfur content of 0.134%, and a product containing 0.090% sulfur is desired.

*a.* If the effluent from the filter is composited, what yield of satisfactory product may be obtained per ton of clay?

*b.* If the effluent from the filter is continually and immediately withdrawn and blended with just sufficient untreated oil to give the desired sulfur content in the blend, what quantity of product may be obtained per ton of clay?

**9.** A laboratory fixed-bed adsorption column filled with a synthetic sulfonic acid cation-exchange resin in the acid form is to be used to remove $Na^+$ ions from an aqueous solution of sodium chloride. The bed depth is 33.5 cm., and the solution to be percolated through the bed contains 0.120 milligram equivalent (meq.) $Na^+$ /cu. cm. At saturation, the resin contains 2.02 meq. $Na^+$/cu. cm. resin. The solution will be passed through the bed at a superficial linear velocity of 0.31 cm./sec. For this resin, Michaels[22] reports that the over-all liquid mass-transfer rate $K'_L a_p = 0.86 v_L^{0.5}$ where $v_L$ is the superficial liquid velocity, cm./sec., and $K'_L a_p$ is expressed as meq. $Na^+$/(sec.)(cu. cm.)(meq./cu. cm.). The relative adsorptivity of $Na^+$ with respect to $H^+$ for this resin is $\alpha = 1.20$, and this is constant for the prevailing concentration level. Define the break-point concentration as 5% of the initial solution concentration, and assume that practical bed exhaustion occurs when the effluent concentration is 95% of the initial. Estimate the volume of effluent at the break point, per unit bed cross section.

(NOTE: For these circumstances, Michaels[22] observed that the adsorption-zone height was 23.8 cm., that the break point occurred after 382 ± 10 cu. cm. effluent/sq. cm. bed cross section was collected and that the hold-up of liquid in the bed was 14.5 ± 2.5 cu. cm. solution/sq. cm. bed cross section. Compare the calculated results with these.)

CHAPTER 12

# DRYING

The term *drying* refers generally to the removal of moisture from a substance. It is so loosely and inconsistently applied that some restriction in its meaning is necessary in the treatment to be given the subject here. For example, a wet solid such as wood, cloth, or paper may be dried by evaporation of the moisture either into a gas stream or without the benefit of the gas to carry away the vapor, but the mechanical removal of such moisture by expression or centrifuging is not ordinarily considered drying. A solution may be "dried" by spraying it in fine droplets into a hot, dry gas, which results in evaporation of the liquid, but evaporation of the solution by boiling in the absence of a gas to carry away the moisture is not ordinarily considered a drying operation. A liquid such as benzene may be "dried" of any small water content by an operation which is really distillation, but the removal of a small amount of acetone by the same process would not usually be called drying. Gases and liquids containing small amounts of water may be dried by adsorption operations, as discussed in Chap. 11. This discussion will be largely limited to the removal of moisture from solids and liquids by evaporation into a gas stream. In practice, the moisture is so frequently water and the gas so frequently air that this combination will provide the basis for most of the discussion. It is important to emphasize, however, that the equipment, techniques, and relationships are equally applicable to other systems as well.

## EQUILIBRIUM

The moisture contained in a wet solid or liquid solution exerts a vapor pressure to an extent depending upon the nature of the moisture, the nature of the solid, and the temperature. If then a wet solid is exposed to a continual supply of fresh gas containing a fixed partial pressure of the vapor, $p$, the solid will either lose moisture by evaporation or gain moisture from the gas until the vapor pressure of the moisture of the solid equals $p$. The solid and the gas are then in equilibrium, and the moisture content of the solid is termed its equilibrium-moisture content at the prevailing conditions.

524

**Insoluble Solids.** A few typical equilibrium-moisture relationships are shown in Fig. 12.1, where the moisture in each case is water. Here the equilibrium partial pressure $p$ of the water vapor in the gas stream has been divided by the vapor pressure of pure water, $P$, to give the relative saturation or relative humidity (see Chap. 7) of the gas, since the curves are then applicable over a modest range of temperatures instead of being useful for one temperature only. Consider the curve for wood. If the wood contained initially a very high moisture content, say 0.35 lb. water/lb. dry solid, and were exposed to a continual supply

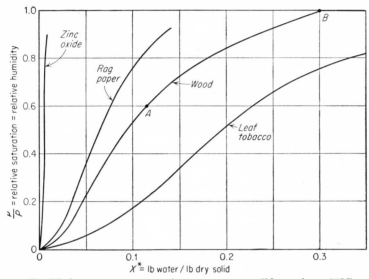

FIG. 12.1. Equilibrium water content of some common solids at about 25°C. (*From "International Critical Tables," vol. 2, pp. 322–325, with permission.*)

of air of 0.6 relative humidity, the wood would lose moisture by evaporation until its equilibrium concentration corresponding to point $A$ on the curve were eventually reached. Further exposure to this air, for even indefinitely long periods, would not bring about additional loss of moisture from the solid. The moisture content could, however, be reduced further by exposure of the solid to air of lower relative humidity, but to remove all the moisture would require exposure to perfectly dry air, corresponding to the origin of the curve. The moisture contained in the wood up to a concentration corresponding to point $B$ in the figure, which exerts a vapor pressure less than that of pure water, may be moisture contained inside the cell walls of the plant structure, moisture in loose chemical combination with the cellulosic material, moisture present as a liquid solution of soluble portions of the solid and as a solid solution, moisture held in small capillaries and crevasses throughout the solid or otherwise adsorbed upon the surface. Such moisture is called *bound water*.[2] If exposed to saturated air, the wood may have any moisture content greater than 0.3 lb./lb. dry solid (point *B*), and moisture in excess of that at *B*, *unbound water*, exerts the vapor pressure of pure water at the prevailing temperature.

The equilibrium moisture for a given species of solid may depend upon the particle size or specific surface, if the moisture is largely physically adsorbed. Different solids have different equilibrium-moisture curves, as shown in the figure. Generally, inorganic solids which are insoluble

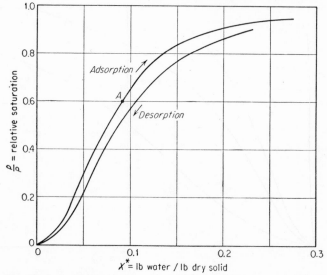

FIG. 12.2. Equilibrium water content of a sulfite pulp, showing hysteresis. [*Seborg, Ind. Eng. Chem.*, **29**, 169 (1937).]

in the liquid and which show no special adsorptive properties, such as the zinc oxide in the figure, show relatively low equilibrium-moisture contents, while spongy, cellular materials, especially those of vegetable origin such as the tobacco in the figure, generally show large equilibrium-moisture contents. The equilibrium partial pressure for a solid is independent of the nature of the dry gas provided the latter is inert to the solid and is the same in the absence of noncondensable gas also. The same solids, if wet with liquids other than water, will show different equilibrium curves. The effect of large changes in temperature may frequently be shown in the form of a reference-substance plot as in Fig. 11.5.[33] It is seen that the equilibrium moisture is similar in many respects to the adsorption equilibria discussed in Chap. 11.

**Hysteresis.** Many solids exhibit different equilibrium-moisture characteristics depending upon whether the equilibrium is reached by condensation (adsorption) or evaporation (desorption) of the moisture. A typical example is shown in Fig. 12.2, and this curve somewhat resembles that of Fig. 11.4. In drying operations, it is the desorption equilibrium which is of particular interest, and this will always show the larger of the two equilibrium-moisture contents for a given partial pressure of vapor. The moisture picked up by a dry solid when exposed to moist air, i.e., the adsorption equilibrium, is sometimes called *regain*, and knowledge of this has practical value in the consideration of drying

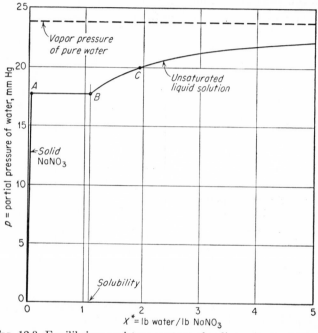

FIG. 12.3. Equilibrium moisture content of sodium nitrate at 25°C.

operations. For example, in the case of Fig. 12.2, it will be of little use to dry the solid to a water content below that corresponding to point $A$ if it is expected to expose the dried material to air of 0.6 relative humidity later. If it is important that the solid be kept at a lower moisture content, it would have to be packaged or stored immediately out of contact with the air in a moisture-impervious container.

**Soluble Solids.** Solids which are soluble in the liquid in question ordinarily show insignificant equilibrium-moisture contents when exposed to gases whose partial pressure of vapor is less than that of the saturated solution of the solid. Refer to Fig. 12.3, where the characteristics of sodium nitrate–water are shown. A saturated solution of sodium nitrate in water at 25°C. exerts a partial pressure of water ($B$) equal to 17.7 mm. Hg, and more dilute solutions exert higher partial pressures, as shown by curve *BC*. When exposed to air containing a partial pressure of water less than 17.7 mm. Hg, a solution will evaporate, and the residual solid will retain only a negligible amount of adsorbed moisture as shown by the curve from the origin to point *A* and will appear dry. If the solid is exposed to air containing a higher water-vapor content, say 20 mm. Hg, moisture will be adsorbed to such an extent that the solid will completely dissolve, or *deliquesce*, to produce the corresponding solution at *C*. Solids of very low solubility, when exposed to ordinary atmospheric air, will not deliquesce since the equilibrium partial pressure of their saturated solutions is greater than that ordinarily found in the air.

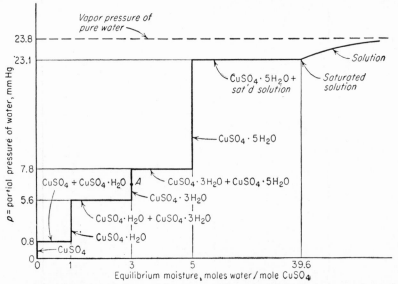

Fig. 12.4. Equilibrium moisture of copper sulfate at 25°C. (not drawn to scale).

Hydrated crystals may show more complicated relationships, such as those of Fig. 12.4 for the system copper sulfate–water at 25°C. Three hydrates are formed in this system, as the figure indicates. The anhydrous salt shows a negligible equilibrium-moisture content, which would in any case consist merely of adsorbed water upon the surface of the crystals. If exposed to air containing a partial pressure of water less than 7.8 and more than 5.6 mm. Hg, the salt will take on sufficient water to form the trihydrate and the crystals will have negligible adsorbed water other than the water of crystallization. The conditions will correspond to a point such as point *A* on the figure. If the moisture content of the air is then reduced to slightly less than 5.6 mm. Hg, the trihydrate will lose moisture (*effloresce*) to form the monohydrate, while at 5.6 mm. Hg any proportion of mono- and trihydrate may coexist. Similarly, if the moisture content of the air is increased to slightly more than 7.8 mm.

Hg, additional moisture will be adsorbed until the pentahydrate is formed. If the moisture content of the air exceeds 23.1 mm. Hg, the salt will deliquesce.

**Definitions.** For convenient reference, certain terms used to describe the moisture content of substances are summarized below.

*Moisture content, wet basis.* The moisture content of a solid or solution is usually described in terms of weight per cent moisture, and unless otherwise qualified this is ordinarily understood to be expressed on the wet basis, i.e., as (lb. moisture/lb. wet solid)100 = [lb. moisture/(lb. dry solid + lb. moisture)]100 = $100X/(1 + X)$.

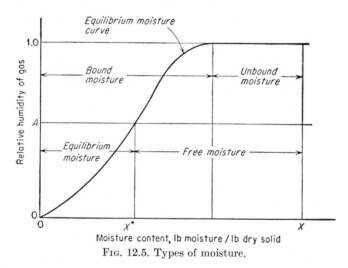

FIG. 12.5. Types of moisture.

*Moisture content, dry basis.* This is expressed as lb. moisture/lb. dry solid = $X$. Percentage moisture, dry basis = $100X$.

*Equilibrium moisture $X^*$.* This is the moisture content of a substance when at equilibrium with a given partial pressure of the vapor.

*Bound moisture.* This refers to the moisture contained by a substance which exerts an equilibrium vapor pressure less than that of the pure liquid at the same temperature.

*Unbound moisture.* This refers to the moisture contained by a substance which exerts an equilibrium vapor pressure equal to that of the pure liquid at the same temperature.

*Free moisture.* Free moisture is that moisture contained by a substance in excess of the equilibrium moisture: $X - X^*$. Only free moisture can be evaporated, and the free water content of a solid depends upon the vapor concentration in the gas.

These relations are shown graphically in Fig. 12.5 for a solid of moisture content $X$ exposed to a gas of relative humidity $A$.

**Illustration 1.**  A wet solid is to be dried from 80 to 5% moisture, wet basis.  Compute the moisture to be evaporated, per 1,000 lb. of dried product.

*Solution*

Initial moisture content $= 0.80/(1 - 0.80) = 4.00$ lb. water/lb. dry solid
Final moisture content $= 0.05/(1 - 0.05) = 0.0527$ lb. water/lb. dry solid
Lb. dry solid in product $= 1,000(0.95) = 950$ lb.
Moisture to be evapd. $= 950(4 - 0.0527) = 3,750$ lb.

## DRYING OPERATIONS

Drying operations may be broadly classified according to whether they are batch or continuous.  These terms are applied specifically from the point of view of the substance being dried.  Thus the operation termed batch drying is usually in fact a semibatch process wherein a quantity of the substance to be dried is exposed to a continually flowing stream of air into which the moisture evaporates.  In continuous operations, the substance to be dried as well as the gas passes continually through the equipment.  No typically stagewise methods are ordinarily used, and all operations involve continuous contact of the gas and the drying substance.

The equipment used for drying may be classified according to any of the following categories:

1. Method of operation, i.e., batch or continuous.  Batch, or semibatch, equipment is operated intermittently or cyclically under unsteady-state conditions: the drier is charged with the substance, which remains in the equipment until dry, whereupon the drier is emptied and recharged with a fresh batch.  Continuous driers are usually operated in steady-state fashion.

2. Method of supplying the heat necessary for evaporation of the moisture.  In *direct* driers, the heat is supplied entirely by direct contact of the substance with the hot gas into which evaporation takes place.  In *indirect* driers, the heat is supplied quite independently of the gas used to carry away the vaporized moisture.  For example, heat may be supplied by conduction through a metal wall in contact with the substance, or less frequently by exposure of the substance to infrared radiation or by dielectric heating.  In the case of the last, the heat is generated inside the solid by a high-frequency electric field.

3. Nature of the substance to be dried.  The substance may be a rigid solid such as wood or fiberboard, a flexible material such as cloth or paper, a granular solid such as a mass of crystals, a thick paste or a thin slurry, or a solution.  If it is a solid, it may be fragile or sturdy. The physical form of the substance and the diverse methods of handling necessary have perhaps the greatest influence on the type of drier used.

## I. BATCH DRYING

Drying in batches is a relatively expensive operation and is consequently limited to small-scale operations, to pilot-plant and development
work, and to drying valuable materials whose total cost will be little
influenced by added expense in the drying operation.

**Direct Driers.**   The construction of such driers depends greatly upon
the nature of the substance being dried.   *Tray driers*, also called cabinet,
compartment, or shelf driers, are used for drying solids which must be

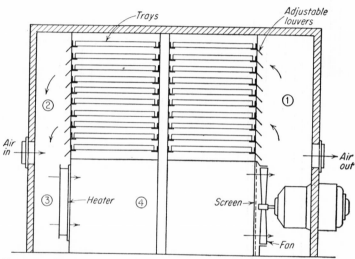

Fig. 12.6. Typical tray drier.   (*Courtesy of Proctor and Schwartz, Inc.*)

supported on trays.   This may include pasty materials such as wet filter
cakes from filter presses, lumpy solids which must be spread upon trays,
and similar materials.   A typical device, shown schematically in Fig.
12.6, consists of a cabinet containing removable trays on which the solid
to be dried is spread.   After loading, the cabinet is closed, and steam-
heated air is blown across and between the trays to evaporate the moisture (cross-circulation drying).   Inert gas rather than air may be used
if the liquid to be evaporated is combustible.   When the solid has reached
the desired degree of dryness, the cabinet is opened and the trays replaced
with a new batch.   Figure 12.7 shows a simple modification, a *truck drier*,
where the trays are racked upon trucks which may be rolled into and
out of the cabinet.   Since the trucks may be loaded and unloaded outside the drier, considerable time may be saved between drying cycles.
Other obvious modifications of the design are also used, depending upon
the nature of the drying substance.   Thus, skeins of fibers such as rayon

may be hung from poles, and wood or boardlike materials may be stacked in piles, the layers separated from each other by spacer blocks.

In the case of granular materials, the solid may be arranged in thin beds supported on screens so that air or other gas may be passed through the beds. This results in very much more rapid drying. A typical device for this purpose, a batch *through-circulation drier*, is shown schematically in Fig. 12.8. Crystalline solids and materials which are naturally granular such as silica gel may be dried in this manner directly.

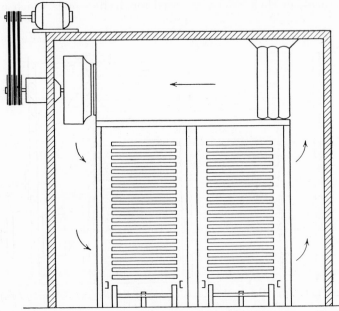

FIG. 12.7. Two-truck drier. (*Courtesy of Proctor and Schwartz, Inc.*)

In the case of others, some sort of preliminary treatment to put them into satisfactory form, *preforming*, is necessary. Pastes, for example, those resulting from precipitation of pigments or other solids, may be preformed by (1) extrusion into short, spaghettilike rods, (2) granulation, i.e., forcing them through screens, or (3) by briquetting.[17]

One of the most important difficulties in the use of driers of the type described is the nonuniformity of moisture content found in the finished product taken from various parts of the dryer. This is largely the result of inadequate and nonuniform air movement inside the drier. It is important to eliminate stagnant air pockets and to maintain reasonably uniform air humidity and temperature throughout the drier. In order to do this, large volumes of air must be blown over the trays, if possible at velocities ranging up to 10 or 20 ft./sec. if the solid will not blow from the trays at these air rates. This may be accomplished by blowing large quantities of heated fresh air only once through the drier, but the loss of heat in the discharged air will then usually be prohibitive in cost. Instead, it is the practice to admit only relatively small quantities of fresh air and to recirculate the bulk of it, sometimes as much as 80 to 95 per cent.[32] This may be done inside the drier, as shown, for example, in Fig. 12.6, with dampers in the inlet and outlet pipes to regulate the extent of recirculation. The louvers at each tray level may then be adjusted so as to ensure as nearly uniform air velocity over each tray as

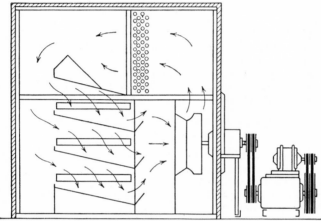

Fig. 12.8. Through-circulation drier. (*Courtesy of Proctor and Schwartz, Inc.*)

possible. Alternatively, the heaters and fans may be installed outside the dryer, with duct-work and dampers to permit more careful control of the relative amounts of fresh and recirculated air admitted to the drier itself. It is important also that the trays in such driers be filled level to the brim but not overloaded, so that uniform free space for air movement is available between trays.

The recirculation of large quantities of air necessarily raises the humidity of the air in the drier considerably above that of the fresh air. Low percentage humidity and consequently reasonably rapid drying rates are then obtained by using as high a temperature as practicable. The drier must then be thoroughly insulated, not only to conserve heat but also to maintain the inside walls at temperatures above the dew point of the air to prevent condensation of moisture upon the walls. Specially conditioned, low-humidity air is not used except where low-temperature drying is necessary to avoid damage to the product.

**Illustration 2.** The drier of Fig. 12.6 contains trays arranged in a tier of 10, each on racks 4 in. apart, each tray 1.5 in. deep. Each tray is 3 ft. wide, and there are 150 sq. ft. of drying surface. It is desired that the air entering the trays (position 1 on the figure) have a dry-bulb temperature of 200°F. and humidity 0.05 lb. water/lb.

dry air.   Atmospheric air enters at 80°F., humidity 0.01.   The air velocity over the
trays at the entrance to the trays is to be 10 ft./sec.   At a time when the solid being
dried is losing water at a constant rate of 60 lb. evaporated/hr., determine the percentage recirculation of air and the conditions of the air in the various parts of the
drier.

   *Solution.*   At position 1, $Y_1 = 0.05$ lb. water/lb. dry air, $t_{G1} = 200°F.$, and the
humid volume (Table 7.1) is $[0.0252 + 0.0405(0.05)](200 + 460) = 17.97$ cu. ft./lb.
dry air.

Free area for flow between trays $= 3(4 - 1.5)11/12 = 6.87$ sq. ft.
   Rate of air flow to trays $= 10(60)(6.87) = 4,120$ cu. ft./min., or $4,120/17.97$
                           $= 230$ lb. dry air/min. (at position 1)

   The rate of evaporation is $^{60}/_{60} = 1.0$ lb. water/min., and the humidity at 2 (Fig.
12.6) is therefore $(0.05 + 1)/230 = 0.0544$ lb. water/lb. dry air.   Assuming adiabatic
drying, the temperature at 2 may be found on the adiabatic saturation line (Fig. 7.6),
drawn through the conditions at 1, and at $Y_2 = 0.0544$, $t_{G2} = 184°F.$

   The condition of the air at 4, and the discharged air, must be the same as at 1.
An over-all water balance about the drier therefore is

$$G(0.05 - 0.01) = 1.0 \text{ lb. water evapd./min.}$$
$$G = 25 \text{ lb. dry air/min. enter and leave}$$

   The quantity of air at 3 and 4 (Fig. 12.6) is therefore $230 + 25 = 255$ lb. dry air/-
min., and at position 4 the humid volume must be 17.97 cu. ft./lb. dry air.   The
volumetric rate through the fan is therefore $255(17.97) = 4,600$ cu. ft./min.   The
percentage of air recycled is $^{230}/_{255}(100) = 90.1\%.$

   The enthalpy of the air at 2 (and at 1) is 99.5 B.t.u./lb. dry air (Fig. 7.6, saturated
enthalpy at the adiabatic-saturation temperature, 116°F.), and that of the fresh air
is 22.4 B.t.u./lb. dry air.   Assuming complete mixing, the enthalpy of the air at 3
is, by an enthalpy balance, $[99.5(230) + 22.4(25)]/255 = 92.0$ B.t.u./lb. dry air.
Since its humidity is 0.05, its dry bulb temperature (Fig. 7.6) is 173.5°F.   The heater
must supply $255(99.5 - 92.0) = 1,910$ B.t.u./min., neglecting heat losses.

   The dew-point temperature of the air (Fig. 7.6) at 1, 3, and 4 is 104.5°F., and at
2 it is 107°F.   The drier should be sufficiently well insulated so that the inside surface
will not fall to a temperature of 107°F.

The general humidity level in the drier may be altered during the
drying cycle.   This may be especially important in the case of certain
solids which warp, shrink, develop surface cracks, or "case-harden" when
dried too rapidly.   A cake of soap of high moisture content, for example, if
exposed to very dry, hot air, will lose moisture by evaporation from the
surface so fast that water will not move rapidly enough from the center
of the cake to the surface to keep pace with the evaporation.   The surface then becomes hard and impervious to moisture (case-hardened), and
drying stops even though the average water content of the cake is still
very high.   In the case of other solids, such as wood, for example,
shrinkage at the surface may cause cracks or warping.   Such substances
should be dried slowly at first with air of high humidity, and drier air
may be used only after the bulk of the water has been removed.

Driers of the type described are relatively cheap to build and have low maintenance costs. They are, however, expensive to operate owing to low heat economy and high labor costs. Each time the drier is opened for unloading and loading, the temperature of the interior falls and all the metal parts of the drier must be heated again to the operating temperature when operation is resumed. Steam consumption for heating the air will generally not be less than 2.5 lb. steam/lb. water evaporated and may be as high as 10, especially for cases where the moisture content of the product is reduced to very low levels.[15] The labor requirement for loading, unloading, and supervision of the drying cycle is high.

**Indirect Driers.** *Vacuum shelf driers* are tray driers whose cabinets, made of cast iron or steel plates, are fitted with tightly closing doors so that they may be operated at subatmospheric pressure. No air is blown or recirculated through such driers. The trays containing the solid to be dried rest upon hollow shelves through which warm water or steam is passed to provide the necessary heat for vaporization of moisture. The heat is conducted to the solid through the metal of the shelves and trays. After loading and sealing, the air in the dryer is evacuated by a mechanical vacuum pump or steam jet ejector, and distillation of the moisture proceeds. The vapors usually pass to a condenser, where they are liquefied and collected, and only noncondensable gas is removed by the pump. *Agitated pan driers*, which may be used to dry pastes or slurries in small batches, are shallow, circular pans, 3 to 6 ft. in diameter and 1 to 2 ft. deep, with flat bottoms and vertical sides. The pans are jacketed for admission of steam or hot water for heating. The paste, or slurry, in the pan is stirred and scraped by a set of rotating plows, in order to expose new material to the heated surface. Moisture is evaporated into the atmosphere in the case of atmospheric pan driers, or the pan may be covered and operated under vacuum. *Vacuum rotary driers* are steam-jacketed cylindrical shells, arranged horizontally, in which a slurry, or paste, may be dried in vacuum. The slurry is stirred by a set of rotating agitator blades attached to a central horizontal shaft which passes through the ends of the cylindrical shell. Vaporized moisture passes through an opening in the top to a condenser, and noncondensable gas is removed by a vacuum pump. The dried solid is discharged through a door in the bottom of the drier.

Driers of this category are expensive to build and to operate. Consequently they are used only for valuable materials which must be dried at low temperatures or in the absence of air to prevent damage, such as certain pharmaceutical products, or where the moisture to be removed is an expensive or poisonous organic solvent which must be recovered more or less completely.

**The Rate of Batch Drying.** In order to set up drying schedules and to determine the size of equipment, it is necessary to know the time which will be required to dry a substance from one moisture content to another under specified conditions. We shall also wish to estimate the influence that different drying conditions will have upon the time for drying. Our knowledge of the mechanism of drying is so incomplete that it is necessary with few exceptions to rely upon at least some experimental measurements for these purposes. Measurements of the rate of batch drying are relatively simple to make and provide much information not only for batch but also for continuous operation.

*Drying Tests.*[27] The rate of drying may be determined for a sample of a substance by suspending it in a cabinet or duct, in a stream of air, from a balance. The weight of the drying sample may then be measured as a function of time. Certain precautions must be observed if the data are to be of maximum utility. The sample should not be too small. Further, the following conditions should resemble as closely as possible those expected to prevail in contemplated large-scale operation: (1) The sample should be similarly supported in a tray or frame. (2) It should have the same ratio of drying to nondrying surface. (3) It should be subjected to similar conditions of radiant-heat transfer. (4) The air should have the same temperature, humidity, and velocity (both speed and direction with respect to the sample). If possible, several tests should be made on samples of different thicknesses. The dry weight of the sample should also be obtained.

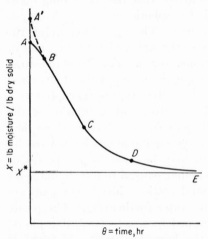

Fig. 12.9. Batch drying, constant drying conditions.

The exposure of the sample to air of constant temperature, humidity, and velocity constitutes drying under *constant drying conditions.*

*Rate-of-drying Curve.* From the data obtained during such a test, a curve of moisture content as a function of time (Fig. 12.9) may be plotted. This will be useful directly in determining the time required for drying larger batches under the same drying conditions. Much information can be obtained if the data are converted to rates of drying, expressed as $N$ lb. moisture evaporated/(hr.)(sq. ft.), and plotted against moisture content, as in Fig. 12.10. This may be done by measuring the slopes of tangents drawn to the curve of Fig. 12.9 or by determining from the curve small changes in moisture content $\Delta X$ for corresponding small changes in time $\Delta\theta$ and calculating the rate as $N = -L_s \, \Delta X/A \, \Delta\theta$.

Here $L_s$ is the weight of dry solid, and $A$ is the wet surface over which the gas blows and through which evaporation takes place in the case of cross-air circulation drying. In the case of through-circulation drying, $A$ is the cross section of the bed measured at right angles to the direction of gas flow.

The rate-of-drying curve is sometimes plotted with the ordinate expressed as lb. moisture evaporated/(hr.)(lb. dry solid), which in the present notation is $-dX/d\theta$.

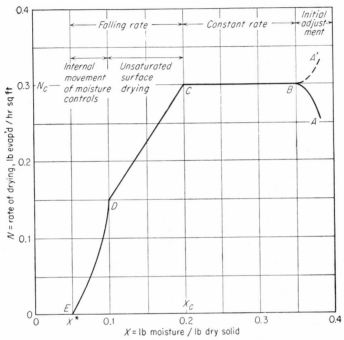

FIG. 12.10. Typical rate-of-drying curve, constant drying conditions.

There are usually two major parts to the rate curve of Fig. 12.10, a period of constant rate and one of falling rate, as marked on the figure. While different solids and different conditions of drying will frequently give rise to curves of very different shape in the falling rate period, the curve shown occurs frequently. Some of the differences which may arise will be considered later, but for the present let us briefly review the reasons generally advanced for the various parts of the curve shown.[10,20,25,28]

If a solid is initially very wet, the surface will be covered with a thin film of liquid which we shall assume is entirely unbound moisture. When it is exposed to relatively dry air, evaporation will take place from the surface. The rate at which moisture evaporates can be described in terms of a gas mass-transfer coefficient $k_Y$ and the difference in humidity of the gas at the liquid surface $Y_s$ and in the main stream $Y$. Thus, for cross-circulation drying

$$N_c = k_Y(Y_s - Y) \tag{12.1}$$

The coefficient $k_Y$ may be expected to remain constant as long as the speed and direction of gas flow past the surface do not change. The humidity $Y_s$ is the saturated humidity at the liquid-surface temperature $t_s$ and will therefore depend upon this temperature. Since evaporation of moisture absorbs latent heat, the liquid surface will come to and remain at an equilibrium temperature such that the rate of heat flow from the surroundings to the surface exactly equals the rate of heat absorption. $Y_s$ therefore remains constant. Since in addition $Y$ remains unchanged under constant drying conditions, the rate of evaporation must remain constant at the value $N_c$, as shown on Figs. 12.9 and 12.10 between points $B$ and $C$. In the beginning, the solid and the liquid surface are usually colder than the ultimate surface temperature $t_s$, and the evaporation rate will increase while the surface temperature rises to its ultimate value during the period $AB$ on these curves. Alternatively the equilibrium temperature $t_s$ may be lower than the initial value, which will give rise to a curve $A'B$ while the initial adjustment occurs. The initial period is usually so short that it is ordinarily ignored in subsequent analysis of the drying times.

When the average moisture content of the solid has reached a value $X_c$, the *critical moisture content* (Fig. 12.10), the surface film of moisture has been so reduced by evaporation that further drying causes dry spots to appear upon the surface and these occupy increasingly larger proportions of the exposed surface as drying proceeds. Since, however, the rate $N$ is computed by means of the constant gross surface $A$, the value of $N$ must fall even though the rate per unit of wet surface remains constant. This gives rise to the first part of the falling-rate period, the period of *unsaturated surface drying*, from points $C$ to $D$ (Figs. 12.9 and 12.10). Ultimately the original surface film of liquid will have entirely evaporated at an average moisture content for the solid corresponding to point $D$. This part of the curve may be missing entirely, or it may constitute the whole of the falling-rate period.

On further drying, the rate at which moisture may move through the solid, as a result of concentration gradients existing between the deeper parts and the surface, is the controlling step. As the moisture concentration generally is lowered by the drying, the rate of internal movement of moisture decreases. In some cases, evaporation may take place beneath the surface of the solid in a plane or zone which retreats deeper into the solid as drying proceeds. In any event, the rate of drying falls even more rapidly than before, as from $D$ to $E$ (Fig. 12.10). At point $E$, the moisture content of the solid has fallen to the equilibrium value $X^*$ for the prevailing air humidity, and drying stops.

*Time of Drying.* If it is desired to determine the time of drying a solid under the same conditions for which a drying curve such as Fig. 12.9 has been completely determined, one need merely read the difference in the times corresponding to the initial and final moisture contents from the curve.

Within limits, it is sometimes possible to estimate the appearance of a rate-of-drying curve such as Fig. 12.10 for conditions different from those used in the experiments. In order to determine the time for drying for such a curve, we may proceed as follows: The rate of drying is, by definition,

$$N = \frac{-L_s}{A} \frac{dX}{d\theta} \tag{12.2}$$

Rearranging and integrating over the time interval while the moisture content changes from its initial value $X_1$ to its final value $X_2$,

$$\theta = \int_0^\theta d\theta = \frac{L_S}{A} \int_{X_2}^{X_1} \frac{dX}{N} \tag{12.3}$$

1. *The constant-rate period.* If the drying takes place entirely within the constant-rate period so that $X_1$ and $X_2 > X_c$ and $N = N_c$, Eq. (12.3) becomes

$$\theta = \frac{L_S(X_1 - X_2)}{A N_c} \tag{12.4}$$

2. *The falling-rate period.* If $X_1$ and $X_2$ are both less than $X_c$, so that drying occurs under conditions of changing $N$, we may proceed as follows:

*a.* General case: For any shape of falling-rate curve whatsoever, Eq. (12.3) may be integrated graphically by determining the area under a curve of $1/N$ as ordinate, $X$ as abscissa, the data for which may be obtained from the rate of drying curve.

*b.* Special case:[3] $N$ is linear in $X$, as in the region $BC$ of Fig. 12.10. In this case,

$$N = mX + b \tag{12.5}$$

where $m$ is the slope of the linear portion of the curve and $b$ is a constant. Substitution in Eq. (12.3) provides

$$\theta = \frac{L_S}{A} \int_{X_2}^{X_1} \frac{dX}{mX + b} = \frac{L_S}{mA} \ln \frac{mX_1 + b}{mX_2 + b} \tag{12.6}$$

But since $N_1 = mX_1 + b$, $N_2 = mX_2 + b$, and $m = (N_1 - N_2)/(X_1 - X_2)$, Eq. (12.6) becomes

$$\theta = \frac{L_S(X_1 - X_2)}{A(N_1 - N_2)} \ln \frac{N_1}{N_2} = \frac{L_S(X_1 - X_2)}{A N_m} \tag{12.7}$$

where $N_m$ is the logarithmic average of the rate $N_1$, at moisture content $X_1$, and $N_2$ at $X_2$.

Frequently the entire falling-rate curve may be taken as a straight line between points $C$ and $E$ (Fig. 12.10). It is often assumed to be so for lack of more detailed data. In this case

$$N = m(X - X^*) = \frac{N_c(X - X^*)}{X_c - X^*} \tag{12.8}$$

and Eq. (12.7) becomes

$$\theta = \frac{L_S(X_c - X^*)}{N_c A} \ln \frac{X_1 - X^*}{X_2 - X^*} \tag{12.9}$$

In any particular drying problem, either or both constant- and falling-rate periods may be involved, depending upon the relative values of $X_1$, $X_2$, and $X_c$. The appropriate equations and limits must then be chosen.

**Illustration 3.** A batch of the solid for which Fig. 12.10 is the drying curve is to be dried from 25 to 6% moisture under conditions identical to those for which the figure applies. The initial weight of the wet solid is 350 lb., and the drying surface is 1 sq. ft./8 lb. dry weight. Determine the time for drying.

*Solution.* The total weight of the batch is unimportant. $L_S/A = 8$. At 25% moisture, $X_1 = 0.25/(1 - 0.25) = 0.333$ lb. moisture/lb. dry solid. At 6% moisture, $X_2 = 0.06/(1 - 0.06) = 0.064$ lb. moisture/lb. dry solid. Inspection of Fig. 12.10 shows that both constant- and falling-rate periods are involved. The limits of moisture content in the equations for the different periods will be chosen accordingly.

*Constant-rate period.* From $X_1 = 0.333$ to $X_c = 0.200$. $N_c = 0.30$.

Eq. (12.4):    $\theta = \dfrac{L_S(X_1 - X_c)}{A N_c} = \dfrac{8(0.333 - 0.200)}{1(0.30)} = 3.54$ hr.

*Falling-rate period.* From $X_c = 0.200$ to $X_2 = 0.064$. Use Eq. (12.3). The following table is prepared from the data of Fig. 12.10:

| $X$ | $N$ | $\dfrac{1}{N}$ |
|---|---|---|
| 0.20 | 0.300 | 3.33 |
| 0.18 | 0.266 | 3.76 |
| 0.16 | 0.239 | 4.18 |
| 0.14 | 0.208 | 4.80 |
| 0.12 | 0.180 | 5.55 |
| 0.10 | 0.150 | 6.67 |
| 0.09 | 0.097 | 10.3 |
| 0.08 | 0.070 | 14.3 |
| 0.07 | 0.043 | 23.3 |
| 0.064 | 0.025 | 40.0 |

A curve, not shown, is prepared of $1/N$ as ordinate, $X$ as abscissa, and the area under the curve between $X = 0.20$ and $X = 0.064$ is 1.06.

Eq. (12.3):    $\theta = \frac{8}{1}(1.06) = 8.48$ hr.

The total drying time is therefore $3.54 + 8.48 = 12.0$ hr.

Alternatively, since the drying curve is straight from $X = 0.20$ to $X = 0.10$, Eq. (12.7) may be used in this range of moisture contents,

$$\theta = \frac{L_S(X_c - X_D)}{A(N_c - N_D)} \ln \frac{N_c}{N_D} = \frac{8(0.20 - 0.10)}{1(0.30 - 0.15)} \ln \frac{0.30}{0.15} = 3.70 \text{ hr.}$$

Graphical integration in the range $X = 0.1$ to $X = 0.064$ provides, through Eq. (12.3), an additional 4.79 hr., so that the total falling-rate time is $3.70 + 4.79 = 8.49$ hr.

As an approximation, the falling-rate period may be represented by a straight line from $C$ to $E$ (Fig. 12.10). The corresponding falling-rate time is, by Eq. (12.9),

$$\theta = \frac{L_S(X_c - X^*)}{N_c A} \ln \frac{X_c - X^*}{X_2 - X^*} = \frac{8(0.20 - 0.05)}{0.3(1)} \ln \frac{0.20 - 0.05}{0.064 - 0.05} = 9.5 \text{ hr.}$$

**The Mechanisms of Batch Drying.** We now consider the various portions of the rate-of-drying curve in more detail. Our present knowledge

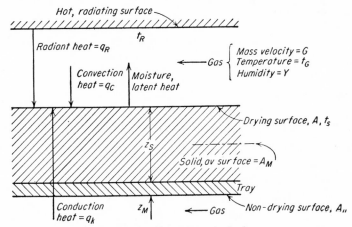

Fig. 12.11. Constant-rate drying.

permits us to describe the drying process in the constant-rate period reasonably well, but our understanding of the falling-rate periods is very limited.

**Cross-circulation Drying.** *The Constant-rate Period.* In this period, where surface evaporation of unbound moisture occurs, it has been shown that the rate of drying is established by a balance of the heat requirements for evaporation and the rate at which heat reaches the surface. Consider the section of a material drying in a stream of gas as shown in Fig. 12.11. The solid of thickness $z_S$ ft. is placed on a tray of thickness $z_M$ ft. The whole is immersed in a stream of drying gas at temperature $t_G°$F. and humidity $Y$ lb. moisture/lb. dry gas, flowing at a mass velocity $G$ lb./(hr.)(sq. ft.). The evaporation of moisture takes place from the upper surface, $A$ sq. ft., which is at a temperature $t_s°$F. The drying surface receives heat from several sources: (1) $q_c$ by convection from the gas stream; (2) $q_k$ by conduction through the solid; (3) $q_R$ by direct radiation from a hot surface at temperature $t_R°$F., as shown, all expressed as B.t.u./ (hr.)(sq. ft.). In accordance with the mechanism discussed earlier, the heat arriving at the surface by these methods is removed by the evaporating moisture, so that the surface temperature remains constant at $t_s$. The entire mechanism resembles the wet-bulb-thermometer process, complicated by the additional source of heat.

The rate of evaporation and the surface temperature may then be obtained by a heat balance.[15,24] If $q$ represents the total heat arriving at the surface, then

$$q = q_c + q_R + q_k \tag{12.10}$$

Neglecting the heat required to superheat the evaporated moisture to the gas temperature and considering only the latent heat of vaporization $\lambda_s$, then the rate of evaporation $N_c$ and the rate of heat flow are related,

$$N_c\lambda_s = q \tag{12.11}$$

The heat received at the surface by convection is controlled by the appropriate convection heat-transfer coefficient $h_c$,

$$q_c = h_c(t_G - t_s) \tag{12.12}$$

The heat received by radiation may be estimated by the usual means[19] and can also be expressed as a heat-transfer coefficient $h_R$,

$$q_R = \varepsilon(1,730)(10^{-12})(T_R^4 - T_s^4) = h_R(t_R - t_s) \tag{12.13}$$

$$h_R = \frac{\varepsilon(1,730)(10^{-12})(T_R^4 - T_s^4)}{t_R - t_s} \tag{12.14}$$

where $\varepsilon$ is the emissivity of the drying surface and $T_R$ and $T_s$ are the absolute temperatures of the radiating and drying surfaces, in degrees Rankine. The heat received by convection and conduction through the solid may be computed by the usual methods for heat transfer through a series of resistances,

$$q_k = U_k(t_G - t_s) \tag{12.15}$$

$$U_k = \frac{1}{(1/h_c)(A/A_u) + (z_M/k_M)(A/A_u) + (z_S/k_S)(A/A_m)} \tag{12.16}$$

where $h_c$, the convection coefficient for the tray, may ordinarily be taken as the same as that for the drying surface, $k_M$ and $k_S$ are the thermal conductivities of the tray material and the drying solid, and $A_u$ and $A_m$ the nondrying surface and the average area of the drying solid, respectively. A thermal resistance at the junction of the drying solid and the tray material, and an effect of radiation to the tray, may be added to the terms of Eq. (12.16), if desired.

Combining Eqs. (12.1) and (12.10) to (12.15) permits calculation of the rate of drying,

$$N_c = \frac{q}{\lambda_s} = \frac{(h_c + U_k)(t_G - t_s) + h_R(t_R - t_s)}{\lambda_s} = k_Y(Y_s - Y) \quad (12.17)$$

The surface temperature must be known in order to use the relationship. This may be obtained by consideration of the left-hand portions of Eq. (12.17), which may be rearranged to read

$$\frac{(Y_s - Y)\lambda_s}{h_c/k_Y} = \left(1 + \frac{U_k}{h_c}\right)(t_G - t_s) + \frac{h_R}{h_c}(t_R - t_s) \quad (12.18)$$

The ratio $h_c/k_Y$ applicable to flow of gases past wet-bulb thermometers [Eqs. (7.33) and (7.34)] may be used for present purposes, and for the system air–water vapor this ratio was shown to be substantially the same as the humid heat of the gas $C_S$. Since $Y_s$ is the saturated humidity of the gas stream corresponding to $t_s$ when unbound moisture is being evaporated, both these quantities may be found by solving Eq. (12.18) simultaneously with the saturated-humidity curve on a psychrometric chart.

If conduction through the solid and radiation effects are absent, Eq. (12.18) reduces to that for the wet-bulb thermometer [Eq. (7.32)] and the surface temperature is the wet-bulb temperature of the gas. The drying surfaces will also be at the wet-bulb temperature if the solid is dried from all surfaces in the absence of radiation. When pans or trays of drying material are placed one above another, as in Figs. 12.6 and 12.7, most of the solid will receive radiation only from the bottom of the pan immediately above it, and unless gas temperatures are very high, this is not likely to be very important. It is essential therefore not to over-emphasize the heat received by radiation in conducting drying tests on single pairs of trays.

The convection heat-transfer coefficient $h_c$ has been measured for both a liquid water surface and for various drying solids, and reasonable agreement has been found. For flow of gas parallel to a smooth surface, it should be possible to determine both $h_c$ and $k_Y$ from curve 5 (Fig. 3.11). For values of Re''' above 15,000, which is the range normally employed, the equation of this curve is

$$\left[ j_H = \frac{h_c}{C_p G} \mathrm{Pr}^{\frac{2}{3}} \right] = \left[ j_D = \frac{k_Y}{G_S} \mathrm{Sc}^{\frac{2}{3}} \right] = 0.036\ \mathrm{Re}'''^{-0.2} \quad (12.19)$$

where Re''' is defined as $lG/\mu$, $l$ being the length of the drying surface in the direction of gas flow. If the gas is air and the length of the surface is 1 ft., Eq. (12.19) provides $h_c = 0.0058G^{0.8}$, whereas in a detailed study of the drying of sand in trays[24] $h_c$ was found to be $0.0128G^{0.8}$. The higher value may be due to roughness of the sand surface. In the absence of more specific data, the following are recommended:

*Air flow parallel to surface, $G$ = 500 to 6,000 lb./(hr.)(sq. ft.) (2 to 25 ft./sec.),*

$$h_c = 0.01 G^{0.8} \tag{12.20}$$

*Air flow perpendicular to surface,[22] $G$ = 800 to 4,000 lb./(hr.)(sq. ft.) (3 to 15 ft./sec.),*

$$h_c = 0.37 G^{0.37} \tag{12.21}$$

The relationships developed in Eqs. (12.17) to (12.21) permit direct estimates of the rate of drying during the constant-rate period, but they should not be considered as complete substitutes for experimental measurements. Perhaps their greatest value is in conjunction with limited experimental data in order to predict the effect of changing the drying conditions.

*Effect of gas velocity.* If radiation and conduction through the solid are negligible, $N_c$ is proportional to $G^{0.8}$ for parallel flow of gas and to $G^{0.37}$ for perpendicular flow. If radiation and conduction are present, the effect of gas rate will be less important.

*Effect of gas temperature.* Increased air temperature increases the quantity $t_G - t_s$ and hence increases $N_c$. In the absence of radiation effects, and neglecting the variation of $\lambda$ over moderate temperature ranges, $N_c$ is directly proportional to $t_G - t_s$.

*Effect of gas humidity.* $N_c$ varies directly as $Y_s - Y$, and consequently increasing the humidity lowers the rate of drying. Usually, changes in $Y$ and $t_G$ involve simultaneous changes in $t_s$ and $Y_s$, and the effects are best estimated by direct application of Eq. (12.17).

*Effect of thickness of drying solid.* If heat conduction through the solid occurs, Eqs. (12.15) and (12.16) indicate lowered values of $N_c$ with increased solid thickness. However, conduction of heat through edge surfaces of pans and trays may be an important source of heat which can result in increased rate of drying if the edge surface is large. If non-drying surfaces are heat-insulated, or if drying occurs from all surfaces of the solid, $N_c$ is independent of thickness. The *time* for drying between fixed moisture contents within the constant-rate period will then be directly proportional to thickness.

**Illustration 4.** An insoluble crystalline solid wet with water is placed in a 2- by 2-ft. rectangular pan, 1 in. deep, made of $\frac{1}{32}$-in.-thick galvanized iron. The pan is placed in an air stream at 150°F., humidity 0.01 lb. water/lb. dry air, flowing parallel to the upper and lower surfaces at a velocity of 10 ft./sec. The surface of the solid is in direct sight of steam-heated pipes whose surface temperature is 250°F.

*a.* Make an estimate of the rate of drying at constant rate.

*b.* Reestimate the rate if the pan were thoroughly heat-insulated and if there were no radiation from the steam pipes.

*Solution.* *a.* $Y = 0.01$ lb. water/lb. dry air, $t_G = 150°F$. The humid volume of the air (Table 7.1) is $[0.0252 + 0.0405(0.01)](150 + 460) = 15.6$ cu. ft./lb. dry air.

$$\rho_G = \text{density of gas} = 1.01/15.6 = 0.0647 \text{ lb./cu. ft.}$$
$$G = 10(3,600)(0.0647) = 2,430 \text{ lb./(hr.)(sq. ft.)}$$

Eq. (12.20):     $h_c = 0.01(2430)^{0.8} = 5.10 \text{ B.t.u./(hr.)(sq. ft.)(°F.)}$

Take the emissivity of the solid as $\varepsilon = 0.94$. $t_R = 250°F$., $T_R = 250 + 460 = 710°R$. Tentatively estimate $t_s$ as $100°F$., and $T_s = 100 + 460 = 560°R$.

Eq. (12.14):     $h_R = \dfrac{0.94(1,730)(10^{-12})(710^4 - 560^4)}{250 - 100} = 1.70 \text{ B.t.u./(hr.)(sq. ft.)(°F.)}$

Take $A_m = A = 2(2) = 4$ sq. ft. The area of the sides of the pan $= 4(2)(\tfrac{1}{12}) = 0.667$ sq. ft., and $A_u = 2(2) + 0.667 = 4.67$ sq. ft. for bottom and sides (this method

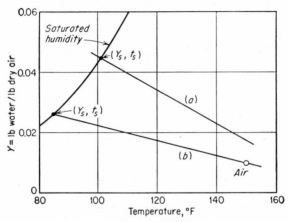

Fig. 12.12. Solution to Illustration 4.

of including the heat transfer through the sides is an oversimplification, but adequate for present purposes). Thermal conductivities are $k_M = 26$ for the metal of the pan, and $k_S = 2$ for the wet solid[24] (this value must be carefully chosen: it may bear no simple relation to the conductivities of either the dry solid or the moisture). $z_S = \tfrac{1}{12} = 0.0833$ ft, $z_M = 1/32(12) = 0.0026$ ft.

Eq. (12.16):     $\dfrac{1}{U_k} = \dfrac{1}{5.10}\dfrac{4}{4.67} + \dfrac{0.0026}{26}\dfrac{4}{4.67} + \dfrac{0.0833}{2}\dfrac{4}{4}$

$U_k = 4.76 \text{ B.t.u./(hr.)(sq. ft.)(°F.)}$

The humid heat of the air (Table 7.1) is $C_S = 0.24 + 0.45(0.01) = 0.245$, and $\lambda_s$ at the estimated $100°F$. is $1,037$ B.t.u./lb.

Eq. (12.18):     $\dfrac{(Y_s - 0.01)1,037}{0.245} = \left(1 + \dfrac{4.76}{5.10}\right)(150 - t_s) + \dfrac{1.70}{5.10}(250 - t_s)$

This reduces to $Y_s = 0.0991 - 0.000541 t_s$, which must be solved simultaneously with the saturated-humidity curve of the psychrometric chart for air–water vapor. This is most conveniently done graphically, as in Fig. 12.12, by plotting the equation on the pertinent portion of the psychrometric chart (Fig. 7.6). The line marked (*a*) on Fig. 12.12 is the above expression, and it intersects the saturated-humidity curve at

$Y_s = 0.0445$, $t_s = 101°F.$, the surface temperature, which is sufficiently close to the 100°F. estimated previously to make recalculation unnecessary. At 101°F., $\lambda_s = 1,036$ B.t.u./lb.

Eq. (12.17):     $N_c = \dfrac{(5.10 + 4.76)(150 - 101) + 1.70(250 - 101)}{1,036}$

$$= 0.712 \text{ lb. water evapd./(hr.)(sq. ft.)}$$

and the evaporation rate is $0.712(4) = 2.848$ lb. water/hr.

*b.* Where no radiation or conduction of heat through the solid occurs, the drying surface assumes the wet-bulb temperature of the air. For the system air-water at this humidity, the adiabatic-saturation lines of the psychrometric chart serve as wet-bulb lines, and on Fig. 12.12 line (*b*) is the adiabatic-saturation line through the point representing the air ($t_G = 150°F.$, $Y = 0.01$). The line intersects the saturated-humidity curve at the wet-bulb conditions, $t_s = 84.5°F.$, $Y_s = 0.026$. At this temperature, $\lambda_s = 1,045$ B.t.u./lb.

Eq. (12.17):     $N_c = \dfrac{h_c(t_G - t_s)}{\lambda_s} = \dfrac{5.10(150 - 84.5)}{1,045} = 0.320 \text{ lb./(hr.)(sq. ft.)}$

and the evaporation rate is $0.320(4) = 1.280$ lb. water/hr.

When the air suffers a considerable change in temperature and humidity in its passage over the solid, as, for example, is indicated in Illustration 2, the rate of drying at the leading and trailing edge of the solid will differ and this accounts in part for the nonuniform drying frequently obtained in tray driers. This may be counteracted in part by periodic reversal of the air flow.

*Movement of Moisture within the Solid.* When surface evaporation occurs, there must be a movement of moisture from the depths of the solid to the surface. The nature of the movement influences the drying during the falling-rate periods. In order to appreciate the diverse nature of the falling-rate portions of the drying curve which have been observed, let us review very briefly some of the theories advanced to explain moisture movement and the relation of these to the falling-rate curves.

1. *Liquid diffusion.* Diffusion of liquid moisture may result because of concentration gradients between the depths of the solid, where the concentration is high, and the surface, where it is low. These gradients are set up during drying from the surface. This method of moisture transport is probably limited to cases where single-phase solid solutions are formed with the moisture, as in the case of soap, glue, gelatin, and the like; and to certain cases where bound moisture is being dried, as in the drying of the last portions of water from clays, flour, textiles, paper, and wood.[13] The general mechanism of this process is described in Chap. 4. It has been found that the moisture diffusivity usually decreases rapidly with decreased moisture content, so that diffusivities calculated in the manner of Illustration 5 (Chap. 4) are average values over the range of concentrations considered.

During the constant-rate period of drying such solids, the surface-moisture concentration is reduced, but the concentration in the depths of the solid remains high. The resulting high diffusivities permit movement of the moisture to the surface as fast as it can be evaporated, and the rate remains constant. When dry spots appear owing to the projection of portions of the solid into the gas film, a period of unsaturated surface evaporation results. The surface eventually dries to the equilibrium moisture content for the prevailing gas. Further drying occurs at rates which are entirely controlled by the diffusion rates within the solid, since these are slow at low moisture contents. If the initial constant-rate drying is very rapid, the period of unsaturated surface evaporation may not appear and the diffusion-controlled falling-rate period begins immediately after the constant-rate period is completed,[26] as in Fig. 12.13.

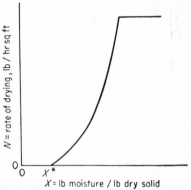

FIG. 12.13. Diffusion-controlled falling rate.[26]

For many cases of drying where the diffusion mechanism has satisfactorily explained the rate of drying as a function of average moisture content, the distribution of moisture within the solid at the various stages of drying has not conformed to this mechanism.[5,13] The superficial applicability of the diffusion mechanism is then apparently accidental.

2. *Capillary movement.*[5,6,13,23] Unbound moisture in granular and porous solids such as clays, sand, paint pigments, and the like, moves through the capillaries and interstices of the solids by a mechanism involving surface tension, in the manner that oil moves through a lamp wick. The capillaries extend from small reservoirs of moisture in the solid to the drying surface. As drying proceeds, at first moisture moves by capillarity to the surface sufficiently rapidly to maintain a uniformly wetted surface and the rate of drying is constant. The water is replaced by air entering the solid through relatively few openings and cracks. The surface moisture is eventually drawn to spaces between the granules of the surface, the wetted area at the surface decreases, and the unsaturated-surface drying period follows. The subsurface reservoirs eventually dry up, the liquid surface recedes into the capillaries, evaporation occurs below the surface in a zone or plane which gradually recedes deeper into the solid, and a second falling-rate period results. During this period, diffusion of vapor within the solid will occur from the place of vaporization to the surface.

In the case of certain pastes dried in pans, the adhesion of the wet cake to the bottom of the pan may not permit ventilation of the subsurface passageways by gas. This may give rise to curves of the sort shown in Fig. 12.14. In this case, the usual constant-rate period prevailed during ($a$). When the surface moisture was first depleted, liquid could not be brought to the surface by the tension in the capillaries since no air could enter to replace the liquid, the surface of moisture receded into the capillaries, and the rate fell during ($b$). The solid eventually crumpled, admitting air to replace the liquid, whereupon capillary action brought this to the surface and the rate rose again, as at ($c$).

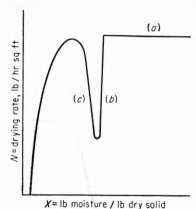

FIG. 12.14. Effect of adhesion of a drying paste to the pan. [*After R. C. Ernst et al., Ind. Eng. Chem.,* **30**, 1119 (1938).]

3. *Vapor diffusion.*[5,23] Especially if heat is supplied to one surface of a solid while drying proceeds from another, the moisture may evaporate beneath the surface and diffuse outward as a vapor. Moisture particles in granular solids, which have been isolated from the main portion of the moisture flowing through capillaries, may also be evaporated below the surface.

4. *Pressure.*[21] Owing to shrinkage of the outside layers of a solid on drying, moisture may be squeezed to the surface.

Usually we can only speculate as to which of the mechanisms is appropriate to a particular solid and must rely on more or less empirical treatment of the experimental rates of drying.

*Unsaturated-surface Drying.* During such a period the rate of drying $N$ will usually vary linearly with moisture content $X$. Since the mechanism of evaporation during this

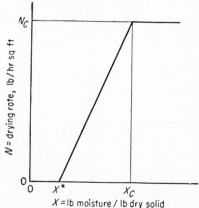

FIG. 12.15. Linear falling rate.

period is the same as that in the constant-rate period, the effects of such variables as temperature, humidity, and velocity of the gas and thickness of the solid are the same as for constant-rate drying.

In some cases this period may constitute the whole of the falling-rate drying, giving rise to a curve of the type shown in Fig. 12.15. Equations (12.8) and (12.9) then apply. Combining Eqs. (12.2), (12.8), and (12.17),

$$- \frac{dX}{d\theta} = \frac{k_Y A (X - X^*)(Y_s - Y)}{L_S(X_c - X^*)} \tag{12.22}$$

Noting that $L_S = z_s A \rho_S$, and letting $k_Y = f(G)$, then

$$- \frac{dX}{d\theta} = \frac{f(G)(X - X^*)(Y_s - Y)}{z_S \rho_S (X_c - X^*)} = \frac{\alpha f(G)(X - X^*)(Y_s - Y)}{z_s} \tag{12.23}$$

where $\alpha = $ a const. This expression is sometimes used as an empirical description of the rates of drying for such cases. Alternatively, defining

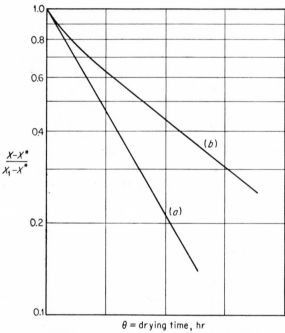

Fig. 12.16. Empirical treatment of falling-rate drying. (a) $N$ varies linearly with $X$, (b) diffusion-controlled falling rate.

the time $\theta$ as that when the moisture content is $X$, Eq. (12.9) is readily transformed into

$$\ln \frac{X - X^*}{X_1 - X^*} = \frac{-N_c \theta}{\rho_s z_s (X_c - X^*)} \tag{12.24}$$

which suggests that falling-rate data of this nature will plot as a straight line, line (a), on the semilogarithmic coordinates of Fig. 12.16. If drying tests are made under the same conditions for samples of different thickness, and so that heat is applied to the solid only through the drying surface, the slopes of such lines on this chart should be proportional to

$-1/z_S$.  The drying time between fixed moisture contents is then directly proportional to the solid thickness.

*Internal-diffusion Controlling.*  If a period of drying is developed where internal diffusion of moisture controls the rate, it can be expected that variables which influence the gas-film coefficients of heat or mass transfer will not influence the rate of drying.  The drying rates should be independent of gas velocity, and humidity will be of importance only in so far as it controls the equilibrium-moisture concentration.  When a semi-logarithmic plot (Fig. 12.16) is prepared from drying data of this type, the curve (*b*) which results resembles those of Fig. 4.3.  For a slab, the curves should be substantially straight at values of the ordinate below 0.6, with slopes proportional to $-1/z_2^S$. The drying time between fixed moisture contents should be proportional to the square of the thickness.  Discrepancies may result because the initial moisture distribution is not uniform throughout the solid if a drying period precedes that for which diffusion controls, and because the diffusivity varies with moisture content.

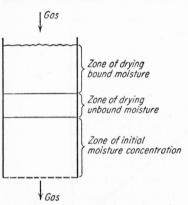

FIG. 12.17.  Through-circulation drying of thick beds of solids.

Attempts have been made to describe rates of drying in the falling-rate period by means of over-all coefficients of heat and mass transfer,[20] but these have not been too successful owing to the change in the individual resistances to transfer in the solid during the course of the drying.

*Critical Moisture Content.*  The available data indicate that the average critical moisture content for a given type of solid depends upon the surface-moisture concentration.  If drying during the constant-rate period is very rapid, and if the solid is thick, then steep concentration gradients are developed within the solid and the falling rate begins at high average moisture contents.  Generally, the critical moisture content will increase with increased drying rate and thickness of solid.  It must usually be measured experimentally.

**Through-circulation Drying.**  When a gas passes through a bed of wet, granular solids, both a constant-rate and a falling-rate period of drying may result and the rate-of-drying curves may appear very much like that shown in Fig. 12.10.[17]  Consider the case where the bed of solids has an appreciable thickness with respect to the size of the particles, as in Fig. 12.17.[1]  The evaporation of unbound moisture into the gas occurs in a relatively narrow zone which moves slowly through the bed, and unless the bed is internally heated, the gas leaving this zone is for all practical purposes saturated at the adiabatic-saturation temperature of the entering gas. This is also the surface temperature of the wet particles. The rate of drying is constant as long as the zone is entirely within the bed. When the zone first reaches the end of the bed, the rate of drying begins to fall because the gas no longer leaves in a saturated condition. In other words, a *desorption* wave passes through the bed and the situation is much like that described for adsorption in fixed beds (Chap. 11). However, the point of view of interest is the moisture content of the solid rather than the concentration changes occurring in the exit gas. In the case of shallow beds composed of large particles, the gas leaves the bed unsaturated from the beginning,[17] but as long as each particle surface remains fully wet, there will still be a constant-rate period. The falling rate then begins when the surface moisture is depleted.

*The Rate of Drying of Unbound Moisture.*[1] Consider a bed of uniform cross section, as in Fig. 12.17, fed with a gas of humidity $Y_1$ at the rate of $G_S$ lb. dry gas/(hr.)(sq. ft. bed cross section). The maximum rate of drying $N_{max}$ will occur if the gas leaving the bed is saturated at the adiabatic-saturation temperature, with humidity $Y_{as}$,

$$N_{max} = G_S(Y_{as} - Y_1) \qquad (12.25)$$

where $N$ is expressed as lb. moisture evaporated/(hr.)(sq. ft. bed cross section). In general, the gas will leave the bed at humidity $Y_2$, and the instantaneous rate of drying is

$$N = G_S(Y_2 - Y_1) \qquad (12.26)$$

For a differential section of the bed where the gas undergoes a change in humidity $dY$ and leaves at a humidity $Y$, the rate of drying is

$$dN = G_S \, dY = k_Y \, dS \, (Y_{as} - Y) \qquad (12.27)$$

where $S$ is the interfacial surface per square foot of bed cross section. Letting $a$ represent the interfacial surface per unit volume of bed whose thickness is $z_S$,

$$dS = a \, dz_S \qquad (12.28)$$

and Eq. (12.27) becomes

$$\int_{Y_1}^{Y_2} \frac{dY}{Y_{as} - Y} = \int_0^{z_S} \frac{k_Y a \, dz_S}{G_S} \qquad (12.29)$$

$$\ln \frac{Y_{as} - Y_1}{Y_{as} - Y_2} = N_{tG} = \frac{k_Y a z_S}{G_S} \qquad (12.30)$$

where $N_{tG}$ is the number of gas transfer units in the bed. This equation is the same as Eq. (7.71), developed for a somewhat similar situation. The mean driving force for evaporation is then the logarithmic mean of

$Y_{as} - Y_1$ and $Y_{as} - Y_2$, in accordance with Eq. (7.72). Combining Eqs. (12.25), (12.26), and (12.30),

$$\frac{N}{N_{max}} = \frac{Y_2 - Y_1}{Y_{as} - Y_1} = 1 - \frac{Y_{as} - Y_2}{Y_{as} - Y_1} = 1 - e^{-N_{tG}} = 1 - e^{-k_Y a z_S / G_S} \quad (12.31)$$

Equation (12.31) provides the rate of drying $N$ if values of $k_Y a$ or $N_{tG}$ can be determined. These have been established for certain special cases as follows:

1. *Particles small* (10 *to* 200 *mesh, or* 0.08 *to* 0.0029 *in. diameter) with respect to bed depth (greater than* 0.45 *in.); drying of unbound water from the surface of nonporous particles.*[1] For this case,† the constant rate is given by $N_{max}$ [Eq. (12.25)]. Equation (12.31) may be used for both constant and falling rates, since at high moisture contents the exponential term becomes negligible. The interfacial surface $a$ varies with moisture content, and it is most convenient to express $N_{tG}$ empirically as

$$N_{tG} = \frac{1.14}{d_p^{0.35}} \left(\frac{d_p G}{\mu}\right)^{0.215} (X \rho_S z_S)^{0.64} \quad (12.32)$$

where $d_p$ is the particle diameter, feet, and $\rho_S$ the apparent density of the bed, lb. dry solid/cu. ft. Through-drying of such beds in the ordinary equipment may involve a pressure drop for gas flow which is too high for practical purposes, especially if the particles are very small. Drying of such beds is done on continuous rotary filters (crystal-filter driers), however.

2. *Particles large* (⅛ *to* ¾ *in. diameter) in shallow beds* (0.4 *to* 2.5 *in. thick); drying of unbound moisture from porous or nonporous particles.* During the constant-rate period the gas leaves the bed unsaturated, and the constant rate of drying is given by Eq. (12.31). For this purpose, $k_Y$ is given by

$$k_Y = j_D G_S / Sc^{\frac{2}{3}} \quad (12.33)$$

and $j_D$ in turn by curve 7 (Fig. 3.11[9,34]). The interfacial surface may be taken as the surface of the particles. For air drying of water from solids, $Sc = 0.6$. Additional experimental data on a large number of preformed materials are also available.[15,17] During the falling-rate period, internal resistance to moisture movement may be important, and no general treatment is available. In many cases[17] it is found that semilogarithmic plots of the form of Fig. 12.16 are useful. If the line on this plot is straight, Eqs. (12.8) and (12.9) are applicable.

† In beds of finely packed solids containing a large percentage of liquid, the liquid is largely forced from between the solid particles by a mechanical process when gas is forced through the bed. See particularly Brownell and Katz, *Chem. Eng. Progr.*, **43,** 537, 601, 703 (1947). Only the last traces of moisture are removed by the drying process considered here.

*Drying of Bound Moisture.* Presumably some adaptation of the methods used for adsorption in fixed beds (Chap. 11) could be made to describe this. No experimental confirmation is available, however.

**Illustration 5.** A cake of a crystalline precipitate is to be dried by drawing air through the cake. The particles of the cake are nonporous, of average diameter 0.008 in., and since they are insoluble in water have negligible equilibrium moisture content. The cake is 0.7 in. thick, and the apparent density is 85 lb. dry solid/cu. ft. It is to be dried from 2.5 to 0.1% moisture. The air will enter the cake at the rate of 175 lb. dry air/(hr.)(sq. ft. bed cross section), at a dry-bulb temperature of 90°F., and 50% humidity. Determine the time for drying.

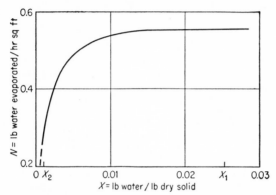

Fig. 12.18. Solution to Illustration 5.

*Solution.* $X_1 = 0.025/(1 - 0.025) = 0.0256$ lb. water/lb. dry solid; $X_2 = 0.001/(1 - 0.001) = 0.001001$ lb. water/lb. dry solid. From Fig. 7.6, $Y_1 = 0.0158$ lb. water/lb. dry air; $t_{as} = 75°F.$ (the adiabatic-saturation temperature) and $Y_{as} = 0.0190$ lb. water/lb. dry air. $G_S = 175$ lb. dry air/(hr.)(sq. ft.)

Approx. av. $G = 175 + 175(0.0158 + 0.0190)/2 = 178$ lb./(hr.)(sq. ft.)
Eq. (12.26): $N_{max} = 175(0.0190 - 0.0158) = 0.56$ lb. evapd./(hr.)(sq. ft.)
$z_S = 0.7/12 = 0.0583$ ft. $d_p = 0.008/12 = 0.000665$ ft. $\rho_S = 85$ lb. dry solid/cu. ft.

Viscosity of air at $(75 + 90)/2 = 82.5°F.$ is 0.018 centipoise, and $\mu = 0.018(2.42) = 0.0286$ lb./ft. hr.
$$d_p G/\mu = 0.000665(178)/0.0286 = 4.14$$
Eq. (12.32): $N_{tG} = \dfrac{1.14(4.14)^{0.215}[X(85)(0.0583)]^{0.64}}{0.000665^{0.35}} = 59.1X^{0.64}$
Eq. (12.31): $N = 0.56(1 - e^{-59.1X^{0.64}})$

The following table gives values of the rate $N$, lb. evaporated/(hr.)(sq. ft.), for various values of $X$, lb. water/lb. dry solid, in accordance with this expression.

| $X$..... | 0.0256 | 0.02 | 0.015 | 0.010 | 0.008 | 0.006 | 0.004 | 0.002 | 0.001 |
|---|---|---|---|---|---|---|---|---|---|
| $N$..... | 0.558 | 0.557 | 0.550 | 0.535 | 0.525 | 0.500 | 0.460 | 0.375 | 0.279 |

These provide the rate-of-drying curve of Fig. 12.18. The time of drying is determined by finding the area under a curve of $1/N$ plotted against $X$, in accordance with

Eq. (12.3). The area under this curve (not shown) is 0.0473. Since $L_S/A = \rho_S z_S = 85(0.0583) = 4.95$ lb. dry solid/sq. ft., the time for drying is, by Eq. (12.3),

$$\theta = 4.95(0.0473) = 0.234 \text{ hr., or } 14 \text{ min.}$$

**Illustration 6.** Wet, porous catalyst pellets in the form of small cylinders, 0.53 in. in diameter and 0.506 in. in height, are to be dried of their water content in a through-circulation drier. The pellets are to be arranged in beds 2 in. deep on screens and are to be dried by air flowing at the rate of 800 lb. dry air/(hr.)(sq. ft. bed cross section), entering at 180°F. dry-bulb temperature, humidity 0.01 lb. water/lb. dry air. The apparent density of the bed is 37.9 lb. dry solid/cu. ft. and the particle surface 86 sq. ft./cu. ft. of bed. Estimate the rate of drying, and the humidity and temperature of the air leaving the bed, during the constant-rate period.

*Solution.* $Y_1 = 0.01$ lb. water/lb. dry air, and, from Fig. 7.6, $Y_{as} = 0.031$ lb. water/lb. dry air at the corresponding adiabatic-saturation temperature (90°F.). $G_S = 800$ lb. dry air/(hr.)(sq. ft.), and the approximate average $G = 800(1.016) = 815$ lb./(hr.)(sq. ft.). The approximate average air viscosity is 0.019 centipoise, or $\mu = 0.019 \, (2.42) = 0.046$ lb./(ft.)(hr.).

The surface of each particle $= [\pi(0.53)^2(2)/4 + \pi(0.53)(0.506)]/144 = 0.0089$ sq. ft. The diameter of a sphere of equal area $= d_p = \sqrt{0.0089/\pi} = 0.0533$ ft. $a = 86$ sq. ft./cu. ft. $z_S = \frac{2}{12} = 0.1667$ ft.

The Reynolds number for the particles (Re″ on Fig. 3.11) $= d_p G/\mu = 0.0533(815)/0.041 = 945$. From curve 7 (Fig. 3.11), $j_D = 0.06$. Sc for air–water vapor $= 0.6$.

Eq. (12.33): $\quad k_Y = 0.06(800)/(0.6)^{2/3} = 67.6$ lb. water/(hr.)(sq. ft.)$(\Delta Y)$
$$N_{tG} = k_Y a z_S/G_S = 67.6(86)(0.1667)/800 = 1.21$$
Eq. (12.25): $\quad N_{max} = G_S(Y_{as} - Y_1) = 800(0.031 - 0.01) = 16.8$ lb./(hr.)(sq. ft.)

Eq. (12.31): $\quad \dfrac{N}{16.8} = \dfrac{Y_2 - 0.01}{0.031 - 0.01} = 1 - e^{-1.21}$

Therefore $N = 11.8$ lb. water evapd./(hr.)(sq. ft.) in the constant-rate period, and $Y_2 = 0.0162$ lb. water/lb. dry air for the exit air. The corresponding exit-air temperature, from the adiabatic-saturation curve for the initial air (Fig. 7.6), is 152°F. Since $L_S/A = \rho_S z_S = 37.9(0.1667) = 6.31$ lb. dry solid/sq. ft.,

Eq. (12.2):
$$-dX/d\theta = N(A/L_S) = 11.8/6.31$$
$$= 1.87 \text{ lb. water evapd./lb. dry solid during constant-rate period}$$

These must be considered as estimates only, subject to check by drying-rate tests.

## II. CONTINUOUS DRYING

Continuous drying offers the advantages that usually the equipment necessary is small relative to the quantity of product, the operation is readily integrated with continuous chemical manufacture without intermediate storage, the product has a more uniform moisture content, and the cost of drying per unit of product is relatively small. As in the case of batch drying, the nature of the equipment used is greatly dependent upon the type of material to be dried. Either direct or indirect heating, and sometimes both, may be used.

In many of the direct driers to be described, the solid is moved through a drier while in contact with a moving gas stream. The gas and solid may flow in parallel or in countercurrent, or the gas may flow across the path of the solid. If heat is neither supplied within the drier nor lost to the surroundings, operation is adiabatic and the gas will lose sensible heat and cool down as the evaporated moisture absorbs latent heat of vaporization. By supplying heat within the drier, the gas may be maintained at constant temperature.

In *countercurrent* adiabatic operation, the hottest gas is in contact with the dryest solid, and the discharged solid is therefore heated to a temperature which may approach that of the entering gas. This provides the most rapid drying, since especially in the case of bound moisture the last traces are the most difficult to remove, and this is done more rapidly at high temperatures. On the other hand, the dry solid may be damaged by being heated to high temperatures in this manner. In addition, the hot discharged solid will carry away considerable sensible heat, thus lowering the thermal efficiency of the drying operation.

In *parallel* adiabatic operation, the wet solid is contacted with the hottest gas. As long as unbound surface moisture is present, the solid will be heated only to the wet-bulb temperature of the gas, and for this reason even heat-sensitive solids may frequently be dried by fairly hot gas in parallel flow. For example, a typical flue gas resulting from combustion of a fuel, which may have a humidity of 0.03 lb. water vapor/lb. dry gas at 800°F., has a wet-bulb temperature of only about 150°F. In any event, the wet-bulb temperature can never exceed the boiling point of the liquid at the prevailing pressure. At the outlet of the drier, the gas will have been considerably cooled, and no damage will result to the dry solid. Parallel flow also permits greater control of the moisture content of the discharged solid, in cases where the solid must not be completely dried, through control of the quantity of gas passing through the drier and consequently its exit temperature and humidity.

**Tunnel Driers.** These direct driers are essentially adaptations of the truck drier to continuous operation. They consist of relatively long tunnels through which trucks, loaded with trays filled with the drying solid, are moved in contact with a current of gas to evaporate the moisture. The trucks may be pulled continuously through the drier by a moving chain, to which they are attached. In a simpler arrangement, the loaded trucks are introduced periodically at one end of the drier, each displacing a truck at the other end. The time of residence in the drier must be sufficiently great to reduce the moisture content of the solid to the desired value. For relatively low-temperature operation the gas is usually steam-heated air, while for higher temperatures, and especially for products which need not be kept scrupulously clean, flue gas from the combustion of a fuel may be used. Parallel or countercurrent flow of gas and solid may be used, or in some cases fans placed along the sides of the tunnel blow the gas through the trucks in crossflow. Operation may be essentially adiabatic, or the gas may be heated by steam coils along its path through the drier, and operation may then be substantially at constant temperature. Part of the gas may be recycled, much as in the case of batch driers, for heat economy. Truck-type tunnel driers may be used for any material which may be dried on trays: crystals, filter cakes, pastes, pottery, and the like.

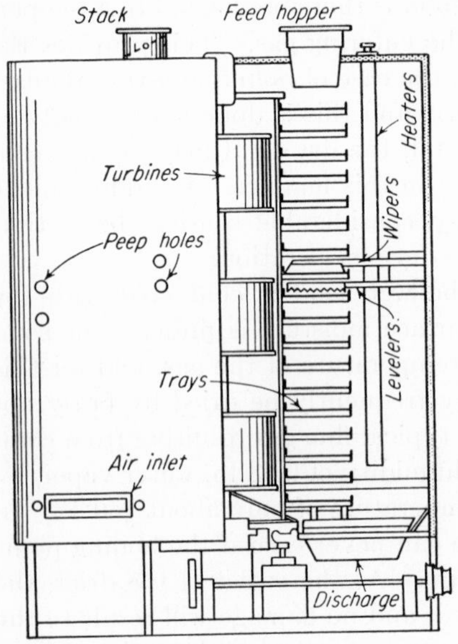

FIG. 12.19. Turbo-type drier. (*Courtesy of Wyssmont Co., Inc.*)

There are many modifications of the tunnel drier which are essentially the same in principle but different in detailed design owing to the nature of the material being dried. For example, skeins of wet yarn may be suspended from poles or racks which move through the tunnel drier. Hides may be stretched on frames which hang from conveyor chains passing through the drier. Material in continuous sheets, such as cloth, may move through the drier under tension, as in a continuous belt over a series of rollers, or may be hung in festoons from moving racks if it is to be dried in the absence of tension.

**Turbo-type Driers.** Solids which ordinarily may be dried on trays, such as powdery and granular materials, heavy sludges and pastes, beads and crystalline solids, may be continuously dried in a turbo-type drier, a form of direct drier.[2] The simplest of these is shown in Fig. 12.19. The drier is fitted with a series of annular trays arranged in a vertical stack. These rotate slowly (from a fraction to 1 r.p.m.) about a vertical shaft. Each tray is provided with a slot cut into the tray, as well as a leveling rake for spreading the solid. Solid fed in at the top is spread upon the top tray to a uniform thickness, and as the tray revolves, the solid is pushed through the slot by a separate wiper rake, to fall upon the tray beneath. In this way, with overturning and respreading on each tray, the solid progresses to the discharge chute at the bottom of the drier. The drying gas flows upward through the drier, is circulated over the trays by slowly revolving turbine fans, and is reheated by internal heating pipes as shown. The rate of drying will be faster than that experienced in a tray-equipped tunnel drier, owing to the frequent reloading of the solid on each tray. Alternative arrangements are possible: external heating of the gas, recirculation of the gas, and arrangements for recovery of evaporated solvents may be provided. In some installations the solid is carried upon a moving, endless conveyor, which is wound about the vertical axis of the drier in a close-pitched, screw-type spiral. These driers are regularly built in sizes ranging from 6 to 20 ft. in diameter and 6 to 25 ft. high. A few installations as tall as 60 ft. have been made.

**Through-circulation Driers.** Granular solids may be arranged in thin beds for through circulation of the gas, and, if necessary, pastes and filter

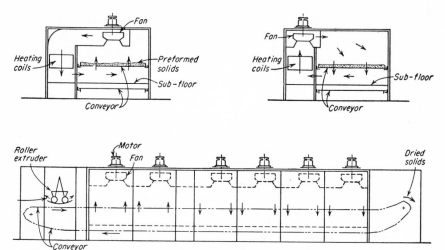

Fig. 12.20. Continuous through-circulation (single-conveyor) drier with roller extruder. (*Courtesy of Proctor and Schwartz, Inc.*)

cakes may be preformed into granules, pellets, or noodles as described in the case of batch driers. In the continuous, through-circulation drier of Fig. 12.20,[14] the solid is spread to a depth of 1.5 to 2 in. upon a moving endless conveyor which passes through the drier. The conveyor is made of perforated plates or woven wire screens in hinged sections in order to avoid failure from repeated flexing of the screen. Fans blow the heated air through the solid, usually upward through the wet solid, and downward after initial drying has occurred. In this way, a more uniform moisture concentration throughout the bed is attained. Much of the gas is usually recycled, and a portion is discarded continuously at each fan position in the drier. For materials which permit the flow of gas through the bed in the manner shown, drying is much more rapid than for tray-type tunnel driers.

**Rotary Driers.** This is a most important group of driers, suitable for handling free-flowing granular materials which may be tumbled about without concern over breakage. Figure 12.21 shows one form of such a drier, a direct countercurrent hot-air drier. The solid to be dried is continuously introduced into one end of a rotating cylinder, as shown, while heated air flows into the other. The cylinder is installed at a small angle to the horizontal, and the solid consequently moves slowly through the device. Inside the drier, lifting flights extending from the cylinder wall for the full length of the drier lift the solid and shower it down in a moving curtain through the air, thus exposing it thoroughly to the drying action

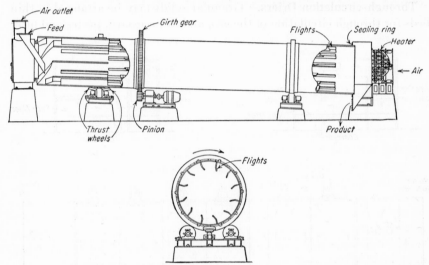

Fig. 12.21. Ruggles-Coles XW hot-air drier, manufactured by Hardinge Co., Inc.

of the gas. This lifting action also assists in the forward motion of the solid. At the feed end of the drier, a few short spiral flights assist in imparting the initial forward motion to the solid before the principal flights are reached. The solid must clearly be one which is neither sticky nor gummy, which might stick to the sides of the drier or tend to "ball" up. In such cases, recycling of a portion of the dried product may nevertheless permit use of a rotary drier.

The drier may be fed with hot flue gas rather than air, and if the gas leaves the drier at a sufficiently high temperature, discharging it through a stack may provide adequate natural draft to provide sufficient gas for drying. Ordinarily, however, an exhaust fan is used to pull the gas through the drier, since this provides more complete control of the gas flow. A dust collector, of the cyclone, filter, or washing type, may be interposed between the fan and the gas exit. A blower may also be provided at the gas entrance, thus maintaining a pressure close to atmospheric in the drier; this prevents leakage of cool air in at the end housings of the drier, and if the pressure is well balanced, outward leakage will also be minimized.

Rotary driers are made for a variety of operations. The following classification includes the major types.[12,29]

1. *Direct heat, countercurrent flow.* For materials which may be heated to high temperatures, such as minerals, sand, limestone, clays, etc., hot flue gas may be used as the drying gas. For substances which should not be heated excessively, such as certain crystalline chemical products like ammonium sulfate and cane sugar, heated air may be used. The general arrangement is that shown in Fig. 12.21, and if flue gas is used, the heating coils are replaced by a furnace burning gas, oil, or coal.

2. *Direct heat, parallel flow.* Solids which may be dried with flue gas without fear of contamination, but which must not be heated to high temperatures for fear of damage, such as gypsum, iron pyrites, and organic materials such as peat and alfalfa, should be dried in a parallel-flow drier. The general construction is much like that of Fig. 12.21, except that the gas and solid both enter at the same end of the drier.

3. *Indirect heat, countercurrent flow.* For solids such as white pigments, and the like, which may be heated to high temperatures but which must remain out of contact with flue gas, the indirect drier indicated schematically in Fig. 12.22a may be used. As an alternative construction, the drier may be enclosed in a brick structure and completely surrounded by the hot flue gases. The air flow in such a drier may be kept to a minimum since the heat is supplied by conduction through the shell or central tube, and finely pulverized solids which dust severely may then be handled. For solids which must not be heated to high temperatures and for which indirect heat is desirable, such as cattle feed, brewers' grains, feathers, and the like, the steam-tube drier, shown in Fig. 12.22b, may be used. This drier may or may not have lifting flights and may be built with one, two, or more concentric rows of steam-heated tubes. The tubes revolve with the drier, necessitating a special rotary joint where the steam is introduced and the condensate removed. This type of drier is frequently used when recovery of the evaporated liquid is necessary.

4. *Direct-indirect.* These driers, more economical to operate than the direct driers, may be used for solids which may be dried at high temperatures by flue gas, especially when fuel costs are high and when large percentages of moisture must be removed from the solid. A typical schematic arrangement is shown in Fig. 12.22c. In such a drier, the hot gas may enter the center tube at 1200 to 1800°F., cool to 400 to 900°F. in its first passage through the drier, and on returning through the annular drying space cool further to 140 to 170°F. at discharge. Lignite, coal,

and coke may be dried in the inert atmosphere of such a drier at relatively high temperatures without danger of burning or dust explosion.

All these driers are available from various manufacturers in standard sizes, ranging from approximately 3 ft. in diameter by 12 ft. long to 10 ft. in diameter by 100 ft. long.

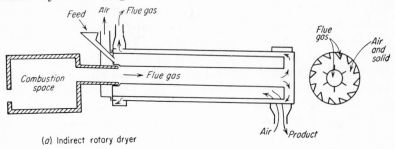

(a) Indirect rotary dryer

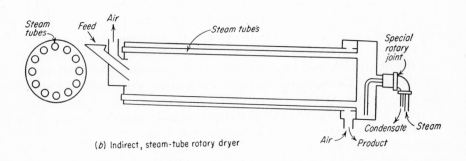

(b) Indirect, steam-tube rotary dryer

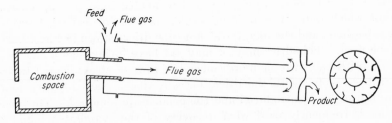

(c) Indirect-direct rotary dryer

Fig. 12.22. Some rotary driers (schematic).

**Hold-up in Rotary Driers.** The average time of passage, or retention time, of the solid in a drier must equal the required drying time if the solid is to emerge at the desired moisture content. Several agencies bring about the movement of the solid particles through a rotary drier. Flight action is the lifting and dropping of particles by the flights on the drier shell: in the absence of air flow, each time the solid is lifted and dropped, it advances a distance equal to the product of the length of the drop and the slope of the drier. Kiln action is the forward rolling of the particles on top of each other in the bottom of the drier, as in a kiln without flights. The particles also bounce in a forward direction after being dropped from the flight. In addition, the forward motion of the solid is hindered by a counterflowing gas or assisted by parallel flow.

The hold-up $v$ of solid is defined as the fraction of the drier volume occupied by the solid at any instant, and the average time of retention $\theta$ may be computed by dividing the hold-up by the volumetric feed rate,

$$\theta = \frac{vZ\pi d^2/4}{(L_S/\rho_S)(\pi d^2/4)} = \frac{Zv\rho_S}{L_S} \qquad (12.34)$$

where $L_S/\rho_S$ is the volumetric feed rate, cu. ft./(hr.)(sq. ft. drier cross section), $L_S$ the rate of flow of dry solids, lb./(hr.)(sq. ft.), $\rho_S$ the apparent solid density, lb. dry solid/cu. ft., and $Z$ the length of the drier, feet. Friedman and Marshall[8] found that the hold-up of a large number of solids under a variety of typical operating conditions could be expressed simply as

$$v = v_0 \pm KG \qquad (12.35)$$

where $v_0$ is the hold-up with no gas flow and $\pm KG$ corrects for the influence of the gas rate, $G$ lb./(hr.)(sq. ft.). The $+$ sign is used for countercurrent flow of gas and solid, the $-$ sign for parallel flow. Hold-up for conditions of no gas flow depends to some extent upon flight design and the nature of the solid, but, under typical conditions and for $v_0$ not exceeding 0.08, their data may be described by

$$v_0 = \frac{0.0037L_S}{\rho_S s n^{0.9} d} \qquad (12.36)$$

where $s$ is the slope of the drier, ft./ft., $n$ the rotational speed, r.p.m., and $d$ the drier diameter, feet. The constant $K$ is dependent upon the properties of the solid, and for rough estimates it may be taken as

$$K = \frac{0.0000933}{\rho_S d_p^{1/2}} \qquad (12.37)$$

where $d_p$ is the average particle diameter, feet. Hold-ups in the range 0.03 to 0.07 appear to be best. Higher hold-up results in increased kiln action, with consequent poor exposure of the solid to the gas, and an increase in power required for operating the dryer.

These empirical relationships are applicable only under conditions of reasonable gas rates which do not cause excessive dusting or blowing of the solid particles from the drier. It is ordinarily desirable to keep dust down to 2 to 5 per cent of the feed material as a maximum, and the corresponding permissible gas rates depend greatly upon the nature of the solid. From 200 to 10,000 lb. gas/(hr.)(sq. ft.) is used, depending upon the solid; for most 35-mesh solids ($d_p$ approximately 0.00137 ft.), 1,000 lb./(hr.)(sq. ft.) is amply safe.[8,15] Dusting is less severe for countercurrent than for parallel flow, since then the damp feed acts to some extent as a dust collector, and it is also influenced by design of feed chutes and end breechings.[8] In any case, it is best to depend upon actual tests for final design and to use the equations for initial estimate only.

Driers are most readily built with length/diameter ratios $Z/d = 4{:}10$. For most purposes, the flights extend from the wall of the drier a distance of 8 to 12 per cent of the diameter, and their number range from $2d$ to $3d$. They should be able to lift the entire solids hold-up, thus minimizing kiln action which leads to low retention time. Rates of rotation are such as to provide peripheral speeds of 40 to 100 ft./min., and the slopes are usually in the range 0 to 0.08 ft./ft.[8] Negative slopes are sometimes necessary in the case of parallel-flow driers.

**Through-circulation Rotary Driers.** Driers of the type indicated in Fig. 12.23 combine the features of the through-circulation and rotary driers. The direct drier shown, the Roto-Louvre,[7] consists of a slowly revolving tapered drum fitted with louvers to support the drying solid and to permit entrance of the hot gas beneath the solid. The hot gas is admitted only to those louvers which are underneath the bed of solid. There is substantially no showering of the solid through the gas stream,

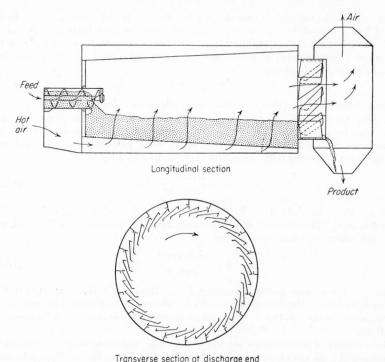

Longitudinal section

Transverse section at discharge end

FIG. 12.23. Continuous through-circulation rotary drier (Roto-Louvre). (*Courtesy of Link-Belt Co.*)

and consequently a minimum of dusting results. The device is satisfactory for both low- and high-temperature drying of the same materials ordinarily treated in a rotary drier.

**Drum Driers.** Fluid and semifluid materials such as solutions, slurries, pastes, and sludges may be dried on an indirect drier, of which Fig. 12.24, a dip-feed drum drier, gives an example. A slowly revolving internally steam-heated metal drum continuously dips into a trough containing the substance to be dried, and a thin film of the substance is retained on the drum surface. The thickness of the film is regulated by a spreader knife, as shown, and as the drum revolves, moisture is evaporated into the surrounding air by heat transferred through the metal of the drum. The dried material is then continuously scraped from the drum surface by a knife.   For such a drier, heat transfer rather than diffusion is the controlling factor.   The liquid or solution is first heated to its boiling point; moisture is then evolved by boiling, at constant temperature if a solute precipitates from a solution at constant concentration, or at increasing temperatures if the concentration change is gradual; and finally the dried solid is heated to approach the temperature of the drum surface.   In the case of slurries or pastes of insoluble solids, the temperature remains

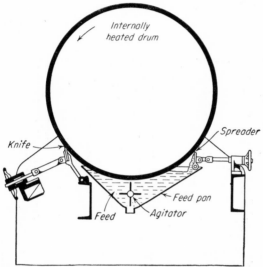

FIG. 12.24.  Dip-feed single-drum drier.   (*Courtesy of Blaw-Knox Co.*)

essentially constant at the solvent boiling point as long as the solid is completely wet and increases only during the last stages of drying.   The vapors are frequently collected by a ventilated hood built directly over the drier.

The ability of various slurries, solutions, and pastes to adhere to a heated drum varies considerably, and diverse methods of feeding the drum are resorted to accordingly.   Slurries of solids dispersed in liquids are frequently fed to the bottom of the drum on an inclined pan, and the excess nonadherent material is recycled to the feed reservoir.   Vegetable glues, and the like, may be pumped against the bottom surface of the drum.   The dip-feed arrangement shown in Fig. 12.24 is useful for heavy sludges, while, for materials which stick to the drum only with difficulty, the feed may be spattered on by a rapidly revolving roll.   Double drum driers, consisting of two drums placed close together and revolving in opposite directions, may be fed from above by admitting the feed into the depression between the drums.   The entire drum drier may, on occasion, be placed inside a large evacuated chamber for low-temperature evaporation of the moisture.

*Cylinder driers* are drum driers used for material in continuous sheet form, such as paper and cloth. The wet solid is fed continuously over the revolving drum, or a series of such drums, each internally heated by steam or other heating fluid.

**Spray Driers.** Solutions, slurries, and pastes may be dried by spraying them as fine droplets into a stream of hot gas in a spray drier.[16,30] One such device is shown in Fig. 12.25. The liquid to be dried is atomized

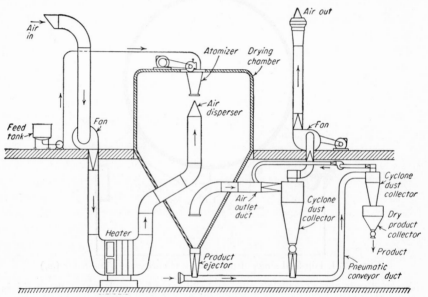

FIG. 12.25. Spray drier. (*Courtesy of Nichols Engineering and Research Corp.*)

and introduced into the large drying chamber, where the droplets are dispersed into a stream of heated air. The particles of liquid evaporate rapidly and dry before they can be carried to the sides of the chamber, and the bulk of the dried powder which results falls to the conical bottom of the chamber to be removed by a stream of air to the dust collector. The principal portion of the exit gas is also led to a dust collector, as shown, before being discharged. Installations may be very large, as much as 40 ft. in diameter and 100 ft. high. Arrangements and detailed designs vary considerably, depending upon the manufacturer. Spray driers are used for a wide variety of products, including such diverse materials as organic and inorganic chemicals, pharmaceuticals, food products such as milk, eggs, and soluble coffee, as well as soap and detergent products.

In order to obtain rapid drying, atomization of the feed must provide small particles of high surface/weight ratio, whose diameter is usually in the range 10 to 60 microns. For this purpose, spray nozzles or rapidly rotating disks may be used. Spray nozzles are of two major types, pressure nozzles in which the liquid is pumped at high pressure and with a rapid circular motion through a small orifice, and two-fluid nozzles in which a gas such as air or steam at relatively low pressures is used to tear the liquid into droplets. Nozzles are relatively inflexible in their operating characteristics and do not permit even moderate variation in liquid-flow rates without large changes in droplet size. They are also subject to rapid erosion and wear. Rotating disks are therefore favored in the chemical industry. These may be plane, vaned, or cup-shaped, up to 12 to 14 in. in diameter, and may rotate at speeds in the range 3,000 to 12,000 r.p.m. The liquid or slurry is fed onto the disk near the center and is centrifugally accelerated to the periphery, from which it is thrown in an umbrella-shaped spray. Appreciable variation in liquid properties and feed rates may be satisfactorily handled, and even thick slurries or pastes may be atomized without clogging the device provided they can be pumped to the disk.

The drying gas, either flue gas or air, may enter at the highest practical temperature, 175 to 1400°F., limited only by the heat sensitivity of the product. Since the contact time for product and gas is so short, relatively high temperatures are feasible. The short time of drying requires effective gas-spray mixing, and attempts to improve upon this account in part for the large number of designs of spray chambers. Cool air is sometimes admitted at the drying-chamber walls, in order to prevent sticking of the product to the sides. The effluent gas may convey all the dried product out of the drier, or else only the fines, but in either case the gas must be passed through some type of dust collector such as cyclones or bag filters, and these are sometimes followed by wet scrubbers for the last traces of dust. Recirculation of hot gas to the drier for purposes of heat economy is not practical, since the dust-recovery operation cannot usually be accomplished without appreciable heat loss.

The drops of liquid reach their terminal velocity in the gas stream quickly, within inches of the atomizing device. Evaporation takes place from the surface of the drops, and in the case of many products solid material may accumulate as an impervious shell at the surface. Since heat is nevertheless rapidly being transmitted to the particles from the hot gas, the entrapped liquid portion of the drop vaporizes and expands the still plastic wall of the drop to 3 to 10 times the original size, eventually exploding a small blowhole in the wall and escaping, to leave a hollow, dried shell of solid as the product. In other cases, the central liquid core diffuses through the shell to the outside, and the reduced internal pressure causes an implosion. In any event, the dried product is frequently in the form of small hollow beads of low bulk density. Some control over the bulk density is usually possible through control of the particle size during atomization or through the temperature of the drying gas (increased gas temperature causes decreased product bulk density by more extensive expansion of the drop contents). For high-density products, the dried beads may be crushed.

Spray drying offers the advantage of extremely rapid drying for heat-sensitive products, a product particle size and density which are controllable within limits, and relatively low operating costs, especially in the case of large-capacity driers. It is rapidly becoming more popular. Although a beginning has been made in the rational design of such driers,[18]

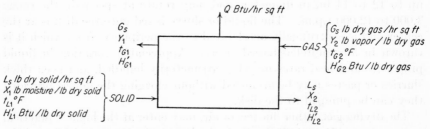

Fig. 12.26. Material and enthalpy balances, continuous driers.

incomplete knowledge concerning drop size, drop trajectories, relative velocity of gas and drop, and rates of drying make it necessary to rely largely on experimental tests for spray-drying designs.

**Miscellaneous Types.** Pulverized and granular solids may be dried by suspending and conveying them in a stream of hot gas through a large pipe to a cyclone-type dust collector, in a system known as *Flash-Drying*.[11] Finely divided solids may be dried as they are moved through a screw conveyor, heated by condensing steam or other medium in a jacket surrounding the conveyor. In such a drier, air need not necessarily be used, and the evaporated moisture may be led directly to a condenser for recovery. Solids which may not be heated to even moderate temperatures may be dried by *freeze drying*. The solid and its moisture are frozen, pelleted if possible, and introduced into a vacuum chamber. The moisture is then sublimed away from the solid, and the necessary heat may be provided by carefully controlled exposure to infrared radiation or by other convenient indirect heating devices, depending upon the nature of the solid. Certain delicate foodstuffs, and pharmaceutical products such as penicillin and blood plasma, are dried in this manner.

**Material and Enthalpy Balances.** A general flow diagram for a continuous drier, arranged for countercurrent flow, is shown in Fig. 12.26. Solid enters at the rate of $L_S$ lb. dry solid/(hr.)(sq. ft.),† is dried from

---

† For purposes of material and enthalpy balances, rates of flow of gas and solid may equally well be expressed as lb./hr.

$X_1$ to $X_2$ lb. moisture/lb. dry solid, and undergoes a temperature change $t_{L1}$ to $t_{L2}$. The gas flows at the rate $G_S$ lb. dry gas/(hr.)(sq. ft.) and undergoes a humidity change $Y_2$ to $Y_1$ lb. moisture/lb. dry gas and a temperature change $t_{G2}$ to $t_{G1}$. A moisture balance is then

$$L_S X_1 + G_S Y_2 = L_S X_2 + G_S Y_1 \tag{12.38}$$

or
$$L_S(X_1 - X_2) = G_S(Y_1 - Y_2) \tag{12.39}$$

The enthalpy of the wet solid is given by Eq. (11.27),

$$H'_L = C_L(t_L - t_0) + X C_A(t_L - t_0) + \Delta H_A \tag{11.27}$$

where $H'_L$ = enthalpy of wet solid at $t_L$, referred to solid and liquid at reference temp. $t_0$, B.t.u./lb. dry solid

$C_L$ = ht. capacity of dry solid, B.t.u./(lb.)(°F.)

$C_A$ = ht. capacity of moisture, as a liquid, B.t.u./(lb.)(°F.)

$\Delta H_A$ = integral ht. of wetting (or of adsorption, hydration, or soln.) referred to pure liquid and solid, at $t_0$, B.t.u./lb. dry solid

Bound moisture will generally exhibit a heat of wetting (see Chap. 11), although data are largely lacking. The enthalpy of the gas, $H'_G$ B.t.u./lb. dry gas, is given by Eq. (7.19). If the net heat lost from the drier is $Q$ B.t.u./hr., the enthalpy balance becomes

$$L_S H'_{L1} + G_S H'_{G2} = L_S H'_{L2} + G_S H'_{G1} + Q \tag{12.40}$$

For adiabatic operation, $Q = 0$, and if heat is added within the drier to an extent greater than the heat losses, $Q$ is negative. If the solid is carried on trucks or other support, the sensible heat of the support should also be included in the balance. Obvious changes in the equations may be made for parallel-flow driers.

**Illustration 7.** An uninsulated, hot-air countercurrent rotary drier of the type shown in Fig. 12.21 is to be used to dry ammonium sulfate from 3.5 to 0.2% moisture. The drier is 4 ft. in diameter, 22 ft. long. Atmospheric air at 75°F., 50% humidity, will be heated by passage over steam coils to 190°F. before it enters the drier, and it is desired that it discharge at 90°F. The solid will enter at 75°F., and it is expected to be discharged at 140°F. One ton of product per hour will be delivered.

Estimate the air and the heat requirements for the drier.

*Solution.* Define rates of flow in terms of lb./hr. $X_2 = 0.2/(100 - 0.2) = 0.0020$; $X_1 = 3.5/(100 - 3.5) = 0.0363$ lb. water/lb. dry solid. $L_S = 2,000(1 - 0.002) = 1,996$ lb. dry solid/hr. The rate of drying is $1,996(0.0363 - 0.0020) = 68.5$ lb. water evapd./hr.

At 75°F., 50% humidity, the absolute humidity of the available air is 0.0095 lb. water/lb. dry air, and this equals $Y_2$. Since $t_{G2} = 190°F.$, and with $t_0 = 32°F.$, the enthalpy of the air entering the drier is (Table 7.1)

$$H'_{G2} = [0.24 + 0.45(0.0095)](190 - 32) + 1,075.2(0.0095) = 48.8 \text{ B.t.u./lb. dry air}$$

For the exit air, $t_{G1} = 90°F.$

$$H'_{G1} = (0.24 + 0.45 Y_1)(90 - 32) + 1,075.2 Y_1 = 13.93 + 1,101.3 Y_1$$

The heat capacity of dry ammonium sulfate is $C_L = 0.36$ and that of water 1.0 B.t.u./(lb.)(°F.). $\Delta H_A$ will be assumed to be negligible for lack of better information. Taking $t_0 = 32°F$. so that enthalpies of gas and solid are consistent, and since $t_{L1} = 75°F$., $t_{L2} = 140°F$., the solid enthalpies, B.t.u./lb. dry solid, are [Eq. (11.27)]

$$H'_{L2} = 0.36(140 - 32) + 0.002(1)(140 - 32) = 39.07$$
$$H'_{L1} = 0.36(75 - 32) + 0.0363(1)(75 - 32) = 17.06$$

The estimated combined natural convection and radiation-heat-transfer coefficient from the drier to the surroundings[19] is 2.0 B.t.u./(hr.)(sq. ft.)(°F.). Taking the mean $\Delta t$ between drier and surroundings as $[(190 - 75) + (90 - 75)]/2 = 65°F$. and the exposed area as $\pi(4)(22) = 277$ sq. ft., the estimated heat loss is

$$Q = 2.0(277)(65) = 36,000 \text{ B.t.u./hr.}$$

Moisture balance [Eq. (12.39)],

$$1,996(0.0363 - 0.0020) = G_S(Y_1 - 0.0095)$$

Enthalpy balance [Eq. (12.40)],

$$1,996(17.06) + G_S(48.8) = 1,996(39.07) + G_S(13.93 + 1,101.3Y_1) + 36,000$$

Solving simultaneously,

$$G_S = 6,450 \text{ lb. dry air/hr.} \qquad Y_1 = 0.0203 \text{ lb. moisture/lb. dry air}$$

The enthalpy of the fresh air (Fig. 7.6) is 21.5 B.t.u./lb. dry air, and hence the heat load for the heater is $6,450(48.8 - 21.5) = 176,000$ B.t.u./hr. If 10 lb./sq. in. gauge steam is used, whose latent heat is 952.1 B.t.u./lb., the steam required is $176,000/952.1 = 185$ lb. steam/hr., or $185/68.5 = 2.7$ lb. steam/lb. water evapd.

## Rate of Drying, Continuous Direct-heat Driers.

Direct-heat driers are best placed in two categories, according to whether high or low temperatures prevail. For operation at temperatures above the boiling point of the moisture to be evaporated, the humidity of the gas has only a minor influence on the rate of drying, and it is easiest to work directly with the rate of heat transfer. At temperatures below the boiling point, mass-transfer driving forces are conveniently established. In any case, it must be emphasized that our imperfect knowledge of the complex drying mechanisms makes experimental testing of the drying necessary. Calculations are useful only for the roughest estimate.

*Drying at High Temperatures.* In a typical situation, three separate zones are distinguished in such driers, recognizable by the variation in temperatures of the gas and solid in the various parts of the drier.[8] Refer to Fig. 12.27, where typical temperatures are shown schematically by the solid lines for a countercurrent drier. In zone I, the preheat zone, the solid is heated by the gas until the rate of heat transfer to the solid is balanced by the heat requirements for evaporation of moisture. Little actual drying will usually occur here. In zone II, the equilibrium temperature of the solid remains substantially constant while surface and unbound moisture are evaporated. At point *B*, the critical moisture of the solid is reached, and, in zone III, unsaturated surface drying and evaporation of bound moisture occur. Assuming that the heat-transfer coefficients remain essentially constant, the decreased rate of evaporation in zone III results in increased solid temperature, and the discharge temperature of the solid approaches the inlet temperature of the gas.

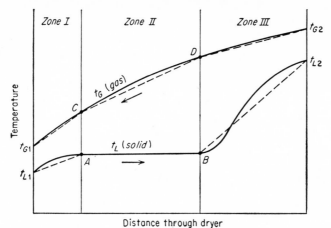

FIG. 12.27. Temperature gradients in a continuous countercurrent drier.

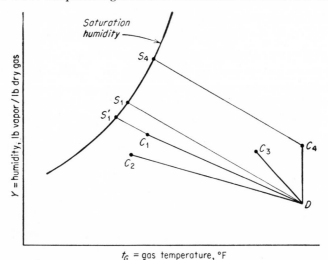

FIG. 12.28. Temperature-humidity relations in continuous driers.

Zone II represents the major portion for many driers, and it is of interest to consider the temperature-humidity relationship of the gas as it passes through this section.[27] On the psychrometric chart (Fig. 12.28), point $D$ represents the gas conditions at the corresponding point $D$ of Fig. 12.27. If drying is adiabatic, i.e., without addition to or loss of heat from the drier, the adiabatic-saturation line $DC_1$ will represent the variation of humidity and temperature of the gas as it passes through this section of the drier, and the conditions of the gas leaving this zone (point $C$, Fig. 12.27) are shown at $C_1$ on Fig. 12.28. The surface temperature of the solid, which can be estimated by the methods described earlier in the case of batch drying, will vary from that at $S_1$ (corresponding to point $B$ of Fig. 12.27) to $S_1'$ (corresponding to point $A$). If radiation and conduction through the solid may be neglected, these are the wet-bulb temperatures corresponding to $D$ and $C_1$, respectively. For the system air-water, whose wet-bulb and adiabatic-saturation temperatures are the same, these will be both given by an extension of the adiabatic-saturation line $DC_1$ to the saturation-humidity curve. Heat losses may cause the gas to follow some such path as $DC_2$. On the other hand, if heat is added to the gas in this section, the path will be represented by a line such as $DC_3$ and, if the gas is kept at constant temperature, by line $DC_4$. In the case of the last, the surface temperature of the solid will vary from that at $S_1$ to that at $S_4$. For any specific drier, the temperatures and humidities may be computed by means of the moisture and enthalpy balances [Eqs. (12.39) and (12.40)] by application of these to each section separately.

Considering only heat transfer from the gas, and neglecting any indirect heat transfer between the solid and the drier itself, the loss in heat from the gas $q_G$ may be equated to that which is transferred to the solid $q$ and the losses $Q$. For a differential length of the drier, $dZ$, this becomes[8]

$$dq_G = dq + dQ \qquad (12.41)$$

Rearranging,

$$dq = dq_G - dQ = U\,dS(t_G - t_L) = Ua(t_G - t_L)\,dZ \qquad (12.42)$$

where $U$ is the over-all heat-transfer coefficient between gas and solid, $t_G - t_L$ the temperature difference for heat transfer, $S$ the interfacial surface per square foot of drier cross section, and $a$ the interfacial surface per cubic foot of drier volume. Then

$$dq = G_sC_s\,dt_G' = Ua(t_G - t_L)\,dZ \qquad (12.43)$$

where $dt_G'$ is the temperature drop experienced by the gas as a result of transfer of heat to the solid only, exclusive of losses, and $C_s$ is the humid heat.

$$dN_{tOG} = \frac{dt_G'}{t_G - t_L} = \frac{Ua\,dZ}{G_sC_s} \qquad (12.44)$$

and if the heat-transfer coefficient is constant,

$$N_{tOG} = \frac{\Delta t_G'}{\Delta t_M} = \frac{Z}{H_{tOG}} \qquad (12.45)$$

$$H_{tOG} = \frac{G_sC_s}{Ua} \qquad (12.46)$$

where $N_{toG}$ is the number of heat-transfer units, $H_{toG}$ the length of the heat-transfer unit, $\Delta t_G'$ the change in gas temperature owing to *heat transfer to the solid only*, and $\Delta t_M$ the appropriate average temperature difference between gas and solid. If the temperature profiles in the drier may be idealized as straight lines, such as the broken lines of Fig. 12.27, then *for each zone taken separately* $\Delta t_M$ is the logarithmic average of the terminal temperature differences and $N_{toG}$ the corresponding number of transfer units for each zone. In the case of zone III, this simplification will be satisfactory for the evaporation of unsaturated surface moisture, but not for bound moisture, or where internal diffusion of moisture controls the rate of drying.

*Tunnel driers.* In drying solids by cross circulation of air over the surface, as in the case of materials on trays or solids in sheet form, the surface temperature in zone II may be estimated through Eq. (12.18). Unless all surfaces are exposed to heat transfer by radiation, this feature of the heat transfer is better ignored and $U$ in Eq. (12.46) may be taken as $h_c + U_k$. This value will also serve in zone I, and in zone III only for cases of unsaturated surface drying. The quantity $a$ may be computed from the method of loading the drier.

*Rotary driers.* The surface of the solid exposed to the drying gas cannot be measured, so that the group $Ua$ must be considered together. Measurements in small countercurrent driers[8] show that $Ua$ is proportional to $G^{0.16}[L_S(1 + K\rho_S^2 G/L_S)]^{1/2}/d$, where $K$ is given by Eq. (12.37). The heat-transfer coefficient is thus influenced by changes in hold-up resulting from changes in gas flow or feed rate of the solid, but not by those resulting from changes in slope or rate of rotation of the drier. In the absence of experimental data, the group $Uad/G^{0.16}$ may be taken as about 10. For economical designs, the exit temperatures of the gas and solid usually should be so chosen as to provide for 1.5 to 2.0 transfer units in the drier.

**Illustration 8.** A preliminary estimate of the size of a countercurrent direct-heat rotary drier for drying an ore flotation concentrate is to be made. The solid is to be delivered from a continuous filter and introduced into the drier at 8% moisture, 80°F., and is to be discharged from the drier at 300°F., 0.5% moisture. There will be 5,000 lb./hr. of dried product. The drying gas is a flue gas analyzing 2.5% $CO_2$, 14.7% $O_2$, 76.0% $N_2$, and 6.8% $H_2O$ by volume. It will enter the drier at 900°F. Heat losses will be estimated at 15% of the heat in the entering gas. The ore concentrate is ground to 200 microns average particle diameter and has a bulk density of 81 lb. dry solid/cu. ft. and a heat capacity 0.2 B.t.u./(lb.)(°F.)(dry). The gas rate ought not to exceed about 500 lb./(hr.)(sq. ft.) to avoid excessive dusting.

*Solution.* $X_1 = 8/(100 - 8) = 0.0870$; $X_2 = 0.5/(100 - 0.5) = 0.00503$ lb. water/lb. dry solid. Define $L_S$ and $G_S$ as lb. dry material/(hr.)(sq. ft.). $L_S = 5,000(1 - 0.005) = 4,975$ lb. dry solid/hr. Water to be evaporated $= 4,975(0.0870 - 0.00503) = 407$ lb./hr.

Basis: 1 mole gas in.   Dry gas $= 1 - 0.068 = 0.932$ mole.

|  | Moles | Lb. | Av. ht. capacity, B.t.u./(lb. mole)(°F.), 900–32°F. |
|---|---|---|---|
| $CO_2$............... | 0.025 | 1.10 | 10.9 |
| $O_2$................ | 0.147 | 4.72 | 7.15 |
| $N_2$................ | 0.760 | 21.3 | 7.15 |
| Total dry wt......... | ..... | 27.1 |  |

Av. mol. wt. dry gas $= 27.1/0.932 = 29.1$ lb./lb. mole, nearly the same as air.

$$Y_2 = 0.068(18.02)/0.932(29.1) = 0.0452 \text{ lb. water/lb. dry gas}$$
$$t_{G2} = 900°F.$$

Av. ht. capacity of dry gas $= \dfrac{0.025(10.9) + (0.147 + 0.760)(7.15)}{0.932(29.1)}$

$$= 0.25 \text{ B.t.u./(lb.)(°F.)}$$

The exit-gas temperature will be tentatively taken as $t_{G1} = 250°F$. This is subject to revision after the number of transfer units are computed. In a manner similar to that above, the average heat capacity of the dry gas, 250 to 32°F., is 0.24 B.t.u./lb. dry gas.

$$\text{Base temperature} = t_0 = 32°F.$$

Eq. (7.19):

$$H'_{G2} = [0.25 + 0.47(0.0452)](900 - 32) + 1,075.2(0.0452) = 283.5 \text{ B.t.u./lb. dry gas}$$
$$H'_{G1} = (0.24 + 0.45Y_1)(250 - 32) + 1,075.2Y_1 = 52.5 + 1,173Y_1$$

Take $\Delta H_A = 0$.

Eq. (11.27):

$$H'_{L1} = 0.2(80 - 32) + 0.0870(1)(80 - 32) = 13.78 \text{ B.t.u./lb. dry solid}$$
$$H'_{L2} = 0.2(300 - 32) + 0.00503(1)(300 - 32) = 53.6 \text{ B.t.u./lb. dry solid}$$
$$Q = \text{ht. loss} = 0.15(283.5)G_S = 42.5G_S \quad \text{B.t.u./hr.}$$

Eq. (12.39):          $407 = G_S(Y_1 - 0.0452)$

Eq. (12.40):

$$4,975(13.78) + G_S(283.5) = 4,975(53.6) + G_S(52.5 + 1,173Y_1) + 42.5G_S$$

Solving simultaneously,

$$G_S = 5,170 \text{ lb. dry gas/hr.}$$
$$Y_1 = 0.1238 \text{ lb. water/lb. dry gas}$$
$$H'_{G1} = 197.6 \text{ B.t.u./lb. dry gas}$$
$$Q = 220,000 \text{ B.t.u./hr.}$$

Assuming that the psychrometric ratio of the gas is the same as that of air, its wet-bulb temperature is found to be [Eq. (7.32)] about 153°F. The surface of the drying solid particles is subject to radiation from the hot walls of the drier, and the surface of the solid in zone II is then estimated to be 160°F. (NOTE: This should be recalculated after the temperature at point $D$, Fig. 12.27, is known, but in this case any change will have no influence on the over-all results.)

For lack of information on the critical moisture content of the solid, which is probably quite low for the conditions found in such a drier, it will be assumed that all moisture is evaporated in zone II at 160°F. Zone I will be taken as a preheat zone for warming the wet solids to 160°F., without drying. Enthalpy of the solid at 160°F.,

$X = 0.0870$ (point $A$, Fig. 12.27) $= 0.2(160 - 32) + 0.0870(1)(160 - 32) = 36.5$ B.t.u./lb. dry solid. Similarly, enthalpy of the solid at 160°F., $X = 0.00503$ (point $B$, Fig. 12.27) $= 25.6$ B.t.u./lb. dry solid.

Assuming heat losses in the three zones are proportional to the number of transfer units in each zone and to the average temperature difference between the gas and the surrounding air (80°F.), the heat losses are apportioned (by a trial-and-error calculation) as 14% in zone I, 65% in zone II, 21% in zone III.

*Calculations for zone* III. Humid ht. of entering gas $= 0.25 + 0.47(0.0452) = 0.272$ B.t.u./(lb. dry gas)(°F.). A heat balance,

$$5,170(0.272)(900 - t_{GD}) = 4,975(53.6 - 25.6) + 0.21(220,000)$$
$$t_{GD} = \text{gas temp. at } D \text{ (Fig. 12.27)} = 768°\text{F.}$$

The change in gas temperature, exclusive of that due to losses, is

$$\Delta t'_G = 4,975(53.6 - 25.6)/5,170(0.272) = 99°\text{F.}$$

Av. temp. difference between gas and solid = av. of $768 - 160 = 608°$F. and $900 - 300 = 600°$F. $= 604°$F. $= \Delta t_M$.

$$N_{tOG} = \Delta t'_G/\Delta t_M = {}^{99}\!\!/_{604} = 0.16$$

*Calculations for zone* I. Humid ht. of exit gas $= 0.24 + 0.45(0.1238) = 0.294$ B.t.u./(lb. dry gas)(°F.). A heat balance,

$$5,170(0.294)(t_{GC} - 250) = 4,975(36.5 - 13.78) + 0.14(220,000)$$
$$t_{GC} = \text{gas temp. at } C \text{ (Fig. 12.27)} = 345°\text{F.}$$
$$\Delta t'_G = 4,975(36.5 - 13.78)/5,170(0.294) = 74°\text{F.}$$
$$\Delta t_M = \text{av. of } 345 - 160 = 185°\text{F. and } 250 - 80 = 170°\text{F.} = 178°\text{F.}$$
$$N_{tOG} = \Delta t'_G/\Delta t_M = {}^{74}\!\!/_{178} = 0.42$$

*Calculations for zone* II

$$\text{Av. humid ht. of gas} = (0.272 + 0.294)/2 = 0.28$$
$$\text{True change in gas temp.} = 768 - 345 = 423°\text{F.}$$
$$\text{Change in temp. due to ht. loss} = 0.65(220,000)/(5,170)(0.28)$$
$$= 99°\text{F.}$$
$$\Delta t'_G \text{ due to ht. transfer to solid} = 423 - 99 = 324°\text{F.}$$
$$\Delta t_M = \frac{(768 - 160) - (345 - 160)}{\ln{[(768 - 160)/(345 - 160)]}} = 360°\text{F.}$$
$$N_{tOG} = \Delta t'_G/\Delta t_M = {}^{324}\!\!/_{360} = 0.90$$
$$\text{Total } N_{tOG} = 0.16 + 0.42 + 0.90 = 1.48$$

*Size of drier.* Standard diameters available are 3, 4, 4.5, and 5 ft. and larger. The cross-sectional area of the 4-ft.-diameter drier is $\pi(4)^2/4 = 12.58$ sq. ft. Expressing the rates of flow as lb. dry material/(hr.)(sq. ft.), $G_S = 5,170/12.58 = 411$, $L_S = 4,975/12.58 = 396$ lb./(hr.)(sq. ft.). This is the only size suitable in view of the permissible gas rate.

Av. $G = G_S(1 + Y_{av}) = 411[1 + (0.0452 + 0.1238)/2] = 446$ lb./(hr.)(sq. ft.). For lack of more specific information take $Ua = 10G^{0.16}/d = 10(446)^{0.16}/4 = 6.6$ B.t.u./(hr.)(cu. ft.)(°F.). $H_{tOG} = G_S C_S/Ua = 411(0.28)/6.6 = 17.5$ ft.

$$Z = N_{tOG}H_{tOG} = 1.48(17.5) = 26.0 \text{ ft.}$$

The nearest standard length is 30 ft.

Take the peripheral speed as 65 ft./min., whence the rate of revolution $= n = 65/4\pi = 5.2$ or 5 r.p.m.

$$d_p = (200 \text{ microns})(3.28)(10^{-6}) = 0.00065 \text{ ft.}$$
$$\rho_S = 81 \text{ lb./cu. ft.}$$
Eq. (12.37):$\qquad K = 0.0000933/81(0.00065)^{1/2} = 0.000045$

Take the hold-up $v = 0.05$, and $KG = 0.000045(446) = 0.02$.

Eq. (12.35):$\quad v_0 = v - KG = 0.05 - 0.02 = 0.03$

Eq. (12.36):$\quad s = \dfrac{0.0037 L_S}{v_0 \rho_S n^{0.9} d} = \dfrac{0.0037(396)}{0.03(81)(5)^{0.9}(4)} = 0.0356$ ft./ft., the drier slope

*Drying at Low Temperatures.* Continuous driers operating at low temperatures may be divided into zones in the same manner as high-temperature driers. Since the surface moisture will evaporate at a comparatively low temperature in zone II, the preheat zone may generally

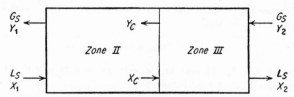

FIG. 12.29. Continuous low-temperature countercurrent drier.

be ignored and only zones II and III need be considered. Refer to Fig. 12.29, which shows an arrangement for countercurrent flow. In zone II, unbound and surface moisture is evaporated as discussed previously, and the moisture content of the solid falls to the critical value $X_c$. The rate of drying in this zone would be constant if it were not for the varying conditions of the gas. In zone III, unsaturated-surface drying and evaporation of bound moisture occur, and the gas humidity rises from its initial value $Y_1$ to $Y_c$. The latter may be calculated by applying the material-balance relation [Eq. (12.39)] to either zone separately. The retention time may be calculated by integration of Eq. (12.3),

$$\theta = \theta_{\text{II}} + \theta_{\text{III}} = \frac{L_S}{A} \left( \int_{X_c}^{X_1} \frac{dX}{N} + \int_{X_2}^{X_c} \frac{dX}{N} \right) \qquad (12.47)$$

where $A/L_S$ is the specific exposed drying surface, sq. ft./lb. dry solid.

*Zone* II, $X > X_c$. The rate $N$ is given by Eq. (12.17), which, when substituted in the first part of Eq. (12.47), provides

$$\theta_{\text{II}} = \frac{L_S}{A} \frac{1}{k_Y} \int_{X_c}^{X_1} \frac{dX}{Y_s - Y} \qquad (12.48)$$

Since $G_s\, dY = L_S\, dX$, Eq. (12.48) becomes

$$\theta_{\text{II}} = \frac{G_s}{L_S} \frac{L_S}{A} \frac{1}{k_Y} \int_{Y_c}^{Y_1} \frac{dY}{Y_s - Y} \qquad (12.49)$$

Integration of Eq. (12.49) must take into account the variation of $Y_s$, the humidity of the gas at the solid surface, with $Y$. If, the gas temperature, for example, is held constant in this zone by application of heat, the path of the gas resembles line $DC_4$ on Fig. 12.28. If furthermore, radiation and conduction effects can be neglected, $Y_s$ for any value of $Y$ on line $DC_4$ is the saturated humidity at the corresponding wet-bulb temperature. Equation (12.49) may then be integrated graphically.

For the case where $Y_s$ is constant, as for adiabatic drying of water into air, Eq. (12.49) becomes

$$\theta_{\text{II}} = \frac{G_S}{L_S} \frac{L_S}{A} \frac{1}{k_Y} \ln \frac{Y_s - Y_c}{Y_s - Y_1} \tag{12.50}$$

*Zone* III, $X < X_c$. Some simplification is necessary for mathematical treatment. For the case where unsaturated-surface drying occurs and the drying rate is dependent strictly upon the conditions prevailing at any instant, independent of the immediate past history of the drying, Eqs. (12.8) and (12.17) apply. These provide

$$N = \frac{N_c(X - X^*)}{X_c - X^*} = \frac{k_Y(Y_s - Y)(X - X^*)}{X_c - X^*} \tag{12.51}$$

When this is substituted in the second part of Eq. (12.47), there results

$$\theta_{\text{III}} = \frac{L_S}{A} \frac{X_c - X^*}{k_Y} \int_{X_2}^{X_c} \frac{dX}{(Y_s - Y)(X - X^*)} \tag{12.52}$$

This may be evaluated graphically after determining the relationship between $X$, $X^*$, $Y_s$, and $Y$. For this purpose, the material balance may be written as

$$Y = Y_2 + (X - X_2) \frac{L_S}{G_S} \tag{12.53}$$

The surface humidity $Y_s$ is found in the manner previously described, and $X^*$ is given by the equilibrium-moisture curve for the appropriate $Y$.

For the special case where the bound moisture is negligible ($X^* = 0$) and $Y_s$ is constant (adiabatic drying), substitution of Eq. (12.53) and its differential $G_S\, dY = L_S\, dX$ in Eq. (12.52) provides

$$\theta_{\text{III}} = \frac{G_S}{L_S} \frac{L_S}{A} \frac{X_c}{k_Y} \int_{Y_2}^{Y_c} \frac{dY}{(Y_s - Y)[(Y - Y_2)G_S/L_S + X_2]} \tag{12.54}$$

$$\theta_{\text{III}} = \frac{G_S}{L_S} \frac{L_S}{A} \frac{X_c}{k_Y} \frac{1}{(Y_s - Y_2)G_S/L_S + X_2} \ln \frac{X_c(Y_s - Y_2)}{X_2(Y_s - Y_c)} \tag{12.55}$$

These methods must not be applied to solids whose internal resistance to movement of moisture is large, where internal diffusion controls the rate of drying, and where casehardening occurs. In these cases, the instantaneous rate of drying under variable conditions is not merely a function of the prevailing conditions but depends upon the immediate past drying history as well. For such solids, the time for drying is best determined experimentally in a carefully planned test which simulates the countercurrent action of the continuous drier.[4]

In applying Eqs. (12.47) to (12.55), it is clear that, should drying take place only above, or only below, the critical moisture content, appropriate changes in the limits of moisture content and gas humidities must be made. In the case of parallel-flow driers, where gas enters at humidity $Y_1$ and leaves at $Y_2$, while solid enters at moisture content $X_1$ and leaves at $X_2$, Eqs. (12.50) and (12.55) become

$$\theta_{II} = \frac{G_s}{L_s}\frac{L_s}{A}\frac{1}{k_Y}\int_{Y_1}^{Y_c}\frac{dY}{Y_s - Y} = \frac{G_s}{L_s}\frac{L_s}{A}\frac{1}{k_Y}\ln\frac{Y_s - Y_1}{Y_s - Y_c} \quad (12.56)$$

$$\theta_{III} = \frac{L_s}{A}\frac{X_c - X^*}{k_Y}\int_{X_2}^{X_c}\frac{dX}{(Y_s - Y)(X - X^*)}$$

$$= \frac{G_s}{L_s}\frac{L_s}{A}\frac{X_c}{k_Y}\frac{1}{(Y_s - Y_c)G_s/L_s - X_2}\ln\frac{X_c(Y_s - Y_2)}{X_2(Y_s - Y_c)} \quad (12.57)$$

**Illustration 9.** Wet rayon skeins, after centrifuging, are to be air-dried from 46 to 8.5% water content in a continuous countercurrent tunnel drier. The skeins are hung on poles which travel through the drier. The air is to enter at 180°F., humidity 0.03 lb. water/lb. dry air, and is to be discharged at a humidity 0.08. The air temperature is to be kept constant at 180°F. by heating coils within the drier. The air rate is to be 1,000 lb./(hr.)(sq. ft.).

The critical moisture content of rayon skeins is 50%, and its per cent equilibrium moisture at 180°F. can be taken as one-fourth of the per cent relative humidity of the air. The rate of drying is then [Simons, Koffolt, and Withrow, *Trans. Am. Inst. Chem. Engrs.*, **39**, 133 (1943)]

$$\frac{-dX}{d\theta} = 0.003G^{1.47}(X - X^*)(Y_W - Y)$$

where $Y_W$ is the saturation humidity of the air at the wet-bulb temperature corresponding to $Y$.

Determine the time the rayon should remain in the drier.

*Solution.* $X_1 = 0.46/(1 - 0.46) = 0.852$; $X_2 = 0.085/(1 - 0.085) = 0.093$ lb. water/lb. dry solid. $Y_1 = 0.08$; $Y_2 = 0.03$ lb. water/lb. dry air. A water balance [Eq. (12.39)],

$$L_s/G_s = (0.08 - 0.03)/(0.852 - 0.093) = 0.0660 \text{ lb. dry solid/lb. dry air}$$

Since the initial moisture content of the rayon is less than the critical, drying takes place entirely within zone III. The form of the rate equation is the same as that of Eq. (12.22), where $k_Y A/L_s(X_c - X^*) = 0.003G^{1.47}$. Rearranging the rate equation,

$$\theta_{III} = \int_0^\theta d\theta = \frac{1}{0.003G^{1.47}}\int_{X_2}^{X_1}\frac{dX}{(X - X^*)(Y_W - Y)}$$

which is in the form of Eq. (12.52). On substituting $G = 1,000$, this becomes

$$\theta_{III} = 0.013\int_{0.093}^{0.852}\frac{dX}{(X - X^*)(Y_W - Y)} \quad (12.58)$$

Consider that part of the drier where the moisture content of the rayon is $X = 0.4$.

Eq. (12.53):   $Y = 0.03 + (0.4 - 0.093)0.066 = 0.0503$ lb. water/lb. dry gas

At 180°F., $Y = 0.0503$, the wet-bulb temperature is 114°F., and the corresponding saturation humidity $Y_W = 0.068$ (Fig. 7.6).

Eq. (7.13):   $$0.0503 = \frac{p}{14.7 - p}\frac{18}{29}$$

$p$ = partial pressure of water = 1.10 lb./sq. in.

The vapor pressure of water at 180°F. = $P = 7.51$ lb./sq. in., and the relative humidity of the air = $(1.10/7.51)100 = 14.63\%$. The equilibrium moisture is $14.6/4 = 3.66\%$, and $X^* = 3.66/(100 - 3.66) = 0.038$ lb. water/lb. dry solid. Therefore

$$\frac{1}{(X - X^*)(Y_W - Y)} = \frac{1}{(0.4 - 0.038)(0.068 - 0.0503)} = 156$$

In a similar fashion, other values of this quantity are calculated for other values of $X$, as follows:

| $X$ | $Y$ | $Y_W$ | Per cent relative humidity | $X^*$ | $\dfrac{1}{(X - X^*)(Y_W - Y)}$ |
|---|---|---|---|---|---|
| 0.852 | 0.080 | 0.0950 | 22.4 | 0.0594 | 84 |
| 0.80 | 0.0767 | 0.0920 | 21.5 | 0.0568 | 88 |
| 0.60 | 0.0635 | 0.0790 | 18.17 | 0.0488 | 117 |
| 0.40 | 0.0503 | 0.0680 | 14.63 | 0.0380 | 156 |
| 0.20 | 0.0371 | 0.0550 | 11.05 | 0.0284 | 325 |
| 0.093 | 0.030 | 0.0490 | 9.04 | 0.0231 | 755 |

The integral of Eq. (12.58) is evaluated graphically by determining the area under a curve of the last column of the table plotted as ordinate against the first column as abscissa (not shown). The area = 151.6, whence, by Eq. (12.58),

$$\theta_{\text{III}} = 0.013(151.6) = 1.97 \text{ or } 2 \text{ hr.} \quad Ans.$$

## NOTATION FOR CHAPTER 12

$a$ = interfacial surface of solid, sq. ft./cu. ft.
$A$ = drying surface, for cross-circulation drying, sq. ft.
   = cross-sectional area of bed perpendicular to the direction of gas flow, for through-circulation drying, sq. ft.
$A_m$ = average cross-sectional area of a drying solid, sq. ft.
$A_u$ = nondrying external surface, sq. ft.
$b$ = a constant
$C_A$ = heat capacity of liquid moisture, B.t.u./(lb.)(°F.)
$C_L$ = heat capacity of dry solid, B.t.u./(lb.)(°F.)
$C_p$ = heat capacity at constant pressure, B.t.u./(lb.)(°F.)
$C_S$ = humid heat of a moist gas, B.t.u./(lb. dry gas)(°F.)
$d$ = differential operator
   = diameter of drier, ft.
$d_p$ = diameter of a particle, ft.
   = diameter of a sphere of same surface as particle, ft.

$D$ = diffusivity, sq. ft./hr.

$e$ = 2.7183

$f$ = function

$G$ = mass velocity of gas, lb. total gas/(hr.)(sq. ft.)

$G_S$ = mass velocity of dry gas, lb. dry gas/(hr.)(sq. ft.)

$h_c$ = heat-transfer film coefficient, for convection, B.t.u./(hr.)(sq. ft.)(°F.)

$h_R$ = heat-transfer film coefficient; for radiation, B.t.u./(hr.)(sq. ft.)(°F.)

$\Delta H_A$ = integral heat of wetting, B.t.u./lb. dry solid

$H'_G$ = enthalpy of a moist gas, B.t.u./lb. dry gas

$H'_L$ = enthalpy of a wet solid, B.t.u./lb. dry solid

$H_{tOG}$ = length of an over-all gas transfer unit, ft.

$j_D$ = as defined by Eq. (12.19)

$j_H$ = as defined by Eq. (12.19)

$k_M$ = thermal conductivity of tray material, B.t.u. (ft.)/(hr.)(sq. ft.)(°F.)

$k_S$ = thermal conductivity of the drying solid, B.t.u. (ft.)/(hr.)(sq. ft.)(°F.)

$k_Y$ = gas-film mass-transfer coefficient, lb. evaporated/(hr.)(sq. ft.)($\Delta Y$)

$K$ = as defined by Eq. (12.37)

$l$ = length of drying surface in direction of gas flow, ft.

$L_S$ = weight of dry solid in a batch, for batch drying, lb.

   = rate of flow of solid, for continuous drying, lb. dry solid/(hr.)(sq. ft.)

$m$ = a constant

$n$ = rate of revolution, r.p.m.

$N$ = rate of drying, lb. moisture evaporated/(hr.)(sq. ft. solid surface)

$N_c$ = constant rate of drying, lb./(hr.)(sq. ft.)

$N_{tG}$ = number of gas transfer units, dimensionless

$N_{tOG}$ = number of over-all gas transfer units, dimensionless

$p$ = partial pressure, atm. (unless otherwise specified)

$P$ = vapor pressure, atm. (unless otherwise specified)

Pr = Prandtl number = $C_p\mu/k$, dimensionless

$q$ = heat received at the drying surface, batch drying, B.t.u./(hr.)(sq. ft. solid surface)

   = heat received by the solid, continuous drying, B.t.u./(hr.)(sq. ft. drier cross section)

$q_c$ = heat transferred by convection, B.t.u./(hr.)(sq. ft. solid surface)

$q_G$ = heat transferred from the gas, B.t.u./(hr.)(sq. ft. drier cross section)

$q_k$ = heat transferred by conduction, B.t.u./(hr.)(sq. ft. solid surface)

$q_R$ = heat transferred by radiation, B.t.u./(hr.)(sq. ft. solid surface)

$Q$ = net heat loss, B.t.u./(hr.)(sq. ft. drier cross section)

$\mathrm{Re}'''$ = Reynolds number = $lG/\mu$, dimensionless

$s$ = slope of a drier, ft./ft.

$S$ = interfacial surface, sq. ft./sq. ft. cross section

Sc = Schmidt number = $\mu/\rho D$, dimensionless

$t_0$ = reference temperature, °F.

$t_G$ = gas temperature, °F.

$t_L$ = solid temperature, °F.

$t_R$ = temperature of radiator, °F.

$t_s$ = temperature of surface, °F.

$T$ = absolute temperature, °R.

$U$ = over-all heat-transfer coefficient, B.t.u./(hr.)(sq. ft.)(°F.)

$v$ = hold-up of solid in a continuous drier, as a volume fraction, cu. ft. solid/cu. ft. drier

$v_0$ = hold-up of solid at no gas flow, cu. ft. solid/cu. ft. drier

$X$ = moisture content of a solid, lb. moisture/lb. dry solid
$X_c$ = critical moisture content, lb. moisture/lb. dry solid
$X^*$ = equilibrium moisture content, lb. moisture/lb. dry solid
$Y$ = humidity of a gas, lb. moisture/lb. dry gas
$z_M$ = thickness of tray material, ft.
$z_S$ = thickness of drying solid, ft.
$Z$ = length of drier, ft.
$\alpha$ = a constant
$\Delta$ = difference
$\varepsilon$ = emissivity of drying surface, dimensionless
$\theta$ = time, hr.
$\lambda_s$ = latent heat of vaporization at $t_s$, B.t.u./lb.
$\mu$ = viscosity, lb./(ft.)(hr.)
$\pi$ = 3.1416
$\rho_G$ = gas density, lb./cu. ft.
$\rho_S$ = apparent solid density, lb. dry solid/cu. ft.

Subscripts:

$as$ = adiabatic-saturation conditions
$c$ = critical
max = maximum
$M$ = average
$s$ = surface
$W$ = wet-bulb conditions
I, II, III = pertaining to zones I, II, and III in a continuous drier

## REFERENCES

1. Allerton, J., L. E. Brownell, and D. L. Katz: *Chem. Eng. Progr.*, **45**, 619 (1949).
2. Berson, M. J.: *Chem. Eng.*, **59**(9), 169 (1952).
3. Brier, J. C., and A. S. Foust: *Trans. Am. Inst. Chem. Engrs.*, **35**, 797 (1939).
4. Broughton, D. B., and H. S. Mickley: *Chem. Eng. Progr.*, **49**, 319 (1953).
5. Ceaglske, N. H., and O. A. Hougen: *Trans. Am. Inst. Chem. Engrs.*, **33**, 283 (1937).
6. Comings, E. W., and T. K. Sherwood: *Ind. Eng. Chem.*, **26**, 1096 (1934).
7. Erisman, J. L.: *Ind. Eng. Chem.*, **30**, 996 (1938).
8. Friedman, S. J., and W. R. Marshall: *Chem. Eng. Progr.*, **45**, 482, 573 (1949).
9. Gamson, B. W., G. Thodos, and O. A. Hougen: *Trans. Am. Inst. Chem. Engrs.*, **39**, 1 (1943).
10. Gilliland, E. R., and T. K. Sherwood: *Ind. Eng. Chem.*, **25**, 1134 (1933).
11. Gordon, C. W.: *Chem. Eng. Progr.*, **45**, 477 (1949).
12. Hardinge Co., Inc.: *Bull.* 16-D.
13. Hougen, O. A., and H. J. McCauley: *Trans. Am. Inst. Chem. Engrs.*, **36**, 183 (1940).
14. Hurxthal, A. O.: *Ind. Eng. Chem.*, **30**, 1004 (1938).
15. Marshall, W. R., and S. J. Friedman: In J. H. Perry, ed., "Chemical Engineers' Handbook," 3d ed., pp. 799ff., McGraw-Hill Book Company, Inc., New York, 1950.
16. —— and E. Seltzer: *Chem. Eng. Progr.*, **46**, 501, 575 (1950).
17. —— and O. A. Hougen: *Trans. Am. Inst. Chem. Engrs.*, **38**, 91 (1942).

18. —— et al.: Chem. Eng. Progr., **48**, 141, 173, 181 (1952); **49**, 169, 226, 417, 480 (1953).
19. McAdams, W. H.: "Heat Transmission," 3d ed., McGraw-Hill Book Company, Inc., New York, 1954.
20. McCready, D. W., and W. L. McCabe: Trans. Am. Inst. Chem. Engrs., **29**, 131 (1933).
21. Mitchell, R. J., J. H. Koffolt, and J. R. Withrow: Trans. Am. Inst. Chem. Engrs., **39**, 156 (1943).
22. Molstad, M. C., P. Farevaag, and J. A. Farrell: Ind. Eng. Chem., **30**, 1131 (1938).
23. Pearse, J. F., T. R. Oliver, and D. M. Newitt: Trans. Inst. Chem. Engrs. (London), **27**, 1, 9 (1949).
24. Shepherd, C. B., C. Haddock, and R. C. Brewer: Ind. Eng. Chem., **30**, 389 (1938).
25. Sherwood, T. K.: Ind. Eng. Chem., **21**, 12, 976 (1929); **22**, 132 (1930); **24**, 307 (1932).
26. ——: Trans. Am. Inst. Chem. Engrs., **27**, 190 (1931).
27. ——: In J. H. Perry, ed., "Chemical Engineers' Handbook," 2d ed., p. 1488, McGraw-Hill Book Company, Inc., New York, 1941.
28. —— and E. W. Comings: Ind. Eng. Chem., **25**, 311 (1933).
29. Smith, B. A.: Ind. Eng. Chem., **30**, 993 (1938).
30. Smith, D. A.: Chem. Eng. Progr., **45**, 703 (1949).
31. Van Marle, D. J.: Ind. Eng. Chem., **30**, 1006 (1938).
32. Victor, V. P.: Chem. Met. Eng., **52**(7), 105 (1945).
33. Whitwell, J. C., and R. K. Toner: Textile Research J., **17**, 99 (1947).
34. Wilke, C. R., and O. A. Hougen: Trans. Am. Inst. Chem. Engrs., **41**, 445 (1945).

## PROBLEMS

**1.** A plant wishes to dry a certain type of fiberboard in sheets 4 by 6 ft. by $\frac{1}{2}$ in. To determine the drying characteristics, a 1- by 1-ft. sample of the board, with the edges sealed so that drying took place from the two large faces only, was suspended from a balance in a laboratory cabinet drier and exposed to a current of hot, dry air. The initial moisture content was 75%. The sheet lost weight at the constant rate of 0.8 lb./hr. until the moisture content fell to 60%, whereupon the drying rate fell. Measurements of the rate of drying were discontinued, but after a long period of exposure to this air it was established that the equilibrium moisture content was 10%. The dry weight of the sample was 2 lb. All moisture contents are on the wet basis.

Determine the time for drying the large sheets from 75 to 20% moisture under the same drying conditions.

**2.** A sample of a porous, manufactured sheet material of mineral origin was dried from both sides by cross circulation of air in a laboratory drier. The sample was 1 ft. square, $\frac{1}{4}$ in. thick, and the edges were sealed. The air velocity over the surface was 10 ft./sec., its dry-bulb temperature was 125°F., and its wet-bulb temperature 70°F. There were no radiation effects. The solid lost moisture at a constant rate of 0.6 lb. water/hr. until the critical moisture content, 15% (wet basis), was reached. In the falling-rate period, the rate of evaporation fell linearly with moisture content until the sample was dry. The equilibrium moisture was negligible. The dry weight of the sheet was 4.0 lb.

Estimate the time for drying sheets of this material 2 by 4 ft. by $\frac{1}{2}$ in. thick from both sides, from 25 to 2% moisture (wet basis), using air of dry-bulb temperature 150°F., but of the same absolute humidity, at a linear velocity over the sheet of 15 ft./-

sec. Assume no change in the critical moisture content with the changed drying conditions.

**3.** Estimate the rate of drying during the constant-rate period for the conditions existing as the air enters the trays of the drier of Illustration 1. The solid being dried is a granular material, of thermal conductivity when wet = 1 B.t.u. (ft.)/(hr.)(sq. ft.) (°F.), and it completely fills the trays. The metal of the trays is stainless steel, 16 B.W.G. (0.065 in. thick). Include in the calculations an estimate of the radiation effect from the undersurface of each tray upon the drying surface.

**4.** A laboratory drying test was made on a 1-sq.-ft. sample of a fibrous boardlike material. The sample was suspended from a balance, its edges were sealed, and drying took place from the two large faces. The air had a dry-bulb temperature of 150°F., wet-bulb temperature 84°F., and its velocity was 5 ft./sec. past the sample. The following are the weights recorded at various times during the test:

| Time, hr. | Wt., lb. | Time, hr. | Wt., lb. | Time, hr. | Wt., lb. | Time, hr. | Wt., lb. |
|-----------|----------|-----------|----------|-----------|----------|-----------|----------|
| 0 | 10.625 | 2.6 | 9.570 | 6.0 | 8.670 | 14 | 8.420 |
| 0.1 | 10.597 | 3.0 | 9.412 | 6.5 | 8.610 | 16 | 8.420 |
| 0.2 | 10.548 | 3.4 | 9.273 | 7.0 | 8.565 | | |
| 0.4 | 10.470 | 3.8 | 9.150 | 7.5 | 8.535 | | |
| 0.8 | 10.305 | 4.2 | 9.045 | 8.0 | 8.507 | | |
| 1.0 | 10.225 | 4.6 | 8.944 | 9.0 | 8.469 | | |
| 1.4 | 10.063 | 5.0 | 8.852 | 10.0 | 8.448 | | |
| 1.8 | 9.900 | 5.4 | 8.772 | 11 | 8.432 | | |
| 2.2 | 9.735 | 5.8 | 8.700 | 12 | 8.423 | | |

The sample was then dried in an oven at 220°F., and the dry weight was 8.301 lb.

*a.* Plot the rate-of-drying curve.

*b.* Estimate the time required for drying the same sheets from 20 to 2% moisture (wet basis) using air of the same temperature and humidity, but with a 50% greater air velocity. Assume the critical moisture remains unchanged.

**5.** A pigment material which has been removed wet from a filter press is to be dried by extruding it into small cylinders and subjecting these to through-circulation drying. The extrusions are $\frac{1}{4}$ in. in diameter, 2 in. long, and are to be placed on screens to a depth of 2.5 in. The surface of the particles is estimated to be 90 sq. ft./cu. ft. of bed and the apparent density 65 lb. dry solid/cu. ft. Air at a mass velocity 700 lb. dry air/(hr.)(sq. ft.) will flow through the bed, entering at 250°F., humidity 0.05 lb. water/lb. dry air.

*a.* Estimate the constant rate of drying to be expected. (NOTE: For long cylinders it is best to take the equivalent diameter as the actual cylinder diameter.)

*b.* Estimate the constant rate of drying to be expected if the filter cake were to be dried on trays by cross circulation of the air over the surface at the same mass velocity, temperature, and humidity. Neglect radiation and heat conduction through the solid.

**6.** A louver-type continuous rotary drier (Fig. 12.23) was used to dry wood chips from 40 to 15% moisture [Horgan, *Trans. Inst. Chem. Engrs.*, **6**, 131 (1928)]. The wood entered at 33°F., while the dried product was discharged at 100°F. at the rate of 3,162 lb./hr. The drying medium was the gas resulting from the combustion of fuel, but for purposes of the present calculation it may be assumed to have the characteristics of air. It entered the drier at 715°F., with a humidity of 0.038 lb. water vapor/lb.

dry gas, at the rate of 275 lb./min. (wet). The gas was discharged at 175°F. The heat capacity of the dry wood may be taken as 0.42 B.t.u./(lb.)(°F.), and the heat of wetting may be ignored. Estimate the heat losses, B.t.u./hr.

**7.** A direct-heat parallel-flow rotary drier, 8 ft. diameter, 60 ft. long, was used to dry chopped alfalfa [see Gutzeit and Spraul, *Chem. Eng. Progr.*, **49**, 380 (1953)]. Over a 5-hr. test period, the drier delivered an average of 2,220 lb./hr. of dried product at 11% moisture and 145°F., when fed with alfalfa containing 79% moisture at 80°F. The drying medium was the combustion products resulting from the burning of 13,074 cu. ft./hr. (80°F., 4 oz. gauge pressure) of natural gas (85% methane, 10% ethane, 5% nitrogen by volume) with air at 80°F., 50% humidity. The gas analyzed 2.9% $CO_2$, 15.8% $O_2$, 81.3% $N_2$ by volume on a dry basis; it entered the drier at 1500°F. and left at 195°F. The heat capacity of dry alfalfa is estimated to be 0.37 B.t.u./(lb.) (°F.), and the heat of wetting may be neglected. Compute the volumetric rate of gas flow through the exhaust fan, cu. ft./min., and the heat losses, B.t.u./hr.

**8.** A direct-heat countercurrent rotary hot-air drier is to be chosen for drying an insoluble crystalline organic solid. The solid will enter at 70°F., containing 20% water. It will be dried by air entering at 310°F., 0.01 lb. water/lb. dry air. The solid is expected to leave at 250°F., with a moisture content 0.3%. One thousand pounds per hour of dried product will be delivered. The specific heat of the dry solid is 0.2 B.t.u./(lb.)(°F.), and its average particle size is 0.5 mm. The superficial air velocity should not exceed 5 ft./sec. in any part of the drier. The drier will be insulated, and heat losses may be neglected for present purposes. Choose a drier from among the following standard sizes, and specify the amount of air which should be used: 36 in. by 10 ft., 36 in. by 20 ft., 48 in. by 25 ft., 54 in. by 30 ft., 60 in. by 35 ft.

**9.** A manufactured material in the form of sheets 2 by 4 ft. by ½ in. is to be continuously dried in an adiabatic countercurrent hot-air tunnel drier at the rate of 100 sheets per hour. The sheets will be supported on a special conveyor carrying the material in tiers 30 sheets high, and they will be dried from both sides. The dry weight of each sheet is 25 lb., and the moisture content will be reduced from 50 to 5% water by air entering at 250°F., humidity 0.01 lb. water/lb. dry air. Forty pounds dry air will be passed through the drier per pound dry solid.

In a small-scale experiment, when dried with air at constant drying conditions, dry-bulb temperature 200°F., wet-bulb temperature 120°F., and at the same velocity to be used in the large drier, the constant drying rate was 0.25 lb. water evaporated/- (hr.)(sq. ft.) and the critical moisture content 30%. The equilibrium moisture content was negligible.

*a.* Calculate the value of $k_Y$ from the data of the small-scale experiment.

*b.* For the large drier, calculate the humidity of the air leaving, and at the point where the solid reaches the critical moisture content.

*c.* Estimate the time of drying in the large drier.

*d.* How many sheets of material will be in the drier at all times?

**10.** A continuous countercurrent hot-air tunnel drier is to be designed to dry a filter-press cake of coarse crystals of an inorganic material, insoluble in water. The filter-press cake will be placed on trays 3 by 3 ft. by 1 in., 20 trays to a truck, with 2 in. between trays. The tunnel drier will have a cross section 6 ft. high by 40 in. wide. The trays have a reinforced screen bottom, so that drying takes place from both top and bottom of each tray. Production is such as to permit introducing one truck load per hour. Each tray contains 65 lb. dry solid, which will enter the drier at 75°F., 50% moisture, and will be dried to negligible moisture content. The critical moisture content is 15%, and the equilibrium moisture is negligible. The trucks are steel, each weighing about 300 lb. The air is to enter at 300°F., humidity 0.03 lb. water/lb.

dry air, and the discharged solid is expected to leave at 275°F.   The air is to be blown over the trays so that the average velocity at the air entrance is to be 15 ft./sec. over the trays.   The specific heat of the dry solid is 0.3 B.t.u./(lb.)(°F.).   The drier is to be well insulated.

*a.* Calculate the length of the drier required.

*b.* The entering air is to be prepared by recycling a portion of the discharged air with atmospheric air (75°F., humidity = 0.01 lb. water/lb. dry air) and heating the mixture to 300°F.   Calculate the percentage of discharge air to be recycled and the heat required.   Calculate the heat also as B.t.u./lb. water evaporated.

# CHAPTER 13

# LEACHING

Leaching is the preferential solution of one or more constituents of a solid mixture by contact with a liquid solvent. This unit operation, one of the oldest in the chemical industries, has been given many names, depending to some extent upon the technique used for carrying it out. *Leaching* and *lixiviation* both originally referred to percolation of the liquid through a fixed bed of the solid, but the former term at least is now used to describe the operation generally, by whatever means it may be done. The term *extraction* is also widely used to describe this operation in particular, although it is applied to all the separation operations as well, whether mass-transfer or mechanical methods are involved. *Decoction* refers specifically to the use of the solvent at its boiling temperature. When the soluble material is largely on the surface of an insoluble solid and is merely washed off by the solvent, the operation is sometimes called *elutriation,* or *elution.* This chapter will also consider these washing operations, since they are frequently intimately associated with leaching.

The metallurgical industries are perhaps the largest users of the leaching operation. Most useful minerals occur in mixtures with large proportions of undesirable constituents, and leaching of the valuable material is a separation method which is frequently applied. For example, copper minerals are preferentially dissolved from certain of their ores by leaching with sulfuric acid or ammoniacal solutions, and gold is separated from its ores with the aid of sodium cyanide solutions. Leaching similarly plays an important part in the metallurgical processing of aluminum, cobalt, manganese, nickel, and zinc. Many naturally occurring organic products are separated from their original structure by leaching. For example, sugar is leached from sugar beets with hot water, vegetable oils are recovered from seeds such as soybeans and cottonseed by leaching with organic solvents, tannin is dissolved out of various tree barks by leaching with water, and many pharmaceutical products are similarly recovered from plant roots and leaves. Tea and coffee are prepared both domestically and industrially by leaching operations. In addition, chemical precipitates are frequently washed of their adhering mother liquors by techniques and in equipment quite similar to those used in true leaching operations, as in the washing of caustic soda liquor from precipitated calcium carbonate following the reaction between soda ash and lime.

**Preparation of the Solid.** The success of a leaching and the technique to be used will very frequently depend upon any prior treatment which may be given the solid.

In some instances, small particles of the soluble material are completely surrounded by a matrix of insoluble matter. The solvent must then diffuse into the mass, and the resulting solution must diffuse out, before a separation can result. This is the situation in the case of many metallurgical materials. Crushing and grinding of such solids will greatly accelerate the leaching action, since then the soluble portions are made more accessible to the solvent. A certain copper ore, for example, can be leached effectively by sulfuric acid solutions within 4 to 8 hr. if ground to pass through a 60-mesh screen, in 5 days if crushed to $\frac{1}{4}$-in. granules, and only in 4 to 6 years if 6-in. lumps are used.[22] Since grinding is expensive, the quality of the ore will have much to do with the choice of size to be leached. In the case of certain gold ores, on the other hand, the tiny metallic particles are scattered throughout a matrix of quartzite which is so impervious to the leaching solvent that it is essential to grind the rock to pass through a 100-mesh screen if leaching is to occur at all. When the soluble substance is more or less uniformly distributed throughout the solid or even in solid solution, the leaching action may provide channels for the passage of fresh solvent and fine grinding may not be necessary. Collapse of the insoluble skeleton which remains after solute removal may then present problems, however.

Vegetable and animal bodies are cellular in structure, and the natural products to be leached from these materials are usually found inside the cells. If the cell walls remain intact upon exposure to a suitable solvent, then the leaching action involves osmotic passage of the solute through the cell walls. This may be a slow process. It is, however, impractical and sometimes undesirable to grind the material sufficiently small to release the contents of individual cells. Thus, sugar beets are cut into thin, wedge-shaped slices called "cossettes" before leaching in order to reduce the time required for the solvent water to reach the individual plant cells. The cells are deliberately left intact, however, so that the sugar will pass through the semipermeable cell walls while the undesirable colloidal and albuminous materials largely remain behind. In the case of many pharmaceutical products recovered from plant roots, stems, and leaves, the plant material is frequently dried before treatment, and this does much toward rupturing the cell walls and releasing the solute for direct action by the solvent. Vegetable seeds and beans, such as soybeans, are usually rolled or flaked to give particles in the size range 0.005 to 0.02 in. The cells are, of course, smaller than this, but they are largely ruptured by the flaking process, and the oils are then more readily contacted by the solvent.

When the solute is adsorbed upon the surface of solid particles or merely dissolved in adhering solution, no grinding or crushing is necessary and the particles may be washed directly.

**Temperature of Leaching.** It is usually desirable to leach at as high a temperature as possible. Higher temperatures result in higher solubility of the solute in the solvent, and consequently higher ultimate concentrations in the leach liquor are possible. The viscosity of the liquid is lower and the diffusivities larger at higher temperatures, and this leads to increased rates of leaching. In the case of some natural products such as sugar beets, however, temperatures which are too high may lead to leaching of excessive amounts of undesirable solutes or chemical deterioration of the solid.

**Methods of Operation and Equipment.** Leaching operations are carried out under batch and semibatch (unsteady-state) as well as under completely continuous (steady-state) conditions. In each category, both stagewise and continuous-contact types of equipment are to be found. Two major handling techniques are used, spraying or trickling the liquid over the solid, and immersing the solid completely in the liquid. The choice of equipment to be used in any case depends greatly upon the physical form of the solids and the difficulties and cost of handling them. This has led in many instances to the use of very specialized types of equipment in certain industries.

## I. UNSTEADY-STATE OPERATION

The unsteady-state operations include those where the solids and liquids are contacted in purely batchwise fashion and also those where a batch of the solid is contacted with a continually flowing stream of the liquid (semibatch method). Coarse solid particles are usually treated in fixed beds by percolation methods, whereas finely divided solids, which may more readily be kept in suspension, may be dispersed throughout the liquid with the help of some sort of agitator.

**In-place Leaching.** This refers to the percolation leaching of minerals in place at the mine, by circulation of the solvent over and through the ore body. It has been applied to the leaching of low-grade copper ores containing less than 0.5 per cent copper, whose value was too low to warrant the expense of mining. It is also regularly used in the removal of salt from deposits below the earth's surface by solution of the salt in water which is pumped down to the deposits.

**Heap Leaching.** Low-grade ores whose mineral values do not warrant the expense of crushing or grinding may be leached in the form of run-of-mine lumps built into huge piles upon impervious ground. The leach liquor is then pumped over the ore and collected as it drains from the heap. Copper has been leached from pyritic ores in this manner, in heaps containing as much as 25,000,000 tons of ore, using over 5,000,000 gal. of leach liquor per day. It may require up to 7 or more years to reduce the copper content of such heaps from 2 to 0.3 per cent.

**Percolation Tanks.** Solids of intermediate size may be conveniently leached by percolation methods in open tanks. The construction of these tanks varies greatly, depending upon the nature of the solid and liquid to be handled and the size of the operation, but they are relatively inexpensive. Small tanks are frequently made of wood, provided that this material is not chemically attacked by the leach liquid. The solid particles to be leached rest upon a false bottom, which in the simplest construction consists of a grating of wooden strips arranged parallel to each other and sufficiently close to support the solid. These in turn may rest upon similar strips arranged at right angles, 6 in. or more apart, so that the leach liquor may flow to a collection pipe leading from the bottom of the tank. For supporting fairly fine particles, the wood grating may be further covered by a coconut matting and a tightly stretched canvas filter cloth, held in place by calking a rope into a groove around the periphery of the false bottom. Small tanks may also be made entirely of metal, with perforated false bottoms upon which a filter cloth is placed, as in the leaching of pharmaceutical products from plants. Very large percolation tanks (150 by 110 by 18 ft. deep) for the leaching of copper ores have been made of reinforced concrete and lined with lead or bituminous mastic. Small tanks may be provided with side doors near the bottom for sluicing away the leached solid, while very large tanks are usually emptied by excavating from the top. Tanks should be filled with solid of as uniform a particle size as practical, since then the percentage of voids will be largest and the pressure drop required for flow of the leaching liquid least. This also leads to uniformity of the extent of leaching individual solid particles and less difficulty with channeling of the liquid through a limited number of passageways through the solid bed.

The operation of such a tank may follow any of several procedures. After the tank is filled with solid, a batch of solvent sufficient completely to immerse the solid may be pumped into the tank and the entire mass may be allowed to steep or soak for a prescribed period of time. During this period the batch of liquid may or may not be circulated over the solid by pumping. The liquid may then be drained from the solid by withdrawing it through the false bottom of the tank. This entire operation then represents a single stage. Repetition of this process will eventually dissolve all the solute. The only solute then retained is that dissolved in the solution wetting the drained solid. This may be washed out by filling the tank with fresh solvent and repeating the operation as many times as necessary. An alternative method is continuously to admit liquid into the tank and continuously to withdraw the resulting solution, with or without recirculation of a portion of the total flow. Such an operation may be equivalent to many stages. Since the solution which results is usually more dense than the solvent, convective mixing is reduced by percolation in the downward direction. Upward flow is sometimes used, nevertheless, in order to avoid clogging of the bed or the filter with fines, but this may result in excessive entrainment of the fines in the overflow liquid. Still a further modification, less frequently used, is to spray the liquid continuously over the top and allow it to trickle downward through the solid without fully immersing the solid at any time.

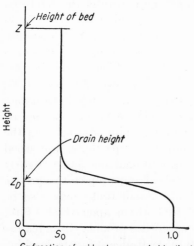

S=fraction of void volume occupied by liquid

FIG. 13.1. Drainage of packed beds.[6]

**Retention of Liquid after Drainage.** Imagine a bed of granular solids whose void space is completely filled with liquid. When the liquid is allowed to drain under the influence of gravity, with admission of air to the voids from the top of the bed, the rate of liquid flow is at first very rapid. The rate gradually falls, and after a relatively long period of time no additional drainage occurs. The bed still contains liquid, however. The fraction of the void volume still occupied by liquid is termed the *residual saturation S*. Figure 13.1 shows the variation of $S$ with height of the bed.[6] In the upper part of the bed the value of $S$ is constant at $S_0$, and this represents the liquid which remains in the crevasses and small angles between the particles as fillets, held in place by surface tension. In the lower part of the bed, the liquid is held up in the voids, filling them completely ($S = 1.0$) by capillary action. The drain height $Z_D$ is defined as the height where the value of $S$ is the average in the range $S_0$ to unity, as shown in the figure. The average value of $S$ for the entire bed will be the area between the ordinate axis and the curve of the figure, divided by the bed height $Z$,

$$S_{av} = \frac{(Z - Z_D)S_0}{Z} + \frac{Z_D}{Z} \qquad (13.1)$$

A large number of measurements of $Z_D$ under a wide variety of conditions showed that, approximately,[6]

$$Z_D = \frac{0.275}{(K/g)^{0.5}(\rho_L/\sigma)} \qquad (13.2)$$

where $K$ is the "permeability" of the bed, $\rho_L$ the liquid density, and $\sigma$ the surface tension of the liquid. The value of $S_0$ was found to depend upon the group $K\rho_L/g\sigma$, called the *capillary number*, as follows:

$$\frac{K\rho_L}{g\sigma} < 0.02: \qquad\qquad\qquad S_0 = 0.075 \qquad\qquad\qquad (13.3)$$

$$\frac{K\rho_L}{g\sigma} \geq 0.02: \qquad\qquad\qquad S_0 = \frac{0.0018}{K\rho_L/g\sigma} \qquad\qquad (13.4)$$

In these expressions it is assumed that drainage has occurred under the action of the force of gravity only and that the contact angle between liquid and solid surfaces is 180°.

The permeability $K$ is the proportionality constant in the flow equation for laminar flow through the bed,

$$G = \frac{K\rho_L \, \Delta P}{\mu_L Z} \qquad\qquad\qquad\qquad (13.5)$$

where $\Delta P$ is the drop in pressure across the bed and $G$ is the mass velocity of flow based on the entire cross section of the bed. Equation (6.26) describes the flow through beds of granular solids, and for laminar flow only the first term of the right-hand side of this expression is used. If $\Delta P/Z$ from this equation is substituted in Eq. (13.5), with Re replaced by $d_p G/\mu_L$, simplification leads to

$$K = \frac{d_p^2 \epsilon^3 g_c}{150(1 - \epsilon)^2} \qquad\qquad\qquad (13.6)$$

where $d_p$ is the diameter of a sphere of the same surface/volume ratio as the particles of the bed and $\epsilon$ is the fractional-void volume. For fibrous material and others whose value of $d_p$ may be difficult to estimate, $K$ may be obtained from Eq. (13.5) after experimental measurement of the pressure drop for laminar flow through the bed.

**Illustration 1.** The sugar remaining in a bed of bone char used for decolorizing is leached by flooding the bed with water, following which the bed is drained of the resulting sugar solution. The bed is 10 ft. deep, the temperature is 150°F., and the sugar solution which drains has a density 71 lb./cu. ft. and a surface tension 66 dynes/cm. The bulk density of the char is 60 lb./cu. ft. and the individual particle density 110 lb./cu. ft. The particles have a specific external surface 80 sq. ft./lb.

Estimate the weight of solution still retained by the bed after dripping of the solution has stopped. Express this also as lb. solution/lb. dry bone char.

*Solution.* The fractional void volume $= \epsilon = 1 -$ (bulk density/particle density) $= 1 - {}^{60}\!/_{110} = 0.455$ cu. ft. voids/cu. ft. bed. The particle surface $= a_p = (80$ sq. ft./lb.)$60 = 4,800$ sq. ft./cu. ft. bed.

Eq. (6.27):     $d_p = 6(1 - \epsilon)/a_p = 6(1 - 0.455)/4,800 = 0.000569$ ft.

Eq. (13.6):     $K = \dfrac{(0.000569)^2(0.455)^3(4.17)(10^8)}{150(1 - 0.455)^2} = 0.285$ cu. ft./hr.$^2$

$\qquad\qquad\qquad \sigma = (66 \text{ dynes/cm.})(6.89)(10^{-5}) = 455(10^{-5})$ lb./ft.

$\qquad\qquad\qquad \dfrac{K\rho_L}{g\sigma} = \dfrac{0.285(71)}{4.17(10^8)(455)(10^{-5})} = 10.67(10^{-6})$

Eq. (13.3):     $S_0 = 0.075$

Eq. (13.2):     $Z_D = \dfrac{0.275}{[0.285/4.17(10^8)]^{0.5}[71/455(10^{-5})]} = 0.675$ ft.

$\qquad\qquad\qquad Z = 10$ ft.

Eq. (13.1):          $S_{av} = \dfrac{(10 - 0.675)(0.075)}{10} + \dfrac{0.675}{10} = 0.1375$

Vol. of liquid retained/vol. of bed = $0.1375\epsilon = 0.1375(0.455) = 0.0625$ cu. ft./cu. ft.
Wt. of liquid in bed          = $0.0625[\pi(3)^2(10)/4]71 = 313$ lb.
Wt. of liquid/wt. of dry solid      = $0.0625(71)/1(60) = 0.073$ lb./lb.

**Countercurrent Multiple Contact. The Shanks System.** Leaching and washing of the leached solute from the percolation tanks by the cocurrent methods described above will inevitably result in weak solutions of the solute.  The strongest solution will result if a countercurrent scheme is used, wherein the final withdrawn solution is taken from contact with the freshest solid and the fresh solvent is added to solid from

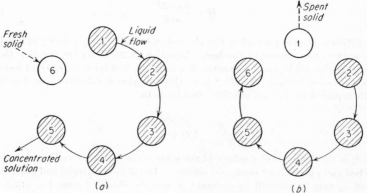

FIG. 13.2. Countercurrent multiple contact, Shanks system.

which most of the solute has already been leached or washed.  In order to avoid moving the solids physically from tank to tank in such a process, the arrangement of Fig. 13.2, shown schematically for a system of six tanks, is used.  This *Shanks system*,† as it is called, is operated in the following manner:

1. Assume at the time of inspecting the system at Fig. 13.2*a* that it has been in operation for some time.  Tank 6 is empty, tanks 1 to 5 are filled with solid, tank 5 most recently and tank 1 for the longest time. Tanks 1 to 5 are also filled with leach liquid, and the most concentrated is in tank 5 since it is in contact with the freshest solid.  Fresh solvent has just been added to tank 1.

2. Withdraw the concentrated solution from tank 5, transfer the liquid from tank 4 to tank 5, from 3 to 4, from 2 to 3, and from 1 to 2.  Add fresh solid to tank 6.

3. Refer to Fig. 13.2*b*.  Discard the spent solid from tank 1.  Transfer

† Named after James Shanks, who first introduced the system in 1841 into England for the leaching of soda ash from the "black ash" of the Le Blanc process.  It was, however, apparently a German development.

the liquid from tank 5 to tank 6, from 4 to 5, from 3 to 4, and from 2 to 3. Add fresh solvent to tank 2. The circumstances are now the same as they were at the start in Fig. 13.2*a*, except that the tank numbers are each advanced by one.

4. Continue the operation in the same manner as before.

After several cycles have been run through in this manner, the concentrations of solution and in the solid in each tank approach very closely the values obtaining in a truly continuous countercurrent multistage leaching. The system can, of course, be operated with any number of tanks, and anywhere from 6 to 16 are common. They need not be arranged in a circle but are better placed in a row, called an "extraction battery," so that additional tanks may be conveniently added to the system if desired. The tanks may be placed at progressively decreasing levels, so that liquid may flow from one to the other by gravity with a minimum of pumping.

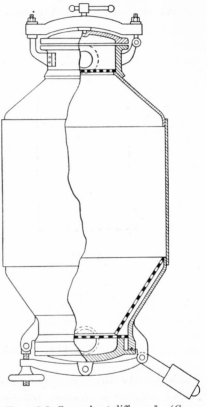

Such leaching tanks and arrangements are used extensively in the metallurgical industries, for recovery of tannins from tree barks and woods, for leaching sodium nitrate from Chilean nitrate-bearing rock (*caliche*), and in many other processes.

**Percolation in Closed Vessels.** When the pressure drop for flow of liquid is too high for gravity flow, closed vessels must be used and the liquid is pumped through the bed of

FIG. 13.3. Sugar-beet diffuser.[7] (*Courtesy of the Institution of Chemical Engineers.*)

solid. Such vessels are sometimes called "diffusers." Closed tanks are also necessary to prevent evaporation losses when the solvent is very volatile or when temperatures above the normal boiling point of the solvent are desired. For example, some tannins are leached with water at 250°F., 50 lb./sq. in. pressure, in closed percolation tanks.

Designs vary considerably, depending upon the application. In the case of leaching of sugar from sugar-beet slices, or cossettes, a diffuser of the type shown in Fig. 13.3 is used. These are arranged in a battery containing up to 16 vessels, and the beets are leached with hot water in the countercurrent fashion of the Shanks system.  Heaters are placed between the diffusers to maintain a solution temperature of 160 to 170°F. In this manner 95 to 98 per cent of the sugar, in beets containing initially about 18 per cent, may be leached to form a solution of 12 per cent concentration.

**Filter-press Leaching.**  Finely divided solids, too fine for treatment by percolation in relatively deep percolation tanks, may be filtered and

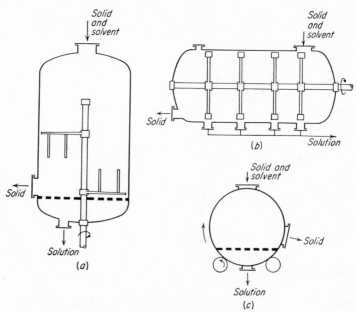

Fig. 13.4. Agitated batch leaching vessels.

leached in the filter press by pumping the solvent through the press cake. This is, of course, common practice in the washing of mother liquor from precipitates which have been filtered.

**Agitated Vessels.**  Channeling of the solvent in percolation or filter-press leaching of fixed beds, with its consequent slow and incomplete leaching, may be avoided by stirring the liquid and solid in leaching vessels.  For coarse solids, many types of stirred or agitated vessels have been devised.  In such cases, closed cylindrical vessels are arranged vertically (Fig. 13.4a) and are fitted with power-driven paddles or stirrers on vertical shafts, as well as false bottoms for drainage of the leach solution at the end of the operation.  In others, the vessels are horizontal, as in Fig. 13.4b, with the stirrer arranged on a horizontal shaft.  In some cases, a horizontal drum is the extraction vessel, and the solid and liquid are

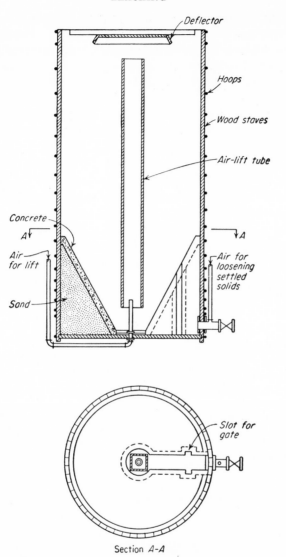

Section *A-A*

FIG. 13.5. Pachuca tank.[16]

tumbled about inside by rotation of the drum on rollers, as in **Fig. 13.4c.**
These devices are operated in batchwise fashion and provide a single
leaching stage. They may be used singly but very frequently also are
used in batteries arranged for countercurrent leaching. They have been
used extensively in the older European and South American installations
for leaching of vegetable oils from seeds,[8] but relatively little in the
United States.[20]

Finely divided solids may be suspended in leaching solvents by agitation, and for batch operation a variety of agitated vessels are used. The simplest is the Pachuca tank (Fig. 13.5), which is employed extensively in the metallurgical industries. These tanks may be constructed of wood, metal, or concrete and may be lined with inert metal such as lead, depending upon the nature of the leaching liquid. Agitation is accomplished by an air lift: the bubbles of air rising through the central tube cause the upward flow of liquid and suspended solid in the tube and consequently vertical circulation of the tank contents. The standard mechanical agitators, with turbine-type impellers, for example, may also be used to keep the finely divided solids suspended in the liquid. After the leaching has been accomplished, the agitation is stopped, the solid is allowed to settle in the same or a separate vessel, and the clear, supernatant liquid may be decanted by siphoning over the top of the tank or by withdrawal through discharge pipes placed at an appropriate level in the side of the tank. If the solids are finely divided and settle to a compressible sludge, the amount of solution retained in the settled solids will be considerable. Agitation and settling with several batches of wash solvent may then be necessary to recover the last traces of solute, and this may be done in a countercurrent fashion. Alternatively, the solid may be filtered and washed in the filter.

**Batch Settling.** The settling characteristics of a slurry consisting of a finely divided solid, of uniform density and reasonably uniform particle size, which is dispersed in a liquid are easily followed by observing a sample of the slurry when allowed to stand undisturbed in a vertical cylinder of transparent glass. If the slurry is initially very dilute, the particles will be observed to settle down through the liquid individually, each at a rate dependent upon the particle size, the relative density of solid and liquid, and the viscosity of the liquid, eventually to collect in a pile at the bottom. Ultimately the liquid becomes clear, but at no time until the end is there a sharp line of demarcation between clear liquid and the settling slurry. For more concentrated slurries, of the sort usually encountered in leaching and washing operations, the behavior is different, however. It will usually be observed that the particles settle more slowly owing to mutual interference (hindered settling). Furthermore, except for a few particles of relatively large size which may be present, there is little classification according to size, and the particles largely settle together. As a result there is usually a reasonably sharp line of demarcation between the clear, supernatant liquor in the upper part of the cylinder and the settling mass of solids in the lower part.

Consider the cylinder of Fig. 13.6, initially filled to a height $Z_0$ with a slurry of uniform concentration $w_0$ weight fraction solids, in which some settling has already taken place. At the time of observation, there is a zone $A$ of clear liquid at the top. Directly beneath this zone $B$, throughout which the solids concentration is reasonably uniform at the initial value $w_0$, as shown by the accompanying graph.[4] In zone $D$ at the bottom, usually called the "compression zone," the particles accumulating from above have come to rest upon each other, and, owing to their weight, liquid is squeezed out from between the particles. For compressible sludges, this results in increasing solids concentration with depth in this zone, as shown by the curve. Zone $C$ is a transition zone between $B$ and $D$, and it may not always be clearly defined. As

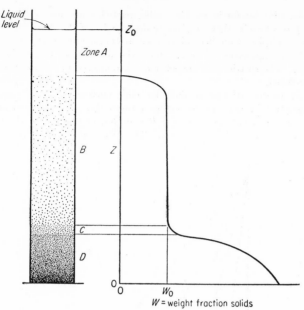

FIG. 13.6. Batch settling.

settling continues beyond the time corresponding to that in the figure, the line of demarcation between zones $A$ and $B$ falls and the height of zone $D$ rises, until even-

tually zone $B$ disappears and only a compression zone containing all the solids remains. This then slowly subsides to some ultimate height.

The rate of settling is usually followed by plotting the height of the line of demarcation between zones $A$ and $B$ against time, as shown by the solid curve of Fig. 13.7. The broken curve represents the position of the upper level of zone $D$. The top of zone $B$ settles at constant rate (curve of $Z$ vs. time straight) from the beginning until zone $B$ has nearly disappeared and all the solids are in the compression zone. The rate of settling of the compression zone to its ultimate height $Z_\infty$ is then relatively slow and is not constant. In a few cases, two constant-rate settling periods may be observed, with substantially no compression period. The appearance of the curves depends not only upon the type of slurry (nature and particle size of the

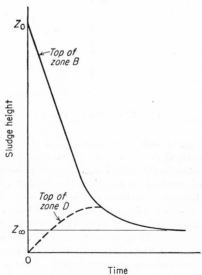

FIG. 13.7. Rate of settling.

solid, and nature of the liquid) but also upon the initial height and concentration of the slurry, as well as the extent of flocculation and whether or not any stirring is done during settling.

*Flocculation.* If the finely divided solid particles are all similarly electrically charged, they repel each other and remain dispersed. If the charge is neutralized by addition, for example, of an electrolyte (flocculating agent) to the mixture, the particles may form aggregates, or flocs. Since the flocs are of larger size, they settle more rapidly. The slurries and suspensions encountered in chemical operations are usually flocculated.

*Stirring.* Very slow stirring, so slow that eddy currents are not formed within the liquid, changes the character of the settling profoundly. The floc structure is altered so that the solids concentration in zone $B$ is no longer uniform at the initial value[5] and zone $D$ may not be clearly defined. The ultimate height of the settled slurry

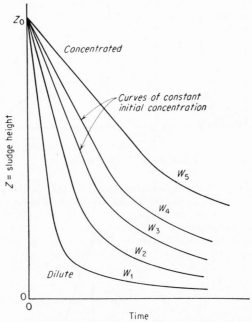

FIG. 13.8. Batch settling of slurries. Effect of slurry concentration.

may be only a fraction of that obtained without stirring[13] owing to breakdown of bridged floc structures in the compression zone, and the ultimate concentration of solids in the settled mass is correspondingly greater. Generally, however, the zones of constant- and falling-rate settling are still observed, although the rates will be different from those obtained without stirring.[23]

*Concentration.* The rate of settling decreases with increased initial concentration of the solids owing to the increase of the effective density and viscosity of the medium through which the particles settle. Figure 13.8 illustrates the effect usually to be expected when slurries of increasing concentration of the same substance are settled in columns of the same height. Various attempts to predict the effect of concentration on the settling rate, from knowledge of the curves at one or more concentrations, have not been tested sufficiently thoroughly to make them of certain value. It has been reasonably well established, however, that the ultimate settled height $Z_\infty$ is related to the initial concentration for any one type of slurry,[13]

$$\frac{Z_\infty}{Z_0} = aw^b \tag{13.7}$$

where $a$ and $b$ are constants which can be determined from measurements of $Z_\infty$ and $Z_0$ for two values of $w$. In the case of stirred settling, the relation may hold only for moderate values of $w$.

*Height.* Refer to Fig. 13.9, which shows settling curves for the same slurry begun at different initial heights. The initial constant settling rate is independent of height, and provided some critical minimum value of $Z_0$ is exceeded, the ultimate value of $Z_\infty/Z_0$ will apparently also be constant. The constant-settling-rate lines both terminate on a line $OA$ radiating from the origin, and in general any line[23] radiating from the origin such as $OB$ will be cut so that line $OC$/line $OB = Z_0/Z_0'$. It follows that the time for a slurry to settle to a fixed fractional height $Z/Z_0$ is proportional to the initial height $Z_0$. In this way it is possible reasonably well to predict the settling curves for deep tanks from results obtained in small laboratory cylinders. In making such laboratory tests, however, it is important[13] to use cylinders at least 3 ft. tall and at least 2 in. in diameter and to maintain all other conditions in the laboratory test identical with those expected to prevail on the large scale.

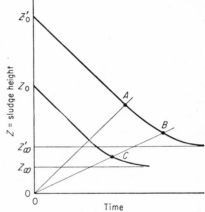

FIG. 13.9. Batch settling of the same slurry at different initial heights.

**Percolation vs. Agitation.** If a solid in the form of large lumps is to be leached, a decision must frequently be made whether to crush it to coarse lumps and leach by percolation or whether to fine-grind it and leach by agitation and settling. No general answer can be given to this problem owing to the diverse leaching characteristics of the various solids and the values of the solute, but among the considerations are the following: Fine grinding is more costly but provides more rapid and possibly more thorough leaching. It suffers the disadvantages that the weight of liquid associated with the settled solid may be as great as the weight of the solid, or more, so that considerable solvent is used in washing the leached solute free of solute and the resulting solution is dilute. Coarsely ground particles, on the other hand, leach more slowly and possibly less thoroughly but on draining may retain relatively little solution, require less washing, and thus provide a more concentrated final solution.

## II. STEADY-STATE (CONTINUOUS) OPERATION

Equipment for continuous steady-state operation may be broadly classified into two major categories, according to whether it operates in stagewise or in continuous-contact fashion. Stagewise equipment may sometimes be assembled in multiple units so as to produce multistage effects, whereas continuous-contact equipment may provide the equivalent of many stages in a single device.

**Leaching during Grinding.** As has been pointed out earlier, many solids require grinding in order to make the soluble portions accessible to the leaching solvents, and if continuous wet grinding is practiced, some of the leaching may be accomplished at this time. As much as 50 to 75 per cent of the soluble gold may be dissolved by grinding the ore in the presence of cyanide solution, for example. Similarly, castor seeds are ground in an attrition mill with solvent for the castor oil.[1] The liquid and solid flow through a grinding mill in parallel and consequently tend to come to a concentration equilibrium. Such operations are therefore single-stage leachings and are usually supplemented by additional agitation or washing operations, as described later.

**Agitated Vessels.** Finely ground solids which can be readily suspended in liquids by agitation may be continuously leached in any of the many types of agitated tanks or vessels. These must be arranged for continuous flow of liquid and solid into and out of the tank and must be carefully designed so that no accumulation of solid occurs. Owing to the thorough mixing ordinarily obtained these devices are single-stage in their action, the liquid and solid tending to come to equilibrium within the vessel.

Mechanically agitated vessels may be used, for which the turbine-type agitator is probably most generally suitable. Pachuca tanks are frequently used in the metallurgical industries. The Dorr agitator (Fig. 13.10) utilizes both the air-lift principle and mechanical raking of the solids and is extensively used in both the metallurgical and the chemical industry for continuous leaching and washing of finely divided solids. The central hollow shaft of the agitator acts as an air lift and at the same time revolves slowly. The arms attached to the bottom of the shaft rake the settled solids toward the center of the tank bottom, where they are lifted by the air lift through the shaft to the revolving launders attached to the top. The launders then distribute the elevated mixture of liquid and solid over the entire cross section of the tank. The rake arms may be lifted to free them of solids which may settle during a shutdown, and they are also provided with auxiliary air lines to assist in freeing them from settled solid. For unevenly sized solids, operation of the agitator may be so adjusted that coarse particles, which may require longer leaching time, remain in the tank for longer periods of time than the finer. These agitators are regularly built in sizes ranging from 5 to 40 ft. in diameter.

The average holding time in an agitated vessel may be calculated by dividing the vessel contents by the rate of flow into the vessel. This

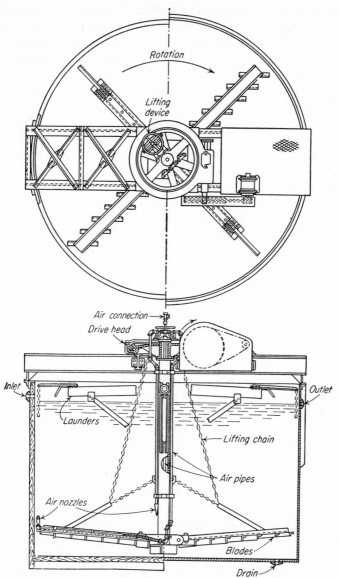

FIG. 13.10. Dorr agitator.   (*Courtesy of The Dorr Co.*)

may be done separately for solid and liquid, and the holding time for
each will be different if the ratio of the amounts of one to the other in
the vessel is different from that in the feed.   The average holding time
of the solid must be sufficient to provide the leaching action required.
Individual solid particles, of course, may short-circuit the tank, by which

is meant that they may pass through in times much shorter than the calculated average, and this will lead to low stage efficiency. Short circuiting may be eliminated by passing the solid-liquid mixture through a series of smaller agitated vessels, one after the other, the sum of whose average holding time is the necessary leach time. This may be readily accomplished with gravity flow of the slurry by placing the individual tanks in the series at progressively lower levels. Three vessels in series are usually sufficient to reduce short circuiting to a negligible amount. It should be noted that, since liquid and solid pass through these vessels in parallel flow, the entire series is still equivalent to only a single stage.

The effluent from continuous agitators may be sent to a filter for separating liquid from solid, upon which the solid may be washed free of dissolved solids, or to a series of thickeners for countercurrent washing.

**Thickeners.** Thickeners are mechanical devices designed especially for continuously increasing the ratio of solid to liquid in a dilute suspension of finely sized particles by settling and decanting, producing a clear liquid and a thickened sludge as two separate products. Thickeners may be used prior to any ordinary filter in order to reduce filtering costs. Owing to the fact that both effluents are pumpable and consequently readily transported, however, thickeners are frequently used to wash leached solids and chemical precipitates free of adhering solution in a continuous multistage countercurrent arrangement, and it is in this application that they are of interest here.

A typical single-compartment thickener of the Dorr Company's design is shown in Fig. 13.11. The thin slurry of liquid and suspended solids enters a large settling tank through a feed well at the top center, in such a manner as to avoid mixing of the slurry with the clear liquid at the top of the tank. The solids settle from the liquid which fills the tank, and the settled sludge is gently directed toward the discharge cone at the bottom by four sets of plow blades or rakes. These revolve slowly so as not to disturb the settled solid unduly. The sludge is pumped from the discharge cone by means of a diaphragm pump. The clear, supernatant liquid overflows into a launder built about the upper periphery of the tank. Thickeners are built in sizes ranging from 6 to 325 ft. in diameter, for handling granular as well as flocculent solids, and of varying detailed design depending upon the size and service. In order to reduce the ground-area requirements, several thickeners operating in parallel, and superimposed as in Fig. 13.12, may be used. Such a device delivers a single sludge product.

The liquid content of the sludge is greatly dependent upon the nature of the solids and liquid and upon the time allowed for settling but in typical cases might be in the range 15 to 75 per cent liquid. The less

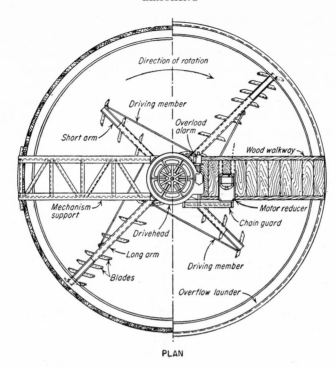

PLAN

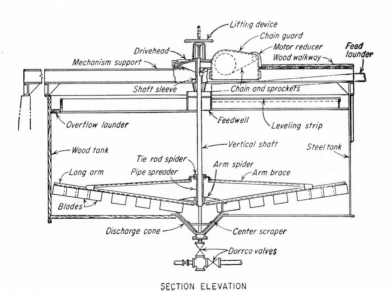

SECTION ELEVATION

FIG. 13.11. Dorr thickener. (*Courtesy of The Dorr Co.*)

liquid retained, the more efficient will be the leaching or washing process which is being carried on.

**Continuous Countercurrent Decantation.**    Leaching equipment such as agitators or grinding mills may discharge their effluent into a cascade of thickeners for continuous countercurrent washing of the finely divided solids free of adhering solute.    The same type of cascade may also be used to wash the solids formed during chemical reactions, as in the manufacture of phosphoric acid, by treatment of phosphate rock with sulfuric

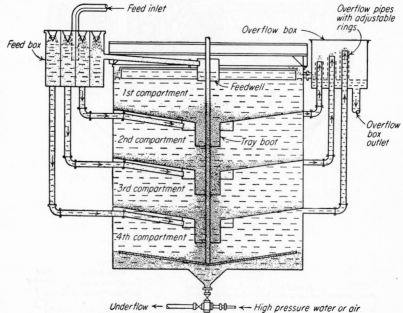

FIG. **13.12.** Dorr balanced-tray thickener.    (*Courtesy of The Dorr Co.*)

acid, or of blanc fixe, by reaction of sulfuric acid and barium sulfide, or of lithopone.

A simple arrangement is shown in Fig. 13.13*a*.    The solids to be leached (or the reagents for a reaction), together with solution from the second thickener, are introduced into the leaching agitators at the left, and the strong solution thus produced is decanted from the solids by the first thickener.    The agitators together with the first thickener then constitute a single stage.    The sludge is passed through the cascade to be washed by the solvent in true countercurrent fashion, and the washed solids are discharged at the right.    There may, of course, be more or fewer than the four stages shown, and the agitators may be replaced by any continuous-leaching device, such as a grinding mill.    Many variations in the flow sheet are regularly made.    For example, the sludge

from each stage may be "repulped," or vigorously beaten with the solvent, between stages in order to improve the washing efficiency.   Figure
13.13*b* shows an arrangement whereby the underflow from the first
thickener is agitated with overflow from the third, for the purpose of
bringing about the additional leaching possible with dilute solution.
The sludge from the final stage may be filtered, as shown, when the solid
is valuable and is to be delivered reasonably dry or when the solute is

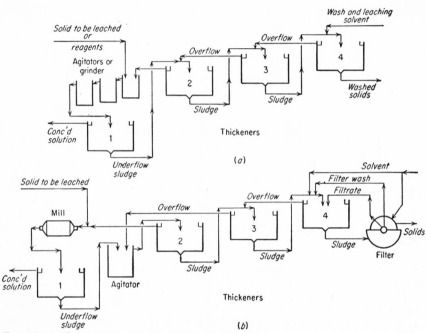

FIG. 13.13.   Continuous countercurrent decantation: (*a*) simple flow sheet and (*b*)
with intermediate agitation and filtration of washed solids.

valuable and solution adhering to the washed solids must be reduced to a
minimum.   For successful operation of these plants, very carefully controlled rates of flow of both sludges and solution are necessary so as not
to disturb the steady-state conditions prevailing.

For small decantation plants, where ground area may be limited, it is
possible to obtain a countercurrent cascade of thickeners built in superimposed fashion into a single shell.

**Continuous Settling.**   The concentrations existing at the various levels of a continuous thickener under steady-state operation differ considerably from those found
in batch settling.   The solid curve of Fig. 13.14 shows typical concentrations during
normal operation,[5] and four clearly defined zones are found in the thickener corresponding to the various sections of the curve.   The feed slurry is diluted as it issues
from the feed well of the thickener, and the bulk of the liquid passes upward to over-

flow into the launder about the thickener periphery. The solid concentration in the top zone is negligible if the overflow is clear. The solids and the remainder of the feed liquid move downward through the lower three zones and leave in the thickened underflow. The solids concentration in the settling zone is much lower than that in the feed, owing to the dilution, but rises rapidly in the compression zone immediately below. In the bottom zone, the action of the rake disturbs arched structures which the settling solids may form, the weight of the solids presses out the liquid, and the concentration rises to the value in the underflow. If the feed rate to the thickener is increased, the concentration of solids in the settling zone rises and reaches a constant maximum value not related to the feed concentration when the settling capacity of

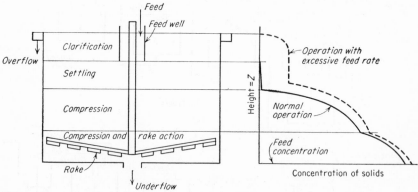

FIG. 13.14. Continuous-thickener characteristics.[5] (*Courtesy of Industrial and Engineering Chemistry.*)

this zone is exceeded. The excess solids, which cannot settle, overflow with the liquid, as indicated by the broken curve of concentrations in Fig. 13.14 for this condition.

The concentration of solids in the underflow sludge for a given rate and concentration of feed may be increased by reducing the rate of withdrawal of sludge. This increases the depth of the compression zone and increases the detention time of the solids within the thickener, although it is important not to raise the level of the compression zone to such an extent that solids appear in the overflow liquid. It is necessary to determine the effects experimentally, which may be done in laboratory equipment of small diameter. Batch-settling tests cannot be used to predict continuous thickener capacities unless extensive experience may be drawn upon to assist in the interpretation of the data.

**Continuous Leaching of Coarse Solids.** Many ingenious devices have been used for moving the solids continuously through a leaching device so that countercurrent action may be obtained. With the exception of the classifiers, which are used principally in the metallurgical industries, these machines were principally developed for the special solids-handling problems arising in the leaching of sugar beets and of vegetable seeds such as cottonseed, soybeans, and the like. Donald[7] has described many of the early devices used for sugar beets. Only the more important of the currently used machines can be described here.

**Classifiers.** Coarse solids may be leached, or more usually washed free of adhering solution or solute, in some types of machinery ordinarily used in the metallurgical industries for classification according to particle size. One such device is shown in Fig. 13.15. The solids are introduced into a tank, which is made with a sloping bottom and which is partly filled with the solvent. The rakes, which are given a reciprocating and circular lifting motion by the driving mechanism, rake the solids upward along the bottom of the tank and out of the liquid. In the upper part of the tank the solids are drained and discharged. The liquid overflows

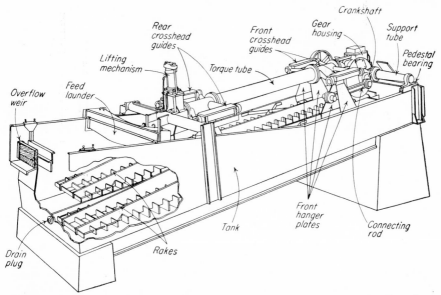

FIG. 13.15. Single Dorr classifier for washing coarse solids. (*Courtesy of The Dorr Co.*)

at the deep end of the tank. The solute concentration in the liquid is reasonably uniform throughout the tank owing to the agitation by the rakes, so that the apparatus produces a single-stage action. Several classifiers may be placed in a cascade for continuous multistage countercurrent action, however, in which case they may be operated by a single drive mechanism.

**Leaching of Vegetable Seeds.** Cottonseeds, soybeans, linseeds (flaxseeds), peanuts, rice bran, castor beans, and many other similar products are regularly leached, or *extracted*, with organic solvents for removing the vegetable oils which they contain. The seeds must usually be specially prepared for most advantageous leaching, and this may involve dehulling, precooking, adjustment of the moisture (water) content, and rolling or flaking. Sometimes a portion of the oil is first removed mechanically by expelling or expression. Leaching solvents are usually petroleum naphthas, for most oils a fraction corresponding closely to hexane, but chlorinated hydrocarbons and the alcohols have also found use. The oil-solvent solution, which usually contains a small amount of finely divided, suspended solids, is called "miscella" and the leached solids "marc." The various leaching devices are usually called "extractors" in this industry.

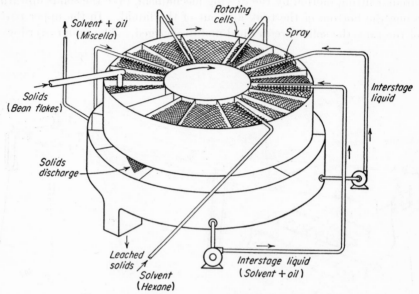

Fig. 13.16. Schematic arrangement of the Rotocel.

The *Rotocel*[17] is essentially a modification of the Shanks system wherein the leaching tanks are continuously moved, in that way permitting continuous introduction and discharge of the solids. Figure 13.16 is a schematic representation of the device, simplified to show the working principle. A circular rotor, containing 18 cells, each fitted with a hinged screen bottom for supporting the solids, slowly revolves above a stationary compartmented tank. As the rotor revolves, each cell passes in turn under a special device for feeding the prepared seeds and then under a series of sprays by which each is periodically drenched with solvent for leaching. After nearly one revolution, the leached contents of each cell are automatically dumped into one of the lower stationary compartments, from which they are continuously conveyed away. The solvent from each spray percolates downward through the solid and the supporting screen into the appropriate compartment of the lower tank, from which it is continuously pumped to the next spray. The leaching is countercurrent, and the strongest solution is taken from the freshest seeds. A number of ingenious mechanical devices are necessary for maintaining smooth operation, and the entire machine is enclosed in a vaportight housing to prevent escape of solvent vapors.

The *Kennedy* extractor,[10,20] a modern arrangement of which is indicated schematically in Fig. 13.17, is another stagewise device which has

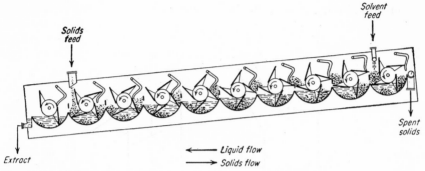

FIG. 13.17. Modern Kennedy extractor. (*Courtesy of The Vulcan Copper and Supply Co.*)

been in use since 1927, originally for leaching tannins from tanbark.[8] It is now used for oilseed and other chemical leaching operations. The solids are leached in a series of tubs and are pushed from one to the next in the cascade by paddles, while the solvent flows in countercurrent. Perforations in the paddles permit drainage of the solids between stages, and the solids are scraped from each paddle as shown. As many tubs may be placed in a cascade as are required.

The other machines described here are of the continuous-contact, rather than the stagewise, type. The *Miag* wheel[18] (Fig. 13.18) is an early German development which is still used extensively in Europe and South America. As the wheel revolves in its casing, the seeds are pushed by the perforated plates countercurrently to the solvent. Screw conveyors are also used in many extractors to carry the solid.

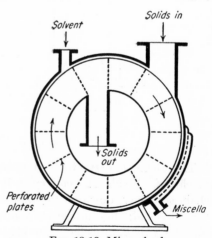

FIG. 13.18. Miag wheel.

In the *Hildebrandt* extractor[18,20] (Fig. 13.19) the solids are conveyed through tubes arranged in U shape. The perforated conveyors rotate at different speeds so that the solids are compacted, particularly in the horizontal leg of the U. Special guide rails along the inside of the tubes prevent the solids from rotating as they are pushed along.   The miscella is discharged through a strainer consisting of a cylindrical sheet, perforated with a number of vertical slots, the inside openings of which are smaller than those outside in order to prevent clogging.   The strainer is kept clear of solid by the scraping action of the conveyor.   Horizontal screw conveyors are also used, as in the *Detrex* system.[12]

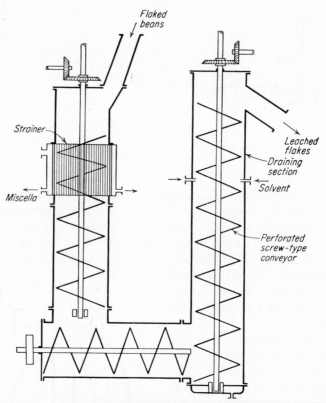

FIG. 13.19. Hildebrandt extractor.

The *Bollman* extractor[20] (Fig. 13.20) is one of several basket-type machines.   Solids are conveyed in perforated baskets attached to a chain conveyor, down on the right and up on the left in the figure.   As they descend, they are leached in parallel flow by a dilute solvent-oil solution ("half miscella") pumped from the bottom of the vessel and sprayed over the baskets at the top.   The liquid percolates through the solids from basket to basket, collects at the bottom as the final strong solution of the oil ("full miscella"), and is removed.   On the ascent, the solids are leached countercurrently by a spray of fresh solvent to provide the half miscella. A short drainage time is provided before the baskets are dumped at the top.

The *Bonotto*-type extractor[18,20] (Fig. 13.21), of which many modifications are in current use, contains a series of circular, slotted plates arranged one above the other. The solids are introduced at the top, spread over the top plate by an arm or rake, pushed through the slot to

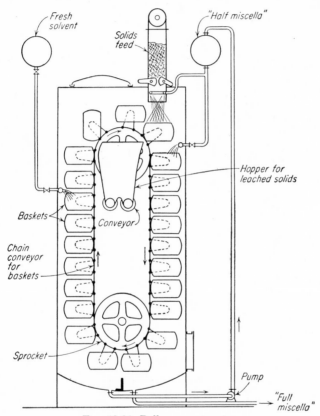

FIG. 13.20. Bollmann extractor.

fall to the next plate below, and so on, to the bottom of the column. Either the rakes or the plates, depending upon the design, are attached to a slowly revolving central shaft. The solvent flows upward through the column, countercurrent to the solids.

Other types of continuous extractors used by the vegetable-oil industry include continuous horizontal filters[2] and horizontal moving screen-type belts[21] for conveying the solids during the leaching operations.

The recovery of solvent from both the miscella and the leached seeds or beans is an essential part of the vegetable-oil extraction process. In the arrangement of operations shown in Fig. 13.22, the miscella is filtered free of entrained, finely divided solids, and the clear solution of oil and solvent is passed first to an evaporator for removal of the bulk of the solvent and finally to a bubble-cap stripping column for removal of the

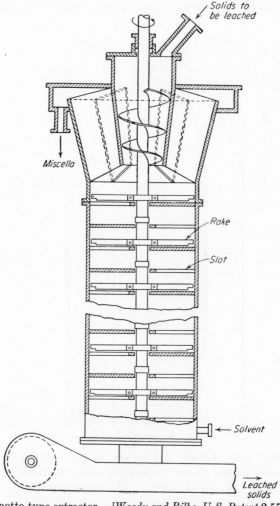

FIG. 13.21. Bonotto-type extractor.    [*Woody and Bilbe, U.S. Patent* 2,551,820 (1951).]

last small quantities.    The solids filtered from the miscella, together with the leached seeds from the extractor, are passed through a steam-jacketed conveyor, where the solvent is evaporated by direct contact of the seeds with steam.    The evaporated solvent and the steam then pass to the evaporators and stripping column.

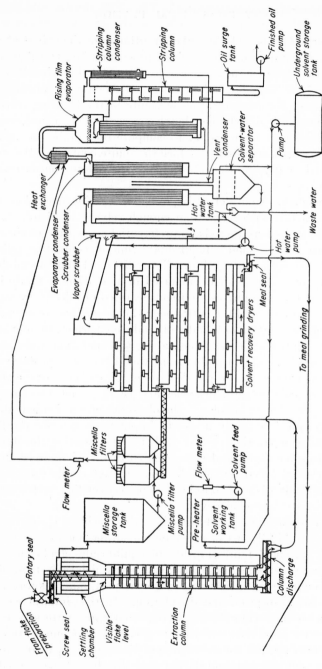

FIG. 13.22. Leaching of vegetable oils and solvent recovery. (Courtesy of The V. D. Anderson Co.)

611

## METHODS OF CALCULATION

It is important to be able to make an estimate of the extent of leaching which may be obtained for a given procedure, i.e., to calculate the amount of soluble substance leached from a solid, knowing the initial solute content of the solid, the number and amount of washings with leaching solvent, the concentration of solute in the leaching solvent, if any, and the method, whether batch or continuous countercurrent. Alternatively, it may be necessary to compute the number of washings, or number of stages, required to reduce the solute content of the solid to some specified value, knowing the amount and solute concentration of the leaching solvent.

**Stage Efficiency.** Consider a simple batch leaching operation, where the solid is leached with more than enough solvent to dissolve all the soluble solute and where there is no preferential adsorption of either solvent or solute by the solid. If adequate time of contact of solid and solvent is permitted, all the solute will be dissolved and the mixture is then a slurry of insoluble solid immersed in a solution of solute in the solvent. The insoluble phases are then separated physically by settling, filtration, or drainage, and the entire operation constitutes one stage. If the mechanical separation of liquid and solid were perfect, there would be no solute associated with the solid leaving the operation and complete separation of solute and insoluble solid would be accomplished with a single stage. This would be an ideal stage, of 100 per cent stage efficiency. In practice, stage efficiencies are usually much less than this: (1) the solute may be incompletely dissolved because of inadequate contact time; (2) most certainly it will be impractical to make the liquid-solid mechanical separation perfect, and the solids leaving the stage will always retain some liquid and its associated dissolved solute. In cases where solute is adsorbed by the solid, even though equilibrium between the liquid and solid phases is obtained, imperfect settling or draining will result in lowered stage efficiency.

**Practical Equilibrium.** In the general case, it will be easiest to make calculations graphically, as in other mass-transfer operations, and this will require graphical representation of equilibrium conditions. It is simplest to use practical equilibrium conditions which take stage efficiencies into account directly, either entirely or in part, much as was done in the case of gas absorption and distillation. In the simplest cases, we must deal with three-component systems containing pure solvent ($A$), insoluble carrier solid ($B$), and soluble solute ($C$). Computations and graphical representation can be made on triangular coordinates for any ternary system of this sort, and the details of this have been worked out.[9] Owing to frequent crowding of the construction into one corner of such a diagram, it is preferable to use a rectangular-coordinate system patterned after that used for fractional adsorption.

The concentration of insoluble solid $B$ in any mixture or slurry will be expressed as $N$ lb. $B$/lb. $(A + C)$, whether the solid is wet with liquid solution or not. Solute $C$ compositions will be expressed as weight fractions on a $B$-free basis: $x =$ wt. fraction $C$ in the effluent solution from a stage ($B$-free basis), and $y =$ wt. fraction $C$ in the solid or slurry ($B$-free basis). The value of $y$ must include all solute $C$ associated with the mixture, including that dissolved in adhering solution as well as undissolved or adsorbed solute. If the solid is dry, as it may be before leaching operations begin, $N$ is the ratio of weights of insoluble to soluble substance, and $y = 1.0$. For pure solvent $A$, $N = 0$, $x = 0$.

The coordinate system then appears as in Fig. 13.23. Consider first a simple case of a mixture of insoluble solid from which all the solute has been leached, suspended in a solution of the solute in a solvent, as represented by point $M_1$ on the figure. The concentration of the clear solution is $x$, and the insoluble solid/solution ratio is $N_{M1}$. Let the insoluble solid be nonadsorbent. If this mixture is allowed to settle, as in a batch-settling tank,

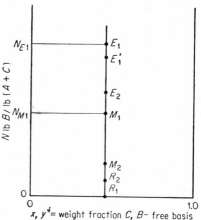

Fig. 13.23. Concentrations in leaching and washing.

the clear liquid which may be drawn off will be represented by point $R_1$ and the remaining sludge will consist of the insoluble solid suspended in a small amount of the solution. The composition of the solution in the sludge will be the same as that of the clear liquid withdrawn, so that $y^* = x$. The concentration of solid $B$ in the sludge $N_{E1}$ will depend upon the length of time $\theta_1$ which was allowed for settling, so that point $E_1$ then represents the slurry. Line $E_1R_1$ is a vertical tie line joining the points representing the two effluent streams, clear liquid and slurry. If the circumstances described were maintained in an actual leaching, points $E_1$ and $R_1$ can be taken as the practical conditions of equilibrium for that leaching. Clearly if less time was allowed for settling, say $\theta_1'$, the sludge would be less concentrated in insoluble solids and might be represented by point $E_1'$. There will be some maximum value of $N$ for the sludge, corresponding to its ultimate settled height, in accordance with the description of batch settling given earlier, but usually in practice insufficient time is allowed for this to be attained. Since the concentration of insoluble solid in a sludge settled for a fixed time depends upon the initial concentration in the slurry, a mixture $M_2$ settled for time $\theta_1$ might result in a sludge corresponding to point $E_2$. If the solid does not settle to give an absolutely clear solution, if too much solution is withdrawn from the settled sludge so that a small amount of solid is carried with it, or if solid $B$ dissolves to a small extent in the solution, the withdrawn solution would be represented by some point such as $R_2$, somewhat above the lower axis of the graph. Similar interpretations may be made for compositions obtained when wet solids are filtered or drained of solution rather than settled, or when continuously thickened.

The settling or thickening characteristics of a slurry depend, as shown earlier, upon the viscosity and relative density of the liquid in which the solid is suspended. Since these in turn depend upon the solution composition, it is possible to obtain experimental data showing the variation of compositions of thickened solids with composition of solution and to plot these on the diagram as practical equilibrium conditions. It is evident, however, that in every case they must be obtained under conditions of time, temperature, and concentrations identical with those pertaining in the plant or process for which the calculations are being made. In the case of drained beds of solids, the equilibrium corresponding to the residual saturation after long-time drainage may be estimated by the methods of Illustration 1. Data for short-time drainage must be obtained experimentally.

In washing operations where the solute is already dissolved, uniform concentration throughout all the solution is rapidly attained, and reduced stage efficiency is most likely to be entirely the result of incomplete drainage or settling. In leaching an undissolved solute interspersed throughout the solid, on the other hand, lowered stage efficiency may be the result of inadequate time of contact as well as incomplete mechanical separation of liquid and solid. In this case it is possible (but not necessary) to distinguish experimentally between the two effects by making measurements of the amount and composition of liquid retained on the solid after short and after long contact time and to use the latter to establish the equilibrium conditions.

Let us now examine a few of the types of equilibrium curves which may be encountered. Figure 13.24a represents data which might be obtained for cases where solute $C$ is infinitely soluble in solvent $A$, so that $x$ and $y$ may have values over the entire range from 0 to 1.0. This would occur in the case of the system soybean oil ($C$)–soybean meal ($B$)–hexane ($A$), where the oil and hexane are infinitely soluble. The curve $DFE$ represents the separated solid under conditions actually to be expected in practice, as discussed above. Curve $GHJ$, the composition of the withdrawn solution, lies above the $N = 0$ axis, and in this case, therefore, either solid $B$ is partly soluble in the solvent or an incompletely settled liquid has been withdrawn. The tie lines such as line $FH$

are not vertical, and this will result (1) if insufficient time of contact with leaching solvent to dissolve all solute is permitted, (2) if preferential adsorption of the solute occurs, or (3) if the solute is soluble in the solid $B$ and distributes unequally between liquid and solid phases at equilibrium. The data may be projected upon a plot of $x$ vs. $y$, as in the manner of adsorption or liquid-extraction equilibria.

Figure 13.24$b$ represents a case where no adsorption of solute occurs, so that withdrawn solution and solution associated with the solid have

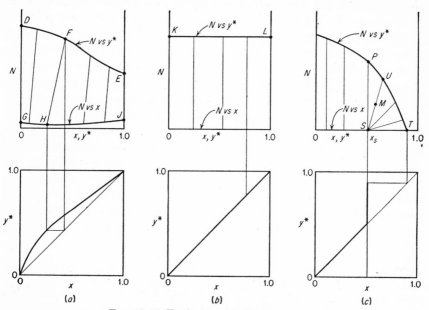

FIG. 13.24. Typical equilibrium diagrams.

the same composition and the tie lines are vertical. This results in an $xy$ curve in the lower figure identical with the 45° line, and a distribution coefficient $m$, defined as $y^*/x$, equals unity. Line $KL$ is horizontal, indicating that the solids are settled or drained to the same extent at all solute concentrations. It is possible to regulate the operation of continuous thickeners so that this will occur, and the conditions are known as "constant underflow." The solution in this case contains no substance $B$, either dissolved or suspended. Figure 13.24$c$ represents a case where solute $C$ has a limited solubility $x_s$ in solvent $A$. No clear solution stronger than $x_s$ can be obtained, so that the tie lines joining slurry and saturated solution must converge, as shown. In this case any mixture $M$ to the right of line $PS$ will settle to give a clear saturated solution $S$ and a slurry $U$ whose composition depends on the position of $M$. Point $T$ represents the composition of pure solid solute after drainage or settling of saturated solution. Since the tie lines to the left of $PS$ are shown vertical, no adsorption occurs and overflow liquids are clear. It will be appreciated that combinations of these various characteristics may appear in a diagram of an actual case.

**Single-stage Leaching.** Consider the single real leaching or washing stage of Fig. 13.25. The circle represents the entire operation, including mixing of solid and leaching solvent and mechanical separation of the resulting insoluble phases by whatever means may be used. Weights of the various streams are expressed as pounds for a batch operation or as lb./hr. [or lb./(hr.)(sq. ft.)] for continuous flow. Since for most purposes the solid $B$ is insoluble in the solvent and a clear liquid leach solution is

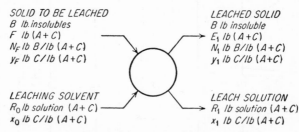

Fig. 13.25. Single-stage leaching or washing.

obtained, the $B$ discharged in the leached solids will be taken as the same as that in the solids to be leached. By definition of $N$,

$$B = N_F F = E_1 N_1 \qquad (13.8)$$

A solute $(C)$ balance,

$$F y_F + R_0 x_0 = E_1 y_1 + R_1 x_1 \qquad (13.9)$$

A solvent $(A)$ balance,

$$F(1 - y_F) + R_0(1 - x_0) = E_1(1 - y_1) + R_1(1 - x_1) \qquad (13.10)$$

and a "solution" (solute + solvent) balance,

$$F + R_0 = E_1 + R_1 = M_1 \qquad (13.11)$$

Mixing the solids to be leached and leaching solvent produces a mixture of $B$-free weight $M_1$ lb. such that

$$N_{M1} = \frac{B}{F + R_0} = \frac{B}{M_1} \qquad (13.12)$$

$$y_{M1} = \frac{y_F F + R_0 x_0}{F + R_0} \qquad (13.13)$$

These relations may be shown on the coordinate system of Fig. 13.26. Point $F$ represents the solids to be leached and $R_0$ the leaching solvent. Point $M_1$, representing the over-all mixture, must fall on the straight line joining $R_0$ and $F$, in accordance with the characteristics of these diagrams described in Chap. 10. Points $E_1$ and $R_1$, representing the effluent streams, are located at opposite ends of the tie line through $M_1$, and their compositions may be read from the diagram. Equation (13.8) permits calculation of the weight of $E_1$ and Eq. (13.11) that of $R_1$. Modification to allow for the presence of $B$ in the liquid withdrawn, necessitating an equilibrium diagram of the type shown in Fig. 13.24a, is readily made by analogy with the corresponding problem in liquid extraction.

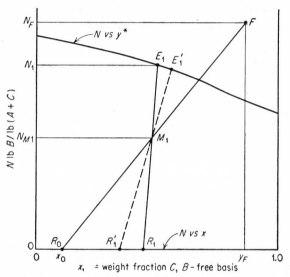

Fig. 13.26. Single-stage leaching or washing.

If the equilibrium data of Fig. 13.26 were obtained experimentally after long contact time of solid and liquid and therefore represent inefficiency of mechanical separation of liquid and solid only, then in a real stage there may be an additional inefficiency owing to short time of contact. The effluent streams may then be represented by points $E_1'$ and $R_1'$ on the figure, and a stage efficiency $(y_F - y_1')/(y_F - y_1)$ may be ascribed to this. In case the equilibrium curve was obtained under conditions of contact time corresponding to the actual leaching, the tie line $E_1R_1$ will give directly the effluent composition.

**Multistage Cocurrent Leaching.** By contacting the leached solids with a fresh batch of leaching solvent, additional solute may be dissolved or washed away from the insoluble material. The calculations for additional stages are merely repetitions of the procedure for a single stage, with the leached solids from any stage becoming the feed solids to the next. Equations (13.8) to (13.13) apply, with only obvious changes in the subscripts to indicate the additional stages. When the number of stages for reducing the solute content of a solute to some specified value must be determined, it must be recalled that we are dealing with real stages, owing to the use of "practical" equilibrium data, and that therefore the number found must be integral. This may require adjustment by trial of either the amount of solute to be leached or the amount and apportioning of solvent to the stages.

**Illustration 2.** Caustic soda is being made by treatment of slaked lime, $Ca(OH)_2$, with a solution of sodium carbonate. The resulting slurry consists of particles of calcium carbonate, $CaCO_3$, suspended in a $10\%$ solution of sodium hydroxide (NaOH), 0.125 lb. suspended solid/lb. solution. This is settled, the clear sodium hydroxide solution withdrawn and replaced by an equal weight of water, and the mixture thoroughly agitated. After repetition of this procedure (a total of two fresh-water washes), what fraction of the original NaOH in the slurry remains unrecovered and therefore lost in the sludge? The settling characteristics of the slurry, determined under conditions representing the practice to be followed in the process [Armstrong and Kammermeyer, *Ind. Eng. Chem.*, **34**, 1228 (1942)], show adsorption of the solute on the solid.

| $x$ = wt. fraction NaOH in clear soln. | $N$ = lb. $CaCO_3$/lb. soln. in settled sludge | $y^*$ = wt. fraction NaOH in soln. of the settled sludge |
|:---:|:---:|:---:|
| 0.0900 | 0.495 | 0.0917 |
| 0.0700 | 0.525 | 0.0762 |
| 0.0473 | 0.568 | 0.0608 |
| 0.0330 | 0.600 | 0.0452 |
| 0.0208 | 0.620 | 0.0295 |
| 0.01187 | 0.650 | 0.0204 |
| 0.00710 | 0.659 | 0.01435 |
| 0.00450 | 0.666 | 0.01015 |

*Solution.* The equilibrium data are plotted in Fig. 13.27. Basis: 1 lb. solution in the original mixture, containing 0.1 lb. NaOH ($C$) and 0.9 lb. $H_2O$ ($A$). $B = 0.125$ lb. $CaCO_3$.

The original mixture corresponds to $M_1$ with $N_{M1} = 0.125$ lb. $CaCO_3$/lb. soln., $y_{M1} = 0.10$ lb. NaOH/lb. soln. $M_1$ is plotted on the figure, and the tie line through this point is drawn. At point $E_1$ representing the settled sludge, $N_1 = 0.47$, $y_1 = 0.100$.

Eq. (13.8):  $E_1 = B/N_1 = 0.125/0.47 = 0.266$ lb. soln. in sludge
$1 - 0.266 = 0.734$ lb. clear soln. withdrawn

*Stage 2.* $R_0 = 0.734$ lb. water added, $x_0 = 0$ lb. NaOH/lb. soln.

Eq. (13.11) adapted to this stage:

$$M_2 = E_1 + R_0 = E_2 + R_2$$
$$M_2 = 0.266 + 0.734 = 1.0 \text{ lb. liquid}$$

Eq. (13.12):  $N_{M2} = B/(E_1 + R_0) = B/M_2 = 0.125/1.0 = 0.125$

$M_2$ is located on line $R_0E_1$ at this value of $N$, and the tie line through $M_2$ is drawn. At $E_2$, $N_2 = 0.62$, $y_2 = 0.035$.

Eq. (13.8):  $E_2 = B/N_2 = 0.125/0.62 = 0.202$ lb.
$1 - 0.202 = 0.798$ lb. clear soln. withdrawn

*Stage* 3.   $R_0 = 0.798$ lb. water added, $x_0 = 0$.

Eq. (13.11):        $M_3 = E_2 + R_0 = 0.202 + 0.798 = 1.0$
$$N_{M3} = B/M_3 = 0.125/1 = 0.125$$

Tie line $E_3R_3$ is located through $M_3$ as in the case of stage 2, and, at $E_3$, $N_3 = 0.662$, $y_3 = 0.012$.  By Eq. (13.8), $E_3 = B/N_3 = 0.125/0.662 = 0.189$ lb. soln. in final sludge.  $E_3y_3 = 0.189(0.012) = 0.00227$ lb. NaOH in sludge, or $(0.00227/0.1)100 = 2.27\%$ of original.

The process permits an appreciable loss and produces three solutions, two of which ($R_2$ and $R_3$) are quite dilute.  It should be compared with the countercurrent washing operation of Illustration 3.

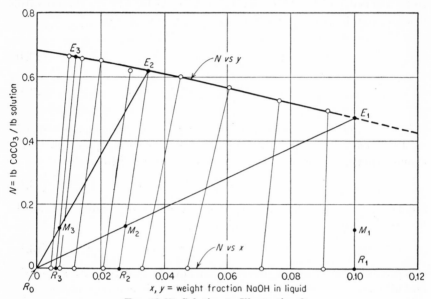

FIG. 13.27. Solution to Illustration 2.

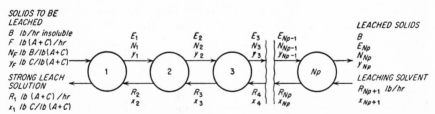

FIG. 13.28. Multistage countercurrent leaching or washing.

**Multistage Countercurrent Leaching.**  A general flow sheet for either leaching or washing is shown in Fig. 13.28.  Operation must necessarily be continuous for steady-state conditions to prevail, although leaching according to the Shanks system will approach the steady state after a large number of cycles have been worked through.  In the flow sheet shown, it is assumed that solid $B$ is insoluble and is not lost in the clear solution, but the procedure outlined below is readily modified to take care of cases where this may not be true.†

A solvent balance for the entire plant is

$$F + R_{Np+1} = R_1 + E_{Np} = M \qquad (13.14)$$

and a "solution" $(A + C)$ balance,

$$Fy_F + R_{Np+1}x_{Np+1} = R_1x_1 + E_{Np}y_{Np} = My_M \qquad (13.15)$$

$M$ represents the hypothetical $B$-free mixture obtained by mixing solids to be leached and leaching solvent. Refer to Fig. 13.29, the operating diagram for the plant. The coordinates of point $M$ are

$$N_M = \frac{B}{F + R_{Np+1}} \qquad (13.16)$$

$$y_M = \frac{Fy_F + R_{Np+1}x_{Np+1}}{F + R_{Np+1}} \qquad (13.17)$$

Points $E_{Np}$ and $R_1$, representing the effluents from the cascade, must lie on a line passing through $M$, and $E_{Np}$ will be on the "practical" equilibrium curve. Equation (13.14) may be rearranged to read

$$F - R_1 = E_{Np} - R_{Np+1} = O \qquad (13.18)$$

Similarly, a solution balance about any number of stages, such as the first three, may be arranged in this form,

$$F - R_1 = E_3 - R_4 = O \qquad (13.19)$$

$O$ represents the constant difference in flow $E - R$ (usually a negative quantity) between each stage. On Fig. 13.29, it can be represented by the intersection of lines $FR_1$ and $E_{Np}R_{Np+1}$ extended, in accordance with the characteristics of these coordinates. Since the effluents from each stage are joined by the practical tie line for the particular conditions which prevail, $E_1$ is found at the end of the tie line through $R_1$. A line from $E_1$ to $O$ provides $R_2$, and so forth. Alternatively the stage constructions may be made on the $x$, $y$ coordinates in the lower part of the figure after first locating the operating line. This may be done by drawing random lines from point $O$ and projecting their intersections with the equilibrium diagram to the lower curve in the usual manner. The operating line has a slope $R/E$, which in the general case will not be constant from stage to stage. The usual staircase construction then establishes the number of stages. The stages are real rather than ideal, the practical equilibrium data having already taken into account the stage efficiency, and hence there must be an integral number. Especially when the number of stages required is the unknown quantity, some trial-and-

† See Illustration 4, for example.

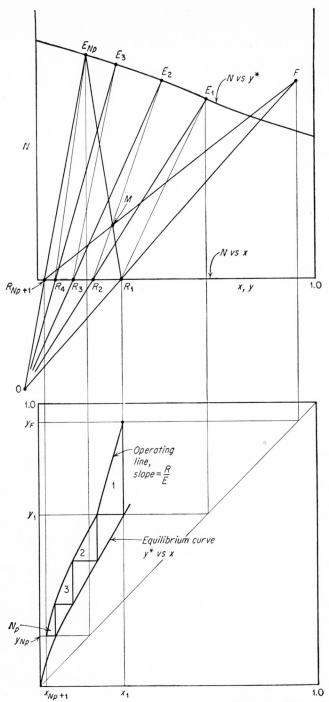

FIG. 13.29. Multistage countercurrent leaching or washing.

error adjustment of the concentrations of the effluents or amount of solvent will be required to obtain an integral number.

If the equilibrium curve of Fig. 13.29 represents inefficiency of mechanical separation of liquid and solid only, and not that resulting from short contact time of solvent and solid, the effect of the latter, if known, may be taken care of by drawing a new equilibrium curve on the $x$, $y$ coordinates. This should be located between the equilibrium curve shown and the operating line, at a fractional distance from the operating line corresponding to the stage efficiency due to the short contact time, in the manner used earlier in gas absorption and distillation.

In the special case where "constant underflow," or constant value of $N$ for all sludges, pertains, the operating line on the $xy$ diagram is straight and of constant slope $R/E$. If in addition the practical equilibrium curve on this plot is straight, so that $m = y^*/x = $ const., then Eqs. (8.22) and (8.23) apply. Adapting the former to the present situation,

$$\frac{y_F - y_{Np}}{y_F - mx_{Np+1}} = \frac{(R/mE)^{Np+1} - (R/mE)}{(R/mE)^{Np+1} - 1} \tag{13.20}$$

Figure 8.15 may be used to solve this rapidly, using $(y_{Np} - mx_{Np+1})/(y_F - mx_{Np+1})$ as ordinate, $R/mE$ as parameter. If in addition the tie lines of the equilibrium diagram are vertical, $m = 1.0$. The form of the equation shown is that which is applicable when the value of $F$ for the feed solids is the same as $E$, so that $R/E$ is constant for all stages, including the first. It frequently may happen, especially in the case where dry solids comprise the feed, that the ratio $R_1/E_1$ for stage 1 will be different from that pertaining to the rest of the cascade. In this case Eq. (13.20) or Fig. 8.15 should be applied to that part of the cascade excluding the first stage, by substitution of $y_1$ for $y_F$ and $N_p$ for $N_p + 1$. In general, the equation or chart may be applied to any part of the cascade where operating line and equilibrium line are both straight, and this may be particularly useful for cases where the solute concentration in the leached solution is very small.

**Illustration 3.** Sodium hydroxide, NaOH, is to be made at the rate of 400 lb./hr. (dry weight) by reaction of soda ash, $Na_2CO_3$, with slaked lime, $Ca(OH)_2$, using a flow sheet of the type shown in Fig. 13.13a. The reagents will be used in stoichiometric proportions, and for simplicity it will be assumed that reaction is complete. Pure water is to be used to wash the calcium carbonate, $CaCO_3$ precipitate, and it is desired to produce as overflow from the first thickener a solution containing 10% NaOH. It will be assumed that the settling data of Illustration 2 apply.

    *a.* If three thickeners are used, determine the amount of wash water required and the percentage of the hydroxide lost in the discharged sludge.

    *b.* How many thickeners would be required to reduce the loss to at least 0.1% of that made?

    *Solution.* a. Mol. wt. of $CaCO_3$ ($B$) = 100, of NaOH ($C$) = 40. NaOH produced = 400 lb./hr. or $^{400}/_{40}$ = 10 lb. moles/hr. $CaCO_3$ produced = $^{10}/_2$ = 5.0 lb. moles/hr.

or $5.0(100) = 500$ lb./hr. $= B$. The water required is that leaving in the strong solution plus that in the final sludge. The amount in the final sludge, according to the settling data, depends upon the NaOH concentration in the final sludge, which is not known. After a trial calculation, it is assumed that the solution in the final sludge

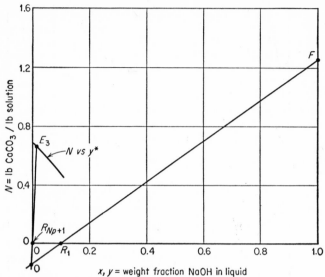

Fig. 13.30. Solution to Illustration 3.

will contain 0.01 wt. fraction NaOH ($y_3 = 0.01$), and the settling data indicate $N_3 = 0.666$ lb. CaCO$_3$/lb. soln. in the final sludge.

$E_3 = B/N_3 = 500/0.666 = 750$ lb./hr. soln. lost
NaOH lost $= E_3y_3 = 750(0.01) = 7.50$ lb./hr.
Water in sludge $= 750 - 7.5 = 742.5$ lb./hr.
NaOH in overflow $= 400 - 7.5 = 392.5$ lb./hr.
$x_1 = 0.1$ wt. fraction NaOH in overflow
$R_1 = 392.5/0.1 = 3,925$ lb. overflow, or strong soln./hr.
Water in $R_1 = 3,925 - 392.5 = 3,532.5$ lb./hr.
Fresh water required $= R_{Np+1} = 3,532.5 + 742.5 = 4,275$ lb./hr.

For purposes of calculation, it may be imagined that the agitators are not present in the flow sheet and that the first thickener is fed with a dry mixture of the reaction products, CaCO$_3$ and NaOH, together with overflow from the second thickener.

$F = 400$ lb. NaOH/hr.     $N_F = B/F = {}^{500}\!/_{400} = 1.25$ lb. CaCO$_3$/lb. NaOH
$y_F = 1.0$ wt. fraction NaOH in the dry solid, CaCO$_3$-free basis

Plot points $R_1$, $E_3$, $R_{Np+1}$, and $F$ on Fig. 13.30, and locate the operating point $O$ at the intersection of lines $FR_1$ and $E_3R_{Np+1}$ extended. The coordinates of point $O$ are $N_O = -0.1419$, $y_O = -0.00213$. (These may be determined analytically, if desired, by simultaneous solution of the equations representing the intersecting lines.) Further computations must be done on an enlarged section of the equilibrium diagram (**Fig. 13.31**). Point $O$ is plotted and the stages stepped off in the usual manner.

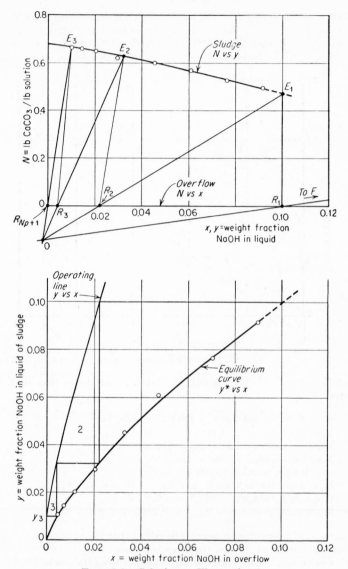

FIG. 13.31. Solution to Illustration 3.

The construction may be projected on to the $xy$ diagram as shown, if desired. Three stages produce a value $y_3 = 0.01$, so that the assumed value of $y_3$ is correct. The NaOH lost in the sludge $= (7.5/400)100 = 1.87\%$ of that made.

*b.*           NaOH lost $= 0.001(400) = 0.4$ lb./hr.
Lb. CaCO$_3$/lb. NaOH in final sludge $= 500/0.4 = 1,250 = N_{Np}/y_{Np}$

In order to determine the liquid content of the final sludge, convert the equilibrium data for dilute mixtures into the following form:

| $N$ | 0.659 | 0.666 | 0.677 | 0.679 | 0.680 |
|---|---|---|---|---|---|
| $y^*$ | 0.01435 | 0.01015 | 0.002† | 0.001† | 0.0005† |
| $\dfrac{N}{y^*}$ | 45.6 | 65.6 | 338 | 679 | 1,360 |

† Estimated values.

By interpolation for $N/y^* = 1,250$, $N_{Np} = 0.680$ lb. $CaCo_3$/lb. soln., and $y_{Np} = 0.680/1,250 = 0.000544$ wt. fraction NaOH in the liquid of the final sludge.

$$E_{Np} = B/N_{Np} = 500/0.680 = 735 \text{ lb./hr.}$$
Water in $E_{Np} = 735 - 0.4 = 734.6$ lb./hr.
NaOH in overflow $= 400 - 0.4 = 399.6$ lb./hr.
$R_1 = 399.6/0.1 = 3,996$ lb./hr.
Water in $R_1 = 3,996 - 399.6 = 3,596$ lb./hr.
Fresh water $= R_{Np+1} = 3,596 + 734.6 = 4,331$ lb./hr.

On the operating diagram (Fig. 13.32) point $O$ is located in the same way as before, and the stages are constructed in the usual fashion. It becomes impractical to continue graphical construction beyond the fourth stage unless considerable magnification of the chart is made, but computations beyond this point may be made with the help of Fig. 8.15. Beyond the fourth stage, the ratio of overflow to liquid in the sludge becomes substantially constant and equal to $R_{Np+1}/E_{Np} = 4,331/735 = 5.90 = R/E$. This is the initial slope of the operating line on the lower part of Fig. 13.32. The slope of the equilibrium curve at these low concentrations is also substantially constant, $m = y^*/x = 0.01015/0.00450 = 2.26$, and $R/mE = 5.90/2.26 = 2.61$. $x_{Np+1} = 0$, and $y_4 = 0.007$. Therefore $(y_{Np} - mx_{Np+1})/(y_4 - mx_{Np+1}) = 0.000544/-0.007 = 0.0777$. From Fig. 8.15, an additional 2.3 stages beyond the 4 computed graphically are required.

An additional two stages (six thickeners) would make $y_{Np}/y_4 = 0.099$, or $y_{Np} = 0.099(0.007) = 0.000693$, corresponding to 0.51 lb. NaOH lost/hr., while an additional three stages (seven thickeners) would make $y_{Np} = 0.0365(0.007) = 0.000255$, corresponding to 0.187 lb. NaOH lost/hr.

It must be emphasized that the cost of these numbers of thickeners probably could not be justified when balanced against the value of the lost NaOH. The very low NaOH loss was specified in order to demonstrate the computation methods.

**Illustration 4.** Flaked soybeans are to be leached with hexane to remove the soybean oil. A 12-in.-thick layer of the flakes (0.009 in. flake thickness) will be fed onto a slowly moving, perforated endless belt which passes under a series of continuously operating sprays.[21] As the solid passes under each spray, it is showered with liquid which percolates through the bed, collects in a trough below the belt, and is recycled by a pump to the spray. The spacing of the sprays is such that the solid is permitted to drain 6 min. before it reaches the next spray. The solvent also passes from trough to trough in a direction countercurrent to that of the moving belt, so that a truly continuous countercurrent stagewise operation is maintained with each spraying and draining constituting one stage. Experiments[21] show that the flakes retain solution after 6 min. drain time to an extent depending upon the oil content of the solution, as follows:

| Wt. % oil in soln. | 0 | 20 | 30 |
|---|---|---|---|
| Lb. soln. retained/lb. insoluble solid | 0.58 | 0.66 | 0.70 |

It will be assumed that the retained solution contains the only oil in the drained flakes.

The soybean flakes enter containing 20% oil and are to be leached to 0.5% oil (on a solvent-free basis). The net forward flow of solvent is to be 1.0 lb. hexane introduced

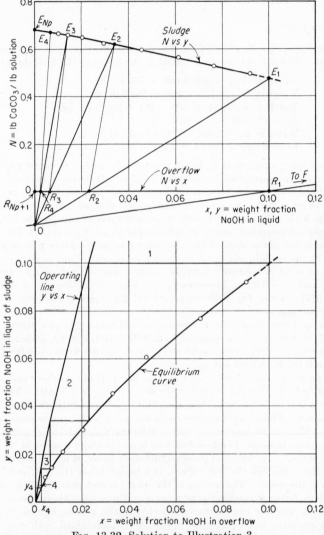

FIG. 13.32. Solution to Illustration 3.

as fresh solvent per pound flakes, and the fresh solvent is free of oil. The solvent draining from the flakes is generally free of solid except in the first stage: the rich miscella contains 10% of the insoluble solid in the feed as a suspended solid, which falls through the perforations of the belt during loading. How many stages are required?

*Solution.* The tie lines are vertical, $x = y^*$. Rearrange the drainage data as follows:

| Per cent oil in soln. $= 100y^*$ | $\dfrac{\text{Lb. soln. retained}}{\text{Lb. insoluble solid}} = \dfrac{1}{N}$ | $N$ | $\dfrac{\text{Lb. oil}}{\text{Lb. insoluble solid}} = \dfrac{y^*}{N}$ |
|:---:|:---:|:---:|:---:|
| 0 | 0.58 | 1.725 | 0 |
| 20 | 0.66 | 1.515 | 0.132 |
| 30 | 0.70 | 1.429 | 0.210 |

Basis: 1 lb. flakes introduced.

*Soybean feed.* $B = 0.8$ lb. insoluble; $F = 0.2$ lb. oil; $N_F = 0.8/0.2 = 4.0$ lb. insoluble solid/lb. oil; $y_F = 1.0$ wt. fraction oil, solid-free basis.

*Solvent.* $R_{Np+1} = 1.0$ lb. hexane; $x_{Np+1} = 0$ wt. fraction oil.

*Leached solids.* Lb. oil/lb. insoluble solid $= 0.005/0.995 = 0.00503$. By interpolation in the equilibrium data, $N_{Np} = 1.718$ lb. solid/lb. soln.

> Insoluble solid lost to miscella $= 0.8(0.1) = 0.08$ lb.
> Insoluble solid in leached solids $= 0.8(0.9) = 0.72$ lb.
> $E_{Np} = 0.72/1.718 = 0.420$ lb. soln. retained
> Lb. oil retained $= 0.00503(0.72) = 0.00362$ lb.
> Lb. hexane retained $= 0.420 - 0.00362 = 0.416$ lb.
> $y_{Np} = 0.00362/0.420 = 0.0086$ wt. fraction oil in retained liquid

*Miscella.* Hexane $= 1 - 0.416 = 0.584$ lb.; oil $= 0.2 - 0.00362 = 0.196$ lb.
$R_1 = 0.584 + 0.196 = 0.780$ lb. clear miscella; $x_1 = 0.196/0.780 = 0.252$ wt. fraction oil in liquid. $N_{R1} = 0.08/0.780 = 0.1027$ lb. insoluble solid/lb. soln.

The operating diagram is shown in Fig. 13.33. Point $R_1$ represents the cloudy miscella and is therefore displaced from the axis of the graph at $N_{R1}$. Point $O$ is located as usual and the stages determined with the $N = 0$ axis for all stages but the first. Between four and five stages are necessary. Adjustment of the amount of solvent or the amount of unextracted oil, by trial, will provide an integral number.

**Rate of Leaching.** The many diverse phenomena encountered in the practice of leaching make it impossible to apply a single theory to explain the leaching action. As has been shown, leaching may involve simple washing of the solution from the surface of a solid, or dissolving of a solute from a matrix of insoluble matter, osmosis, and possibly other mechanisms. Our knowledge of these is very limited. The washing of a solution from the surface of impervious solid particles may be expected to be very rapid, requiring only the blending of solution and solvent, and stage efficiencies are then quite likely to be governed entirely by the completeness of the mechanical separation of liquid from solid.

Leaching of a solute from the internal parts of a solid, on the other hand, will be relatively slow. Solids made up of a skeletal structure of insoluble substance, with the pores impregnated with the solute, can be described in terms of a pore-shape factor, as outlined in Chap. 4. The factor is a function of the solid, independent of the nature of the solute and solvent, and is a measure of the complexity of the path through which the solute diffuses. In the case of natural products such as plant materials, the complexity of the structure may make application of these methods difficult. Wood, for example, will show different rates of leaching of an impregnating solute depending upon whether diffusion is in a direction parallel to or across the grain of the wood.[19] If solutes must

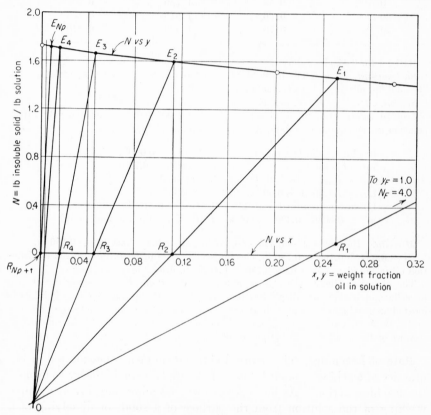

FIG. 13.33. Solution to Illustration 4.

pass through cell walls by dialysis, it may not be possible to apply the concept at all. The rates of diffusion of soybean oil from soybean flakes, which do not permit simple interpretation, have been attributed to the presence of several types of structures in the matrix[15] as well as to the presence of a slowly dissolving constituent in the oil.[11,14] That the leached oil is composed of several differently behaving substances is evident from the different properties of oil obtained after short and long leaching times. These examples serve to indicate the complexity of many practical leaching processes; very little study has actually been given them. When solids such as these are immersed in leaching solvents, it is reasonable to suppose that the resistance to mass transfer within the solid itself is likely to be the controlling resistance and that of the liquid surrounding the solid to be quite minor.[3] In such cases increasing the rate of movement of liquid past the solid surface will not appreciably influence the rate of leaching.

## NOTATION FOR CHAPTER 13

$a$ = a constant

$a_p$ = surface of particles, sq. ft./cu. ft. of packed space

$A$ = pure leaching solvent

$b$ = a constant

$B$ = insoluble carrier solid, lb. (in a batch operation) or lb./hr. or lb./(hr.) (sq. ft.) (in a continuous operation)

$C$ = soluble solute

$d_p$ = diameter of a sphere of same surface/volume ratio as a particle, ft.

$E$ = solvent and solute associated with the leached solids, lb. (in a batch operation) or lb./hr. or lb./(hr.)(sq. ft.) (in a continuous operation)

$F$ = solute and solvent in solids to be leached, lb. (in a batch operation) or lb./hr. or lb./(hr.)(sq. ft.) (in a continuous operation)

$g$ = acceleration due to gravity, ft./hr.$^2$

$g_c$ = conversion factor, $4.17(10^8)$ lb. mass (ft.)/(lb. force)(hr.)$^2$

$G$ = mass velocity, lb./(hr.)(sq. ft.)

$K$ = permeability, cu. ft./hr.$^2$

$m$ = slope of equilibrium curve, $dy^*/dx$, dimensionless

$M$ = solvent and solute content of a slurry or mixture, lb. (in a batch operation) or lb./hr. or lb./(hr.)(sq. ft.) (in a continuous operation)

$N$ = ratio of weight of insoluble solid to weight of solute and solvent, lb. $B$/lb. $(A + C)$

$N_p$ = number of stages, dimensionless

$\Delta P$ = pressure drop, lb./sq. ft.

$R$ = solvent and solute in a leaching solution, lb. (in a batch operation) or lb./hr. or lb./(hr.)(sq. ft.) (in a continuous operation)

$S$ = residual saturation of a bed of solids, fraction of void volume occupied by liquid, dimensionless

$S_0$ = residual saturation in the upper part of a packed bed, dimensionless

$S_{av}$ = average residual saturation, dimensionless

$w$ = concentration of insoluble solids in a slurry, weight fraction

$x$ = concentration of solute in solution, weight fraction, $B$-free basis

$y$ = concentration of solute in a mixture, weight fraction, $B$-free basis

$y^*$ = value of $y$ at equilibrium

$Z$ = height of a percolation bed or of a settling solid, ft.

$Z_D$ = drain height, ft.

$Z_0$ = initial height of a slurry, ft.

$Z_\infty$ = ultimate height of settled solids, ft.

$\epsilon$ = fractional void volume of a packed bed, dimensionless

$\theta$ = time, hr.

$\mu_L$ = liquid viscosity, lb./(ft.)(hr.)

$\rho_L$ = liquid density, lb./cu. ft.

$\sigma$ = surface tension, lb./ft. = (dynes/cm.)$(6.89)(10^{-5})$

Subscripts:

    1, 2, etc. = stage 1, stage 2, etc.
        $F$ = feed; solids to be leached
        $S$ = saturated

## REFERENCES

1. Anon.: *Chem. Inds.*, **64**, 926 (1949).
2. Anon.: *Chem. Eng.*, **61**(7), 324 (1954).
3. Boucher, D. F., J. C. Brier, and J. O. Osburn: *Trans. Am. Inst. Chem. Engrs.*, **38**, 967 (1942).
4. Comings, E. W.: *Ind. Eng. Chem.*, **32**, 663 (1940).
5. ———, C. E. Pruiss, and C. De Bord: *Ind. Eng. Chem.*, **46**, 1164 (1954).
6. Dombrowski, H. S., and L. E. Brownell: *Ind. Eng. Chem.*, **46**, 1267 (1954).
7. Donald, M. B.: *Trans. Inst. Chem. Engrs.*, **15**, 77 (1937).
8. Donlan, T. R.: Recovery of Fats and Oils, paper presented before the North Jersey Section, American Chemical Society, January, 1953.
9. Elgin, J. C.: *Trans. Am. Inst. Chem. Engrs.*, **32**, 457 (1936).
10. Fitz, G. R., and G. G. Low: U.S. Patent 2,567,474 (Sept. 11, 1951).
11. Goss, W. H.: *Oil & Soap*, **23**, 348 (1946).
12. Hamacher, J. D., and R. W. Barns: U. S. Patent 2,547,577 (Apr. 3, 1951).
13. Kammermeyer, K.: *Ind. Eng. Chem.*, **33**, 1484 (1941).
14. Karnofsky, G.: *J. Am. Oil Chemists' Soc.*, **26**, 564 (1949).
15. King, C. O., D. L. Katz, and J. C. Brier: *Trans. Am. Inst. Chem. Engrs.*, **40**, 533 (1944).
16. Liddell, D. M.: "Handbook of Non-ferrous Metallurgy," 2d ed., McGraw-Hill Book Company, Inc., New York, 1945.
17. McCubbins, K., and G. J. Ritz: *Chem. Inds.*, **66**, 354 (1950).
18. Markley, K. S., and W. H. Goss: "Soybean Chemistry and Technology," Chemical Publishing Company, Inc., New York, 1944.
19. Osburn, J. Q., and D. L. Katz: *Trans. Am. Inst. Chem. Engrs.*, **40**, 511 (1944).
20. Scofield, E. P.: *Chem. Eng.*, **58**(1), 127 (1951).
21. Smith, C. T.: *J. Am. Oil Chemists' Soc.*, **28**, 274 (1951).
22. Van Arsdale, G. D.: "Hydrometallurgy of Base Metals," McGraw-Hill Book Company, Inc., New York, 1953.
23 Work, L. T., and A. S. Kohler: *Ind. Eng. Chem.*, **32**, 1329 (1940).

## PROBLEMS

**1.** A 3-ft.-diameter tank fitted with a false bottom and canvas filter is partly filled with 2,000 lb. (dry weight) of sea sand wet with sea water. The sand is allowed to drain until it stops dripping, whereupon 1,500 lb. fresh water is added and recirculated to reach a uniform salt concentration. The sand is again allowed to drain until dripping stops and is then removed from the tank and dried. Estimate the salt content of the dried sand.

The sand particles have an average particle size $d_p$ = 0.0013 ft., a particle density 166 lb./cu. ft., and a bulk density 93 lb. (dry weight)/cu. ft. Sea water contains 3.5% salt; its density is 63.6 lb./cu. ft. and surface tension 73.6 dynes/cm. The surface tension of water is 72.8 dynes/cm.

**2.** Derive expressions for the coordinates of point $O$ $(y_O, N_O)$ (Fig. 13.29), and check the results by determining the numerical values in the case of Illustration 3a.

**3.** In order to eliminate the solids in the final miscella of Illustration 4, it is decided to pass liquid from stage 3 to stage 1, where the liquid will contact fresh solids. The drained liquid from stage 1, containing the suspended solids, will then be passed to stage 2, where it is filtered by passage of the liquid through the bed of solids in this stage. The final miscella is then withdrawn as a clear solution from stage 2. How many stages will then be required for the same solvent/seeds ratio and the same oil concentration in the discharged solids?

**4.** A mineral containing 20% elemental sulfur is to be leached with hot gas oil, in which the sulfur is soluble to the extent of 10% by weight. The solvent will be repeatedly pumped over the batch of ground mineral, using 1.5 lb. fresh solvent/lb. mineral. After no further solution of sulfur is obtained, the liquid will be drained and replaced with a fresh batch of 1.5 lb. oil/lb. original mineral, and the operation repeated. On drainage, the solid materials retain the solution to the extent of one-tenth the weight of undissolved solid (sulfur and gangue). No preferential adsorption takes place.

*a.* Calculate the equilibrium data, and plot them in the usual manner.

*b.* Determine the amount of sulfur unextracted and the sulfur concentration of the composited leach liquors.

*c.* Repeat (*b*) for the case where a two-stage Shanks system is used, with 3 lb. fresh solvent/lb. unleached solid. Assume steady state has been reached.

**5.** Aluminum sulfate, $Al_2(SO_4)_3$, is to be produced by action of sulfuric acid, $H_2SO_4$, on bauxite in a series of agitators, with a cascade of continuous thickeners to wash the insoluble mud free of aluminum sulfate.

$$Al_2O_3 + 3H_2SO_4 \rightarrow Al_2(SO_4)_3 + 3H_2O$$

The flow sheet is similar to that of Fig. 13.13*a*. The reaction agitators are fed with (1) 25 tons bauxite/day, containing 50% $Al_2O_3$ and the rest insoluble; (2) the theoretical quantity of aqueous acid containing 60% $H_2SO_4$; and (3) the overflow from the second thickener. Assume the reaction is complete. The strong product solution is to contain 22% $Al_2(SO_4)_3$, and no more than 2% of the $Al_2(SO_4)_3$ produced is to be lost in the washed mud. The last thickener is to be fed with pure wash water. The underflow from each thickener will contain 4 lb. liquid/lb. insoluble solid, and the concentration of solubles in the liquid of the underflow for each thickener may be assumed to be the same as that in the overflow. Calculate the number of thickeners required and the amount of wash water required per day.

(NOTE: In solving this problem, be certain to account for the water in the acid as well as that produced by the reaction. Adapt Fig. 8.15 to all but the first thickener in the cascade.)

**6.** Barium, occurring naturally as the sulfate, $BaSO_4$, is put in water-soluble form by heating with coal, thus reducing the sulfate to the sulfide, $BaS$. The resulting reaction mixture, barium "black ash" containing 65% soluble $BaS$, is to be leached with water. One hundred tons black ash per day is fed to a tube mill, together with the overflow from the second of a cascade of thickeners, and the effluent from the mill is fed to the first thickener. All the barium is dissolved in the mill. The strong solution overflowing from the first thickener is to contain 20% $BaS$ by weight. The thickeners will each deliver a sludge containing 1.5 lb. liquid/lb. insoluble solid. The solution in the overflow and that in the sludge leaving any thickener may be assumed to have the same $BaS$ concentration. It is desired to keep the $BaS$ lost with the final sludge to at most 2 lb./day.

*a.* How many thickeners are required? [Adapt Eq. (8.23) to all except the first thickener.]

*b.* It is decided to pass the final leached sludge to a continuous filter, as in Fig. 13.13*b*, where the liquid content of the filtered solids will be reduced to 15% by weight. The filtrate will be returned to the last thickener, but the filter cake will not be washed. How many thickeners will then be required?

**7.** In the manufacture of potassium nitrate, $KNO_3$, potassium chloride, $KCl$, is added to a hot, concentrated aqueous solution of sodium nitrate, $NaNO_3$,

$$KCl + NaNO_3 \rightleftharpoons KNO_3 + NaCl$$

Owing to its relatively low solubility, part of the sodium chloride, $NaCl$, precipitates and is filtered off. A little water is added to the filtrate to prevent further precipitation of $NaCl$, the mixture is cooled to 20°C., and pure $KNO_3$ crystallizes. The resulting slurry contains, per 100 lb. precipitated $KNO_3$, 239 lb. of a solution analyzing 21.3% $KNO_3$, 21.6% $NaCl$, and 57.1% water. The slurry is fed to the first of a cascade of four continuous classifiers, where each 100 lb. of crystals is countercurrently washed with 75 lb. of a saturated solution of $KNO_3$, containing 24.0% $KNO_3$, in order to free them of $NaCl$. The wet crystals leaving each classifier retain 25% liquid, and the liquid overflows are clear. The washed crystals discharged from the fourth classifier, containing 25% liquid, are sent to a continuous drier. All liquid except that discharged with the washed crystals leaves in the overflow from the first classifier. Equilibrium between solid and liquid is attained in each classifier, and the clear overflows have the same composition as the liquid retained by the crystals. The solubility of $KNO_3$ in $NaCl$ solutions ($KNO_3$ is the equilibrium solid phase) at the prevailing temperature is given by the following table:

| % NaCl......... | 0 | 6.9 | 12.6 | 17.8 | 21.6 |
|---|---|---|---|---|---|
| % KNO₃........ | 24.0 | 23.3 | 22.6 | 22.0 | 21.3 |

*a.* Plot the equilibrium data [$N$ = lb. $KNO_3$/lb. ($NaCl + H_2O$) for both clear overflow and wet crystals; $x$ and $y$ = lb. $NaCl$/lb. ($NaCl + H_2O$)].

*b.* Calculate the per cent $NaCl$ content which may be expected on the dried $KNO_3$ product.

PART V

# CONTACT OF MISCIBLE PHASES

CHAPTER 14

# THE LESS CONVENTIONAL OPERATIONS

The operations described in this chapter are concerned with the separations which may be obtained by countercurrent contact of completely miscible fluids, usually with some sort of permeable screen or membrane arranged to prevent the fluids from mixing rapidly. They have had very limited application, because of the difficulties in providing an adequate permeable screen, because the rate of separation is slow, or because they are very expensive. The first, dialysis, is concerned with separation of liquid solutions and the others with mixtures of gases.

## DIALYSIS

Dialysis is the separation of substances of different molecular sizes in a liquid solution by virtue of their different rates of diffusion through a suitable membrane. In practice, the solution is separated from a quantity of the solvent by the membrane. Solvent and the solute of small molecular size may then pass through the membrane relatively easily, while the passage of the larger molecules is more difficult. It is practical to attempt separations only of substances whose molecular sizes differ appreciably, such as crystalline from colloidal substances, if good separations at reasonable rates are to be expected.

Practical industrial applications are relatively few, owing to the low rates of separation which can be obtained and to the relatively poor selectivity of the available membranes. The most important application is the separation of sodium hydroxide, NaOH, from hemicellulose in the solutions of the viscose-rayon process.[17,20] These contain roughly 17 per cent NaOH and 1.5 to 2.5 per cent hemicellulose, and the latter must largely be separated before the caustic may be reused. The liquid is dialyzed with water to give a solution containing roughly 9 per cent NaOH and 0.08 per cent hemicellulose, which amount is not objectionable, with 90 to 93 per cent recovery of the caustic. Higher caustic recoveries are not attempted, since if the NaOH content of the original liquid is reduced below about 1 per cent, the hemicellulose precipitates and interferes with the dialysis. Dialysis has also been used to separate sugar from colloidal materials in the solutions resulting from the leaching of sugar beets.   It finds further application on a laboratory scale in the removal of electrolytes and the smaller, water-soluble organic molecules from biological materials such as serums, proteins, hormones, and enzymes.

**Membranes.**   It is possible to make membranes which are highly selective.   For example, a membrane of gelatinous copper ferrocyanide, if precipitated within a porous porcelain which acts as a support, is capable of preventing the passage of ordinary solutes such as sugar and glycerin and even smaller ionic particles such as are found in salt solutions and yet permits passage of water.   If a solution is separated from pure water by such a membrane, water passes through the membrane in the direction solvent to solution, in the direction of water-concentration drop, and dilutes the solution.   This is known as osmosis.   Membranes which are so selective, however, have such low permeabilities that the rate of movement of water is exceedingly slow even if a considerable pressure difference is maintained across the membrane in the direction of flow. For practical applications, membranes which have much larger pore openings, and which do not require such extensive mechanical support, are necessary.   Thin sheet materials such as Cellophane, parchment paper, mercerized cotton, and denitrated nitrocellulose are used.   The sheets contain a myriad of small pores whose diameters (of the order of magnitude $10^{-6}$ cm.) are very nonuniform.   Since most crystalline materials in solution have molecular diameters of the order of $10^{-8}$ cm., the membranes are incapable of separating these substances and are useful only in incompletely separating colloidal from noncolloidal materials. The membranes must be thin (0.002 to 0.01 cm. thick when dry, usually swollen when wet) so as to minimize the resistance to mass transfer.

The selectivity of the membrane is probably partly the result of a mechanical-sieve action, whereby the larger particles are screened out, especially in the case of the large pore diameters found in commercial membranes.   To some extent, the passage of solvent and small molecules may follow selective adsorption onto the surface, and blocking of the pores to the passage of larger molecules by the film of adsorbate then contributes to the selectivity.   In some instances, a substance may dissolve in the membrane and pass through by the process of structure-insensitive diffusion (see Chap. 4).   A combination of these actions probably frequently occurs.

**The Dialysis Operation.**   Consider the schematic representation of a batch dialysis in Fig. 14.1.[8]   The solution to be dialyzed contains large and small solute molecules, represented schematically as shown at (a), and it is separated initially from a batch of pure solvent by a suitable membrane.   The solvent immediately begins to move through the membrane and into the solution by osmosis, and since it ordinarily has a lower specific gravity than the solution, a convection current of rising solvent develops on the left of the membrane as at (b) in the figure. If the liquids are not agitated, the solvent spreads out in a layer over the top of the solution and will mix with the solution only very slowly. The solute particles also diffuse through the membrane into the solvent, the smaller ones rapidly but the larger only very slowly. Since the solution formed on the right side of the membrane will generally be more dense than the solvent, it will tend to stratify at the bottom of the vessel, as shown. In transparent vessels, this "gravity stratification," as it is

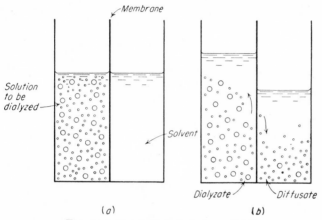

FIG. 14.1. Batch dialysis (schematic).[8]

known, is clearly discernible. Owing to the osmotic flow of solvent, the volume of the *dialyzate*, or dialyzed solution, will increase at the expense of the *diffusate*. If the membrane is permeable to both solutes, the solutions on either side will eventually come to the same concentrations and an equilibrium will be established. Because the larger molecules dialyze only very slowly, however, it is possible to make a separation by periodically replacing the diffusate with fresh solvent before equilibrium is established. The concentration of the dialyzate may be kept relatively high, and the rate of dialysis maintained at a reasonable level, by careful withdrawal of the layer of solvent at the top.

Alternatively, a continuous rather than a batchwise operation may be carried out in the countercurrent manner shown schematically in Fig. 14.2. The solutions flow in such a direction as to take advantage of the tendency toward stratification: the liquid to be dialyzed is introduced at the bottom and withdrawn at the top, while the diffusate flows downward. The membrane is arranged vertically for this reason also, and if membrane supports in the form of ribs or splines are used, they should be arranged vertically so as not to interfere with the natural convection currents.   The solutions on either side of the membrane are of different densities, and the mechanical strain on the flimsy membrane resulting from the different hydrostatic pressures can be lessened by withdrawing the diffusate and dialyzate from the cell at different levels, as shown.

**Dialysis Equipment.**   There are two major types of continuous dialyzers in regular use.   The Webcell dialyzer of the Brosites Machine Co. (Fig. 14.3) utilizes the principles developed in Fig. 14.2 directly. The membranes are placed between metal frames arranged in a manner

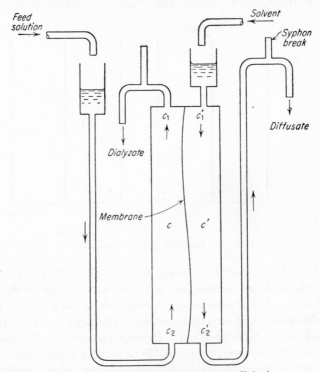

FIG. 14.2. Continuous countercurrent dialysis.

reminiscent of the ordinary filter press.   A mechanical support built into the frames, not shown in the sketch, may also be used.   Holes in the frames and the membranes form continuous conduits for the liquids when the entire assemblage is pressed tightly together.   Feed solution to be dialyzed is distributed to alternate frames and flows upward past the membranes, and the dialyzate discharges through a channel at the top. Solvent, in a similar manner, enters the remaining frames and flows downward, and the diffusate leaves through a channel at the bottom.   The liquids flow under the force of gravity, as shown schematically in Fig. 14.2, and are not pumped through the dialyzer.   In the larger units particularly, where many frames may be used, there may be several channels in the frames for introducing feed and solvent, each leading to separate groups of frames. In this way, more equitable distribution of the flow is obtained.

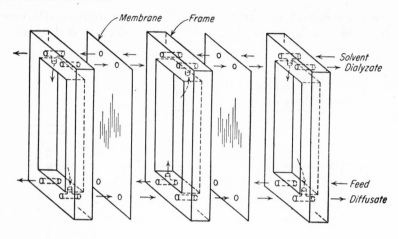

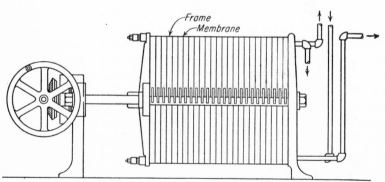

FIG. 14.3. Brosites Machine Co. filter-press-type dialyzer. [*U.S. Patent* 2,399,471 (1946).]

In the Cerini dialyzer (Fig. 14.4), the membranes, usually of mercerized cotton, are sewn into sacks and supported on metal frames. These are suspended in a baffled tank through which the solution to be dialyzed flows. The dialyzing solvent then passes through the inside of the sacks.

**Rate of Dialysis.** Consider the mass transfer of a readily dialyzed solute of small molecular size in the apparatus of Fig. 14.2. At some level in the apparatus where the concentrations of this solute are $c$ and

$c'$ in the two streams, the local rate of transfer $N$ lb. moles solute/-(hr.)(sq. ft. membrane surface) is

$$N = K(c - c')$$ (14.1)

where $K$ is an over-all mass-transfer coefficient. The resistance to mass transfer resides in the two liquids, which may be characterized by mass-

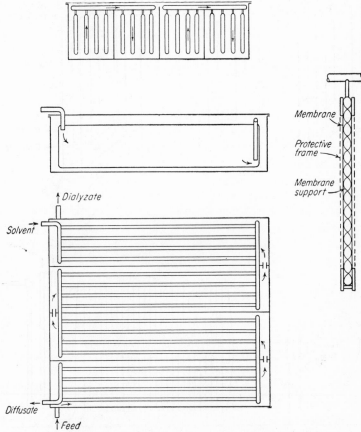

FIG. 14.4. Cerini dialyzer. [*U.S. Patent* 1,719,754 (1929).]

transfer coefficients $k_L$ and $k'_L$, and in the membrane, to which a coefficient $k_M$ may be assigned,

$$\frac{1}{K} = \frac{1}{k_L} + \frac{1}{k_M} + \frac{1}{k'_L}$$ (14.2)

Assuming that $K$ and the volumetric-flow rates of the liquids remain constant from the top to the bottom of the membrane, an average concentration difference for the length of the membrane may be used,[9]

$$\Delta c_{av} = \frac{(c_1 - c_1') - (c_2 - c_2')}{\ln\left[(c_1 - c_1')/(c_2 - c_2')\right]} \qquad (14.3)$$

where the subscripts 1 and 2 refer to the terminal conditions (Fig. 14.2). Then

$$N = K \Delta c_{av} \qquad (14.4)$$

where $N$ is now the average mass-transfer rate for the entire apparatus. In reality, the volumes of solutions change considerably owing to the osmotic transfer of solvent. Furthermore, $K$ varies from top to bottom of the membrane as a result of both variations of the solute diffusivity with concentration and variation of the effective liquid-film thicknesses. Nevertheless, at least in the case of dialysis of sodium hydroxide solutions, it has been established[19] that Eq. (14.4) is entirely adequate for ordinary purposes, owing to the fact that the errors incurred in its use tend to offset each other.

There are very few data on the mass-transfer coefficients. For each liquid, $k_L = D/z$, where $z$ is the effective liquid-film thickness and $D$ is the solute diffusivity. At the typically low rates of flow used in caustic soda dialysis (0.1 to 0.2 ft./hr. superficial linear velocity past the membrane), the value of $z$ is approximately 0.0016 ft. (0.05 cm.).[16,19] Actually, the natural convection currents resulting from density differences are larger than the superficial velocities, and these probably control the liquid-film thicknesses. The coefficient for the membrane can be expressed in terms of an effective membrane thickness $z_M$, such that $k_M = D/z_M$, and $z_M$ in turn can be described by the product of the real membrane thickness and a pore-shape factor (see Chap. 4). For readily dialyzed solutes, the pore-shape factor for parchment membranes is in the range 1.5 to 3 if the wet thickness of the membrane is used[19] and in the range 9 to 20 for most commercial membranes when based on the dry thickness.[16] As a result, the resistance to mass transfer is about equally divided between the membrane and the two liquid films for readily dialyzed solutes.

Attempts to reduce the effective liquid-film thickness by increasing the velocity of liquid flow, through the use of tortuous paths for the liquids, have been made, but no quantitative data are available for measuring their effectiveness. It seems likely that only very high velocities will have an appreciable influence on the over-all coefficient, and these lead to difficulties in the support of the membrane. Increasing the temperature of the dialysis operation is likely to be a more effective method of decreasing the over-all resistance to mass transfer, since the diffusivities (for both liquid film and membrane) increase rapidly with increased temperature. For example, $D$ for NaOH in water increases by about 50 per cent if the temperature is increased from 60 to 95°F. Maintaining the dialyzate warm and the diffusate cold will improve the rate of solute diffusion and at the same time retard the osmotic transfer of solvent into the dialyzate.

Equations (14.1) to (14.4) may also be written for the difficultly dialyzed solute. Owing to the very large particle size with respect to the diameter of the membrane pores, the principal resistance to mass transfer will reside in the membrane for this solute. Pore-shape factors for structure-sensitive diffusion in a membrane are constant for all solutes

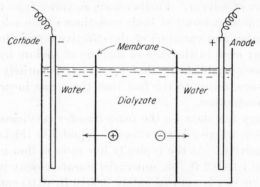

FIG. 14.5. Electrodialysis.

which are small with respect to the pore diameter, as indicated in Chap. 4. But in any practical dialysis, the great difference in particle diameters necessary for effective separation results in a different factor for the two solutes and a given membrane. These can be estimated for membranes whose pore diameters are uniform and known,[16] but generally it will be necessary to resort to experiment to determine the extent to which the solutes of a mixture will be separated by dialysis.

**Electrodialysis.** When electrolytic crystalline substances are to be separated from colloids in solution by dialysis methods, the rate of removal of the ions can be considerably increased by imposing an electromotive force across the membrane, as in Fig. 14.5. Here the solution to be dialyzed is placed in the central compartment, separated from the anode and cathode compartments by the semipermeable membrane. The ions then move through the membrane toward the electrodes much more rapidly than in ordinary dialysis. In practice, two difficulties arise. The first is due to the electroosmotic transfer of water through the membranes, usually from the anode to the cathode compartments, which not only dilutes the dialyzate but also carries the ions back into the central compartment. The second is due to the tendency of the membranes to assume an electric charge on each face, positive on that side facing the cathode, negative on the side facing the anode. The inner face of the membrane nearest the cathode then tends to accumulate hydroxyl ions which give an alkaline reaction, while the inner face of the membrane nearest the anode tends to give an acid reaction. This may bring about undesirable effects such as coagulation or precipitation of many colloids. Electrodialysis has been used extensively in biological laboratory work, but not industrially.

If the membrane nearest the cathode were permeable only to cations but impermeable to anions, and if the other membrane were permeable to anions but not cations, it would be possible to remove the ions from an electrolyte solution more efficiently since the backward flow of ions would then cease. Membranes are now available, made from ion-exchange resins, which are nearly perfectly semipermeable.[13] Thus, a cation-exchange resin membrane exchanges cations and is permeable to these but will offer considerable resistance to the passage of anions. Similarly, an anion-exchange resin membrane is preferentially permeable to anions. Devices and processes using them have been proposed, particularly for converting sea water to potable water, but as yet none has had commercial application.

## GAS SEPARATIONS

The principles of separating gas mixtures by gaseous diffusion, atmolysis, and thermal diffusion have been known for some time, the first indeed since 1829. They are inherently expensive and difficult operations, and until the Second World War only limited laboratory-scale applications had been made of them for the separation of isotopes of the elements. The war brought about the only industrial-scale application, the separation of the uranium isotopes by gaseous diffusion and thermal diffusion.

**Gaseous Diffusion.** We have seen [Eq. (4.23)] that if a pure gas flows through a diaphragm or barrier containing small holes (whose diameter is of the order of one-tenth the mean free path of the molecules) under conditions of small pressure drop, the rate of flow is inversely proportional to the square root of the molecular weight of the gas and to the drop in pressure across the barrier. If the gas is a binary mixture of components of different molecular weight, the relative rates of flow of the components through the barrier will be different and a separation becomes possible.

Refer to Fig. 14.6, where a single gaseous-diffusion stage is shown. The binary feed contains $x_F$ mole fraction $A$, of low molecular weight $M_A$, and $1 - x_F$ mole fraction $B$, of high molecular weight $M_B$. If the downstream pressure is substantially zero and if only an infinitesimal portion of the feed gas is permitted to pass through the barrier, the composition of the diffused gas $y$ mole fraction $A$ will be enriched in comparison with that of the feed,

$$\frac{y}{1-y} = \frac{x_F}{1-x_F}\left(\frac{M_B}{M_A}\right)^{\frac{1}{2}}$$        (14.5)

Rearranging, this becomes

$$\alpha' = \frac{y/(1-y)}{x_F/(1-x_F)} = \left(\frac{M_B}{M_A}\right)^{\frac{1}{2}}$$        (14.6)

The quantity $\alpha'$ is then a measure of the enrichment obtained under these conditions.† If any measurable portion of the gas passes through the barrier, the remaining portion is then impoverished in component $A$ and the average value of $\alpha'$ must necessarily be smaller than that given by

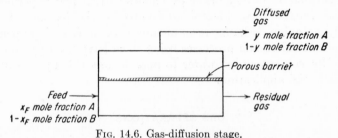

Fig. 14.6. Gas-diffusion stage.

Eq. (14.6).[15] For most economical construction and operation of a multistage device, half the gas will be passed through the barrier,[7] so that appreciable reduction in $\alpha'$ will occur in practical cases. In any practical stage, $\alpha'$ will be still further reduced by any back diffusion of the enriched diffused portion and by nonseparative flow following Poiseuille's law [Eq. (4.19)]. It is necessary to operate at low pressures in order to minimize the latter.

Since the diffused gas may still not be enriched appreciably in comparison with the feed, it may be sent to another stage; additional stages may then be used for still further enrichment, thus leading to a cascade of stages as in Fig. 14.7.[2] Similarly the undiffused gas from any stage may be recycled to the preceding stage for further treatment, and the cascade develops the usual "enriching" and "stripping" sections on either side of the point of introducing the feed. Since the quantity of gas passing forward toward either product becomes less with each stage,

† $\alpha'$ should not be confused with the equilibrium separability for other processes involving contact of immiscible phases, such as relative volatility for distillation, relative adsorptivity for adsorption, or selectivity for liquid extraction. In operations such as gaseous diffusion, equilibrium between the two separated portions of the gas would, of course, mean identical compositions throughout, since the portions are completely miscible, whereupon $\alpha'$ becomes equal to unity.

the size of the stage may be progressively reduced in passing from the feed to the products. Alternatively, instead of very large stages near the center of the cascade, a large number of small units may be operated in parallel, as shown in the figure. Since, however, all the units operating in parallel bring about identical composition changes, together they

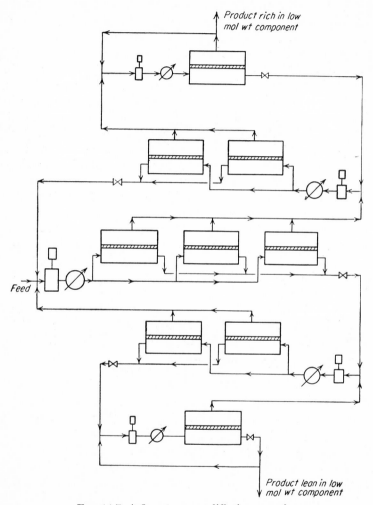

FIG. 14.7. A five-stage gas-diffusion cascade.

affect the enrichment of only one stage, so that the arrangement of Fig. 14.7 is considered as containing only five stages. It is a further characteristic of the gas-diffusion cascade that the gas must be compressed between stages, and the heat developed by the compression must be removed by a cooler as shown in the figure. In the "ideal" cascade, for which the number of stages and the work of compression are the least, the number of stages required is given by the Fenske equation [Eq. (9.99)], with the relative volatility replaced by the actual enrichment $\alpha'$ obtained per stage.[7]

The work of compression, the size and expense of constructing and operating the cascade, and the engineering problems associated with making adequate barriers make gas diffusion useful as a separation method only in cases where other, more conventional methods such as distillation, extraction, adsorption, and the like, are unusually difficult or impossible. This may especially be the case in the separation of isotopes of the elements. The conventional operations described in the earlier chapters of this book depend essentially on differences in the chemical properties of compounds which lead to their unequal distribution between immiscible phases. Two compounds which differ only because an element in one is replaced by its isotope in the other will frequently show such small differences in their distribution that the conventional methods become impractical.

Such is the case for separation of the isotopes of uranium $U^{235}$ and $U^{238}$, and the gas-diffusion plant built during the Second World War at Oak Ridge, Tennessee, to separate the gaseous uranium hexafluorides is the only large-scale application of this operation.[14] The compounds $U^{235}F_6$ and $U^{238}F_6$ have molecular weights 349 and 352, respectively, so that the differential enrichment per stage, by Eq. (14.6), is $\alpha' = (352/349)^{1/2} = 1.0043$. This is reduced when half the gas is permitted to diffuse in each stage to 1.003. If then a feed, made from natural uranium and containing 0.71 per cent $U^{235}F_6$, is to be separated into products containing 99 and 0.1 per cent $U^{235}F_6$, respectively, Eq. (9.99) indicates that

$$\frac{\log\,(99/1)(99.9/0.1)}{\log 1.003} - 1 = 3,067 \text{ stages}$$

would be required. The enrichment per stage actually realized is less than 1.003, and approximately 4,000 stages are used. For each mole of $U^{235}F_6$-rich product withdrawn, some 70,000,000 moles of gas are recycled between the stages, which requires enormous power for pumps and unprecedented quantities of cooling water. The power plant for this installation is rated at 238,000 kw. The nature of the porous barrier has not been disclosed, but the requirements that it contain tremendous numbers of holes of diameter measured in hundredths of microns, be able to withstand a difference in pressure on either side of roughly 1 atm., be chemically indifferent to the very reactive gas, and be capable of being mass-produced in quantities that must be measured in acres are indicative of its unusual properties. Other engineering features of this extraordinary plant have also been described.[14]

Benedict[1,2] has considered applications of gaseous diffusion to other isotope separations, and Kammermeyer[12,15] has demonstrated the use of porous glass barriers. Kammermeyer[4] has also investigated the use of plastic membranes through which the gases diffuse after solution in the plastic, in which case the separation depends upon the differences in the solubilities of the gases and their diffusivities in the plastic.

**Atmolysis, or Mass Diffusion.** If a gas mixture such as hydrogen and nitrogen were permitted to diffuse against a countercurrent of some vapor

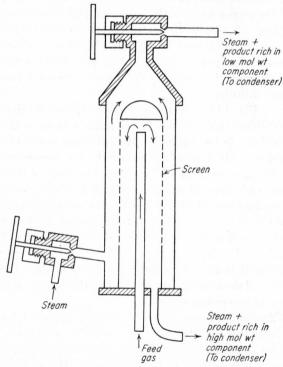

Steam + product rich in low mol wt component (To condenser)

Screen

Steam

Steam + product rich in high mol wt component (To condenser)

Feed gas

FIG. 14.8. Atmolysis apparatus of Maier.[18]

such as steam, a separation or enrichment of the hydrogen-nitrogen mixture would be obtainable since the rate of diffusion of hydrogen through steam is nearly 3.5 times that of nitrogen. Such an operation was studied in an apparatus of the sort shown in Fig. 14.8 by Maier.[18] The gas mixture to be separated flows downward through the inner tube, while steam or other vapor is admitted to the outer jacket. A relatively coarse screen separates the two streams. After careful adjustment of the valves so that the pressures on either side of the screen are nearly alike, it is found that the low-molecular-weight component of the gas diffuses more rapidly into the outer chamber, so that the effluent at the top is rich in this component. The steam passing through the screen concentrates the component of high molecular weight in the effluent at the bottom. The steam in the effluent streams may then be condensed to provide the product gases. The screen is necessary to prevent bulk flow with reasonable control of the pressure, and Maier found it possible to use screens made of such materials as porous Alundum, metallic plate perforated with $\frac{1}{64}$-in. holes, and rolled 100-mesh copper screening. The requirements for the screen, in other words, are far less exacting than those for the barrier of the gas-diffusion process. For cases where the pressures on either side of the screen are exactly balanced, the differential enrichment factor per stage, $\alpha'$, equals the ratio of the diffusivities of the gases through the vapor. This may be considerably increased at the expense of greatly increased vapor consumption by permitting a moderate bulk flow of vapor through the screen. The process does not require the low pressures of gas diffusion.

The device of Fig. 14.8 is a single stage, and, for effective separations of gases whose diffusivities are nearly the same, a cascade of stages much as for gas diffusion will be required. Benedict and Boas[3] have suggested the use of a column which provides essentially a countercurrent continuous contact of two streams of the gas in a crossflow of the steam, thus producing the equivalent of many stages in a single device. For the difficult separations for which such a device might be considered, the columns would then be cascaded in order to permit gradual reduction of the cross section for flow in the direction of the products, as in Fig. 14.7. The steam and condensing requirements for the process are very large,[3] and no commercial installations have yet been made. Cichelli *et al.*[5] have discussed and demonstrated a variant of the process which does not require the use of a separating screen.

**Thermal Diffusion.** If two reservoirs containing a gas mixture are connected by a tube and maintained at different temperatures, it is found that the heavier molecules concentrate in the cooler reservoir, while the lighter molecules concentrate in the warmer.[11] If the molecules are of equal masses, those of smaller diameter tend to concentrate in the region of higher temperature. This movement under an imposed temperature gradient is known as thermal diffusion, and the effect can be multiplied by using the apparatus first described by Clusius and Dickel,[6] shown schematically in Fig. 14.9. Natural convection currents develop in the annular space as shown, owing to the change in gas density with temperature, and these, combined with the tendency to separate by thermal diffusion in the horizontal direction, provide a continuous-contact arrangement which may be equivalent to many stages. In a well-designed column, the height of a transfer unit may be only a few centimeters. Even so, a cascade of columns in the general arrangement of

Fig. 14.7 would be required for large degrees of separation. The cold wall of the column would ordinarily be kept at the lowest possible temperature provided by the available cooling water, and a hot-wall temperature of 600 to 900°F. will be preferred.[1] The heat requirements are exceedingly large, and with one exception the process has been used only on a small scale for the separation of isotopes. During the Second World War, the process was used temporarily on a large scale for the separation of the uranium isotopes in the form of the hexafluorides, while waiting for the completion of the gas-diffusion plant.[10] The thermal diffusion phenomenon is also known to occur in liquid solution, where it has been known as the *Soret effect*.

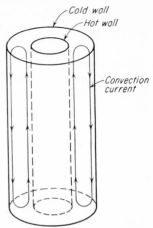

FIG. 14.9. Thermal-diffusion column.[1] (*Courtesy of the American Institute of Chemical Engineers.*)

Table 14.1 indicates the results of calculations by Benedict[1,3] for the separation of 100 gm./day of $C^{13}$, 90 per cent pure, from natural carbon (1.06 per cent $C^{13}$), using $C^{12}H_4$ and $C^{13}H_4$ and the gas processes just described. The figures are not entirely comparable owing to the different yields of product assumed, but they indicate the unusual size of plant and energy requirements for such a separation.

TABLE 14.1. SEPARATION OF 100 GM./DAY OF $C^{13}H_4$ FROM $C^{12}H_4$
Product to be 90 per cent pure

| Process | Yield, % of $C^{13}$ | Surface or stages required | Energy or steam consumption |
|---|---|---|---|
| Thermal diffusion...... | 50 | 280,000 sq. ft. | 75,600 kw. |
| Gaseous diffusion...... | 50 | 345 stages | 149 kw. |
| Atmolysis, stagewise... | 10 | 677 stages, 70,000 sq. ft. screen area | 54,400 lb. steam/hr. |
| Atmolysis, column..... | 10 | 43,020 sq. ft. screen area | 38,600 lb. steam/hr. |

## NOTATION FOR CHAPTER 14

$A$ = component of smaller molecular weight
$B$ = component of larger molecular weight
$c$ = solute concentration in dialyzate, lb. moles/cu. ft.
$c'$ = solute concentration in diffusate, lb. moles/cu. ft.
$\Delta c_{av}$ = average concentration difference, lb. moles/cu. ft.
$D$ = diffusivity, sq. ft./hr.

$k_L$, $k'_L$ = liquid mass-transfer film coefficients, lb. moles/(hr.)(sq. ft.)($\Delta c$)

$k_M$ = membrane mass-transfer coefficient, lb. moles/(hr.)(sq. ft.)($\Delta c$)

$K$ = over-all mass-transfer coefficient, lb. moles/(hr.)(sq. ft.)($\Delta c$)

ln = natural logarithm

$M$ = molecular weight, lb./lb. mole

$N$ = rate of mass transfer, lb. moles/(hr.)(sq. ft.)

$x_F$ = concentration of $A$ in feed gas, mole fraction

$y$ = concentration of $A$ in separated gas, mole fraction

$z$ = effective liquid-film thickness, ft.

$z_M$ = effective membrane thickness, ft.

$\alpha'$ = relative enrichment, $\dfrac{\text{moles } A/\text{mole } B \text{ in product}}{\text{moles } A/\text{mole } B \text{ in feed}}$

## REFERENCES

1. Benedict, M.: *Chem. Eng. Progr.*, **43**, 41 (1947).
2. ———: In R. E. Kirk and D. F. Othmer, eds., "Encyclopedia of Chemical Technology," vol. 5, p. 76, Interscience Encyclopedia, Inc., New York, 1950.
3. ——— and A. Boas: *Chem. Eng. Progr.*, **47**, 51, 111 (1951).
4. Brubacher, D. W., and K. Kammermeyer: *Ind. Eng. Chem.*, **44**, 1465 (1952); **45**, 1148 (1953); **46**, 733, 739 (1954).
5. Cichelli, M. T., W. E. Weatherford, and J. R. Bowman: *Chem. Eng. Progr.*, **47**, 63, 123 (1951).
6. Clusius, K., and G. Dickel: *Z. physik. Chem.*, **B44**, 397 (1939).
7. Cohen, K.: "The Theory of Isotope Separation," G. M. Murphy, ed., National Nuclear Energy Series, Manhattan Project Technical Section, Division III, vol. IB, McGraw-Hill Book Company, Inc., New York, 1951.
8. Daniel, F. K.: In R. E. Kirk and D. F. Othmer, eds., "Encyclopedia of Chemical Technology," vol. 5, p. 1, Interscience Encyclopedia, Inc., New York, 1950.
9. Enyon, D. J.: *J. Soc. Chem. Ind. (London)*, **52**, 173T (1933).
10. Fox, M. C.: *Chem. Eng.*, **52**(12), 102 (1945).
11. Grew, K. E., and T. L. Ibbs: "Thermal Diffusion in Gases," Cambridge University Press, London, 1952.
12. Hagerbaumer, D. H., and K. Kammermeyer: *Chem. Eng. Progr., Symposium Ser.* 10, **50**, 25 (1954).
13. Hiester, N. K., and R. C. Philips: *Chem. Eng.*, **61**(10), 161 (1954).
14. Hogerton, J. F.: *Chem. Eng.*, **52**(12), 98 (1945).
15. Huckins, E., and K. Kammermeyer: *Chem. Eng. Progr.*, **49**, 180, 294 (1953).
16. Lane, J. A.: In J. H. Perry, ed., "Chemical Engineers' Handbook," 3d ed., p. 753, McGraw-Hill Book Company, Inc., New York, 1950.
17. Lee, J. A.: *Chem. Met. Eng.*, **42**, 483 (1935).
18. Maier, C. G.: "Mechanical Concentration of Gases," *U.S. Bur. Mines Bull.* 431 (1940).
19. Marshall, R. D., and J. A. Storrow: *Ind. Eng. Chem.*, **43**, 2934 (1951); **44**, 1165 (1952).
20. Vollrath, H. B.: *Chem. Met. Eng.*, **43**, 303 (1936).

# INDEX

Absorbers, reboiled, 249, 250
  (*See also* Gas-liquid operations, equipment for)
Absorption (*see* Gas absorption)
Absorption factor, definition, 219
  in gas absorption, 219–221, 232
  most economical, 221, 244
Activated adsorption, 448
Activated alumina, 450
Activated carbon, 450
  for aqueous solutions, 468, 469
  deterioration of, 478
  for fixed beds, 500
  for Hypersorbers, 487
Activated clay, 450, 468
Activation of adsorbents, 450, 470
Activity coefficient, 264
Adhesion, effect of, in drying, 548
Adiabatic cooling curves, 165, 166
  for air–water vapor, chart, *facing* 162
Adiabatic processes, in adsorption, 489
  definition, 155
  in drying, 569, 570, 575
  in gas absorption, 215–217
  in gas-liquid contact, 165, 166, 173–184
  in humidification-cooling, 181–184
Adsorbate, definition, 451
Adsorbents, activation of, 450, 470
  influence of, on equilibria, 453, 459, 463
  list of, 448–450
  properties of, 448–450
  repeated use of, 475
  for stagewise adsorption, 468
Adsorption, 2, 4, 447–520, 586
  apparent, 461–466
  chemisorption, 448
  continuous contact, 483–517
    adsorption wave, 498–500, 504–511
    adsorption zone, 499, 507
    chromatography, 504
    enthalpy balances, 489
    in fixed beds, 497–511
      rate of, 504–511
    fractionation processes, 484–487, 492–497

Adsorption, continuous contact, ion exchange, 511–517
  one component adsorbed, 488–492
  percolation, 503, 504
  steady-state operation, 484–497
  transfer units, 490, 495
  two components adsorbed, 492–497
  unsteady-state operation, 497–511
  vapors and solvent recovery, 500–503
  effect of, in leaching operations, 586
  equipment for, continuous, 484–488
    fixed beds, 497–504, 513
    Hypersorbers, 484–487
    moving beds, 484–488
    percolation, 503, 513
    solvent recovery, 500–502
    stagewise, 467–470
  fractional, 2, 4, 484–487, 492–497
  heat of, 454–457
  hysteresis in, 453, 526, 527
  ion exchange, 511–520
  negative, 464–466
  operations, classification of, 466–467
  physical, definition, 448
  potential, 454
  properties of adsorbents, 448–450
  reflux ratio, 486, 493–497
  reversible, 448
  stagewise, 466–484
    adsorbents for, 468
    application of Freundlich equation, 471, 474
    contact filtration, 466–484
    equipment for, 467–470
    minimum adsorbent, 474, 477
    multistage cocurrent, 472–476
    multistage countercurrent, 476–482
    single-stage, 470–472
Adsorption equilibria, 450–466
  effect on, of pressure, 461
    of temperature, 453, 461
  Freundlich equation, 462, 464
  hysteresis, 453
  liquids, 461–466
  single gases and vapors, 450–457

651